Video Game Bible
1985-2002

National Library of Canada Cataloguing in Publication

Video game Bible, 1985-2002 / Andy Slaven ... [et al.].
ISBN 1-55369-731-6
  I. Slaven, Andy, 1977-
GV1469.3.V52 2002   794.8'0973'075   C2002-903242-3

TRAFFORD

This book was published *on-demand* in cooperation with Trafford Publishing.
On-demand publishing is a unique process and service of making a book available for retail sale to the public taking advantage of on-demand manufacturing and Internet marketing.
On-demand publishing includes promotions, retail sales, manufacturing, order fulfilment, accounting and collecting royalties on behalf of the author.

Suite 6E, 2333 Government St., Victoria, B.C. V8T 4P4, CANADA
Phone   250-383-6864   Toll-free 1-888-232-4444 (Canada & US)
Fax   250-383-6804   E-mail   sales@trafford.com
Web site www.trafford.com   TRAFFORD PUBLISHING IS A DIVISION OF TRAFFORD HOLDINGS LTD.
Trafford Catalogue #02-0544   www.trafford.com/robots/02-0544.html

10   9   8   7   6   5   4   3   2   1

A historical reference to every U.S. video game console that has come and gone, from 1985-2002.

Video Game Bible

Volume 1

EDITOR IN CHIEF
Andy Slaven

STAFF WRITERS
Michael Collins
Lucus Barnes
Vincent Yang

CONTRIBUTING WRITERS
Charlie Reneke
Michael Thomasson
Joe Kudrna

COVER ART
Andy Slaven

COVER MODEL
Kyle Yamauchi

DEDICATED TO:
David Barnes

SPECIAL THANKS TO:

Andrew Walker, Dan and Melba Slaven, Lee Hunt, Lee Hewitt, Nick Matheys, Steve Jacobs of **FX Video Game Exchange,** Adam Harvey, Frank Cifaldi of "**www.theredeye.net**", Andrew Deehr, Mark Callahan, Joe Santulli, Leonard Herman, Cindy Kuethe, Paul Rieselman, John Craeger, to everyone that emailed me game scans, all the members at the VGB message board, and to everyone else that helped out by either contributing or offering support. I am sure that a lot of names have been left off of this list by accident, and for that I apologize.

Table of Contents

 # Editor's Enlightenment

Video game collecting vs. video game playing. There is a rift in the video game market dividing collectors and players. While some choose to horde every game available, others choose to purchase only those games that will be played from start to finish with only a few breaks. And still there are some that not only collect video games, but also play them and critique them objectively. This guide should be beneficial to anyone who plays and/or collects video games for any U.S. system starting with the Nintendo Entertainment System (NES) through the Sega Dreamcast (with the notable exception of the Sony Playstation).

Many of you might look at the table of contents and scratch your head at some of the systems listed. We have decided to provide coverage for not only the systems that did well in the American market, but also for those that were never embraced fully by the public (not necessarily bad, simply not successful). What you might notice while reading sections devoted to the more obscure systems is that many of the games for them are unique to that system. And in addition to these games being unique, you will notice that our comments on some of them suggest that they are amazing...and this is often the case. Even though a system wasn't very popular or even very good, most of them have at least one title that stands out.

Classic vs. Neo-Classic There is little doubt that the classic era of gaming is very thoroughly documented. But have you tried to find a reliable Sega Genesis release list? How about an SNES list? The truth is, most of these systems have partial coverage on many websites, but rarely can a complete list be found for any of them, and trying to sort out what is rare and what is expensive is usually more work than it is worth.

While those from the "Age of Atari" have done well for themselves and can now look nostalgically back on their childhood and the fond memories of their Pong systems, a new generation has come of age. Those of us who remember our childhood as being filled with after school NES playing or lunchroom fights breaking out over the superiority of the SNES over the Genesis (or visa versa) will certainly understand our fondness of the Neo-Classic era. One day our children might look at us in the same light we view the classic gamers, but even when that day comes, just remember that you'll always be, on average, 15 years younger than a classic gamer. :)

So, after nearly two years of gathering release information, we have finally compiled the most complete listings for these systems anywhere. And while it may be the case that a few obscure games have been left out of these listings accidentally, you will not find a more complete listing, or more accurate information on the neo-classic era than the book you are holding right now.

We have made every effort to ensure our information is 100% correct, however we expect that some errors have been made. If you notice an error in any of our sections, please let us know about it so that it may be corrected in this guide's second volume.

So why do you prefer the "Neo-Classics?" Aside from the need for a reliable guide on the subject listed above, the reasons that the VGB staff has chosen to concentrate on the neo-classics are greatly varied. While all the staff members have their own opinions on the subject, it pretty much all falls into a melting pot of good game play, good story line, and good memories. The "good memories" part is true of any type of collection, but the "game play" and "story line" stand out in this hobby. While it is true that the classic games often had good story lines, and the success of a game squarely rested on good game play (in the lack of discernable graphics), it's the amount of innovation in these fields that stands out in the neo-classic era.

Role Playing Games (RPG's) began to take shape, dialog became important to progression in games, characters became more realistic, control became more responsive, etc. New and innovative controllers were made. Stereo sound became standard. Games were becoming something more than a test of dexterity. And game players began to expect more. This expectation drove the industry to keep evolving, and even when a system "failed," its innovative features were recycled and often used in other systems. The Neo-Classic era is responsible for the huge advances in video games over the past 15 years, and these systems live on in every Playstation 2, Xbox, and Game Cube…and every system to come.

All of the authors featured within this guide hope that you not only find it informative, but also enjoyable. The inclusion of unusual game facts at the bottom of each page was done to keep the guide interesting even in sections that would otherwise hold little interest for you. Personal opinions about most games have also been included to help in selecting games that will be more enjoyable, and selected photos of games within each section have been displayed on each page. Each system features an overview that gives general information not intended for diehard collectors alone, but instead it is intended as a basic introduction that should be enjoyed by the average gamer. *Allez Cuisine!!*

Andy

Rarity

The number listed directly after the publisher in a game's absolute rarity. This means that the rarity of a game is not only judged in comparison to other games for that particular system, but instead it is considered by total number produced and its availability. Typically, the total number produced is the only factor considered, but in a few instances, certain games that were made in very small quantities are readily available due to the game's demand. While this game may not be nearly as common as others, it would still be readily available. Typically, a "10" refers to games with less than 150 copies known to exist. A "9" is typically a game with less than 2000 copies made, an "8" would have less than 5000 copies made and a "7" would have less than 20,000 copies made. Rarities below "7" are very subjective, but we have done our best to make them as accurate as possible. A "3" is used for games that were released in quantity, and are considered to be of average rarity. But like any other collectable, rarity is not the only factor, and rarity does not always dictate what the price value of a game is.

Price

Pricing is typically the most disputed portion of any guide of this nature. The prices listed should give a price that can be reasonably paid or received for a game when dealing directly with the buyer/seller, but do not apply to online auction sites. These sites inflate prices as they reflect the highest amount that a single person was willing to pay, not what the game is actually worth.

Prices are not derived from the rarity value, but instead are a reflection of what the game is actually worth. Often a more common game will be more expensive due to the fact that it is a better game and is more desirable. Likewise, a very bad game that is in short supply will only demand a relatively small price.

For the purposes of this guide, CD-based game prices are listed for games **with jewel case and instructions** and **cartridge game prices are listed for loose games.** As a general rule, games in their original boxes demand about 20% higher than a loose game. This rule also applies to CD-based games that include both jewel cases and boxes, such as 3DO and TG-16 games.

Any systems that are contrary to these general rules will have a note after the introduction to explain further how pricing should be interpreted.

Sample Page

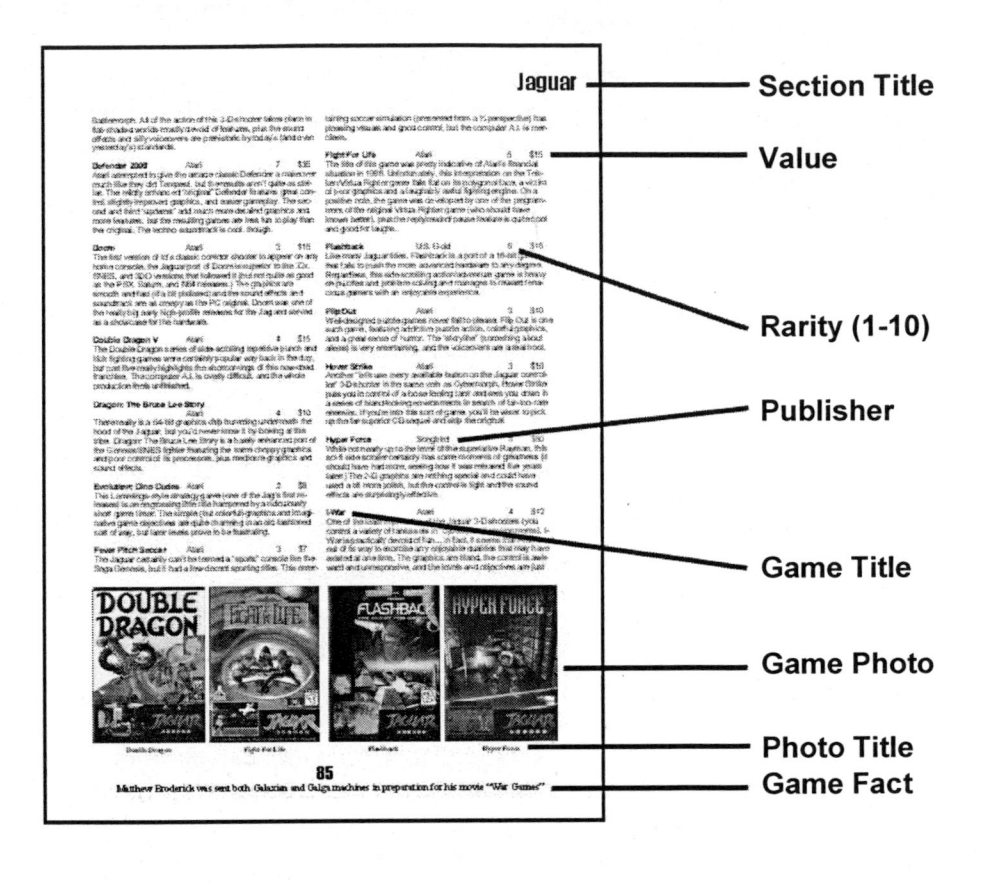

Jaguar — Section Title

— Value

— Rarity (1-10)

— Publisher

— Game Title

— Game Photo

— Photo Title
— Game Fact

The page layout used in this book offers a quick reference that clearly shows the rarity, price, and publisher, as well as an overview that does not interfere with your ability to quickly determine the value of a game. When bidding at online auction sites, these precious seconds may be all it takes to secure a copy of Metal Slug for the Neo-Geo instead of a dozen Super Mario Bros. carts. It is important to note that **THE RARITY VALUE IS NOT A GAME REVIEW GRADE.** It is a rarity value only and does not reflect the quality of the game in any way whatsoever.

The photos used within the book are not designed to show only the rare items, but instead represent a wide variety of games for the system. Included not only as a historical account of the box art used, but also as a reference guide to show various styles of art used on various systems. Once a general feel for what a certain system's boxes look like, it will become easier to find that system's games in a variety of situations. Each box scan is clearly labeled below the picture, and while not every photo is on the same page as its listing, each is within one page of their respective listing.

Finally, a fun game fact is listed below the page number. There is no order to these facts, and they cover many facets of video game history. Included simply to make this guide more fun to read, these should give you a reason to visit chapters for systems that you don't yet own.

U.S. Systems

For the purposes of this book, a system is defined as:
A device that accepts interchangeable media, uses a television as its primary output and must include an interface for interaction with that media. A console must, through either design or practice, have a primary function of playing media designed for entertainment, rather than practical application.

The Virtual Boy is a notable exception within this section due to its lack of any TV output. For convenience, it is included in this section of the book as it best fits within this section.

3DO

By: Andy Slaven

The 3DO platform is perhaps one of the most misunderstood video game platforms ever created simply due to the mass of incorrect information available for it on the internet. 3DO itself is not a console, but a conglomerate of technology that was created and treated like a franchise. A true 32-bit machine with 16-bit stereo sound, the technology used to make a 3DO system was sold to various companies so that they could make their respective versions of this gaming platform. The two U.S. producers of the 3DO system were Panasonic and Goldstar. Sanyo and Samsung also built models, but of these two companies, only Sanyo released a consumer model, and it was exclusive to Japan.

This franchising arrangement was responsible for one of the most unique marketing schemes in video game history. Typically, video game hardware companies make their respective systems and sell the hardware at a loss, relying on software sales to not only make up the difference, but to generate a profit as well. But since neither Panasonic nor Goldstar was going to be making a profit on the sale of software, this tried and true method would not be a feasible way to sell their 3DO systems. Instead, after each unit was made, these respective companies would have to generate a profit from the system itself. In addition to making a profit for themselves, 3DO would also collect a royalty for each system sold, and would also make a profit from each software title marketed that featured the 3DO logo. As a result, when Panasonic introduced the FZ-1 model to the U.S. public in October of 1993, it carried with it the hefty price of $700! Goldstar released their model shortly after the FZ-1 debuted, and also carried a $700 price tag, though it had less RAM and lacked an internal cooling fan, causing problems for several games that were later released. In addition to this exorbitant price tag, the system also carried the stigma of being a "multimedia device" designed to run all sorts of software, not just games. This meant that a large portion of early titles was classified as edutainment, reducing the overall appeal the average consumer.

Within a year of Panasonic's initial release, improvements in hardware manufacturing and reduced component costs allowed the price of the FZ-1 to be reduced to $500 nationwide, though the Goldstar model only saw regional reductions in price based on unit sales (which were far less than those of the Panasonic model). As sales waned for the Goldstar model, an MPEG adapter was made available with a Total Recall pack-in movie, and was only compatible with the Goldstar unit. This $150 extra did not increase the sales of the Goldstar 3DO system as was hoped, and Panasonic quickly had a firm grip on the small, but loyal, 3DO following.

In 1995, Panasonic released the last U.S. version of the 3DO system in the form of the Panasonic FZ-10. This model featured lower grade components and as a result was sold at the relatively low price of $300. Instead of a front loading CD tray, like the FZ-1 and Goldstar models, the FZ-10 featured a flip-top lid and was notably lighter than the FZ-1. Unlike the first two models released, this newer (and much more common) model featured a readily accessible memory manager. This allowed for game data to be manipulated in order to free up space for other games, instead of waiting for the unit to fill up and require an immediate deletion in order to save a current game.

All three U.S. systems featured a unique controller configuration since the system itself only featured one control port. The controller itself came equipped with a passthrough plug for the use of additional controllers. This design would support up to 8 controllers simultaneously, though it quickly became cumbersome when playing with more than two people. Also, during fighting games, an unscrupulous "first player" could simply wiggle the connection with the second controller for that added edge. The controller itself, regardless of brand, featured three main action buttons, two shoulder buttons, and a start/play button in the center. This button configuration proved adequate for all games but one: Super Street Fighter 2 Turbo. A special Capcom controller could only be ordered via mail-in offer after buying that game, and offered 6 action buttons.

With the introduction of the Sony Playstation, Sega Saturn and the Nintendo 64, the 3DO quickly became nothing more than a footnote in video game history. However, its legacy is a large title of games, many of which are of very high quality. Those that think that the 3DO company lost money in this bargain aren't giving the genius Trip Hawkins (CEO of 3DO) proper credit. Due to the marketing agreement, 3DO was assured a profit from day one. Not only did they receive a royalty from all software sales from 3rd party developers, but they also received a per unit royalty from both Panasonic and Goldstar in addition to the initial payment for use of the 3DO technology. And to add to 3DO's pint, during the stages of 3DO's continuing development for the video game system, a technology known as "M2" was developed. Originally planned as the basis for a new 3DO system, the project was scrapped as competition from Sony, Sega and Nintendo began to prove insurmountable. This technology was then sold to Matsushita, the parent company of Panasonic for the sum of $100,000,000.00! So don't feel too bad for 3DO, because thanks to the brilliance of Trip Hawkins, they came out further ahead on hardware design profits than any other video game company in history.

Without a doubt, the 3DO was ahead of its time, and carried with it a fatal price tag as proof. Starting as a multimedia device, much like the Phillips CD-i, the 3DO made the successful conversion to be considered a gaming system where the Phillips technology would not. The consoles are among the most resilient CD based systems ever made, and the majority of them still work perfectly. A testament to innovation in the video game industry, the 3DO is perhaps the best example of technology from which newer consoles were built. From the successful use of internal RAM to the failed controller configuration, it is this type of engineering that makes the Neo-Classic era stand apart from any other. An "intermediate system" or "missing link" of sorts in video game history, the 3DO will forever remain as one of the greatest consoles ever made, regardless of its overall lack of consumer support.

3DO

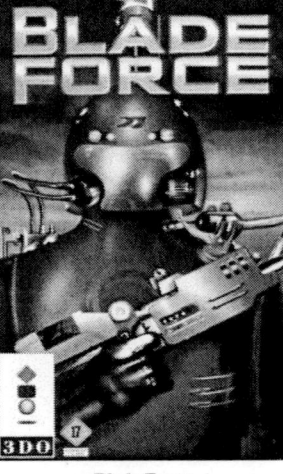

| 3D Atlas | Ballz: The Director's Cut | Blade Force | Brain Dead 13 |

20ᵗʰ Century Video Almanac
                    Software Toolworks   3 $5
An interactive history lesson of the 20ᵗʰ century, an intuitive interface and large amounts of information make this title interesting to play around with. For a long time, this title was one of the few places that footage of the Challenger explosion could be found, though a version does exist that does not include this footage.

3D Atlas   Electronic Arts   3 $5
Simply an interactive atlas of the world, this title includes topographical overviews in video format to give a real feeling of a 3-D environment. Not very interesting for anyone other than aspiring topographers however.

Alone In The Dark   Electronic Arts   3 $7
Where the entire cinematic horror adventure genre started, this title utilizes shock value and immersing environments to inspire a feeling of horror. The control scheme can become a bit tricky if the camera view is obstructed, or if it begins to shift too often, but otherwise a very good early installment in this ever growing genre.

Alone In The Dark 2   Electronic Arts   5 $10
Not quite as enthralling as the first installment, a shift of environment to that of a ship takes away a bit of the creepy feeling, however change might be a good thing for gamers unfamiliar with the series. While the location might be questionable, the story line is where most gamers began to complain. While it is still an entertaining horror game with slight graphical improvements over the first installment, it is certainly lacking in key areas.

Animals!: San Diego Zoo Presents, The
                    Software Toolworks   3 $5
Take an interactive tour of the San Diego Zoo and view information on the animals within. This was part of the early drive to increase the number of interactive learning media that was quickly replaced with an emphasis on gaming. This title really holds no interest for gamers, and with the widespread use of the internet, it is even lacking as a research tool.

B.C. Racers   Goldstar / LG Electronics 5 $12
This kart racing game uses cavemen instead of the often seen franchised characters. Unfortunately, the tracks are extremely difficult and uninspired, and night courses can become impossi-

ble to see at times. It can be fun, but frustration often detracts from this all too quickly after beginning a game.

Ballz: The Directors Cut   PF. Magic   4 $8
A standard fighting game with a twist: the characters are completely comprised of spherical body parts. A real display of 3DO power, the fact that this many onscreen 3-D objects could be animated and displayed with minimal slowdown was a real breakthrough for the industry. The fighting engine is relatively simple, but in a time when 2-D fighters were all too common, this was a nice change of pace and still offers a nice variation to a diluted genre.

BattleChess   Interplay   5 $12
The classic rules of chess apply to this title, but instead of simply taking a piece, you are treated to an animation of one piece beating the other to death using a variety of techniques. Breathing life back into a classic game, this title should be a favorite among fans of chess.

BattleSport   3DO   3 $8
Choose your vehicle and participate in this soccer style sport that is played from within your vehicle. Various power-ups and fast paced action make this a sort of hybrid between combat racing games and a sports game. This should be entertaining for fans of games such as those found in the Twisted Metal series.

Blade Force   3DO   3 $10
A helicopter attack game that takes place among various levels, the futuristic setting will make this entertaining for some, but demanding gamers will be a bit bored with the repetitious nature of the game.

Blonde Justice   Vivid Interactive   4 $5
This adult title offers very little interaction, as is the case with most adult titles, and even less fun. Necessary to complete a your 3DO collection, but hardly worth owning otherwise.

Brain Dead 13   ReadySoft   4 $10
Played in the style of Dragon's Lair, this interactive movie/cartoon features some very nice graphics and challenging game play. Though the interaction is basically limited to pushing a specific button at the right time, the difficulty level and good length make this an enjoyable installment to this lost genre.

10

Asteroids was so popular in Japan that it caused a national coin shortage!

Burning Soldier   Panasonic   3 $8
This rapid fire shooter, has graphics that could definitely be improved, and the overall length is ridiculous. This game can easily be beaten within just a few hours of game play, if not less.

Bust-A-Move   Panasonic   5 $15
One of the most addictive games ever, this title requires that you shoot balloons of various colors into an encroaching wall of even more balloons. When three balloons of the same color come in contact, they disappear, taking with them any others that are supported. The two player mode is especially entertaining as your small victories create a setback for your opponent. Perhaps even more addictive than Tetris, don't expect to play this game for less than an hour.

Cannon Fodder   Sensible Software 5 $12
Very popular in the U.K., this title wasn't released in the U.S. until long after its European release. Played with an overhead view, you control a squad of soldiers, portrayed by cute looking characters, in a melee of shooting action against your opponent.

Captain Quazar   3DO   3 $10
This shooter features a character that was apparently an attempt by 3DO to create a franchised character to become their mascot. While the cartoon-like graphics in this game are nice and the control is very solid, Captain Quazar just didn't have the qualities to become a successful mascot. Despite the lack of mascot status, this title is still very enjoyable.

Carrier: Fortress At Sea
          Panasonic / Discovery Channel 4 $9
In this game, in the same style as Alone In the Dark and Resident Evil, you take on a supernatural force of opponents in this horror game. Control, however, is absolutely horrible and completely ruins what could have been a good game. Also, this title doesn't offer much of a challenge or a very long story.

Casper   Interplay   4 $12
When this game was released, the graphics were among some of the best on any system. The childish theme kept it from reaching a more mainstream audience, but otherwise this title is a lot of fun. Granted, the game play can become monotonous as you wander from room to room searching for keys and passages, so it should be played in moderation.

Corpse Killer   Digital Pictures 3 $5
One of the best versions of this title, but even the 3DO can't save this game from being bad. Grainy graphics and inaccurate control make this title more frustrating than entertaining.

Coven, The   Vivid Interactive 4 $5
An adult title for the 3DO, this Vivid "game" offers very little interaction and even less game play.

Cowboy Casino   IntelliPlay   4 $8
This game does not depict a full casino, but instead a western style bar featuring several types of poker. This title should have included much more before attaching the word "casino" to its name. Your opponents are occasionally accompanied by a FMV sequence to make a snide comment, but this isn't enough to keep the game from growing old.

C.P.U. Bach, Sid Meier's   MicroProse 4 $12
Perhaps the most innovative title for the 3DO, this isn't actually a game. Once this disk is in the 3DO, it will turn the system into a music generating machine. Choose the instruments that you want to hear and the style of music you want, then sit back and watch several different types of visuals to accompany the unique songs made in the same style as Bach. It is absolutely incredible to see this title in action and is a definite must-have for the 3DO.

Crash 'N Burn   Crystal Dynamics 2 $7
Racing and fighting rolled into one. This combat shooter offers cheesy video clips of the different drivers, a modest selection of weapons, and some very unique tracks. While the feeling of speed is lacking in some areas and the combat engine could have been improved a bit, this title is still a lot of fun when played with multiple people.

Creature Shock   Virgin / Argonaut 5 $12
A rail shooter, this game really only allows for control over the direction you are shooting. Available in much better form on the Saturn and PSX, this early version quickly becomes predictable and often boring.

Crime Patrol   American Laser Games 3 $10
Ported from the superior arcade version, this is still one of the best shooters for the 3DO. Advancing through the ranks from a rookie all the way up to Captain, accuracy is emphasized for both scoring and advancement, though it can be fun to see what else you can shoot.

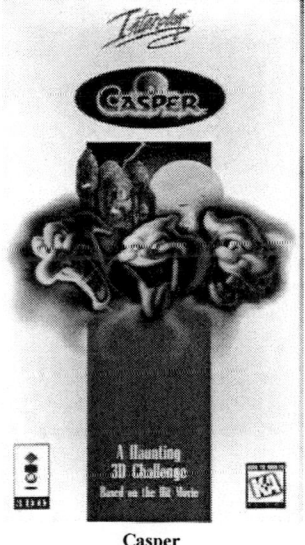

Casper   Cowboy Casino   Sid Meier's C.P.U. Bach   Crime Patrol

Neo-Geo cartridges weigh about 375 grams.

The Daedalus Encounter   Dennis Miller: That's News To Me

Dino Park Tycoon   Dragon Lore

Cyberdillo   **Panasonic**   **4**   **$12**
This humorous fist person shooter is full of toilet humor and a 70's feel. Childish in nature and disappointing in its overall presentation, the humor wears off and the realization that this game isn't very good quickly sets in. If you're a fan of fart jokes and South Park, this title may keep your interest, but otherwise it is just a very odd FPS.

Cyberia   **Interplay**   **3**   **$8**
On a mission to destroy a hijacked doomsday weapon, you are a computer hacker sent to infect the control system used to activate this device. Featuring graphics that were considered amazing for their time, this title is entertaining and should offer a good amount of game play.

D   **Warp / Panasonic**   **4**   **$15**
A definite favorite of vampire fans, this time-based game is represented very well on the 3DO. The best version available at the time, this title is available in a slightly improved version on several other formats including the Sega Saturn.

Daedalus Encounter, The   **Panasonic**   **4**   **$15**
Starring Tia Carrere, this four CD game is a series of puzzles and FMV sequences. Some of the best digitized video on the system, it can become a little bland after a while. The puzzles, while simple in concept, can be very challenging and often seem impossible. Usually taking the form of rearranging certain pieces of an indecipherable lock, if you are unable to solve them, you will die.

DeathKeep   **SSI / Mindscape**   **5**   **$15**
Dungeons and Dragons on the 3DO was something that made a lot of gamers happy. Though this title lacks the same formula that made Slayer such a success, this game is still amazing. Great graphics and an easy to use interface make this mythical journey into the Deathkeep a completely immersing experience.

Demolition Man   **Virgin**   **4**   **$12**
Based on the movie by the same name, this title will find you playing the role of John Spartan in your quest to stop crime in the future. After being cryogenically frozen, you are awakened to a world of unknown technology, though control and graphics could have been improved quite a bit before this game was released.

Dennis Miller: That's News to Me
     Sanctuary Woods   **4**   **$6**
An unusual title, this CD offers video segments of Dennis Miller performing comical segments that comment on "current" culture. Of course, since this title was released in 1994, the segments are humorously dated.

Digital Dreamware   **Virgin**   **5**   **$10**
A kaleidoscope of colors and sound are used in this title for the sheer enjoyment of watching and listening. There really is no game aspect to this title however.

Dino Park Tycoon   **MECC**   **6**   **$18**
Design, build and run a dinosaur based theme park, much in the same fashion as Themepark. This is an obvious attempt to make money off of Jurassic Park's popularity at the time of this game's release.

Doom   **Art Data / ID**   **4**   **$12**
The popular first person shooter makes a truncated appearance on the 3DO with grainy graphics, less than stellar sound, and average control. While not really a bad version of the game, it is best played on a PC.

Dragon Lore   **Mindscape**   **5**   **$18**
This expansive adventure spans four CD's and offers some of the most impressive visuals on the system. A point and click adventure with the occasional action sequence, Dragon Lore is a relatively slow paced game designed for an older audience. Announced long before its completion, this title is sure to please those expecting a purely still-framed adventure, and sure to upset those expecting a completely action based adventure.

Dragon's Lair   **Readysoft**   **3**   **$7**
The classic game makes an appearance on the 3DO, though at the same time a superior version was also available on the CD-i. Pushing a specific button at the right time will see your character, Dirk, progress. Pressing the wrong button will see him turned into a pile of bones.

Drug Wars   **American Laser Games**   **4**   **$8**
Actually Crime Patrol 2, this installment sees more of the same digitized shooting. Best played in the arcade, this title also made an appearance on the CD-i.

Endlessly　　　　Vivid Interactive　4　$5
This adult game from vivid offers small amounts of interaction and grainy 32-bit nudity…not much in the way of a game.

Escape From Monster Manor
　　　　　Electronic Arts　4　$10
An average first person shooter that places you within a strange mansion, strange creatures will block your passage from the top floor of the house to the underground tunnels that you must eventually work though. An interesting story line is explained at the beginning of the game and does add some depth to an otherwise typical FPS.

ESPN Beach Volleyball　IntelliPlay　6　$8
Seemingly a strange sport to necessitate its own title, this was a poor seller and is difficult to find today.

ESPN Baseball: Interactive Hitting
　　　　　IntelliPlay　4　$5
Interact with the FMV sequences in this title designed to improve your hitting skills.

ESPN Golf: Lower Score w/ Tom Kite
　　　　　IntelliPlay　3　$3
Learn to hone your golf skills with your 3DO and Tom Kite. Ok, let's be honest, this isn't any fun, even for golfers. Interactive menus allow you to watch FMV segments featuring golf tips.

ESPN Let's Go Skiing　IntelliPlay　5　$8
The only way to learn how to ski is to go skiiing, but this title might give you some of the basic knowledge necessary not to break your neck on your first real outing.

ESPN Let's Play Soccer　IntelliPlay　4　$5
Basic instructions on how to improve your soccer game are included in this title

ESPN Step Aerobics　IntelliPlay　4　$5
Follow the exercises portrayed in FMV sequences in this title.

Family Feud　　　　GameTek　4　$7
An electronic version of the long defunct game show, this title was an obvious attempt at gaining more support from older consumers (read: those who could afford $700 for a game console.)

Fatty Bear's Birthday Surprise
　　　　Humongous Entertainment　3　$4

Fatty Bear's Funpack
　　　　Humongous Entertainment　3　$4
A variety of interactive activities are used to entertain children while they learn basic academic skills.

FIFA International Soccer
　　　　　Electronic Arts　2　$7
Stunning graphics for its time and incredible game play made this title the forerunner in the soccer game genre. It quickly became the benchmark for all other soccer games to be compared to.

Flashback: The Quest For Identity
　　　　US Gold / Delphine Software　4　$8
An amazingly unique graphical style makes this game stand out from others as being very enjoyable to simply look at. On a quest to seek the truth about your identity, you will face puzzles and interesting level designs in this entertaining title.

Flying Nightmares　DoMark　5　$12
An excellent harrier flight simulation, the flight stick is almost a necessity. Very difficult not only because of the complexity of control, but also because of its realistic portrayal of the confusion seen in combat situations. The control is not difficult because it is bad however, but instead because it is very realistic. This is not an arcade style flight simulation, but instead of a similar quality to those found on PC's of the time.

Foes of Ali　　　　Electronic Arts　4　$8
Unique to the 3DO platform, this title has controls that feel a bit sluggish for a boxing game. Nice graphics and a variety of boxers keep it entertaining, but it is hard to get past the slow reaction time of the fighters.

Fun 'n Games　　Panasonic　4　$5
Though typically childish in nature, the variety of puzzles and games found on this title make it enjoyable by more than just children. The challenge is extremely low however, and won't hold much interest, if any, for seasoned gamers.

Gex　　　　Crystal Dynamics　2　$5
This gecko was very popular in his day, and made appearances

Fatty Bear's Funpack

Flashback: The Quest for Identity

Flying Nightmares　　　　　　**Foes of Ali**

Jungle Hunt was originally titled Jungle King, but was changed after the estate of Edgar Rice Burroughs threatened to sue.

3DO

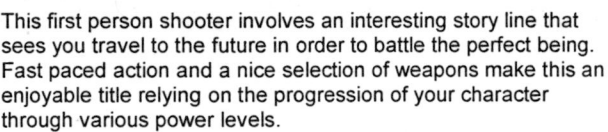

| Gunslinger Collection | Icebreaker | Immercenary | Johnny Bazookatone |

on several systems. An action game with very nice graphics, this title is enjoyable though not revolutionary.

Gridders   Tetragon   4 $8
In this puzzle game based around large shifting cubes, you must maneuver properly to not only avoid being crushed, but also to clear each level. Not only testing your mind, but also your thumbs, speed is essential in solving the stages within this game.

Guardian War   Panasonic   4 $8
An early attempt at a 3-D RPG, this title offers control that is difficult to get used to, graphics that are lacking, and a story line that is less than interesting. A good concept that was later used in several other games, this title simply couldn't deliver the experience that was obviously intended.

Gunslinger Collection 3-in-1
               American Laser Games   6 $22
This is a collection of Mad Dog McCree, Mad Dog McCree 2 and Crime Patrol within one package. No improvements to any of these games have been made however, and this collection was simply sold to foster both support for American Laser Games and to offer the consumer a cheaper alternative to buying the three games seperately.

Hell: A Cyberpunk Thriller   Take 2 Interactive 5 $8
The cover art was enough to coax enough people into buying this game, and to disappoint them in the game as well. Expectations of a great interactive game were dashed as consumers were greeted with a complicated interface and small amounts of true interaction and decision making.

Horde, The   Crystal Dynamics 3 $7
This strategy game offers simple control and features interlaced FMV sequences to progress the story line.

IceBreaker   Panasonic   3 $6
In this interesting puzzle game you must clear each level before moving on to the next. Fans of Tetris and Bust-A-Move should enjoy this 3-D puzzler. Simple, but nice graphics, and easy control make the challenging game play an exercise for the mind, not the thumbs.

Immercenary
           Electronic Arts / Five Miles Out   4 $7

This first person shooter involves an interesting story line that sees you travel to the future in order to battle the perfect being. Fast paced action and a nice selection of weapons make this an enjoyable title relying on the progression of your character through various power levels.

Immortal Desire   Vivid Interactive   4 $5
Yet another adult title from vivid...just horrible.

Incredible Machine, The   Dynamix   4 $12
Build humorous chain reactions from various parts in order to complete certain onscreen tasks. A very unique title, this is something typically only seen in Japan. This puzzle game will not only test your mind, but will also require you to be very creative.

Iron Angel of the Apocalypse
               Synergy Inc.   3 $7
Slow frame rates and a reduced action window haunt this first person shooter, though it does contain some interesting cinemas. The story line can almost make you forget about the bad game play, almost.

Iron Angel of the Apocalypse: The Return
               Synergy Inc.   4 $9
More of the same offers nice cinemas and a good story, and the game play seems to have improved a bit, but not to the level necessary to make it very fun. Both this title and the first installment could have been much better had more time been spent figuring a way to make it run at full speed on the 3DO.

It's A Bird's Life with Shelly Duvall
               Sanctuary Woods 3 $2
Shelly narrates this interactive title about...birds. Not very interesting or interactive, this was an early title used by 3DO to help market the system as a multimedia device instead of a simple game machine.

Jammit   GTE   4 $7
This basketball game, (also available on the Genesis and SNES) doesn't offer any outstanding upgrades, though the control does seem to be a bit improved. Several modes of play offer variations in an otherwise average street-ball game.

John Madden Football   Electronic Arts 2 $3
The most successful football video game franchise in history

14

There are 240 dots on a Pac-Man board.

made an impressive appearance on the 3DO with this installment. While it could have certainly featured improved graphics, the solid game play and style that made the series popular remain intact.

Johnny Bazookatone   US Gold   3 $8
This platform shooter features cartoon-like graphics and solid control. Available on both the PSX and Saturn, the 3DO version has a rough feel when compared to other ports.

Jurassic Park Interactive
Universal Interactive Studios   2 $5
Once regarded as a reason to own a 3DO, this title is absolutely horrible! A collection of miniature games, such as an Asteroids clone, is really all this title has to offer. Nice graphics occasionally grace an otherwise horrible title.

Killing Time   3DO   4 $8
First person shooters rely on precise control, and this game is severely lacking in that area. Numerous enemies will surround you in this game, typically because you are simply unable to guide your character away from them. Very violent when you're able to actually shoot your enemies, this game could have been much better had just a bit more effort been put forth on refining it.

Kingdom: The Far Reaches
Interplay   4 $10
Select the area you wish to explore and then utilize a Dragon's Lair style control scheme to see your character safely through the dangers within. Without a linear story line as found in Dragon's Lair, this game offers more of a challenge and more replay value, though it can become frustrating after dying in the same spot a dozen times.

Last Bounty Hunter, The
American Laser Games   6 $12
This digitized shooter is easy to master after the enemy patterns are learned. Very similar in style to the Mad Dog McCree games, this title can be more fun to watch than it is to play, so set the VCR to record so that you can watch it after it is completed.

Lemmings   Psygnosis   4 $8
A puzzle game with action elements, your job is to save the lemmings from their instinctive fate of mass suicide. Utilizing their specific abilities, your must safely guide them to the end of each of the 125 levels.

Life Stage: Virtual House, The
Panasonic   6 $12
One of the earlier releases for the 3DO, this title is actually an interactive building project of sorts in which a living space can be created and toured. Available in mass when the 3DO was launched, this title suffered from poor sales and is becoming more difficult to find, though it offers no real game play value.

Lost Files of Sherlock Holmes, The
Electronic Arts   4 $15
A very unique Sherlock Holmes title from the time, instead of relying completely on a point and click interface and grainy FMV, this version uses animated sequences and quality FMV sequences. Some areas of this game might become tedious, but overall, this title will offer a fair amount of challenge for even the best sleuths. The first time this game is played, it will offer around 60 hours of game play, far superior to other games of its day.

Lost Eden   Virgin / Cryo   5 $15
A point and click first person adventure game, this title features a world where dinosaurs and humans live side by side. In a quest to save Eden from a rogue dinosaur you must unlock the ancient secrets of the citadel and create new ones to continue protecting the world. This game plays in a similar fashion to that of Dragon Lore or Myst and offers full screen animations.

Love Bites   Vivid Interactive   4 $5
Little interaction, no story line, and once again a disappointing entry by Vivid.

Lucienne's Quest   Panasonic / Microcabin   7 $35
One of the few RPG's available for the 3DO, this title is not only very entertaining, but very desirable and very rare. With a quality story line and an isometric view, this game really is unique on the 3DO and will not be easy to find.

Mad Dog McCree
American Laser Games   4 $8
Digitized opponents face you in this head to head fast draw contest that requires the game gun from American Laser Games.

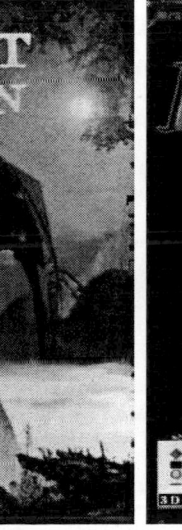

Jurassic Park Interactive   **Kingdom: The Far Reaches**   **Lost Eden**   **Lucienne's Quest**

The first Pong machine broke on the first night because too many quarters had been inserted!

3DO

| Mind Teazzer | The Need for Speed | Oceans Below | Off-World Interceptor |

Mad Dog McCree 2: The Lost Gold
American Laser Games 4 $8
Basically the same as the first Mad Dog McCree, this title offers new opponents, though little else in the way of change.

Mathemagics L3 interactive 5 $5
Learn to calculate cubed roots and multiply three digit numbers in your head with the help of this title. While this might seem very boring, it can be interesting to find shortcuts to otherwise complicated math problems. And while solving long division problems won't boost you into a more popular crowd, neither will playing more entertaining games on the 3DO.

Mazer American Laser Games 5 $10
Different from all the other American Laser Games titles on the 3DO, this actually isn't a digitized shooter, but instead an action game that allows you to select one of four characters, each with a different power. Supporting up to two players at once, the game play itself is relatively simple. Destroy the oncoming army of robots while trying to knock out their control unit. Once the unit is destroyed, a boss will appear in order to stop you. Once the boss is destroyed, you move along to the next level and the next until the game is finished. This game is much easier when played with two people, especially considering the possible combinations of special powers available.

MegaRace Mindscape 4 $8
Available for the Sega CD as well, this futuristic racing game is actually a depiction of a virtual reality race seen through the eyes of characters within the game. Though better than the Sega CD version, this title still lacks a real feeling of speed and features often poorly designed courses.

Microcosm Psygnosis 3 $5
An early 3-D shooter using nice backgrounds, this game is obviously dated, and was already aged when it was released on the 3DO. Once impressive, this title has become boring and repetitive.

Mind Teazzer Vivid Interactive 5 $10
Just when you thought every Vivid game for the 3DO was absolutely horrible, along comes Mind Teazzer and proves that at least one adult title isn't worth all the criticism. Don't misunderstand now, the game is still bad, but at least in this puzzle game there is a good level of interaction. It just happens to include nude women to make it more interesting.

Myst Panasonic 4 $8
The classic point and click puzzle adventure is less than impressive on the 3DO. Very grainy graphics make the main appeal of this game a burden instead of an asset. The mouse controller does make this title more enjoyable however.

Need For Speed, The Electronic Arts 3 $8
Real cars and realistic courses are featured in this game, and the extreme feeling of speed really help this title stand out. Pushing a Lamborghini to 200 mph in heavy downtown traffic is an incredible challenge, and the spectacular wrecks that are sure to result make this first installment to the popular series a lot of fun.

NeuroDancer: Journey Into The Neuronet
Pixis Interactive 4 $7
This is an adult title in which the sole purpose is to gain enough credits to pay for a virtual stripper to dance for you. Limited interaction and a sleazy feel make this a collector's game only, though it is still more of a game than most of the Vivid titles.

Night Trap Digital Pictures / Virgin 4 $15
The most controversial FMV title ever made for a home console leaps from the Sega CD to the 3DO with slightly improved video and game play. Still a mediocre title at best, it remains a cult classic.

Novastorm Psygnosis 3 $5
A favorite among gamers on other systems, the 3DO version of Novastorm simply doesn't do this title justice. Quite simply, this is possibly the worst version of this space shooter ever made.

Oceans Below Software Toolworks 4 $4
Study the ocean and its creatures in this interactive title. Not a game, but instead one of the titles used by 3DO to help advertise the system as a multimedia device.

Off-World Interceptor Crystal Dynamics 3 $7
Taking monster trucks to a distant planet seems like a great idea, and this version of the game makes it enjoyable. Low gravity and big tires are all that are needed for some incredible racing action in these off road courses.

Olympic Soccer Panasonic 4 $8
While this game might have been considered one of the greats, the fact that the far superior FIFA title was also available for this

Qix is pronounced "kicks."

system made this title come in a distant second.

Olympic Summer Games   Panasonic   4 $8
How quickly can you push the buttons on your 3DO controller? Compete in both track and field events in this title that features nice graphics and sound. Unfortunately there isn't much skill involved, but it is fun regardless.

Out Of This World   Interplay   4 $10
Gorgeous graphics make this version of Out of this World the best looking version to date. Beautiful environments and an interesting story line make this one of the better games for this system.

Panzer General   Mindscape / SSI   3 $6
Take the role of a German general and control a Panzer unit. Your strategic prowess will be challenged by this game, though after playing several times patterns begin to form within your opponent's decisions.

PaTaank   PF. Magic   4 $8
Ever want to play pinball…as the ball? This is similar in concept as you control a disc within an arena, changing course by utilizing different features within the arena itself. Nice graphics and solid control, coupled with a very creative idea make this fun title a must-have for the 3DO.

Perfect General, The   Kirin Entertainment   3 $7
Complex controls and a large number of options allow you to control the red or blue armies into battle. While a bit difficult to get used to, once a good understanding of the game has been acquired, it becomes both challenging and fun. A strategy game at heart, the "cute" graphics seem an odd choice but can quickly be overlooked when you realize the depth that can be found within this game.

PGA Tour Golf '96   Electronic Arts   3 $5

Pebble Beach Golf Links
T&E Soft / Panasonic   2 $5
Golfing next to the ocean makes it "links", just in case you didn't know. Digitized graphics make the environment and players look especially nice, and control is solid. This is a nice golf installment that was ahead of the others released around the same time.

Phoenix 3   3DO   4 $8
Digitized platform games are somewhat of an oddity, and this title proves why there aren't more of them. Horrible graphics and questionable control make the bad sound and music less noticeable, but overall there is little about this game that is enjoyable. The cover art on the box is nice, but that is pretty much where enjoyment of this game will end.

Plumbers Don't Wear Ties
Kirin Entertainment   4 $7
While technically an adult title, this game is nothing more than a multiple choice adventure in which you attempt to lure a woman into your life. The wrong choices often result in humorous outcomes, though they can't save this title from being horrible. Interestingly though, a code does allow for the "censored" bars to be removed, but only to find that they weren't covering anything interesting in the first place.

PO'ed   Any Channel   3 $8
Force your way through a variety of interesting enemies in this first person shooter with a large variety of weapons, often resulting in a very violent ending. Fast paced action, nice graphics and gallons of blood helped push this title to other systems including the PSX.

Primal Rage
Goldstar / LG Electronics / Time Warner Int.   4 $10
This fighting game offers a variety of primitive creatures to fight with. Amazingly popular in the arcades, this version is a nice conversion, though the characters aren't nearly as large as those found in the arcade. Control is solid however, and this is a nice fighting title for the 3DO.

Psychic Detective   Electronic Arts   3 $8
In this FMV adventure you must use your psychic powers to solve the case, you are able to view what others are seeing. A game of "being in the right place at the right time" will find you playing through several times in order to see the appropriate clues as they happen. Running in real time, if you access the mind of the wrong person, you might just have to start over so that you can try again. Regardless of your findings, the game will continue to play in real time, leading to frequent frustration and a feeling of helplessness as you realize your interaction is completely passive.

Out of this World   Panzer General   Plumbers Don't Wear Ties   Psychic Detective

Walter Cronkite said that his idea of retirement was, "To sit all day in a big, dark room playing Space Invaders.

3DO

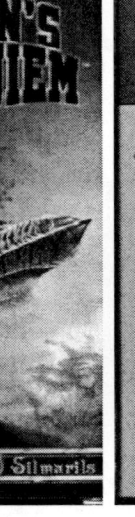

| Quarantine | Quarterback Attack | Robinson's Requiem | Sesame Street Numbers |

Putt-Putt's Fun Pack
Humongous Entertainment 3 $5
This child's interactive media offers early age learning material in a variety of simple games.

Putt-Putt Goes To The Moon
Humongous Entertainment 4 $5
This child's game has a space theme, but offers the basic early learning games and material found in so many other children's games.

Putt-Putt's Joins The Parade
Humongous Entertainment 3 $5

Quarantine GameTek 3 $8
Driving a car with cross hairs as a hood ornament should be enough for anyone to buy this game, but awful control and graphics don't help this game stand out. The sheer amount of violence in this game will make it enjoyable for fans of games like Twisted Metal however.

Quarterback Attack Digital Pictures 4 $7
What was originally an interesting concept turns into a dismal failure. Taking the role of a quarterback through first person interaction is portrayed with the use of FMV, but horrible control and limited scenarios turn this title into an exercise in frustration.

Real Pinball Panasonic 4 $8
Realistic table design and accurate control make this game stand apart from most other pinball games.

Return Fire Prolific / Silent Software 3 $10
Making headlines when first released, Return Fire still remains an amazing vehicle shooter. Numerous maps, multiple vehicles and the ability to blow everything up make this one of the best games for the system. Extremely addictive game play will keep you entertained for hours.

Return Fire: Maps O' Death
Prolific 4 $12
More of the same, but taking place on different maps, this installment continues to offer the same fun found in the first game. You can never blow up enough stuff, and this game is proof of that.

Rise Of The Robots Absolute 4 $6
An average 2-D fighting game at best, ROTR could have been refined quite a bit. Available on many other systems, this version features a few video sequences no different than those found in the CD32 version.

Road Rash Electronic Arts 3 $8
Swinging chains (and anything else you can find) at your opponents while riding a motorcycle is a lot of fun in this version of the popular game. An amazing soundtrack of various groups helps to make this title stand out in the field of combat racers.

Robinson's Requiem Readysoft 5 $15
As part of an elite team crash landed on a hostile planet, your job in this first person adventure is to explore your surroundings and find a way off this planet. A mixture of RPG, adventure and action elements make this an interesting title that should offer a good level of challenge for most gamers.

Samurai Shodown Crystal Dynamics 4 $12
Putting the Neo-Geo on the map, this game simply isn't the same caliber game on any other console. While a good attempt was made for the 3DO version, the graphics, sound and control all suffer in the conversion.

Scramble Cobra Panasonic 4 $7
The box would have you believe that this game is some sort of simulation with various weapons systems at your control, but instead it is nothing more than a mediocre side scrolling helicopter game like so many others. Poor sound and low graphical quality aren't enough to make it horrible however, and solid control saves this title from being a complete failure.

Seal Of The Pharoah Panasonic 4 $8
This corridor exploring game finds you inside of a pyramid trying to unlock its secrets. Primitive graphics by today's standards, this title may offer mild entertainment for retrogamers.

Sesame Street Numbers Electronic Arts 5 $7
Utilizing Sesame Street characters, children can use this interactive software to improve their numerical skills.

Sewer Shark Digital Pictures 3 $5
A horrible FMV rail shooter, this title was originally packaged with the Sega CD, but it is amazing that anyone would actually buy it separately. Though there are slight graphical improve-

18

The three missile bases in Missile Command are called Alpha, Omega, and Delta.

ments, the sheer boredom of this game become evident after only a few minutes.

Sex
Vivid Interactive   4 $5
A horrible entry to the game market from Vivid, like all of its other titles this adult game offers little interaction and grainy FMV sequences of women in various states of undress.

Shadow: War of Succession
Tribeca Digital Studios   4 $6
This horrible fighting game features digitized characters and bad control. The best aspect of this game is the fact that it is short and relatively easy to finish. Once you have played this, it is doubtful you ever will again. Consider playing Way of the Warrior, but without any of the positive qualities and you might have a feel for what this title is like.

Shanghai: Triple Threat   Activision   3 $8
The ancient Chinese game of mahjong makes its appearance on nearly ever video console ever made, and the 3DO offers no exception. Amusing animations accompany the removal of each tile, though this version offers nothing that any other mahjong game doesn't.

Shock Wave
Electronic Arts   2 $5
This shooter places you behind the space craft to destroy the enemy threat. Various level designs keep it relatively interesting, and FMV sequences are used to help progress the story line.

Shock Wave: Operation Jumpgate
Electronic Arts   2 $7
Expanding on the series, this is a good shooter, but becomes stagnate after a few minutes of play time.

Shockwave 2: Beyond The Gate
Electronic Arts   4 $10
It is very surprising that this franchise actually lasted for three games. Slightly improved graphics and improvements to the sound are included in this installment, but it really offers nothing in the way of major innovation to the series.

Silly Classix: At the Museum
VideoactV   5 $12

Slam 'N Jam '95   Crystal Dynamics   4 $10
Absolutely stunning graphics and simple controls made this game stand out in the field of basketball games. Even by today's standards, this title is a lot of fun to play. And while real teams and players weren't officially used, close inspection of the players' faces will show that they were indeed used, but instead placed on different teams.

Slayer   SSI   3 $15
One of the best Dungeons and Dragons action games available, the normally despised random level design give this title enormous replay value. The ability to tailor dungeons with 10 to 100 levels add a great challenge to this game. Different characters can be customized, multiple weapons and items can be collected along the way, and an easy interface make this first person action game amazing.

SlopeStyle   L3 Interactive   4 $5
Before snowboarding was a staple of the video game industry, this interactive title was released for the 3DO. But, instead of tricking off of everything on the slope, this is an interactive learning cube, concentrating on the learning aspect of the sport. Don't expect any actual game play from this title.

Snow Job: Staring Tracy Scoggins
3DO   5 $15
Not much fun by traditional standards, this game still offers a very unique experience. Featuring 360 degree views of real environments and numerous items to add to your inventory, this title offers a very high level of difficulty even for seasoned players. Typically driven by a point and click interface, the occasional action sequence speeds things up from time to time. If you're looking for a change of pace, this game should offer both challenge and entertainment for those open to a new type of video game.

Soccer Kid   3DO   4 $12
You might expect this to be a soccer game, but instead it is actually a platform game utilizing a "soccer kid" and his soccer ball. This interesting game uses some nice cartoon-like graphics and solid control. You should definitely give this game a try if you get the chance, though it isn't really a must-have.

Space Ace   Readysoft   3 $7
One of many appearances of this title on a home platform, this version isn't quite as good as the CD-i version that was released

Shanghai: Triple-Threat   Slam 'N Jam '95   Snow Job: Staring Tracy Scoggins   Soccer Kid

Nintendo originally approached Atari to market and distribute the NES. Sega later did the same with the Genesis.

3DO

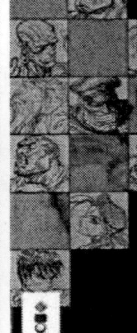

Space Shuttle	Starblade
Strahl	Super Street Fighter II Turbo

around the same time.

Space Hulk: Vengeance of the Blood Angels
Electronic Arts   3 $8
Command a five man team, or go it alone in this first person shooter/strategy game. Battling against the Genestalkers, a hideous alien race, the various levels of control in this game offer a large amount of replay value.

Space Pirates   American Laser Games   5 $12
This FMV shooting game features some horribly dressed actors that you will be only too glad to shoot. The video quality is poor, and the sound isn't worth noting, plus the game gun accuracy seems to be way off in this title. Often firing at the same target several times, even when you're sure of a hit, will result in multiple misses.

Space Shuttle
The Software Toolworks / Amazing Media   5 $10
An interactive tour of the space shuttle and every aspect of its operations, this isn't a game, but instead a multimedia title designed for reference.

Star Control 2   Crystal Dynamics   4 $18
Possibly the best game made for the 3DO, this expansive action oriented space RPG offers a staggering number of locations to visit. Each star can be explored, every planet and moon can be orbited and researched, in addition to landing on many of them in your quest to seek raw materials necessary to improve your space craft. Form alliances with alien races, utilize their technology, fight numerous enemy races in great actions sequences, and explore the galaxy in this amazing title from Crystal Dynamics. Amazing CG sequences compliment the game to round out an outstanding video game experience.

Star Fighter   3DO   4 $8
This polygon based space shooter is viewed from behind the ship and is basically an updated version of Guardian. The sluggish control takes a while to get used to, but it becomes second nature after a little practice.

Star Wars Chess   LucusArts   6 $15
In the same style as Battle Chess, this game features animations to depict your opponent's individual character's demise. This time around, however, the traditional characters are replaced with prominent characters from the Star Wars movies.

Star Wars: Rebel Assault   LucasArts   3 $10
Available on a variety of systems, the 3DO does a nice job of portraying the space flights and intense battles depicted within the game. Solid control and stereo sound made this version one of the best at its time of release, though more recent versions on more powerful systems will make this version seem ancient by comparison.

Starblade   Panasonic / Namco   3 $7
The largest problem with this title is the inability to reverse the control style so that pressing down makes the ship fly upward. Aside from that complaint, the graphics are nice and the sound is decent, though the voice-overs are comically bad. This does the arcade version justice, though the original is still better.

Station Invasion   3DO   2 $6
An interactive game show intended for adults, this title features various mini-games and questions that should be played by multiple people to be enjoyed.

Stellar 7: Draxon's Revenge
Dynamix   3 $7
An early polygon based shooting game, this was state of the art for the time. Very little in the way of terrain, maneuver your customizable ship through the flat levels in an effort to destroy increasingly cunning enemies.

Strahl   Panasonic   4 $10
This interactive cartoon is similar in style to Dragon's Lair, except the appropriate button selection is displayed onscreen at the appropriate time. Simply an exercise in how quickly you can press the correct button, the amazing animation makes the game more enjoyable for onlookers.

Super Street Fighter II Turbo
Panasonic   4 $12
A surprise entry to the 3DO library, few believed that a game of this popularity would make an appearance on the struggling 3DO platform. A special controller was even released for this title, and though it isn't arcade perfect by any stretch of the imagination, it remains a solid translation of a great 2-D fighter.

Super Wing Commander
Origin / Electronic Arts   4 $12
In place of the regular Wing Commander, the 3DO receives this "super" version of the game. Nice graphics stand out as the

20

high point in this space simulation, though the fail to impress as they originally did when the game was originally released.

SuperModels Go Wild   **Vivid Interactive**   4 $5
32-bit nudity with little interaction, this is standard fare for the adult titles on the 3DO.

Supreme Warrior   **Digital Pictures**   3 $5
First person FMV is utilized in this horrible fighting game from Digital Pictures. What could have been a great game quickly turned sour due to bad control and horrible video quality.

Syndicate
          BullFrog / Electronic Arts   3 $8
Attempt to reunify the world by deploying different agents of varied skills in this action oriented strategy game. A bit unusual when compared to other strategy games due to the direct interaction with your agents, this title is entertaining and challenging for both strategy game buffs and novices alike.

ThemePark
          BullFrog / Electronic Arts   3 $10
Design, build and run the day to day operations of your own theme park. Part of the growing simulation genre that saw some very strange variations, this solid title remains a favorite of many 3DO owners.

ToonTime ...in the Classroom
          VideoactV   5 $10

Total Eclipse   **Crystal Dynamics**   2 $5
One of the first games made for the 3DO, this version suffers from slow down and an overall lack of any feeling of speed. Later released on the Playstation, this game offers little challenge to the experienced gamer. Your job is to simply destroy everything on screen, which can often cause boredom to set in quickly.

Trip'd   **Panasonic / Warp**   3 $8
A simple Tetris like game with one major problem: stagnate game play. The levels offer very little variation and the music never changes. An otherwise fun game that offers more variation than a standard game of Tetris, monotony will very quickly set in.

Twisted: The Game Show   **Electronic Arts**   2 $7
An interactive talk show with outlandish questions and events, this title was geared toward an adult crowd, though the content isn't inappropriate for children.

VR Stalker   **Morpheus Interactive**   3 $7
An average flying combat game, this title is played from behind the ship as you clear multiple levels of numerous enemies. This title does not stand out, though at the time, it's use of polygons was a novelty.

Virtuoso   **Elite / Data East**   4 $10
Three main missions and 24 total levels comprise the entirety of this game in which you play the virtual image of a rock star. Your character is actually playing a game, and you are controlling him within it. Various weapons are available in this shooter, and stylish graphics make it enjoyable to watch as well as play.

Waialae Country Club   **Panasonic**   2 $6
One of many average golf simulations for the time, this title features digitized characters and environments. Concentrating on realism of control and environments, it seems to fall a bit short if the game makers' intended goal, though it is still enjoyable.

Way of the Warrior
          Universal Interactive Studios   3 $15
Perhaps the most loved and hated game on the 3DO, Naughty Dog's first video game is never short of controversy. Done in the same style as Mortal Kombat, digitized characters and overly gruesome fatalities grace this game with a unique style and feel, regardless of it's obvious roots in the MK series. Numerous hidden characters and levels only add to the fun of this very cheesy game, and a soundtrack by White Zombie make it stand out as a true great in the fighting genre. Don't mistake the outstanding qualities of this game as an endorsement of its fighting engine's prowess however. The fighting aspect of this game is probably the worst part. Bad controls and choppy character animations would make the average player turn away in disgust, but the overall feel of the game, b-movie feel and sheer fun of ripping your opponent's heart out to watch it beat in your hand for the last time are just too much to ignore. Regardless of the arguments for or against this title, it must be played at least once to understand the appeal.

Trip'd

Virtuoso

Waialae Country Club

Way of the Warrior

The character Dan from Street Fighter Alpha was designed to be a parody of Ryo Sakazani from Art of Fighting.

3DO

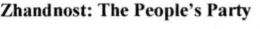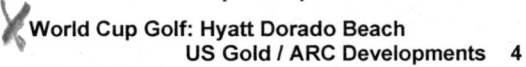

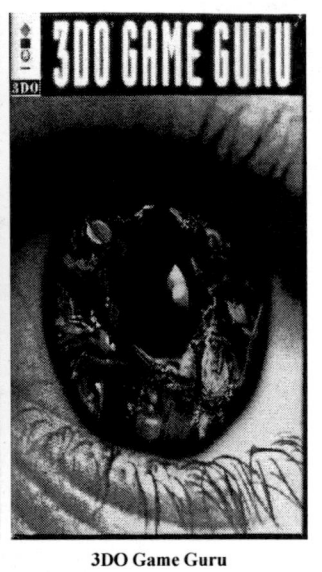

| Wicked 18 | Wolfenstein 3D | Zhandnost: The People's Party | 3DO Game Guru |

Who Shot Johnny Rock?
American Laser Games 3 $8
Very challenging at first, once the enemy patterns are learned the game becomes more enjoyable, though never easy. Similar in style to Mad Dog McCree, this title supports the difficult to find 3DO game gun.

Wicked 18 T & E Soft / Panasonic 3 $12
If you find golf boring, this game should change your mind. With variations to the normal game such as lava traps, floating stone pillars, and eccentrically designed courses, this round of golf is extremely challenging and entertaining. While it seems frustration would quickly set in after hitting a stone wall built into the fairway, the fun involved with this inventive course is enough to overcome any other apparent flaws in the game. Good control and sound, coupled with great graphics and awesome design make this a must-have for the 3DO.

Wing Commander III: Heart of the Tiger
Origin / Electronic Arts 2 $12
The classic space story continues with this digitized installment. Featuring some nice FMV sequences and solid shooting action, this title should be enjoyable for both fans of the series and new gamers alike.

Winner Take All Vivid 5 $7
This softcore porn game by Vivid offers little real interaction, as usual

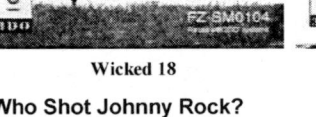
Wolfenstein 3D Interplay 3 $7
The true pioneer that made first person shooters a reality, this game lets you maneuver through the often monotonous hallways of a Nazi controlled castle in search of loot, all while defending yourself from mutated creatures and Nazi soldiers.

Woody Woodpecker & Friends: Volume 1
MCA Home Video, Inc. 8 $40
This cartoon based title is among the most difficult title to find for the 3DO, as are the two subsequent volumes.

Woody Woodpecker & Friends: Volume 2
MCA Home Video, Inc. 8 $40

Woody Woodpecker & Friends: Volume 3
MCA Home Video, Inc. 8 $40

World Cup Golf: Hyatt Dorado Beach
US Gold / ARC Developments 4 $6
This substandard golf game for the 3DOfeatures unresponsive control, causing massive hooks or slices. The environments look nice, but nothing stands out above other golf titles.

World Cup Striker U.S. Gold 4 $7

Zhadnost: The People's Party
3DO 3 $8
An entertaining variety show of sorts, this game is intended for multi-players and offers more fun for adults than children.

DEMO CD's, SAMPLE DISKS and Misc.

3DO Game Guru	3DO	4	$15
3DO Interactive Sampler CD #1, The	3DO	1	$1
3DO Interactive Sampler CD #2, The	3DO	1	$1
3DO Interactive Sampler CD #3, The	3DO	2	$3
3DO Interactive Sampler CD #4, The	3DO	2	$3
3DO Buffet	Interplay	2	$4
Season's Greetings 1995 Calendar	Panasonic	4	$7
Panasonic Real Sampler CD Version 1	Panasonic	3	$1
Panasonic Real Sampler CD Version 2 (w/ Photo CD)	Panasonic	5	$5
Sample This!	Crystal Dynamics	1	$1
Virtual Vivid Sampler	Vivid Interactive	5	$8

HARDWARE

Goldstar 3DO   **Goldstar**   **5**   **$55**
This model features a front loading tray and sturdy construction, though this model suffers more problems than either of the Panasonic models.

Panasonic 3DO FZ-1   **Panasonic**   **4**   **$40**
The first 3DO system, this model features a front loading CD tray and is of the highest quality. Very heavy and extremely well built, this is the most resilient version of the 3DO.

Panasonic 3DO FZ-10   **Panasonic**   **2**   **$30**
Created to reduce costs, this is the second version of the Panasonic 3DO featuring a flip-top lid and reduced-cost components. Still a well built machine, this model just lacks the styling that made the FZ-1 such a great looking machine.

Flightstick PRO   **CH Products**   **6**   **$30**
Nearly a necessity for playing Flying Nightmares, this is one of the best quality flight sticks made for any home console to date. Highly sought after and In short supply, this is a must-have controller for any serious 3DO fan.

Game Gun   **American Laser Games 7**   **$30**
Why this gun is so uncommon is something only ALG can answer, but it is EXTREMELY difficult to come by. However, this controller can be bypassed by using a series of adaptors so that a Genesis Justifier light gun can be used on the 3DO (though these adapters are as difficult to find as the Game Gun is.)

Goldstar Controller   **Goldstar**   **2**   **$4**
Cheaply built and prone to problems with the directional pad, these controllers can be found regularly and inexpensively.

MPEG Adapter   **Goldstar**   **8**   **$30**
Released as an effort to make the Goldstar 3DO stand out from the Panasonic version, this unit was a failure even though it included Total Recall for free. Many stores sent their stock back to Goldstar, making this accessory relatively rare, but still undesirable by most.

Panasonic Controller   **Panasonic**   **1**   **$5**
More common than the Goldstar model but featuring better workmanship, this is the best choice for a standard 3DO controller.

Panasonic Mouse   **Panasonic**   **4**   **$10**
This controller is very useful for point and click interface games such as Myst and Hell. Quickly sent to bargain bins due to poor sales, this is becoming increasingly difficult to find.

Street Fighter 2 Controller Capcom   **5**   **$14**
Available only through a mail in offer after buying Super Street Fighter 2 Turbo, this is a difficult controller to come by, though a much more common version exists for the SNES. It was designed so that the right hand could be inverted, and offered 6 action buttons instead of 5 (3 action buttons + 2 shoulder buttons.)

The 3DO will not only play nearly any game from any region, but it will also play copied games.

Amiga CDTV
By: Andy Slaven

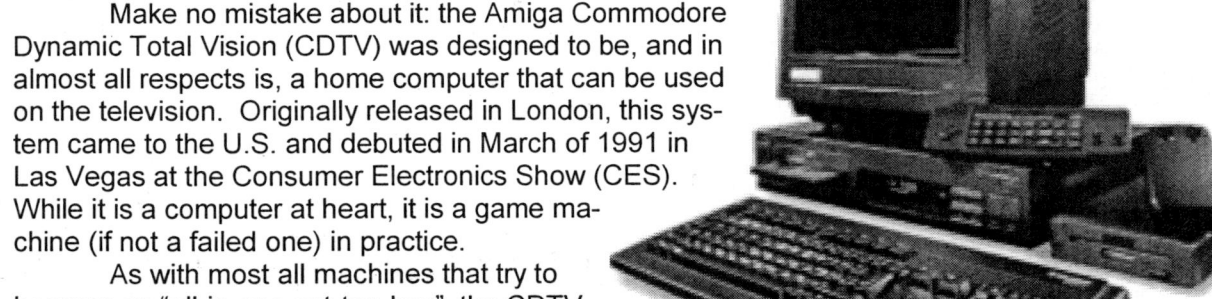

Make no mistake about it: the Amiga Commodore Dynamic Total Vision (CDTV) was designed to be, and in almost all respects is, a home computer that can be used on the television. Originally released in London, this system came to the U.S. and debuted in March of 1991 in Las Vegas at the Consumer Electronics Show (CES). While it is a computer at heart, it is a game machine (if not a failed one) in practice.

As with most all machines that try to become an "all-in-one set-top-box", the CDTV was a "jack of all trades and master of none". You'll notice that this was the case with the Bandai Pippin as well. And, unless things change drastically in the future, the Microsoft Xbox will almost assuredly meet with the same fate as these fossil systems.

Designed to fit snuggly into a consumer's stereo cabinet or on top of the television, the goal of this machine was to bring interactivity into the home. With an infrared controller, optional keyboard, extra disc drive, etc., this system could be much more than was originally stated by Commodore (pictured above is the full system with optional monitor and other accessories). And probably the intention of the company was to get "the box" into the consumer's home, and THEN announce all the "wonderful extras" that were available at a "nominal fee".

An amazing console, if for no other reason than its nearly complete obscurity, the CDTV has some good games to offer, but most are available on cheaper and easier to find consoles. As a piece of functional computer/gaming hardware, it's basically worthless. But as a piece of gaming history, a piece of nostalgia, or a piece in a complete gaming hardware collection...it's absolutely necessary as well as priceless.

An interesting fact is that the CDTV software can be played on the newer Commodore Amiga CD32 and some Amiga computer systems. The CD32 is more reliable and usually easier to find, although it often demands a higher price. Both of these consoles were much more popular in Europe, but both were released to a timid audience in the U.S.

Based around a Motorola MC68000, and with a clock speed of 7 MHz, it was able to hold its own as a computer. Some models were installed with 512 kb and others with 1 Mb RAM. Unfortunately for Commodore, the unit was shipping with Workbench 1.3 (the Amiga operating system it used), but the new Amiga computers were already being installed with Workbench 2.0.

It was intentionally separated from any computers in the stores where it was sold at the request of Commodore. Keep in mind that at the time only 10% of Americans used a computer at home, and only 15% used a computer at work. It was Commodore's wish to make this the "VCR of the future." But in the end, computer buyers thought it wasn't enough of a computer, and non-computer users thought it was too much of a computer. Without much of an impact on the U.S. market, Commodore's first video game console quietly disappeared.

***Note: Due to the seemingly borderless distribution of software for the CDTV, the list compiled also includes games specifically intended for Europe, but were redistributed in the U.S. Only gaming software was listed, and games that were designed specifically for children were omitted. No application software of any type was mentioned in this section.

The Sega CD will not play import games, but will play copied games.

| Battlestorm | The Case of the Cautious Condor | The Curse of RA | Defender of the Crown |

17 bit Collection Almathers 5 $10
A collection of partial games and viewable demos of other games to be released.

17 bit Collection 2 Almathers 5 $10
Similar to the first volume, but obviously with different demos.

Air Warrior On-Line 4 $18
A surprisingly fun flight simulator, especially for its day. You will face off against a screen full of other pilots looking to shoot you down. Graphics are quite dated, and the control can sometimes feel questionable, but considering its age and the technological disadvantages it faced on this system, it was pulled off rather well.

Alistair In Outer Space Altered Images 5 $12
Suited for children 5-9, this title is an interactive story book following Alistair's adventures.

All Dogs Go To Heaven - Talking Electric Crayon
Merit 4 $5
A child's game based on the Disney movie of the same name, the object is basically little more than to color different pictures.

Battle Chess Interplay 4 $5
Animated death blows performed either by or on your characters make this chess game more enjoyable than the regular type.

Battlestorm Titus 5 $9
Your job is to defeat the Katlomarians before they take over the galaxy in this space oriented game. Your opponents fly "battlestorm starships" and are capable of enormous destruction. This is an interesting game, and worth the time if you have this system.

The Case Of The Cautious Condor
Tiger Media 3 $14
A 30 minute time limit makes this game nearly impossible to beat on the first try. Set in the 1930's and drawing almost every imaginable cliché from detective movies, this game will be a big hit with any fans of classic cinema. Also available on the Amiga CD32, this is one of the best titles available. With a simple point and click interface and nicely done voice-overs, this is a "must have" for the system.

Casino Games Sean Software 6 $15
Ten unique audio tracks make this casino simulation better than most others of the time, but a relatively small choice of games within the casino and any lack of reality make the replay value relatively low.

CDTV Remix 2 Microdeal 5 $6
You will be able to create music and alter existing music with this program. Similar to MTV Music Generator for the Sony Playstation, but much more basic.

Chaos in Andromeda - Eyes Of The Eagle
On-Line 5 $7
You must rescue a missing scientist in this futuristic role playing game set on the planet of Koranis 12. You are able to personalize your character, and the world map is very large compared to other games of the time.

Covergirl Strip Poker On-Line 4 $5
Just as it sounds, this game is an adult title where the object is to win enough hands of poker to "undress" your female opponents.

Classic Board Games Merit 3 $3
Backgammon, Chess and Draughts are all available on this compilation game. A variable level of difficulty adds to the replay value of this game. Also, a two player mode is available so that you can play against your friends.

Curse Of RA, The Softgold 5 $8
Yet another puzzle game for the system, this one is based on clearing levels by deciphering different symbols. With numerous levels and the ability to create your own, this game will keep your interest for quite a while.

Defender Of The Crown CDTV Publishing 4 $7
A classic game that appears on the PC as well as many consoles, this version delivers not only good game play, but also features full stereo and speech.

Defender Of The Crown II CDTV Publishing 3 $10
Not as popular on consoles, this game is still a favorite among PC owners. With improvements to the interface and new hiresolution graphics, this game is almost guaranteed to please those who enjoyed the first installment.

Demo Collection Almathera 4 $3
A collection of partially playable games available at some stores, and while very inexpensive to obtain, it may be worth the time to pick one up considering the fact that most CDTV games are played for a short period of time.

Demo Collection 2 Almathera 5 $3
More difficult to find than the first volume, but still very inexpensive due to the lack of collectors interested in demo CD's.

Dinosaurs For Hire Wright 3 $2
This "game" is simply an animated story about dinosaurs.

E.S.S. Mega Tomahawk 7 $20
European Space Simulator (E.S.S.) is a very bad simulator involving the maintenance of a space shuttle in the near future.

Control, graphics and sound all suffer in this rare CDTV release.

Falcon   Mirrorsoft   7 $28
A very good version of the PC flight simulator, it is surprisingly responsive and well designed. The level of detail on this antiquated system will surprise most.

Fantastic Voyage   Centaur Software   5 $10
Based on the cult classic of the same name, you must pilot a miniaturized submarine through a man's body in order to repair brain damage caused by an attempt on that man's life.

Future Wars: Adventures In Time
           Interplay   8 $30
Puzzle solving, time travel and fighting mutants are all brought together in this title which also includes very good music and sound effects. ***Interplay insists that they released this game for the CDTV, which is good enough proof for VGB, however it may have only been released in Germany.

Games, The   Ocean   5 $5
In this interesting twist to the sports genre, you take the place of the team's manager instead of the athletes themselves. You must design and maintain training routines in order to optimize the athletes' performances.

Global Chaos   Hex   4 $4
This CD includes revolutionary music (for the time) and computer generated graphics. It also features the game "Top Banana".

Guy Spy and the Crystals of Armageddon
           Readysoft   3 $5
Unadvertised, and originally packaged with the PC version, this Dragon's Lair style game is very entertaining and difficult to come by.

Hound Of The Baskervilles, The
           On-Line   5 $10
Sherlock Holmes at his best. A classic story-turned-interactive title, this "game" was marketed toward children as an early learning tool, but the amount of interaction and use of Characters from the Sherlock Holmes stories classifies this title with other games for the system instead of a typical interactive book.

Indiana Jones and the Last Crusade
           Lucas Arts   10 $250
This is the rarest of all the CDTV releases, with only a few known copies, almost all of which are European. It also has difficulty running properly on some machines.

Labyrinth of Time   Electronic Arts   6 $18
Similar in fashion to Myst and other point-and-click adventures, this game places you within a labyrinth where time travel is necessary in order to meet your objectives. Nice visuals and a sometimes eerie soundtrack make this a fun title to play for stress relief. Many consider this title to be the best game available for the system. With amazing graphics, a very realistic experience, and the eerie sound track mentioned above, this highly sought after title is sure to please anyone who is able to find it.

Lemmings   Psygnosis   3 $5
Available on many platforms, you control a mass of lemmings in their quest through 100 levels.

Logical   Softgold   5 $10
This game is a 100 level puzzle based on grouping colored marbles into different groups. It is addictive, but not nearly as much as other puzzle games such as Tetris.

Mind Run   Crealude   3 $5
While considered to be an "educational" title by many, this is a puzzle game relying more on intelligence than skill. It is still a game however, regardless of the fact that it tests your mind instead of your thumbs.

Murder Makes Strange Deadfellows
           Tiger Media   7 $20
Made by the same geniuses behind The Case of the Cautious Condor, this game is surprisingly bad. Set in a haunted house, and using a similar style as before, this title lacks the feeling of their first game. It just doesn't seem to captivate an audience of onlookers in the same way, and as such isn't nearly as much fun to play.

Music Maker   CDTV Publishing   4 $5
This very basic music altering program allows you to create simple tracks with either sound effects or instrumentation.

North Pole Expedition   Virgin   8 $40
This is an interesting interactive trivia game where your decisions either help you advance or hinder your progress. Extremely difficult to find, but fun to play in multi-player mode.

Pinball Dreams   21st Century   6 $15
Supporting play for up to 8 people and sporting 4 different pinball machines in increasing difficulty, this title is definitely more fun when played with friends.

Pool   Virgin   5 $8
While the geometry seems a little off and the physics aren't up to speed with modern systems, this is one of the better pool simulations of its time.

Power Pinball   Karma Soft   4 $7
A mediocre pinball title at best, this game didn't surface until 1995, years after it had originally been completed. It was made available first through mail order catalogs, and then later through discount stores that carried old software.

Guy Spy and the Crystals of Armageddon   The Hound of the Baskervilles   Lemmings   Logical

The Dreamcast's Shenmue was originally slated as a Saturn release.

Sherlock Holmes Consulting Detective   Sim City   Super Games Pak   Xenon 2

Prehistrorik   **Titus**   **5**   **$7**
An arcade style game that places you in a time when cavemen and dinosaurs roamed the earth...although historically inaccurate it is still fun to play.

PREY - An Alien Encounter Kirk Moreno MM   3 $5
In this fully 3-D animated adventure, you play the role of a security guard stationed on a colony within the asteroid belt. You must save the colony before aliens completely invade.

Psycho Killer   **On-Line**   **3**   **$6**
This is a suspense game in which you must defeat a psychotic killer and save the potential victim being held captive. Unfortunately for anyone who likes playing games, this really isn't very entertaining. Grainy video clips and overall bad game design really take away from what might have been an enjoyable title.

Raffles   **Edge Interactive**   **4**   **$5**
Your objective is simple. Find the hidden treasure within an expansive mansion. This is a relatively entertaining game that some might actually enjoy. But don't expect too much excitement as the gameplay itself is simplistic and often monotonous.

Sherlock Holmes Consulting Detective
                    Icom   **6**   **$18**
Taking on the role of Sherlock Holmes, you will try and solve "The Mummy's Curse", "The Case of the Mystified Murderess", and "The Case of the Tin Soldier". And while available on several other systems, the CDTV does a very good job of handling both the video and speech of the decent actors.

Sim City   **Infrogames**   **5**   **$10**
A very popular game that is available for almost every platform after the Nintendo Entertainment System (for which only a prototype exists). Build and manage cities while taking care of problems as they arise. This is one of the best known and most enjoyable games for the CDTV. With so many different versions to choose from, the CDTV is hardly the first place one would think to look, but it is a very good translation nonetheless.

Sim Earth Planet Simulator Ocean   6 $16
Quite simply, you play God in this game. Your objective is to maintain the welfare of life forms that are evolving on Earth.

Snoopy: The Case Of The Missing Blanket
                    Edge Interactive   **5**   **$5**
You take the role of Snoopy as a detective determined to find Linus's lost blanket. This is an interactive cartoon geared toward children but should also be fun for Peanuts fans.

Space Wars   **Odyssey**   **4**   **$12**
Even more classic than Pong, Space Wars pits you in an environment with either a sun, black hole, or simply empty space. Your craft will show damage and be affected by it. A must-have

for classic gamers and CDTV collectors, but not really for anyone else.

Spirit of Excalibur   **Virgin**   **6**   **$12**
This is similar in style to the game Dark Seed, but this version is text-heavy. It takes a little while to get used to, but definitely a fun game for this system.

Super Games Pak   **Odyssey**   **4**   **$5**
Jailbreak, Byteman and Deathbots are featured on this compilation disc. Both Jailbreak and Byteman are very addictive games, but Deathbots is perhaps one of the worst games ever made. This game also includes a 14 minute animated movie advertising the upcoming Lunar Rescue and is very interesting for anyone interested in the history of video games.

Team Yankee
                    Entertainment International 5 $8
While the name would indicate that you are about to play a baseball simulation, it is actually a tank simulation. You control 4 tank crews and have access to TOW missiles, laser range finders, night vision and a slew of other features.

Tiebreak   **Starbyte**   **5**   **$15**
This 1992 release is a basic tennis game. And while fun at times, control and graphical limitations really tax one's patience.

Town With No Name   **On-Line**   **3**   **$7**
This interactive cartoon takes place in the American West and pits you against a gang. It is mildly entertaining, and is relatively long when compared to other interactive cartoons of the time.

Trivial Pursuit   **Hom Abbot**   **5**   **$10**
Based on the very popular board game of the same name, this is the only two disc CDTV game ever released. The information stored on these discs only takes up a total of 448 megs, but was split over two CD's so that two separate sets of questions could be played. Once the first set of questions had been completely run through enough times to finally lose their appeal or challenge, the second disc could be put in for a completely new challenge.

Turrican   **Softgold**   **5**   **$12**
Certainly not a system exclusive, but it is a fun game. With 13 levels and 9 different weapon systems, this future-set game is fun for a little while.

Turrican II
                    Softgold   **6**   **$18**
This sequel offers 12 levels of play on 5 different worlds. Large enemies and improved graphics make this game more enjoyable than the first installment, but the 20 unique music tracks are what make this title stand above many other games on this system.

Sega completed a Saturn version of Virtua Fighter 3, but opted not to release it.

CDTV

Ultimate Basketball   Context Systems   4 $10
One of the few sports games available for this system, it is passable at best, but much less enjoyable than so many other basketball games of its day.

Welcome to CDTV   Commodore   2 $2
The pack-in CD with the CDTV unit, this disc contains demos of software and games that would be available on the CDTV.

Will-Bridge Practice Collection
                              Will-Bridge   7 $35
Actually a series of bridge games, five of which were slated to be produced, not all of them have been verified to exist. The first 3 have been documented, and the fourth volume has been reported, but not verified.

Wrath of the Demon   Readysoft   4 $7
A decent attempt at a 3-D game, this is a fantasy based title set in a world similar to that of Dungeons & Dragons.

Xenon 2: Megablast   Bitmap Brothers 8 $30
A vertically scrolling shooter, this game is well designed and is still enjoyable to play today. Unfortunately for non-collectors who just want a good game, it is very difficult to come by. But fortunately for collectors, as rare as it is, it rarely demands a price of more than $30-$35.

normal CDTV controller.

Unreleased Games

As with any system, there are unreleased prototypes that are always being discovered. Until recently in fact, the Game Indiana Jones and the Last Crusade was believed to be an unreleased game as well. While this CDTV section is the most complete game software listing available, the system's nearly complete lack of documentation makes the task of cataloging these games with 100% accuracy nearly impossible.

It is not our policy to list unconfirmed games as being released, nor do we offer coverage in the area of prototypes, but if you have any evidence of the existence of a CDTV game not listed, please let us know. As you can see below, the existence of a previously though unreleased game called Loom has recently been questioned. A complete box for this game was found, leading to the possibility of the game's true existence, in final form.

HARDWARE

CDTV Unit   Commodore   5 $90

CDTV Controller   Commodore   4 $15
Wider than a typical game controller, this device has multiple function keys in the center, along with a directional pad and two action buttons.

CDTV Keyboard   Commodore   6 $35
Relatively standard in design, this was a necessity to use the CDTV for application software.

CDTV 56k Memory Card   Commodore   6 $15

CDTV 256k Memory Card   Commodore   7 $25

CDTV Mouse   Commodore   6 $15
Rudimentary in design, this mouse features two awkward buttons and average tracking ability.

CDTV Track Ball   Commodore   7 $45
Featuring both a trackball and function buttons, this device combines the usefulness of a mouse and the function keys of a

Indiana Jones and the Last Crusade   Loom

Dragon's Lair was produced by Don Bluth, an animator who has also worked on films such as Robin Hood and The Rescuers.

Amiga CD32

By: Andy Slaven

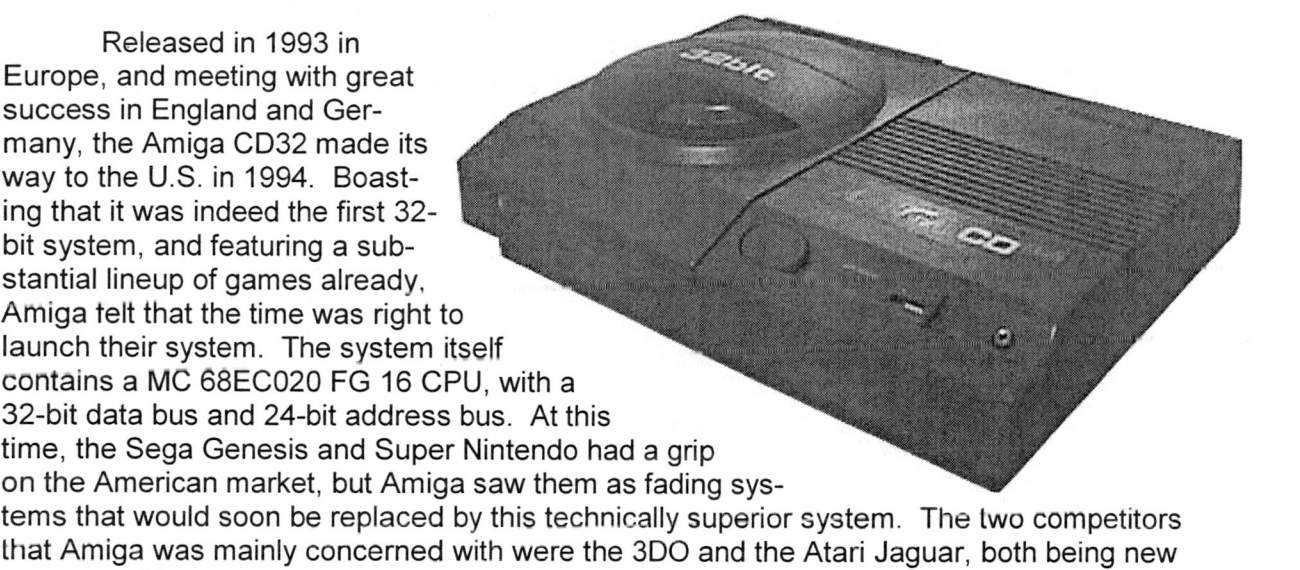

Released in 1993 in Europe, and meeting with great success in England and Germany, the Amiga CD32 made its way to the U.S. in 1994. Boasting that it was indeed the first 32-bit system, and featuring a substantial lineup of games already, Amiga felt that the time was right to launch their system. The system itself contains a MC 68EC020 FG 16 CPU, with a 32-bit data bus and 24-bit address bus. At this time, the Sega Genesis and Super Nintendo had a grip on the American market, but Amiga saw them as fading systems that would soon be replaced by this technically superior system. The two competitors that Amiga was mainly concerned with were the 3DO and the Atari Jaguar, both being new systems with enormous potential.

Sporting one of the strangest controller designs to date, the control pad actually appears to be inverted and is a bit awkward to get used to, but with six action buttons, it offered more versatility than most other controllers of the time. Perhaps, much to Amiga's disappointment, the most memorable portion of any magazine ad was, in fact, this controller.

Perhaps one of the largest faults of the system was the fact that a large portion of games catered to European tastes. There are an extraordinary number of Soccer titles available for the system, most of which are given the European name of "football". It is only natural that many American gamers were disappointed in their game selection when they realized that they had indeed bought a soccer game, and not the American football they were wanting. Also, regardless of the power of the system, most of the games have a "grainy" feel to them, almost as if they were unfinished or rushed to production. In reality, a large portion of the games on the CD32 were simply ports of Amiga 12000 games, or in some cases, direct ports of Commodore 64 games. A few mainstream games did manage to appear on the system however, and it was even graced by a Street Fighter 2 game (though it is horribly bad). As a rule of thumb, games that were released on both the CD32 and another system of the time are less refined on the CD32.

In addition to being a straightforward video game console, the CD32 can be installed with a FMV cartridge that allows for the use of VCD's, adding yet another function to the system. Upgrades to the system can be made that will essentially turn it into a substantially powerful (for the time) Amiga computer. With the addition of the right parts in the proper configuration, the CD32 was far superior to the Amiga 1200, one of the most popular Amiga computers at the time.

The marketing scheme that Amiga used seemed to be nearly non-existent, and nearly everyone who was aware of this system already owned one of the many computers in Amiga's lineup. Most of the advertisements made for this system were printed in Amiga-based maga-

CD32

zines, though a few forgettable examples did appear in mainstream magazines for the short duration of the CD32's life.

A fatal combination of poor advertising and overall low quality games was enough to see the Amiga CD32 fall victim to poor sales. In actuality, most gamers were never aware of this system's existence. Most gamers today have no recollection of the system at all, and those that do rarely owned one. As a result of this, most items associated with this system are relatively rare, though the prices are extraordinarily low. This is typical of other systems that suffered from the same fate, such as the Amiga CDTV and the Memorex VIS, though neither sport such a large library of games. The opposite is true in Europe however, where this system was one of the more successful systems during this time period.

Aside from the fact that nearly nobody knew of the system, the timing of this system's release simply couldn't have been worse. Instead of fading away, both the Sega Genesis and Super Nintendo seemed to be growing in strength and popularity. By the time the Playstation rolled around in 1995, any fading hopes of Amiga that the CD32 would find an audience were completely destroyed, leaving these systems in bargain bins and garage sales across the country.

More notable than the system itself, or any of its games, is the extremely small, but loyal fan base that is still in existence today. Homebrew games, though not covered here, are still being made by gamers around the world, and new uses for the CD32 are still being uncovered every day, each one reverently finding its place among news releases on various CD32 fan sites.

The Amiga CD32 came and went with barely a whisper to the gaming community. One can't help but wonder if it would have really had a chance at succeeding if its existence had only been known by the mainstream market. While not substantially ahead of its time, and certainly not behind the times technologically, it is probably a safe assumption that the CD32 could have been a competitive platform had Amiga simply run a more successful marketing campaign.

In 1998, Nintendo's call center held a party to celebrate their 64 millionth call!

| Alien Breed: Tower Assault | Arabian Nights | Battletoads | Beavers |

7 gates of Jambala   Thalion   5 $8

Akira   Neo   6 $25
Featuring a few cinematic sequences from the classic anime movie, this title might appear to be a lot of fun at first, but it quickly becomes apparent that this is simply a collection of mini games that don't offer a lot of fun. While enough game play will eventually cause some enjoyment to be had, it would have been best for a title sporting this name to be an anime style adventure.

Alfred Chicken   Mindscape   4 $6
In a fight against the evil Meka-Chickens, you must maneuver through 11 levels of various design in order to rescue Billy Egg and his brothers. Featuring some of the best control and graphics of any platform game on the CD32, this title is entertaining to play and maintains a level of fun throughout.

Alien Breed 2   Team 17   4 $6

Alien Breed: Tower Assault
                 Team 17   5 $8
Featuring both Alien Breed 2 and Alien Breed: Tower Assault in one package, the game can be selected from the opening sequence. Tower Assault will have you battle through five multi-floored towers filled with the living dead and aliens. Alien Breed 2 features updated graphics and sound over its first release, but plays the same.

Alien Breed 3D   Team 17   4 $10
Quite simply, this is a Doom clone, but that doesn't make it a bad thing. While the CD32 wasn't specifically designed to handle these types of graphics, it does a nice job of recreating the environments and does a nice job of making the player feel like they're actually within the game. Granted, by today's standards, this game is pretty horrible, but was one of the best console games of this type released during this time.

Alien Breed SE '92   Team 17   5 $8
This title contains an upgraded version of Alien Breed with larger levels and updated missions, as well as an entirely separate game named Qwak. Qwak supports two player action in a platform/puzzle game that can be very addictive. Described on the package as being "super-playable", the solid control is not a disappointment, though it can become frustrating while working through the more difficult levels.

All Terrain Racing   Team 17   4 $6
An overhead racing game with over 40 3-D tracks and multiple weapons upgrades, this title offers a lot of variation that helps make up for the questionable control and graphics. As you progress, the computer racers increase in difficulty to the point of near cheating, making the later levels extremely difficult.

Arabian Nights   Buzz   4 $6
Take the role of Sinbad Junior, an apprentice gardener, in an attempt to save the princess Laila in this side scrolling platform adventure. The control in this game is adequate and the environments are sufficiently different to allow for extended play in what would otherwise be a repetitive game.

Arcade Pool   Team 17   5 $10
An overhead pool game with realistic geometry and authentic sound, this title is better than others of the time. Featured in this game is 8-Ball, 9-Ball, Straight Pool, Speed Pool, and variations of Snooker.

Assasination   Team 17   5 $8

Banshee   Core Design   4 $8
Showing both detail in level design and in small animations used to add enjoyment to the game, this flying shooter is both solidly controlled and nice looking. While this type of game is relatively common across the board, it should definitely be tried by CD32 owners that are fans of arcade style vertically scrolling shooters.

Base Jumpers   Rasputin   5 $8

Battle Chess   Interplay   4 $8
Where normal chess can often become boring, Battle Chess adds animations to show exactly how your opponent's character is defeated. Often humorous, the death scenes are different for each character, and most have two unique animations.

Battletoads   Rare / Mindscape   4 $6
Based on the franchise that was obviously created to contend with the success of the Teenage Mutant Ninja Turtles, this is a side scrolling platform adventure in which you must rescue not only a princess, but your buddy Pimple as well. The graphics are a bit better than those found in NES games, though the control is a bit lacking and can cause for frustrating deaths from time to time.

Beavers   Unique   5 $8

Beneath a Steel Sky   Virgin   4 $12
An animated graphic adventure, this game feels and plays very much like games in the Shadowgate series and is often considered to be one of the best titles available for the CD32, though typically only by RPG fans. After successfully solving puzzles that help you progress, you will be treated to a relatively well done animation sequence and then presented with a new set of problems to solve.

Gradius was the first Konami game to feature the infamous "Konami Code", which includes "up up down down left right left right"

CD32

Benefactor   Digital Illusions   4 $6
This is just a very fun action oriented puzzle game, made by the creators of Lemmings. You will need to rely on the special abilities of various "merrymen" in order to get you through each of the 61 levels that await. The levels become more complex very quickly, and you must rely on more than one of the merrymen's abilities to get you through the stage.

Big 6, The   Codemasters   5 $8

Black Viper   Neo   4 $6
A futuristic motorcycle racing game that gives you a bike mounted with machine guns, this title suffers from "pop-up" quite often. And while the graphics are 3-D, this game's visuals leave a lot to be desired.

Brian the Lion   Psygnosis   5 $8
Playing the part of Brian, your goal in this platform game is to rescue your friend Chris from the evil dragon Geeza. While some are huge fans of this game, others find it repetitive and annoying. But since it is a CD32 title, it shouldn't cost you too much to make your own decision.

Brutal: Paws of Fury   Gametek   4 $6
This fighting game features animal fighters instead of the stock human characters. And while the idea is a nice break from so many other 2-D fighters of the time, better versions are available for several other consoles.

Brutal Football   Millenium   4 $10
Perhaps the most violent sports title ever, this football game features four monstrous breeds in a no-holds-barred competition to the death...or victory, whichever one comes first. Even the box promises "laughs and blood".

Bubba 'N Stix   Core Design   4 $8
An interesting concept, and also available in better form on the Sega Genesis, this title will have you control Bubba and use Stix as a weapon/tool of sorts. Stix can be used for a variety of purposes, even a snorkel, but you will actually control Bubba throughout this mission to get safely back to Earth after having been kidnapped by aliens.

Bubble and Squeak   Audiogenic   4 $6
A fun platform game featuring a unique duo, the game itself features average level designs but solid game play and can be very enjoyable.

Bump 'n Burn   Granslam   4 $6

Cannon Fodder   Virgin   4 $8
More common in European countries, this title is a fun and entertaining battle strategy game. Also available on several other consoles, this title was mostly ignored in the U.S. until it was

past its prime. Now it has a relatively loyal fan base in the U.S., and still manages to please simulation fans.

Case of the Cautious Condor   Airwave Adventure   4 $10
An "interactive adventure", this game is controlled through a series of still screens and live voice actors. The acting is surprisingly good, though often filled with cliches and racial stereotypes. Set in 1930's England aboard a "flying boat", you play the role of a detective trying to find a murderer. But quickly after the plane takes off, another murder takes place, and you only have 30 minutes to solve the case. This is a very surprising success for the CD32. With artwork seemingly from the 1930's, period dialog, and top quality voice actors, this title should be in any CD32 owner's library.

Castles II - Siege and Conquest   Interplay   4 $8
A strategy title based on your ability to forge and maintain alliances, this game takes place in the fictional world of Bretagne. Most of the game itself takes place on an over world map, and since not every situation can be solved peacefully, you must occasionally do battle in order to bring peace to the land and eventually become king.

CD32 Sports Football   Commodore   4 $5
This game allows you to either coach, play, or actually watch a game. While the concept is good enough, the graphics and control in this game simply aren't enough to make this game playable.

Cedric   Neo   5 $8
An average looking platform game, this title allows you to jump on your enemies to kill them, ala Mario. However, the game is not just a simple platform title, but also adds elements of an RPG such as examining objects and more of an exploration feel than one of being driven to the end of a level.

Chambers of Shaolin   Grandslam / Unique   4 $8

Chaos Engine, The   Bitmap Brothers   4 $6
Form a party of two of the six available characters, The Thug, Preacher, Mercenary, Gentleman, Navvie, or the Brigand, and do battle in four worlds and 16 levels of overhead action. Armed with a variety of weapons, over 25 in total, brute force will be key in killing off the hordes of monsters that the chaos engine has created. Featuring very nicely detailed environments and solid control, this title stands out as one of the better games available for the CD32.

Chuck Rock   Core Design   5 $8
Take the role of Chuck on your quest to rescue your wife, Ophelia, from her kidnapper, the evil Gary Gritter. With 500 action screens, this title will keep you busy for a while, though it

Brutal Football

Bubba 'N Stix

Cannon Fodder   The Chaos Engine

32

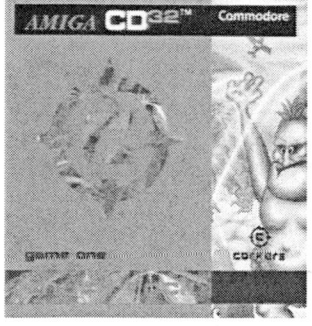

| Chuck Rock | Chuck Rock II: Son of Chuck | Dark Seed | Diggers/Oscar |

doesn't have the same level of control seen on other consoles.

Chuck Rock 2 - Son of Chuck
Core Design   4 $8
This time around, you are Chuck Jr. Featuring similar game play and graphics, this title lacks the same amount of character that made the first installment such a success on several consoles, though it can still be fun for short periods of time.

Clockwiser   Rasputin   5 $8

Clue, The   Neo   4 $8
A strategy based adventure of sorts, this is not a remake of the popular board game, but instead is a game set in 1950's London, and you are a thief. Your job is to burglarize various locations, though half of the game is spent getting to these locations. A unique and fun game, this title is best played on the Amiga computer with the keyboard.

D/Generation   Mindscape   4 $6
Your job is to confront and bring down an escaped "biometric weapon" created by a company known as Genoq. You will be placed on the 80th floor of their headquarters and must fight your way to the 89th floor, but each room you enter will be filled with not only a variety of puzzles to be solved, but also more biometric weapons. This is an isometric action game and should keep most action fans pretty happy, though the storyline will keep it interesting for those that typically aren't interested in isometric action games.

Dangerous Streets   Flair   4 $4
This is simply an awful fighting game with a partial screen view, choppy animation and poor quality sound. It is extremely difficult to keep track of how much damage you have taken or given with the noticeable absence of a life meter, and when a round is completed, the loser simply disappears from the screen. This is an obviously rushed attempt at joining the 2-D fighting game craze that the world seemed to be in after Street Fighter 2 was released.

Dark Seed   Cyberdreams   6 $35
Inspired by the works of H.R. Giger, this game is a point and click adventure in which you play the role of Mike Dawson, an average guy that happened to be in the wrong place at the wrong time. He has been implanted with the seed of an alien, and only has three days to get it out of his head. This game is one of the most desirable for the CD32 and features some of the best box art ever seen.

Death Mask   Alternative   5 $8
Originally released in early 1995, this game had been under production for quite a while before it was actually released. Sold as an answer to Doom, this title simply can't stand up to the competition.

Deep Core   Ice   4 $6
Featuring one of the best introduction video sequences seen on the system, this title gets off to a good start, but slows down a bit for the action. A platform game featuring a uniformly eerie level design throughout, this game can become repetitious, but is certainly fun to play. Featuring 9 atmospheric levels, 6 weapons systems, and numerous power-ups and sub levels, this game will take a while to master completely.

Defender of the Crown 2
Cinemaware / Commodore   4 $6
With the success of its predecessor, this sequel adds improved graphics and expanded game play. While this title didn't reach the same level of success as the original it is a very strong strategy game with occasional action sequences that are used to represent the confrontation of besieging armies. Build your fame and increase your control over medieval England with carefully plotted decisions.

Dennis   Ocean   1   ¢0

Diggers   Millenium   4 $6
One of the more common games for the CD32, this game is very similar in concept to the teamwork type of play seen in Lemmings, and is often thought of as a Lemmings clone, though not nearly as much fun.

Diggers/Oscar   Millenium   6 $10
This is simply a compilation of both Diggers and Oscar on one CD, in their original forms.

Disposable Hero   Gremlin   5 $8
One of many side scrolling shooters for the CD32, this title features both average control and graphics, keeping it from standing out in any area. Though, despite its mediocrity, it is still an enjoyable title if you're a fan of this genre.

Donk   Supervision   5 $10

Dragonstone   Core Design   4 $8

Emerald Mines   Almathera   5 $12
This is simply a Boulderdash clone, but the odd thing is, many people feel that it is superior to the original. Of course there will be improvements in graphics over the years, but many feel that the overall experience, including control, are far superior on the CD32.

Exile   Audiogenic   5 $8
This scrolling action title was first released long ago as a BBS system, and simply got a facelift for its appearance on the

Turning a system on and off quickly in order to see strange onscreen effects is known as "frying."

CD32

CD32, though this title really didn't deserve a game of its own.

F17 Challenge   Team 17   4 $6
While this Pole Position clone does look nice and feature some impressive backgrounds for a CD32 title, the control simply doesn't seem to be as responsive as it should be. Instead, gamers are left with a "hard left" or "hard right" option only, making any subtle turns an impossibility.

Fantastic Voyage   Centaur Software   4 $12
This title is based on the classic film by the same name, and is simply an updated version of the CDTV version, though the improvements are difficult to see.

Fears   Manyk   4 $8
An average Doom clone at best, this title is easily outdone by games like Alien Breed 3-D, though it is interesting to note that this is a product of a computer gaming race to create the first Doom clone to market for the Amiga 1200 computer series.

Fields of Glory   Microprose   5 $10
A strategy gamer's dream in 1993 upon its release, this game takes place in 1815, and you control thousands of troops in Napoleonic Era battlefield. Featuring both map screens and direct control screens (shown from overhead), this title will occasionally surprise you with a short cinematic used to progress the story, or to show an untimely demise of one of your generals.

FIFA International Soccer   Electronic Arts   4 $6
Considered the benchmark in video game soccer, this title features solid game play and enjoyable graphics, though it is the fluid motion and real feeling of control that makes this game stand out.

Fightin' Spirit   Neo   4 $6
Short on fighting games, the CD32 was surprisingly graced with this sleeper hit. The characters are large and easily controllable, much better than other fighters such as Dangerous Streets, but about on par with Shadow Fighter.

Final Gate, The   Bigg Wolf   4 $8

Fire & Ice   Renegade   4 $8
Considered one of the best platform games of its day, this title demonstrates the CD32's often untapped ability to render gorgeous levels and well controlled characters. A constantly increasing level of challenge will keep most gamers busy, and its relatively unknown status (when compared to other platform games such as Super Mario Bros.) should make this an interesting game for almost anyone.

Fire Force   Ice   4 $6
Very similar in play and style to games like Bloody Wolf and Metal Slug, this is a side scrolling combat game in which you

are allowed the use of various military weaponry and explosives. While it isn't nearly as addictive as the aforementioned Metal Slug, it is still a fun title that will probably capture at least a few hours of your time.

Flimbo's Quest   System 3   5 $8
Once considered to be a "cute" title, age has really ravaged what many once thought of as a fun platform game.

Flink   Psygnosis   5 $8

Fly Harder   Buzz   4 $6
This is a fun scrolling flight shooter, and is basically a Thrust clone of sorts. You must avoid both ground based and air based fire and obstacles, this title should entertain those looking for a quick action game, though it can become tiresome after only a few levels.

Football Glory   Black Legend   4 $6
A good rule of thumb on the CD 32 is to simply replace the word "football" with "soccer". This title was released to go head-to-head with Sensible Soccer, and quite simply it lost. It is a very good arcade style soccer game simply not up to par with Sensible Soccer.

Frontier: Elite II   Gametek   4 $8
An interesting mix of genres helped make this one of the best Amiga games to date. With a mixture of strategy, action and even some simulation, your goal is to basically do what you want to. You can start up trade routs, buy your own ship, join the military, etc. While this is an enjoyable title, it is best played on an Amiga computer.

Fury of the Furries   Mindscape   4 $6
Take the role of a round and furry creature known as Tiny in your quest to rescue the King from "The Wicked One". There are eight levels, but you will be able to transform yourself into various objects to make the task a bit easier.

Fuzzball   System 3   5 $8

Gamers Delight   GTI   4 $6

Genesia   Mindscape   5 $10
Often referred to as a Populous clone, this title really can stand on its own merits. The objective is to find a suitable area for colonizing, then build a city in which economic prosperity must occur in order to continue expanding. It is a lot of fun for simulation fans, and might actually interest those just trying to have an hour's worth of fun, though this title can easily take weeks away from your life, not just hours.

Global Effect   Millenium   4 $8
This is similar in concept and execution to that of Sim Earth,

Fire & Ice

Fire Force

Fly Harder

Fury of the Furries

In the Saturn version of Area 51, shoot the first 3 humans without hitting anything else. See what happens!

| Global Effect | Guardian | Heimdall 2 | James Pond 2: Robocod |

though this version features more of a preachy attitude that closely watches things like global warming (evidence that this was created when children still believed what they learned from Captain Planet instead of leading scientists that made one thing clear: that global warming is nothing but a plot by environmental groups to get rich off of the American public's sympathy for all things green.)

Gloom   **Black Magic**   4 $6
When the term "Doom clone" is used, this is often the first game that comes to mind. It really does appear that everything was simply taken from Doom, slightly altered (and sometimes not at all), and placed on this disc.

Guardian   **Acid Software**   4 $6
Polygon based games were in their infancy when this shooter was released. Viewed from behind your ship, you must destroy all the invading ships before they take control of the planet. An original story line places you in the role of a "guardian" left on different planets to protect it from invasion. Taking place during a time when the universe is collapsing in on itself, habitable planets are in short supply, and you are the only defense against those that wish to take the planet for their own.

Gulp   **Ice**   5 $10

Gunship 2000   **Microprose**   4 $8
This is a nice looking helicopter gunship simulator that offers 5 types of helicopters to choose from and some of the best graphics on the system.

Heimdall 2   **Core Design**   4 $10
Play the role of Heimdall after he gives up his divinity so that you can recover the pieces of the Sacred Amulet and stop the evil Loki. Featuring isometric action and a graphical style completely unique to this game, this title is sure to please fans of the action/RPG genre.

Humans 1+ 2   **Gametek**   4 $6
A combination of the first two games in the series, this Lemmings clone stresses teamwork and offers interesting puzzle situations that must be solved with the special skills of each person involved.

Humans 3   **Gametek**   5 $8
A surprising release for the CD32, this continuation of the series is more of the same type of fun, offering both new levels and new basic skills of the humans involved.

Impossible Mision 2025   **Microprose**   4 $10
Elvin Atombender (the bad guy) has built a high security tower and filled it with various types of centry robots. Your job is to break in and destroy these robots before he can use them to

take over the world. The plot is extremely cheesy, and the game itself is pretty simple, but it plays well and looks nice.

International Karate Plus   **System 3**   4 $5
This is basically the exact same game that showed up on the C64, and actually may have made the transition without any changes at all. If you have the original, there is no reason to buy this version.

International Sensible Soccer
         Sensible Software 4 $8
Considered to be the best soccer game on the CD32, this was the standard by which all other soccer games were judged. This title did for the CD32 what the FIFA series did for other systems.

James Pond 2: Robocod   **Millenium**   4 $6
This side scrolling platform game is available on several consoles and features colorful levels as well as cute character animations.

James Pond 3: Operation Starfish
         Millenium   5 $8
Available only for the Sega Genesis and the CD32, this game offers slight graphical improvements over the second installment, though the Genesis version is much better.

Jet Strike   **Rasputin / Granslam**   4 $8
A simple side scrolling jet plane shooter, this game has little to offer that others in the genre don't.

John Barnes' European Football
         Buzz   4 $6
Granted, this title is named after a soccer great, but even so, the game is average at best. Viewed from overhead, but scrolling sideways, this game just doesn't seem to move correctly. And even though the title offers effects such as varying weather, it still fails to impress.

Jungle Strike   **Ocean**   4 $6
The sequel to Desert Strike, this title was also available on several other consoles, and is best played on them.

Kang Fu   **Great Effects Development**   5 $8
Take the role of Klont the kangaroo in this side scrolling combat adventure. On a mission to save your baby and those of other kangaroo families, you will traverse through dangerous levels, but will also be supplied from time to time with various weapons to ease the undertaking of your journey. Fun in both concept and execution, this is a platform game that was made with a light heart and should be enjoyable for those simply looking for a platform challenge.

The tub in E. Honda's stage on the SNES doesn't overflow upon victory like the arcade version.

Kick Off 3   Anco   4 $8
If there is any soccer game that comes close to rivaling the seat of Sensible Soccer, this would be it. And to this day the debate is often seen as to which is better, though it is typically not something you would hear anywhere but European countries.

Kid Chaos   Ocean   4 $6

Kingpin   Team 17   4 $8
A surprisingly good looking bowling game, this title offers a fine balance of both challenge and fun, though it is a bit on the challenging side.

Labyrinth of Time, The   Electronic Arts   4 $12
Very similar in style to Myst, this game places you within a very unique world where you must explore a seemingly endless variety of rooms and passages. An extremely immersing experience, the well orchestrated sound track and stunning still frame animations are among the best on the system. While certainly not the choice for fans of action games, this title will require extensive thought and reasoning to complete.

Lamborghini American Challenge
    Titus   4 $6

Last Ninja 3   System 3   4 $6
With an equal balance of stealth and force, this isometric ninja game was a very refreshing break from other games from this period. Amazing graphics for its day, Last Ninja 3 should definitely be tried by any CD32 owner, though it won't be for everyone. One minor complaint about this title is the truncated action screen that was used so that the environments could be rendered quickly enough. A border with weapons and statistics is displayed to the left and below the action screen, taking up a full 3rd of the total area.

Legacy of Soracil   Gremlin   5 $8

Legends   Manyk   5 $8

Lemmings   Psygnosis   4 $6
Take control of various lemmings with special abilities to safely guide the entire group to safety. Available on seemingly every platform ever made, the CD32 version offers nice backgrounds and character animations, though the control seems a bit "soft", making control commands seem delayed.

Liberation - Captive 2   Mindscape   4 $6
Set in a futuristic world that has been exploited and over-commercialized, you must control four droids in an effort to free innocents that are being held against their will. Utilizing both digitized speech and FMV sequences, this title is an enjoyable game, though often a bit tricky.

Litil Divil   Gremlin Interactive   4 $8
You are on a journey to get a pizza for the Devil himself in this game, and must travel through the depths of Hell to get it. The control seems a bit rigid and fighting movements seem unresponsive, though this is common for this title regardless of platform.

Lost in Mine   Marksoft   5 $8

Lost Vikings, The   Interplay   4 $8
This is a fun adventure/puzzle title in which you control one of three Vikings that have been abducted. Each character has his own weapon and individual strengths. This is an enjoyable title that puts fun ahead of all else.

Lotus Trilogy, The Classic   Gremlin   4 $8
Featuring cars from the Lotus line, this game (or variations of it) were also released on other U.S. platforms, though like the car, they never received much recognition in the U.S.

Lunar-C   Mindscape   5 $8

Manchester United   Krisalis   4 $6
Also available on the SNES in Europe, this soccer title is basically the same game. Though this title was most probably heavily distributed in Europe, it is difficult to find in the U.S., and is often a PAL version.

Marvins Marvelous Adventure
    21st Century   5 $10

Mean Arenas   Ice   4 $6
This is a maze game that tries to interject humor by featuring Buzz and Bob, the arena announcers that will occasionally burst into the action by "commentating". Voice sampling was a big deal in 1993 and is overused in this game, taking any fun that this title had to offer and quickly replacing it with irritation. Basically an updated version of Pac-Man, but without the charming simplicity.

Microcosm   Psygnosis   4 $5
One of the first rail shooters that featured realistic graphics, this game has aged poorly. Very limited control is used while piloting your ship through the human body, in this, an obvious rendition of the classic film "Fantastic Voyage".

Mitre Soccer Superstars   Flair   4 $6
With quite a few soccer titles on the CD32, it is hard for any to stand out, and this game gets shuffled into the "soccer deck" with relative ease.

Morph   Millenium   5 $8

| The Labyrinth of Time | Last Ninja 3 | The Lost Vikings | Mean Arenas |

In August of 2000, 55% of gamers thought that broadband gaming for consoles was "right around the corner."

Morph   Myth: History in the Making   Pirates! Gold   Project-X/F17 Challenge

Myth: History in the Making
System 3   4 $6
A side scrolling platform game, this title has a similar feel to Rygar for the NES, though the control can seem a bit off at times. Nice environments can't save this game from becoming just one in an ocean of platformers.

Naughty Ones   Interactivision   5 $6

Nick Faldo's Golf   Grandslam Interactive   4 $8
This game was originally released on the Commodore 64 in 1992, and definitely shows its age, but it did make the transition with several upgrades.

Nigel Mansell's World Championship
Gremlin Graphics   4 $6
A Formula One racing simulation, this game suffers from the fact that it just doesn't feel fast. The graphics are relatively nice, but certainly not as good as those found on the SNES or Genesis versions.

No Second Prize   Thalion   5 $10
This 3-D motorcycle game shows some early uses of polygon graphics and can be fun for an occasional play, though it is doubtful that anyone will ever become addicted to a game such as this.

Odyssey   OTM   4 $8

Oscar   Flair   4 $5
Play through several side scrolling platform levels, each with its own movie theme such as Sci-Fi, Horror, or Western. The game itself is very average, though it does suffer from "soft" control, meaning that the characters seem to react slowly to your commands, often causing frustrating deaths.

Overkill   Mindscape   4 $6
This side scrolling shooter is basically an updated version of Defender, though not nearly as addictive. It should be entertaining for both fans of the genre and retro-gamers alike, though more intricate side scrolling shooters such as R-Type are preferred by most.

PGA Euro Tour Golf   Ocean   4 $6
This is simply one of many golf simulators available at this time, though this title does feature a few nice holes that are recreated well with the CD32's graphics.

Pierre le Chef is Out to Lunch
Mindscape   5 $8
This is just a good humored fun game that appeals to both young and old, though it is often overlooked because its title would appear to be that of a child's game. Taking the role of

Pierre, you will travel through six countries in search of the right vegetables, that just happen to be revolting. To make things worse, your nemesis, "le Chef Noir" is working against you in your quest. With bonus levels and warp zones, this game has more to offer than first appears, and sporting some of the best looking levels to be found in any 1993 release, this title should be entertaining for any platformer fan.

Pinball Fantasies   Digital Illusions   5 $12
Featuring four different tables, this is actually the sequel to the Amiga computer game known as Pinball Dreams. While the first title wasn't much to play, this game is regarded as the best pinball game available on any Amiga platform.

Pinball Illusions   Digital Illusions   4 $8
With three different pinball machines to choose from and very detailed and smooth graphics, this title shouldn't be missed by any pinball fan.

Plinky   Millenium   5 $10

Pirates GOLD   Microprose   6 $12
This is a naval simulation in which you take control of your own ship and do battle with various others on the high seas. Pilot the ship from an overhead map view, and even board and fight hand to hand with the opposing ship's captain. A broad level of interaction throughout this game make it very interesting, even if some of the situations are overly simplified with the archaic graphical style of the maritime events.

Power Drive   US Gold   4 $6

Premiere   Core Design   5 $8

Prey: Alien Encounter
Sent to asteroid KG-42 because of lost contact with the colonists, you begin this adventure game with the strong suspicion that the entire storyline was stolen from the 1979 movie Alien...and you'd be right.

Project X   Team 17   4 $6
A side scrolling shooter, this title features some very nice graphics for the system and solid control.

Project-X/F17 Challenge   Team 17   4 $8
This title combines the game Project-X with the game F17 Challenge on one disc. Both titles are also available separately.

Quik the Thunder Rabbit   Titus / Paragon   5 $10
If you get tired of playing this game and dying, enter "SUCOLOKU" for your password entry and you'll be invincible. Enjoy!

After saving a game of Zelda for the NES, what button were you supposed to hold down when turning off the power?

Qwak   Team 17   5 $8

Rise of the Robots   Mirage / Time Warner   4 $6
Available on several systems, this once popular game just does-
n't utilize the CD32's potential. Very slow control can ruin this 2-
D fighting game despite the games relatively good graphics.
Animations between rounds do make this version stand apart
from cartridge version of the game, but not enough to make it
any more enjoyable. Very short and very easy, this game
should have had more refinements before it was released.

Roadkill   Vision / Acid Software   4 $6
A fun overhead driving/combat game, this title features various
cars to choose from and a driving style similar to that seen in
the first two Grand Theft Auto games.

Ryder Cup Golf   Ocean   4 $6
This is a decent golfing game with often realistic looking courses
and still manages to capture all the frustration felt when you
slice one onto the cart path.

Sabre Team   Krisalis Software   5 $8
A decent isometric shooter, this title features some nice graphical effects for a CD32 title, though at times slight slowdown
might be experienced.

Seek & Destroy   Mindscape   5 $8

Sensible Soccer (Limited Edition)
                     Sensible Software   6 $12
Sensible Soccer is one of the best soccer games available on
any platform, and this version does a nice job of showing off the
ease of control necessary to make a soccer game successful.

Sexual Fantasies   Better Concepts   5 $6
If you ever wanted to look at naked women in 256 colors, well,
here's your chance. Once considered to be an impressive
showing of image processing, titles such as these are now a
joke among collectors and rarely worth anything.

Shadow Fighter   Gremlin Interactive   4 $8
One of the few fighting games released on the CD32, this game
is nearly as good as Fightin' Spirit, though it lacks the same
style that made the latter a better game overall.

Silly Putty   System 3   5 $10
Yes, you get to play as a ball of Silly Putty in this fun platform
puzzle game, judging jumps and making precision moves to
complete each level.

Simon the Sorcerer   Adventure Soft   4 $6
Play the role of Simon in this cute adventure to save the Wizard
known as Calypso.

Skeleton Krew   Core Design   4 $6
A very nice looking isometric action game, this title features
smooth character animation and also utilizes a view slightly
more removed than other isometrics, giving you a better view of
the playing field and what you are about to face.

Sleepwalker   Ocean   5 $10

Soccer Kid   Krisalis Software   5 $8
Aptly named, you play a soccer kid, but instead of actually playing soccer, you will use your soccer ball as a weapon through
various side scrolling platform levels. This title was made available for several systems, including a recent release on the Atari
Jaguar by Songbird.

Speedball 2   Renegade   4 $6
This title plays similarly to Sensible Soccer with one notable
exception...you are encouraged to beat the hell out of your opponents. A very fun game, this title was one of the few CD32
games to receive any mainstream press.

Speris Legacy   Binary Emotions   5 $8

Spherical Worlds   Neo   5 $8
An overhead shooter, this title offers addictive game play, but
once you stop playing, it is difficult to get back into the game.

Star Crusader   Gametek   5 $12
This 3-D space shooter is very similar in style to Wing Commander, though it hardly received the same amount of recognition.

Striker Elite   Team 17   4 $6
Believe it or not, it's another soccer game on the CD32, and
again, it is about average, though this game does offer a good
deal of speed often neglected in other soccer games.

Strip Pot   Artworx   4 $6

Sub War 2050   Microprose   5 $10
Viewed from inside the cockpit, this is a futuristic submarine
fighting game, and can be a lot of fun if submarines are your
sort of thing.

Summer Olympix   Flair   4 $8
Compete in the 100 meter sprint, archery, skeet, kayaking, javelin, long jump, boxing and swimming in this humorous sports
game. While the graphics aren't the best around, they do their
job, and the game is fun overall.

Super Frog   Team 17   4 $6
A side scrolling platform game, this title features very clean and
sharp graphics, and the control is very solid. Take on the role of
the "super frog" as you traverse detailed levels that are crea-

Roadkill   Simon the Sorcerer

Skeleton Krew   Super Frog

Super Methane Bros.

Super Stardust

Trolls

UFO: Enemy Unknown

tively designed.

Super League Manager	Audiogenic	5	$8

Super Loopz	Audiogenic	4	$10

Super Methane Bros. Apache Software 4 $10
Play as one of the two brothers, each aptly equipped with a gas mask, in this side scrolling platform game that features both solid control and often enjoyable level design.

Super Putty	System 3	4	$6

Super Skidmarks Acid 4 $6
This is a fun racing game that even offers the option of pulling trailers, for whatever reason, and yes the cars leave skidmarks on the ground.

Super Stardust Bloodlust / Team 17 4 $6
An updated version of Asteroids, those that are not of the school that the original one never be improved upon might want to take a look at this game. While it doesn't sport the official name of Asteroids, it is certainly clear where this beautiful game got its inspiration. With great control, nice animations and impressive backgrounds, this title should be tried by anyone who enjoyed Asteroids.

Super Street Fighter 2 Turbo
Gametek 5 $10
Simply a faster version of Street Fighter 2, it is surprising that this game was released for the CD32 at all considering the system's limited popularity. This is an absolutely horrible version of the game that once took the nation by storm, and should probably be avoided by pretty much everyone.

Surf Ninjas Flair 4 $6
Taking the two most popular sports in Japan (surfing and killing people while dressed in black pajamas and shooting carpenter nails affixed with a red tassel through bamboo shoots, ala American Ninja), this game is actually based on the movie by the same name. This game isn't much better than its movie inspiration however.

Syndicate Bullfrog 4 $6
Control up to four of your soldiers in this overhead futuristic shooting game. Your objective is to free the world from enemy syndicates by killing everything in your path.

Theme Park Bullfrog 5 $10
Create and run your own theme park in this title. And while this is a fun game for simulation fans, a much better version can be found on the Atari Jaguar.

Thomas Tank Pinball	Alternative Software	6	$12

Top Gear 2 Gremlin 5 $12
This game looks and feels much like Sega's Out-Run, though the graphics are a bit better and the control seems a bit more flexible.

Total Carnage Ice 4 $6
A port of the arcade game by the same name, this title features two player simultaneous action and is best played this way. An overhead view is used in this game, making it similar in style to Ikari Warriors, though the graphics in this game are notably better. Fans of shoot 'em ups should enjoy this game, especially when played with a friend.

Tower of Souls	Black Legend	4	$8

Traps 'n Treasures	Krisalis	5	$10

Trivial Pursuit Ocean 5 $10
This board game is brought to the CD32 in this title, and though there are numerous questions to be answered, they will occasionally cycle through again. But, due to the category system, this game features more replay than other titles of this nature, such as Jeopardy.

Trolls Flair Software 4 $6
Originally released in 1993 for the Commodore 64, this is one of several titles to be brought to this system directly from the C64 with only minor upgrades to graphics and control.

UFO: Enemy Unknown Microprose 4 $10
A very intricate simulation that will take hours just to get used to, this game is definitely not one that is to be played for just a few minutes at a time. Construct bases and manage your resources while mounting a defense against possible attacks. Expand your control across the globe and continue building. Fans of combat simulations and management simulations alike should enjoy this game, and will easily be able to spend over 50 hours building their empire.

Ultimate Body Blows Team 17 4 $6
Take control of one of 22 characters in this, the third installment in the Body Blows series. The characters within this game are simply a combination of the first two games. This title isn't bad as far as fighting games on the CD32 are concerned, though it would be laughable by many other consoles' standards.

Universe	Core Design	5	$8

Vital Light Millenium 4 $6
A long and intricate opening sequence of an incoming spaceship and very detailed scenes of the cityscape would make you

39

In 1989, Nintendo Power magazine boasted over one million subscribers.

CD32

think that this game was some sort of epic adventure. But when all the cinemas are over, and the "announcers" are done talking to you, the real game begins. A falling block game that features two player support, the object isn't to align the blocks, but instead to change the color of the different sections to the same hue, causing them to explode. It can get very tricky as the blocks begin to move faster however, so it will take some practice to become proficient.

Wembley International Soccer
Audiogenic   4 $6
Basically the same as the version made available for the Amiga computer line, this is one of many average soccer games on this system.

Wendetta 2175   Epic Marketing   5 $10
Overall, this space shooter is of relatively high quality, though you can expect to see the CD32 trademark of occasionally rough edges and a grainy appearance.

Whales Voyage   Neo   4 $10
This is a nice space exploration game in which you will not only need to explore new planets, but also act as an ambassador to the new races that you come across during your travels. While games like Star Control II have mastered this type of genre, this game should be enjoyable as well.

Whizz   Flair   5 $8
An isometric platform action game, this title is nearly ruined by the horrible control, a common problem on both this and the Amiga computer versions of the game. One advantage that this game has over its computer counterpart is the fact that the CD32 controller is easier to use than a mouse.

Wild Cup Soccer   Millenium   4 $8
The soccer version of Brutal Sports Football, this title features both fun soccer playing and beating up your opponents.

Wing Commander   Origin   4 $12
Amazing graphics were this game's selling point when it was first released on the Amiga computer, and while still entertaining, the graphics have definitely aged quite a bit. The CD32 does a very good job of handling this game and is one of the better titles in the CD32 library.

Worms   Team 17 / Ocean   4 $8
Released for quite a few systems of the time, this is a turn-based strategy game with a 60 second/turn time limit. You will control several squads during your attacks against the enemy, and this game is very enjoyable, though best played on a system like the Saturn or PSX.

Your Privacy Assured
Dark Unicon Productions   5 $8
One of the few adult titles on the CD32, this game features not only adult images, but also features hundreds of adult stories and games.

Zool   Gremlin Graphics   4 $8
Take the role of Zool, a ninja in the "Nth Dimension" in this side scrolling platform game with cartoon like environments and very colorful backgrounds. The control in this game is actually pretty solid and enjoyable.

Zool 2   Gremlin Graphics   4 $8
This game contains six bosses over 18 levels within the "Nth Dimension". You are able to control either Zool, or his buddy Zooz, on your quest to defeat Krool and save the Nth Dimension.

HARDWARE

Amiga CD32   Amiga   4 $125

Standard Control   Amiga   4 $12
One of the most unique controller designs in history, this controller features an "inverted" design in which the gripping nubs point upward (as opposed to those that face downward on the PSX controller.) It has four main action buttons, two shoulder buttons and a start button.

FMV Module   Amiga   7 $60
This simply allowed for the play of VCD's on a CD32.

Wild Cup Soccer   Zool

40

Atari 7800

By: Michael Collins

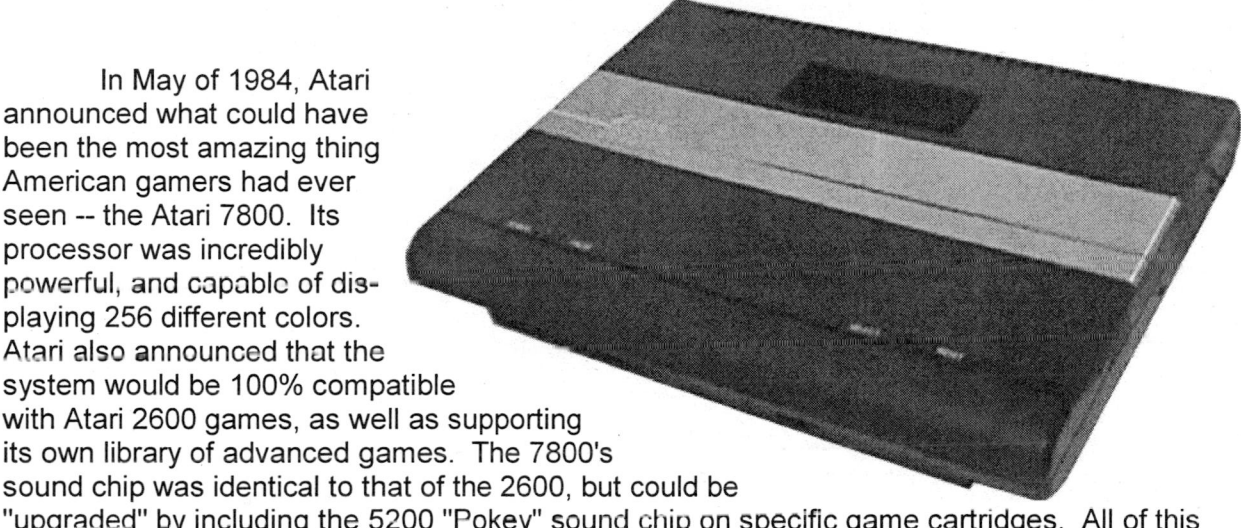

In May of 1984, Atari announced what could have been the most amazing thing American gamers had ever seen -- the Atari 7800. Its processor was incredibly powerful, and capable of displaying 256 different colors. Atari also announced that the system would be 100% compatible with Atari 2600 games, as well as supporting its own library of advanced games. The 7800's sound chip was identical to that of the 2600, but could be "upgraded" by including the 5200 "Pokey" sound chip on specific game cartridges. All of this sounds just wonderful, but there were problems and good reasons for the financial failure of the Atari 7800.

An interesting feature of the Atari 7800 was its cartridge validation technique. Since video game machines were often party to unlicensed third party software, Atari decided to make the 7800 "hack proof". The 7800 would, by default, only play Atari 2600 games. But when an official 7800 cartridge was inserted, containing the validation key, the graphics chip code named "Marie" would unlock its full potential and allow the 7800 game to be recognized. While this feature was added in order to keep unlicensed software from flooding the system's library, the added bonus was the fact that the system could play all VCS games without any problems, plus add the pause feature of the 7800's console.

The combination of the sale of Atari to Jack Tramiel and the crash of 1984 put the 7800 on the backburner, and for far too long. By the time Atari released the system, it didn't have much of a chance against the competition. In 1986, the 7800 debuted with only three titles available for purchase, none of which caught the eye of many gamers. The success of Nintendo's NES completely overshadowed the 7800, and Sega's Master System wasn't helping Atari, either.

As Nintendo prepared to release their wildly successful Famicom system in the U.S., they looked for someone who would be able to handle distribution. The naturally sought out Atari since they had, at the time, the most successful release of any system in history. A deal was on the table and ready to be completed when Atari executives backed out of the bargain due to a misunderstanding over Coleco's use of Donky Kong on the ADAM computer system. Coleco argued that since the ADAM took cartridges it was technically a video game system and didn't infringe on Atari's rights to the home computer rights of Donky Kong.

Atari was enraged and assumed that Nintendo had gone behind their backs. It was at this time that Atari readied plans to release the 7800 that had been lying dormant for three years, thinking that they could use this delay to their advantage. By the time Atari realized that Nintendo had been honest with them, Nintendo had seen Atari's quarterly reports. Seeing that

7800

Atari was doing much worse then originally thought, Nintendo decided to market the Famicom in the U.S. as the Nintendo Entertainment System (NES) themselves.

Other video game consoles aside, Atari had competition even from itself. The 7800 was not the only system they were trying to sell; they were pushing the Atari 2600 Jr., the XEGS, and the rest of their 8-bit computer line as well. In trying to do so much, they ended up doing so little - the 7800 didn't get the attention it deserved, even from Atari, and drifted off into video game oblivion much sooner than it should have.

Not surprisingly, there wasn't a plethora of add-ons or peripherals for Atari's new gaming console. The joysticks that were included with the system were dubbed the Atari Pro-Line Controllers, and, thankfully were more comfortable (and more reliable) than their predecessors, the 5200 joysticks. Although there were several light gun games available for the 7800, there was never actually a gun made specifically for the system. However, there are several that work well with it, such as the gun that was packed in with the XEGS. Other peripherals for the system were pretty much nonexistent, aside from two that were never released: a 5200 adapter and a keyboard.

Hardcore 7800 fans may also be interested in purchasing a High Score Cart, if they can find one. The cart was announced by Atari in 1984, and would for the first time allow gamers to actually save their high scores for their favorite games at home. Although Atari never brought the cartridge into mass production, Curt Vendel did release the cart in 2000, to a limited, yet surely ecstatic group of collectors.

As far as games for the 7800 go, there certainly isn't a lack of them. Although only about sixty 7800 games were released domestically, the entire 2600 library (save about three or four of them) can be played on the 7800 in their full glory. Many of the 7800 versions of the classic Atari arcade games are the best available for any Atari console. Several, such as Asteroids, have great two-player simultaneous gameplay modes that just cannot be found elsewhere. Best of all, none of the aforementioned 7800 games are very rare, and many of them are actually fairly common, so the 7800 is a great system to collect for.

The first 250,000 copies of the NES game Maniac Mansion allowed you to microwave a hamster. It was later removed.

Centipede

Commando

Crack'ed

Donkey Kong

Ace of Aces   Atari   3 $5
As can be inferred from the name of this game, Ace of Aces is an air combat game. It is a decent one, with nice graphics, deep gameplay, and somewhat difficult controls. For some, this game can be rewarding, but it still gets repetetive after a while.

Alien Brigade   Atari   3 $5
Since there aren't as many light gun games available for the 7800 as there are for the SMS, for instance, any of them deserve a look if you're a fan of them. Alien Brigade is one of the better ones out there. It has some cool levels, a nice variety of weapons, and shooting aliens is always a lot of fun.

Asteroids   Atari   1 $3
Even though this game is pretty much a rehashed and somewhat updated version of the original, it is still a great game. Updated graphics and a really nice simultaneous two-player mode make it a great game for anybody who couldn't get enough of this game in the arcades or on their 2600 at home.

Ballblazer   Atari   3 $5
At the time of its release, there was nothing like Ballblazer out there. It's a sort of pseudo-soccer game, played in the first person. The gameplay is rather simple, but it's lots of fun, especially with a friend, and the 3D graphics look great on the 7800.

Barnyard Blaster   Atari   2 $4
Light gun game fans should stick with Alien Brigade for their 7800 blasting cravings. Barnyard Blaster is a fairly decent game, but the inability to set the difficulty on an easy game really takes away from what could have and should have been a great title.

Basketbrawl   Atari   3 $7
The folks at Atari really should have just stuck with a "normal" basketball game mold when making this. Instead, they added in the ability to punch and fight during games, and this just doesn't work at all. The only real reason to play this game is for a good laugh with your friends.

Centipede   Atari   1 $3
We've all seen Centipede before, and this is a great version of it. However, the updated graphics and simultaneous two-player mode can't keep this game from being the same old thing. For those who still love zapping all of those bugs though, this is one of the best versions you can get of the game.

Choplifter!   Atari   3 $5
Choplifter! is one of those games that some people will have a blast with and others will just want to blast from sheer frustration. The object of the game is to save hostages from your enemies. Sounds simple, but the controls are a little awkward, and the game itself is difficult without having to worry about that.

Commando   Atari   4 $12
Combat similar in style to Ikari Warriors is featured in this game.

Crack'ed   Atari   3 $5
While the concept of Crack'ed seems like a cool one, the execution of it is horrible. The object of the game is to save eggs in several nests on the screen from the baddies who want to take them. However, the game should have supported the light gun, because it is a major pain to drag the crosshair cursor around the screen with the joystick controller.

Crossbow   Atari   3 $5
For a light gun game, Crossbow has a surprisingly refreshing feel. The game requires players to help their on-screen friends along their way by shooting anything in their path. The game is also set in medieval times, which is uncommon for light gun games.

Dark Chambers   Atari   2 $4
It may not say "Gauntlet" in the title, but that is essentially what this game is. Dark Chambers is a solid game, but is certainly a clone. The two-player mode is also of note, because it adds some spice to the life of Dark Chambers.

Desert Falcon   Atari   2 $4
Desert Falcon is a pretty decent shooter. The gameplay is interesting, partially due to the ability to pick up power-ups, and the graphics are amazing.

Dig Dug   Atari   2 $4
Even though this version does echo of "too little, too late," Dig Dug on the 7800 is certainly one of the best ports of it to date. Great graphics and the same addictive gameplay as the arcade original make this one that should not be missed.

Donkey Kong   Atari   2 $4
It may not be arcade-perfect, but this version of Donkey Kong is many times better than the 2600 version. The graphics are ridiculously better, and there is a third screen to play on (as compared to two on the 2600). For some, this game might seem like a re-hash, but for those who are still looking for a

The American release of Super Mario Bros. 2 was originally a Japanese game titled Doki Doki Panic.

good home port, this is one of the better ones.

Donkey Kong, Jr. Atari 2 $4
For those of you who can't get enough of the big gorilla, Donkey Kong, Jr. is probably your best bet. It has great graphics, and thankfully, all four screens to play on. It still isn't arcade perfect, but is as close as you'll get on the 7800.

Double Dragon Activision 5 $15
If you don't own a SMS or NES, this port of Double Dragon will probably do. It is, as always, a big challenge, pretty much fun, and the two-player mode is great. However, after playing this game so much on the NES and SMS control pads, the 7800's joystick just feels awkward.

F-18 Hornet Absolute Entertainment 5 $12

Fatal Run Atari 4 $12
I am reminded of Fatal Run when I think of State of Emergency on the PS2. The gameplay itself has no major connection -- the object of Fatal Run is to destroy enemy cars. However, the replay value of the two games is similar -- the first few minutes are great, but after that, it just seems old. Nice graphics don't save this one.

Fight Night Atari 3 $5

Food Fight Atari 3 $5
Ever been in a food fight before? That's what this game is, essentially. Players must dodge food flying at them, and although it may sound silly, this game is addictive! The difficulty level is perfect, and although the graphics aren't up to par with some 7800 games, that's not what it's about anyway.

Galaga Atari 2 $5
As with the 7800 version of Double Dragon, this port of the arcade original is a decent one, but isn't up to par with other versions. The gameplay is still very addictive, but it just doesn't feel quite right.

Hat Trick Atari 2 $4
Many sports games don't age well with time, and this is either one of them, or one that was never good in the first place. The graphics are sharp, but animation is choppy. While the single-player mode is pretty poor, the two-player mode is at least decent.

Ikari Warriors Atari 4 $8
For gamers who don't have an NES, this version of Ikari Warri-

ors will suffice. While it may not look as pretty at a glance, the gameplay is still intact, and shooting all of your enemies is still a ton of fun. Two-player mode is even more fun than the single-player mode.

Impossible Mission Atari 4 $10
In the words of Alanis Morisette, "Isn't it ironic?" This game really is impossible! Certain objects in the game cannot be collected, and therefor the game cannot be beaten. However, for the European readers out there, the PAL version was fixed before release.

Jinks Atari 2 $4
Jinks is a decent game, but could have been much better if a few things had been tweaked. The controls need some editing, and the game needs a little more variation. It is a Breakout offshoot, but Breakout is a much better game.

Joust Atari 1 $3
Although not exactly arcade perfect, this port of the arcade game is probably as close as you'll get to the original on a home console. The controls do take some getting used to, but they do their job. For those unfamiliar with the game, it's simple. The object is to ride around on your flying bird, jousing your opponents off of their birds. All kinds of fun.

Karateka Atari 3 $5
Stick with Kung Fu on the NES for your karate-chopping desires. The controls in this game are simply horrid, and even when they work at all, the game is just boring and uneventful. Stay away from this one.

Kung-Fu Master Absolute Entertainment 4 $15
For the few people out there who don't have an NES but do have a 7800, this is a nice choice for a Kung Fu game. The similarities to the NES's Kung Fu are ridiculous, but this game has nice visuals, gameplay, and decent sound. It certainly isn't the best game on the 7800, but is still a fair one.

Mario Bros. Atari 3 $5
It's the classic Mario Bros. arcade game, on the 7800. Although it has been released many, many times on a number of consoles, this port of the classic is a great one. Check this one out if you're a fan of the game.

Mat Mania Challenge Atari 4 $8
Mat Mania is much like many wrestling games of the time - boring and uneventful. Although there is an impressive list of moves at players' disposals, it just isn't enough to keep this

Double Dragon   Galga   Mario Bros.   Mat Mania Challenge

The Japanese thought that the real SMB 2 game was too strange and difficult for U.S. gamers.

Mean 18 Ultimate Golf   **Pete Rose Baseball**   **Planet Smashers**   **Rampage**

game from being a real stinker as compared to the fighting games of today that we've all become used to.

Mean 18 Ultimate Golf   Atari   6 $25

Meltdown   Atari   4 $10
Meltdown is a light gun game, and although it has a few strategy elements, it is just plain boring. The graphics are dull, the gameplay is dull, and the sounds are dull. It is probably better to just stay away from this one.

Midnight Mutants   Atari   4 $8
Midnight Mutants is one of the best reasons to buy a 7800, if you don't have one already. It is a sort of pseudo-RPG with lots of cool action and exploration, all for the goal of saving "Grandpa," who is better known from his role in "The Munsters." As stated already, this is one of the best reasons to own a 7800.

Motor Psycho   Atari   4 $10
Motor Psycho is a motorcycle racing game, and while it is a little bit of fun, the poor controls and repetitive gameplay take too much away from it.

Ms. Pac-Man   Atari   1 $4
This is pretty much just a re-released version of an old game. The game is playable, but is hardly as good as it should have been considering the 7800's potential. However, Ms. Pac-Man has seen so many re-releases in recent years that there are better versions now available.

Ninja Golf   Atari   4 $8
Yes, you read it correctly. This is a ninja golf game. After taking a swing at the ball and watching it fly, players must fight several ninjas on the way to the ball. It may sound wacky, and it is, but it is surprisingly enjoyable.

One-on-One Basketball   Atari   2 $3
For fans of classic sports games, One-on-One basketball is one of the best. It has nice graphics, nice gameplay, and has aged surprisingly well.

Pete Rose Baseball   Absolute Entertainment   5 $15
It's really too bad that when a baseball game is endorsed by one of the best players of all time that the game isn't necessarily as good. This game is about as cool as Pete's ban from baseball, and that isn't very cool at all. Poor controls and graphics make this one to stay away from.

Planet Smashers   Atari   4 $12

Pole Position II   Atari   1 $2
Atari must have desired their own demise, because when they shipped this game with every 7800, they shipped a very average game. Boring graphics, old gameplay, and not much else were just a few of the things that probably turned many gamers off to the 7800.

Rampage   Activision   5 $15
Again, Rampage makes a pretty good port to a home console. The graphics and sounds are good, and it is still fun (at least for a while) to completetly destroy town after town after town.

Realsports Baseball   Atari   1 $2
Baseball fans should look elsewhere. Either that, or they should only look at -- not play -- this game. The graphics are great, but the gameplay itself is just boring and doesn't feel at all like a real baseball game. If you do play this game at all, though, stick to the two-player mode.

Robotron: 2084   Atari   3 $5
If you liked the arcade game, you'll love being able to have this game at your home. The 7800 version of this robot-killer is a great one, with nice graphics, decent sound, and all of the intense gameplay intact. Recommended.

Scrapyard Dog   Atari   2 $4
The platformer genre was not fairly represented on the 7800, and this is a perfect example of this sad fact. Although the game is somewhat decent, it is just dull and boring. The main character is somewhat of a prude, and the game doesn't really give players much of a reason to care about playing it.

Summer Games   Atari   3 $5
For fans of button-mashers with multiple events, this is a great title. However, I'm not sure how many fans of games like this there are out there. Summer games is a decent title, and one of the better ones like it. It is especially enjoyable with a group of friends, since it supports up to eight players.

Super Huey UH-IX   Atari   3 $7
This game is about as much fun as Silent Service was on the NES, but instead of controlling a submarine, gamers take flight in a Super Huey UH-IX helicopter. As with Silent service, the game feels more like a chore than a game, and because of this, is too tedious to be worth playing.

Warrior, released in 1979 by Cinematronics, was the first two-player fighting game.

7800

Super Skateboardin'
Absolute Entertainment   4 $8

The idea behind Super Skateboardin' is simple: skateboard through the factory, and turn off all of the lights and machines. The visuals are pretty nice, and the game is actually pretty much fun. For those interested, this game was programmed by David Crane, of Atari 2600 Pitfall fame.

Tank Command
Froggo   7 $35

This is a roaming tank shooter that offers wave after wave of enemy targets. Fun for a quick game, this title can quickly become monotonous.

Title Match Pro Wrestling
Absolute Entertainment   4 $12

An otherwise standard wrestling game, this title features some very nice crowd and environment effects, and displays some of the nicest lighting effects on the system.

Tomcat F-14 Fighter Simulator
Absolute Entertainment   4 $12

Touchdown Football
Atari   3 $7

If you're looking for sports games, the 7800 is not the right machine to find them on, and Touchdown Football is a perfect testament to this. The graphics are nice, but that's about it.

Tower Toppler
Atari   2 $4

Tower Toppler is a fairly simple game. The object of it is to get your creature to the top of several towers unharmed, and then repeat. The difficulty changes in time, of course, and the graphics in this game are some of the very best on the 7800.

Water Ski
Froggo   6 $20

One of only two Froggo games released for the 7800 (the other being Tank Command), this game could have been a lot better than it was. The main problem with it is the control, which makes the game nearly unplayable at times.

Winter Games
Atari   2 $3

While Summer Games was a pretty solid game, Winter Games is even better. It may just be that I'm a sucker for winter video games more so than summer ones, but the events in this game are more exciting, the graphics cooler, and everything seems to come together well. As is the case with Summer Games, Winter Games supports up to eight-player multiplayer action.

Xenophobe
Atari   4 $8

Xevious
Atari   2 $3

Xevious has always been a great game, and for those who don't have a home version of it yet, this is probably the best. The game is a shooter, and although it is repetitive (as many shooters are), it is still a blast from the past.

HARDWARE

Atari 7800	Atari	3	$35
7800 Joystick	Atari	2	$5

Tank Command

Tower Toppler

Water Ski

Xenophobe

The official number of Tengen's Tetris game that were actually recalled: 268

Atari Jaguar
By: Lucus Barnes and Andy Slaven

The Atari Jaguar was released in late 1993 and claimed the title of "World's first 64-bit console," though this claim remains disputed even today. Originally released for $250, this system came with one controller and the cartridge Cybermorph. Considering the fact that many systems no longer came packaged with a game, this was a nice feature. The controller design was unlike anything that had been seen before on a home console and featured not only the standard directional pad on the left, but three main action buttons and a keypad that would accept overlays for games requiring complex controls. Later, the Jaguar was sold without a game at a reduced price, and Cybermorph was sold in a boxed version separately.

Third party support for the Jaguar was much better than it had been for Atari's past few video game systems, though there were few game releases directly after launch. The one game that really turned the eyes of the video game world toward the Jaguar was Alien vs. Predator. With some of the best first person graphics seen on a home console, a changeable character story line, and great movie inspired situations and environments, this title was unlike anything gamers had ever seen. Unfortunately Atari wasn't able to follow this game with other similarly successful titles, though Tempest 2000 is another notable game for this system.

A debate rages on within the gaming community as to the Jaguar's actual bit count. While toted as the world's first 64-bit system, there are those who would argue this claim. The system itself contains a total of five processors divided among three separate chips, two of which are named named "Tom" and "Jerry". The third chip is a Motorola 68000 (16-bit) that served as the CPU for several systems released before the Jaguar. The real debate lies within the bit values for the separate chips used in this overall system, with both the blitter and object processor (Tom) being the only true 64-bit components used. The other chip (Jerry) doesn't contain any 64-bit components, and this is where the argument really begins. The designers of the Jaguar contend that all the components that need to be 64-bit are, and those that don't need to be, aren't. Part of the reason so many games have little or no improvement over 16-bit consoles such as the SNES is due to the fact that many programmers didn't use the Jaguar to its full potential, but instead used the 68000 chip as the main processor. However you view this argument, it is normally agreed upon that the Jaguar is a 64-bit "system," meaning that it has the capability to function as a 64-bit unit when considered as a whole, but also has 16-bit components that are supplemental.

The Jaguar had several unique accessories that were released for the system, including the Jag Link cable that allowed for two Jaguar systems within 100 feet to be connected for independently viewed action. While this is a very good idea, and far ahead if its time, poor sales of the system meant that this device had only a small potential market, and as such not many were sold. Also, a virtual reality visor was planned for release, but only made it to the prototype stage. Resembling a professional grade visor and fitting over eyeglasses if necessary, this accessory would have surely helped raise Jaguar sales, though it was eventually deemed too expensive and cancelled. Only a few of these have surfaced and demand well over $1000 when they do. Only one game is known to be supported by this device, though it is rumored that different versions of the VR unit are compatible with other games (None of these have been confirmed however.)

In 1995 Atari released the Jaguar CD in hopes of continuing the lifecycle of the Jaguar, much in the same way Sega had used the Sega CD. This system reached a miniscule consumer base and did nothing to prolong the life of the Jaguar. In 1996 Atari went through restructuring that would lead to the official end of the Jaguar. Though already considered a dead system by most, it wasn't until the sale of the Jaguar technology to Hasbro in 1998 that would drive the final nail into the Jaguar's coffin.

Then came along a company called Songbird Productions to resurrect this system. Releasing professionally developed and produced games for the Atari Jaguar as recently as 2002, and plans to continue doing so, Songbird has breathed new life into a system that was destined to become a footnote in video game history. While it is not the policy of the VGB guide to list "homebrew" games as being officially released, Songbird games should not be confused with these. Each game is sold in its own full color box, the cart features a full color label, and the quality of these titles is top notch.

What was destined to remain a collector-only system is making a resurgence of sorts, not only with an active fan base on the internet, but now with the continuation of games for the system as well. Perhaps in a few more years the Atari Jaguar will be viewed as the system that didn't reach its potential until a decade after its release.

Jaguar controller shown 3/4 size

What game requires the player to toss food to animals while moving through an altered Nazi maze?

Atari Karts   **Battle Sphere**   **Breakout 2000**   **Cannon Fodder**

Air Cars   ICD   8 $70
The Jaguar library is LOADED (since this is the Jag section, we're being real loose with the terms "library" and "loaded") with 3-D shooters (Cybermorph, I-War, Hover Strike, etc.) Sadly, this dull-sounding and drab-looking mission based snoozer is probably the worst of the lot. Air Cars was one of the final "regular production" Jag releases, and mostly available through mail order.

Alien vs. Predator   Atari   5 $40
Widely considered to be THE best game ever released for the Jaguar, this dark and atmospheric corridor shooter is packed full of genuine scares and still manages to impress today's jaded gamers with its smooth graphics and game play. This game allows you to choose to play as either an Alien, a Predator, or a Marine. One of the best selling of all Jag games, AvP still commands top dollar since most collectors won't let go of their copies.

Atari Karts   Atari   7 $40
Atari naturally threw their hat into the Mario Kart ring, and the resulting game is surprisingly entertaining. The graphics and scrolling may be 16-bit in quality, but they're certainly nice 16-bit. The frame rate is smooth and fast, the control is tight, and the characters design is imaginative (some charters must be unlocked.) Overall, Atari Karts rates as one of the best (and certainly most sought-after) racers on the Jag.

Attack of the Mutant Penguins
**   Atari   6 $25**
No, it's not related to Attack of the Killer Tomatoes. This action/strategy/shooter hybrid sports an odd title that might lead you to dismiss it as just another mindless piece of Jaguar fluff, but the game itself is a solid (if short) bit of entertainment. The colorful isometric graphics are very appealing, but the soundtrack is practically nonexistent.

Battle Sphere   Scatologic   8 $180
Unlike most consoles that simply die and stay buried, the Jaguar has been breathing its death wheeze for years now. A 3-D shooter in the tradition of Wing Commander (and even the original 2600 Star Raiders), Battlesphere is widely regarded as one of the Jag's better (and most expensive!) games. It's too bad the early Jaguar games didn't look and play like this one... the cat might have roared a lot louder and longer.

Breakout 2000   Telegames   7 $35
Atari graced the Jaguar with several "updates" to their classic arcade games including this title based on the simplistic yet

amazingly addictive "reflex test" game (the original version is also included). The graphics are presented from a pseudo 3-D perspective, but the overall visual presentation fails to impress. The real problem is the control... the Jaguar digital pad simply can't emulate the precise movement of a paddle.

Brutal Sports Football
**   Telegames   3 $8**
The concept of a literally "brutal" game of football played by roughneck characters armed with weapons and power-ups is very appealing. In fact, it's truly bizarre that no one has taken the concept further. Unfortunately, choppy framerates and very stupid computer opponents sideline the detailed graphics and good control.

Bubsy in Fractured Furry Tales
**   Atari   4 $12**
One of the better platform games available for the Jag (as if there were a lot to choose from), this Sonic wannabe sports nice control and very colorful graphics. The one-hit kills will get on your nerves, as will some of Bubsy's one-liners. Unfortunately, it's looks and plays almost exactly like the SNES and Genesis versions.

Cannon Fodder   Virgin   4 $12
This thoroughly enjoyable war-based action/simulation has a lot going for it and will prove rewarding for those willing to invest the time necessary to master it. Based on a series of computer games, Cannon Fodder is a mission-based affair with cartoonish graphics, a good soundtrack, entertaining sound effects, and excellent control.

Checkered Flag   Atari   2 $5
Imitation might be the sincerest form of flattery, but this Virtua Racing clone is rendered nearly unplayable by Atari's attempt to provide analog-like control to the digital controller (the longer you hold down the control pad, the sharper the turn.) The polygonal models and colorful backgrounds are actually quite nice for a pre-Playstation/Saturn 3-D racer, but the control is a complete wreck.

Club Drive   Atari   3 $10
Do you like blocky and plain graphics, really poor track design, sloppy control, and a maddening soundtrack? If so, Club Drive is the perfect game for you (and you call yourself a "gamer.") There is really nothing at all to recommend about this awful "racer", other than cheap laughs.

Cybermorph   Atari   2 $4
As the original pack-in title, Cybermorph is the most common of

JAG

all the Jag games and hasn't aged nearly as well as its sequel, Battlemorph. All of the action of this 3-D shooter takes place in flat-shaded worlds mostly devoid of features, plus the sound effects and silly voiceovers are prehistoric by today's (and even yesterday's) standards.

Defender 2000　　Atari　　　　7　$35
Atari attempted to give the arcade classic Defender a makeover much like they did Tempest, but the results aren't quite as stellar. The mildly enhanced "original" Defender features great control, slightly improved graphics, and easier gameplay. The second and third "updates" add much more detailed graphics and more features, but the resulting games are less fun to play than the original. The techno soundtrack is cool, though.

Doom　　Atari　　　　3　$15
The first version of Id's classic corridor shooter to appear on any home console, the Jaguar port of Doom is superior to the 32x, SNES, and 3DO versions that followed it (but not quite as good as the PSX, Saturn, and N64 releases.) The graphics are smooth and fast (if a bit pixilated) and the sound effects and soundtrack are as creepy as the PC original. Doom was one of the really big early high-profile releases for the Jag and served as a showcase for the hardware.

Double Dragon V　　Atari　　　　4　$15
The Double Dragon series of side-scrolling repetitive punch and kick fighting games were certainly popular way back in the day, but part five really highlights the shortcomings of this now-dead franchise. The computer A.I. is overly difficult, and the whole production feels unfinished.

Dragon: The Bruce Lee Story
　　　　　　　　　　Atari　　　　4　$10
There really is a 64-bit graphics chip humming underneath the hood of the Jaguar, but you'd never know it by looking at this tripe. Dragon: The Bruce Lee Story is a barely enhanced port of the Genesis/SNES fighter featuring the same choppy graphics and poor control of its processors, plus mediocre graphics and sound effects.

Evolution: Dino Dudes　Atari　　2　$8
This Lemmings-style strategy game (one of the Jag's first releases) is an engrossing little title hampered by a ridiculously short game timer. The simple (but colorful) graphics and imaginative game objectives are quite charming in an old-fashioned sort of way, but later levels prove to be frustrating.

Fever Pitch Soccer　　Atari　　3　$7
The Jaguar certainly can't be termed a "sports" console like the

Sega Genesis, but it had a few decent sporting titles. This entertaining soccer simulation (presented from a ¾ perspective) has pleasing visuals and good control, but the computer A.I. is merciless.

Fight For Life　　Atari　　　　5　$15
The title of this game was pretty indicative of Atari's financial situation in 1996. Unfortunately, this interpretation on the Tekken/Virtua Fighter genre falls flat on its polygonal face, a victim of poor graphics and a laughably awful fighting engine. On a positive note, the game was developed by one of the programmers of the original Virtua Fighter game (who should have known better), plus the replay/rewind/pause feature is quite cool and good for laughs.

Flashback　　U.S. Gold　　　　5　$15
Like many Jaguar titles, Flashback is a port of a 16-bit game that fails to push the more advanced hardware to any degree. Regardless, this side-scrolling action/adventure game is heavy on puzzles and problem solving and manages to reward tenacious gamers with an enjoyable experience.

Flip Out　　Atari　　　　3　$10
Well-designed puzzle games never fail to please. Flip Out is one such game, featuring addictive puzzle action, colorful graphics, and a great sense of humor. The "storyline" (something about aliens) is very entertaining, and the voiceovers are a real hoot.

Hover Strike　　Atari　　　　3　$10
Another "let's use every available button on the Jaguar controller" 3-D shooter in the same vein as Cybermorph, Hover Strike puts you in control of a loose-feeling tank and sets you down in a series of bland-looking environments in search of far-too-rare enemies. If you're into this sort of game, you'll be wiser to pick up the far-superior CD sequel and skip the original.

Hyper Force　　Songbird　　　　8　$50
While not nearly up to the level of the superlative Rayman, this sci-fi side-scroller certainly has some moments of greatness (it should have had more, seeing how it was released five years later!) The 2-D graphics are nothing special and could have used a bit more polish, but the control is tight and the sound effects are surprisingly effective.

I-War　　Atari　　　　4　$12
One of the least impressive of the Jaguar 3-D shooters (you control a variety of tanks sets in "cyberspace" environments), I-War is practically devoid of fun... in fact, it seems that Atari went out of its way to exorcise any enjoyable qualities that may have existed at one time. The graphics are bland, the control is awk-

Double Dragon　　　　　Fight For Life

Flashback　　　　　Hyper Force

50

Iron Soldier   Missle Command 3D   Power Drive Rally   Rayman

ward and unresponsive, and the levels and objectives are just plain boring.

International Sensible Soccer
Telegames   3 $10
Who on earth came up with this game's title? SENSIBLE SOCCER?!? Sadly, the game's execution is no better than its title. The control is awkward, the graphics are decidedly 16-bit in nature, and there are numerous bugs whizzing around.

Iron Soldier   Atari   2 $10
Widely considered to be one of the best games in the Jaguar library, Iron Soldier is an action-packed 3-D mech-style shooter similar to the popular PC title Mechwarrior. Destruction runs rampant, and there is a fair amount of strategy involved as well. There was nothing quite like Iron Soldier available for home consoles at the time of it's release, and it's still fun today (part three even made it out for the Playstation.)

Iron Soldier 2   Telegames   7 $50
Also available in a more common CD format, the cartridge version of the sequel to the popular (for the Jaguar) mech shooter isn't all that different from the first game. The graphics have been improved slightly and the missions are more varied, plus the difficulty level has been increased quite a bit over that of the cartridge version. The CD version contains better music and extra cinemas.

Kasumi Ninja   Atari   2 $10
Atari's first fighter for the Jaguar was a big disappointment and helped create the misconception that the Jag wasn't much more powerful than its 16-bit competitors. The choppy 2-D graphics look like something from a bad Genesis game, the control is imprecise (the huge Jag controller doesn't help), and the characters are unbalanced.

Missile Command 3-D   Atari   5 $20
Another one of Atari's "updates" to a classic arcade favorite, Missile Command 3-D falls somewhere between the excellent Tempest 2000 and the mediocre Breakout 2000. The original Missile Command is still a lot of fun, but 3D Missile command is something of a disappointment. Virtual Missile Command is the most intriguing of the three, partly because it was supposed to be one of the original games to support the unreleased VR Headset (and partly because it takes place underwater.)

NBA Jam T.E.   Atari   5 $15
Midway's popular arcade quarter-muncher made an appearance on most every console and handheld of the era, and the Jaguar port is one of the console's best games (as well as its best

sports title.) All the features from the arcade parent are present, including the big heads, scaling graphics, outrageous hidden characters, and trademark voiceovers.

Pinball Fantasies   Computer West   4 $12
Not many gamers clamor for pinball titles, especially mediocre ones based on old 16-bit games. There's really not much to recommend about Pinball Fantasies unless you enjoy unrealistic physics and bland graphics. Go find a real pinball machine instead!

Pitfall: The Mayan Adventures
Atari   5 $15
Like the Sega 32x, the Atari Jaguar was home to a number of games that were nothing more than mildly enhanced Genesis and Super Nintendo titles. This beautiful 2-D platform game (based on the revolutionary Atari 2600 game, which is also included) is great fun, but it's not much different from the earlier releases.

Power Drive Rally   Time/Warner   3 $10
It's kind of odd to say that one of the most entertaining games on the Jaguar is an overhead racing affair similar to Micro Machines, but that's the way it is. Regardless, Power Drive Rally is great fun, featuring beautiful 2-D graphics, a very smooth frame rate, and excellent control.

Protector   Songbird   8 $50
Perfection is rarely improved upon, but perfection is rarely achieved. If you're a Defender fan (and if you're not, you should be), you'll find a lot to like about this well-done clone. Songbird did a great job with the control, graphics, and sound effects, and the gameplay is classic old-school shooting action.

Protector SE   Songbird   8 $50
Overall improvements are sure to be featured in this release, along with new features, in this special edition of an already great game.

Raiden   Atari   3 $10
A "classic" (as in outdated) port of an overhead arcade shooter might have been a poor choice for a first-generation Jaguar offering, but you certainly can't fault the accuracy of the translation. The shooting action is fast and furious, and the graphics are intense and sprite-filled, making Raiden one of the best Jag games for those with fast reflexes and a love for huge explosions.

Rayman   Ubi Soft   6 $30
Most gamers have conveniently forgotten that Ubi Soft's popular

JAG

Rayman mascot began his career on the Jag, only later appearing on the PSX, Saturn, N64, Dreamcast, GB, and GBA. The original shows off the glorious 2-D power of the Jaguar, and the control is as sweet as ever. The Jaguar might have stood a chance if it had been graced with more games like Rayman!

Ruiner Pinball   Atari   5 $12
It's not as bad as Pinball Fantasies, but Ruiner pinball still fails to convey the "feel" of a true pinball game. The graphics are flashy and colorful, but the physics are completely unrealistic.

Skyhammer   Songbird   8 $50
Developed by the same folks behind Alien vs. Predator (Rebellion), Shyhammer combines the 3-D antics of Decent with futuristic environments reminiscent of the classic sci-fi movie Blade Runner. The graphics are quite nice for a Jaguar game, but the control is a bit slow and the framerates are choppy.

Soccer Kid   Songbird   8 $50
No, it's not a sports title... it's a 2-D platform game starring a ball-kicking soccer kid (silly, we know.) It's certainly not up to the level of Rayman or even Bubsy, but the game controls nicely and the graphics are pretty enough.

Space War 2000   B&C ComputerVisions   8 $70
Not a regular production release at all, this unfinished prototype was made available at the 2001 CGE and through mail order. It's a 3-D shooter that looks to have a lot of potential, but it's simply not playable enough to rate it as a "real" game. Perhaps it will be finished and re-released in the future... we can only hope!

Super Burnout   Atari   3 $10
Widely viewed as the best racing game on the Jaguar, Super Burnout utilizes scaling 2-D sprites instead of taking the more modern polygonal route. This rather old-fashioned approach still works surprisingly well, and the sense of speed (coupled with tight control) is quite impressive.

Supercross 3D   Atari   4 $12
Atari's first (and only) dirt bike racing game for the Jaguar is something of a mixed bag... the graphics, control, and overall gameplay are better than average, but the choppy and slow framerate is problematic and harms an otherwise good racer.

Syndicate   Ocean   5 $15
This port of the popular PC game rates as one of the best games in the Jaguar library, and with good reason. It's a wonderfully complex, bloody, and entertaining action/strategy title that will keep you busy for weeks (just be prepared to fight with

the complex controls for a while.)

Tempest 2000   Atari   2 $15
Quite possibly the coolest remake of a classic arcade game ever made, Tempest 2000 rates as one of the shiniest jewels in the Jaguar's crown (more of a tiara, really.) Along with classic Tempest you'll find two great upgrades loaded with fantastic psychedelic graphics, cool new weapons, and a completely awesome techno soundtrack. The only flaw in this otherwise stellar game is the lack of a paddle controller.

Theme Park   Ocean   5 $15
One of the biggest time-killers of all time (along with Sim City), Theme Park puts you in control of the day-to-day operations of an amusement park (including employee relations, fast-food selection, and ride design.) It might sound dull, but give it a chance and you'll be completely and utterly hooked.

Towers II: Plight of the Stargazer
**   Telegames   7 $50**
An intriguing combination of Doom-style gameplay and basic role-playing game elements, Towers II manages to be one of those rare titles that will entertain both arcade game fans and RPG enthusiasts alike. The graphics are and framerate are quite smooth, while the RPG "extras" are incorporated very well into the overall game structure.

Trevor McFur in the Crescent Galaxy
**   Atari   2 $5**
Atari shot itself in the foot when it decided to launch its shiny new Jaguar console right along side next to this dreadful horizontal 2-D shooter. The rendered graphics are nice, but the storyline is awful and the one-hit kills are simply inexcusable. At least you can laugh at the lion people.

Troy Aikman NFL Football   Williams   3 $8
As the only "real" football simulation ever released for the Jaguar (Brutal Sports Football doesn't quite qualify), Troy Aikman football provides an entertaining skins diversion but doesn't look or feel much different than the Genesis/SNES games of the same name (which weren't that special, either.)

Ultra Vortex   Atari   3 $15
Often cited as a favorite among Jaguar fans, Ultra Vortex is an excellent Mortal Kombat clone with an extra emphasis on gore and violence. The 2-D graphics are quite lovely from a 1995 standpoint, featuring sharp digitalized fighters (a few are rendered) and lush backgrounds. The control and soundtrack are excellent as well.

| Soccer Kid | Tempest 2000 | Towers II: Plight of the | Theme Park |

When Sonic replaced the game Altered Beast as the Genesis pack-in game, those with Altered Beast could mail off for a free copy of Sonic.

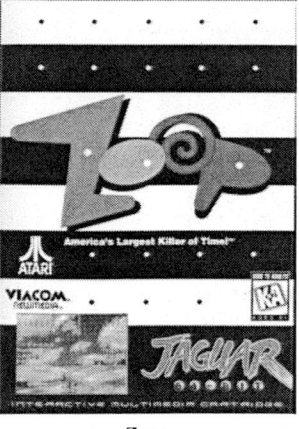

| Wolfenstein 3D | Zero 5 | Zool 2 | Zoop |

Val D'Isere Skiing And Snowboarding
Atari   3 $8

This upgraded port of the Super Nintendo ski title Tommy Moe's Winter Extreme betters its predecessor in several key areas, including graphics and overall variety. Unfortunately, the original game wasn't that good to start off with, and neither is this one.

White Men Can't Jump   Atari   3 $8

Games based on movie licenses are nothing new, but this two-on-two arcade-style game based on the entertaining comedy manages to seem fresh and different. Originally bundled with the Team Tap (a four-player adaptor), WMCJ sports bland graphics but the excellent control and fast gameplay make up for its visual deficiencies.

Wolfenstein 3D   Atari   4 $12

Widely viewed as the granddaddy of all first person shooters (though similar games came before it). Wolfenstein 3-D dropped the 2-D side-scrolling pretenses of its PC ancestors in favor of 3-D Nazis and mutants. It doesn't compare that well to Doom or AvP, but it's still great historical fun and way better than the awful SNES port.

Worms   Telegames   7 $50

Quite possibly the most underrated game in the entire Jaguar library, this action/shooter/strategy/party game isn't that great as a single-player experience but is a total and complete blast when played with three slightly inebriated friends. The 2-D graphics are colorful and smooth, and the sound effects are a riot.

Zero 5   Telegames   7 $50

Games that consist of several different sub-games generally don't play too well, usually because none of the individual games are strong enough to merit a separate release. Zero 5 is a 3-D space shooter at heart, but none of the three different games manage to rise above the level of mediocre. This is a shame, as Zero 5 sports some of the best graphics and music that the Jaguar ever produced. As a technological display, Zero 5 is great. As a game, it's pretty lame.

Zool 2   Atari   2 $7

Has anyone played (or even heard of) the original Zool? Most people haven't heard of the sequel, either, but lots of decent games never get the recognition they deserve. Zool 2 is a fairly standard 2-D platform game with decent graphics and excellent control, but its lack of overall originality is one of the big reasons why you'll never see Zool 3.

Zoop   Atari   5 $10

The best puzzle games are easy to learn, reel you in quickly, and gradually ramp up the difficulty level. Zoop isn't difficult to understand (though it's a bit deeper than your average puzzle game) and it can certainly be addictive, but the difficulty increases way too early on to warrant a hearty recommendation. This one is best suited for gamers with great hand/eye coordination.

HARDWARE

Atari Jaguar   Atari   4 $30

Cat Box   Atari   5 $20

This device plugs into the Jaguar and offers a variety of video and audio output options.

Jag Link   Atari   5 $12

This is a networking cable that allowed for multiple Jaguars to be connected up to 100 feet, and allowed for independently viewed action.

Jaguar Controller   Atari   2 $7

Standard with three main action buttons and a keypad, this design was a bit awkward at first, but is necessary for more complex games such as Alien vs. Predator.

Pro Controller   Atari   5 $12

This controller featured three more action buttons (actually repositioned 7, 8 & 9 buttons) and two trigger buttons (repositioned 4 & 6 buttons.)

Team Tap   Atari   2 $5

Connect up to four people per port with this multi-tap device.

The Saturn was the game system of choice on the Drew Carey Show.

JAG CD

Atari Jaguar CD
By: Lucus Barnes and Andy Slaven

Atari released an add-on system for the Atari Jaguar in 1995 dubbed, creatively enough, the Atari Jaguar CD. Priced at $150, this system included not only two demo discs for Tempest 2000 and Myst, but also included full versions of Blue Lightning and Vid Grid. Built into the system itself was a program known as the VLM (Virtual Light Machine) that would generate colorful graphics to accompany audio CD's when played in the unit.

The Jaguar CD is equipped with a 2x speed CD-ROM that uses proprietary software in order to prevent the pirating of discs, and to allow for the use of up to 790 megabytes instead of the standard 650. As with most CD systems of the day, this unit could also play audio CD and CD+G formats, though the latter never seemed to gather much of a following. Both forms of audio CD's use an onscreen interface to easily facilitate their use, and the VLM on this system (known by different names on other systems such as the 3DO) is considered to be the best available on any home console.

In similar fashion to the Sega 32x, this system interfaces with the base system via the cartridge port, and allows for cartridges to be played through a pass-through slot on top. The system itself is an odd shape, rounded and oblong, and quickly gained the nickname "football." One feature that is noticeably absent from the system is internal RAM used for saving game information. Instead, a separate cartridge called the Memory Track was sold to facilitate game saves. The reason for releasing a separate memory device instead of including it was to reduce the overall cost, and as a consequence, a lower price tag. With the necessity of a Jaguar in addition to the Jaguar CD, the lowest possible price was essential to help promote sales.

The main problem that Atari would face with the launch of the Jaguar CD was not going to be the quality of games it could produce, but instead the lack of developers willing to create those games. Both Sony and Sega had released their next generation consoles (the PSX and Saturn respectively), and this created not only competition within the consumer market, but more importantly in the developer market. The prospect that the PSX offered to many developers was too great an opportunity for many to pass up, and still others were already investing heavily in the success of the Saturn. As a result, Atari's fledgling system was left in the cold with little hope of receiving much attention from either consumers or developers.

It is estimated that Capcom sold well over 50,000 Street Fighter II arcade machines.

Both poor sales and a lack of software for the system mounted, and in 1996 Atari went through major restructuring. At this point the system was all but forgotten, though it technically survived until 1998 when the technology was sold to Hasbro. While the system is quite capable of producing high quality graphics and game play, it never reached its full potential, and even the fanatical Jaguar fan base pays little attention to this short lived system. By far, the greatest feature on this machine is the VLM and should definitely be experienced first hand. Unfortunately, the Achilles heel of this machine is the fact that it is very fragile, and more often than not, systems found in the wild will prove to be defective.

Due to the lack of sales of hardware, the Atari Jaguar CD is becoming a difficult item to find. A seemingly steady stream of these systems is available on the internet brand new, but the knowledge that this system was never made in very large numbers keeps both the demand and price high. Even since the beginning of 2002 prices on these systems have risen over 20%, changing from the average $85-$100 price, to an ever increasing $120. Regardless of the fact that the Jaguar CD has some quality games for it, it is the lack of quantity that drives many retro-gamers away from this purchase, making it one of the many systems with appeal only to the collectors' market.

The makers of Mortal Kombat originally wanted either Steven Segal or Jean Claude Van Damme. Both refused.

JAG CD

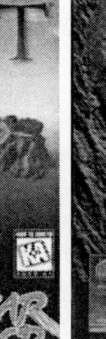

Baldies   **Iron Soldier 2**   **Myst**   **Primal Rage**

Baldies   Atari   5 $15
The Jaguar CD certainly wasn't a hot seller, so it's doubtful that many gamers have played Baldies. This is a shame, as it's a really cute and entertaining action/strategy game with a great sense of humor. The graphics are decidedly 16-bit in nature and the Jaguar control pad simply wasn't meant for this type of game, but there's a lot of fun to be had here nevertheless.

Battlemorph   Atari   4 $10
Widely viewed as one of the best of the CD releases, this sequel to the original console pack-in game Cybermorph improves on its predecessor in every conceivable way. The graphics are far better, the soundtrack is awesome, and the missions (some of which occur underwater) are full of challenge and variety.

Blue Lightning   Atari   4 $5
Why on earth Atari chose to make this waste of plastic the pack-in game for the CD peripheral is a complete mystery, but we suppose misery really does love company (Battlemorph would have been a far better choice). A pseudo 3-D shooter similar to Afterburner (and based on the Atari Lynx game of the same name), Blue Lightning looks, sounds, and plays just like a bad 16-bit cart. If it weren't for the computer-rendered intermissions, you'd be hard pressed to find ANY evidence of 64-bit shenanigans.

Brain Dead 13   Readysoft   5 $15
If you enjoy the "push-a-button-and-see-what-happens" gameplay of Dragon's Lair and Space Ace, you'll love this game (the rest of us will move onto something else.) You can't fault the quality of the beautiful cartoon animation, but the entire concept of "guessing" what button to push in order to proceed is totally antiquated.

Dragon's Lair   Readysoft   4 $10
This beautiful "interactive" cartoon disguised as a videogame was an arcade phenomenon in the 1980's, and many believed that Dragon's Lair was the future of the gaming industry. Fortunately, the novelty of the trial-and-error gameplay wore off FAST. The Jaguar port is faithful to the arcade original (aside from some slightly rougher-looking visuals) and the never-ending "your dead" animation is as maddening as ever.

Highlander   Atari   5 $12
Another oft-overlooked Jaguar CD game, Highlander is actually based more on the bizarre cartoon series and less on the movie franchise. The gameplay is similar to that of Resident Evil in that you lead a 3-D polygonal character throughout a 2-D world comprised of pre-rendered backgrounds. The sketchy control issues prevalent of the genre are in full force here and the game

is a wee bit short, but Highlander has its moments.

Hover Strike: Unconquered Lands
     Atari   4 $10
The original Hover Strike is pretty bad by all accounts, and most Jaguar fans weren't expecting much from the CD sequel. Those few tenacious gamers who did manage to keep an open mind were pleasantly surprised, as the it's far superior to the original. The basic gameplay remains the same, but the control is much tighter and the graphics are much cleaner and feature loads of texture mapping. The musical score is especially well done.

Iron Soldier 2   Telegames   6 $40
Also available on a more rare cartridge format, this sequel to the popular (for the Jaguar) mech shooter isn't all that different from the first game, aside from some slightly better graphics and more missions (plus the difficulty level has been cranked up past that of the already formidable original.) The CD version contains music and cinemas not included on the cart.

Myst   Atari   4 $10
Widely accredited as the "game" that brought the gaming experience to the masses (on the PC and Apple, at least), Myst is really just a bunch of REALLY obscure (as in massively frustrating) puzzles wrapped up in some lush pre-rendered visuals. It's probably great fun to newbies (it sold millions) but most Jaguar fans will be bored.

Primal Rage   Time Warner   6 $20
The arcade versions of the gun shooters Area 51 and Maximum Force were powered by modified Jaguar chipsets (called the CoJag arcade board.) It's been rumored that the arcade games T-Mek (which only saw a home release on the Sega 32x) and Primal Rage (which appeared on every console and handheld of the era) were also originally CoJag games. This is untrue, as both titles run off entirely different hardware. Nevertheless, people expected the Jaguar CD port of the inexplicably popular Jurassic era themed fighter to be arcade-perfect. It's not quite flawless (the loading times are long and the characters are smaller) but everything else is pretty much the same, including the shallow fighting engine.

Space Ace   Readysoft   4 $10
Really nothing more than Dragon's Lair in space, Space Ace features the same gorgeous (albeit washed-out) cartoon visuals and "make a guess" gameplay of Dragon's Lair and Brain Dead 13. Gamers had grown tired of this type of game by the time it made its late appearance in arcades, and Space Ace was a big commercial disappointment.

The uniforms and weapons used to make the game Night Trap were recently found in California. They were all sold to a private collector.

Vid Grid Atari 4 $5
Quite possibly the strangest title in the Jaguar library, Vid Grid is a puzzle game of sorts where the objective is to de-scramble images from popular music videos from artists like Aerosmith, Van Halen, and Jimi Hendrix. It sounds silly, but there's just enough innovation present to provide an entertaining experience. The video and sound quality is about what you'd expect from the Jaguar CD. Best of all, Vid Grid came packed free with the CD unit.

World Tour Racing Telegames 6 $40
A lot of Jaguar fans were really excited when Telegames announced World Tour Racing for the Jaguar CD, and a lot of gamers were really disappointed when they finally sat down to play it. The game's FMV is awesome, but you can't build a game around FMV. Sadly, the choppy framerate and poor control conspired to leave this mediocre racer mired in the pit stop.

DEMO CD's

Myst Sampler Atari 4 $2
This short "teaser" version of the full-length Myst was included with Jaguar CD peripheral. Your exploration is limited to the library.

Tempest 2000 Soundtrack
  Atari 4 $5
No, it's not a game. Yes, it's the soundtrack to the Tempest 2000 game cart. The already excellent techno music has been enhanced, re-mixed, and several new tunes have been added.

HARDWARE

Atari Jaguar CD Atari 4 $80

Memory Track Atari 5 $15

World Tour Racing

Memory Track

Shelly Duvall's A Birds Life was nearly the pack-in game for the 3DO.

Bandai Pippin @world
By: Andy Slaven and Joe Kudrna

The Pippin @world is by far the rarest video game console ever released in the U.S. Originally released in December of 1995, and officially released as the Pippin Atmark in March of 1996 in Japan, this model was white and is much more plentiful than the black U.S. model. Japan seemed relatively willing to accept such a machine as nearly 200 titles were released for it, but these titles were only exclusive to Japan...but, unfortunately for American consumers, only in Japanese. But with no region coding of any type, Japanese games can be played on U.S. systems, and a large amount of them do not require an understanding of the Japanese language.

Believed to be the result of a project known as "Pea Pod", Apple had originally envisioned a multimedia system similar in function to that of the CD-i. But Bandai had plans of marketing this machine as a game console, one that would eventually compete with the Saturn and Playstation. It wasn't until midway through the design process that internet capabilities became an area of interest, and were eventually added into the scheme of things by Apple's designers. The U.S. version, known as the Pippin @world, was released in November of 1996, included a 28.8 Motorola Surfermodem and cost $500.

Estimates place the actual number of U.S. consumer units at around 2,000-10,000 consumer units sold. The U.S. development unit, like the Japanese version, is also white, making the black version a very rare find indeed. The thinking behind making so many development units available was to entice as many companies as possible to make games for the system. With a total of 16 titles released in the U.S., it is obvious that this tactic did not work.

This system is actually powered by a 66 megahertz, 32-bit PowerPC 603 processor, which made it a very powerful system for its day. A 4x speed CD-ROM and 16 bit audio output also makes this unit capable of doing things other systems weren't able to do. Unfortunately, the Pippin was never used to its potential. Though a very powerful system, the one major weakness of the Pippin was its inability to produce quality 3-D output.

The Pippin is actually capable of playing several types of CD's, including audio and CD+G, but was not designed to play VCD's (video compact discs). While this capability seems like it could have easily been added, VCD's had virtually no market in the U.S., and Japan's LD (laserdisc) market was doing very well, so it seemed unlikely that this feature would ever be used. This does not mean that the Pippin is incapable of playing video, however. When used as a computer, the Pippin was able to play back video in Macintosh compatible formats, but the "auto-boot" feature needed to make VCD's readily playable for those without knowledge of how to use a computer was not a feature.

While Apple actually designed the hardware used in the Pippin and Mitsubishi manufactured the units, the technology was licensed to Bandai so that they could handle distribution worldwide. After the system's release in Japan however, Apple began to lose interest in the project since profits weren't nearly what was expected. It was Bandai's sole responsibility to market this system, and with Apple in serious financial difficulty during this time, there was no feasible way that Apple could help promote this system. Unfortunately for Bandai, part of their agreement with Apple forbid the use of the term "computer" to promote the system, and it could not be sold to businesses or for the purposes of rental. After the November 1996 U.S. release, Apple had all but disowned the system completely. This put an enormous burden on Bandai, and the U.S. Pippin sale and production were halted by mid 1997.

While Bandai's Pippin @world never reached even a fraction of its potential, it is extremely collectable. Software for this system, however, is nearly impossible to come by. Edutainment titles were often discarded when the child it was bought for reached an age where it was no longer enjoyable. Interactive guides were thrown away as the internet became more accessible. Games were pawned or thrown away when newer game systems were introduced. And with the prospect that as few as 2,000 people may have owned one of these machines while it was still supported, it only makes sense that very few games would be left for collectors to find.

In the end, a company called DayStar (Don't call them a pyramid scheme...it's more like a trapezoid) bought the left over stock, and was the largest single seller of the system within the U.S. One former DayStar employee placed sales of the unit through their distribution chain as high as 2,000 units. Katz Media would eventually buy rights to distribution in Europe and begin distribution of developer kits, though this company would later become bankrupt.

Oddly enough however, in recent years, small amounts of Pippin software have been surfacing. It is believed that instead of destroying the software that had been made for the U.S. release, the unsold copies were stored in the hope that they could either be sold in Japan or repackaged for sale on compatible Macintosh systems. It has been documented that unsold U.S. consoles were repackaged and sent to Japan for distribution, so doing so with the software seems a very likely possibility.

Regardless of its actual performance, both in sales and in software, the @world is by far one of the best looking and most capable systems ever created. While it may only remain a footnote in the history of video games, this very unique system will remain the centerpiece of many collections.

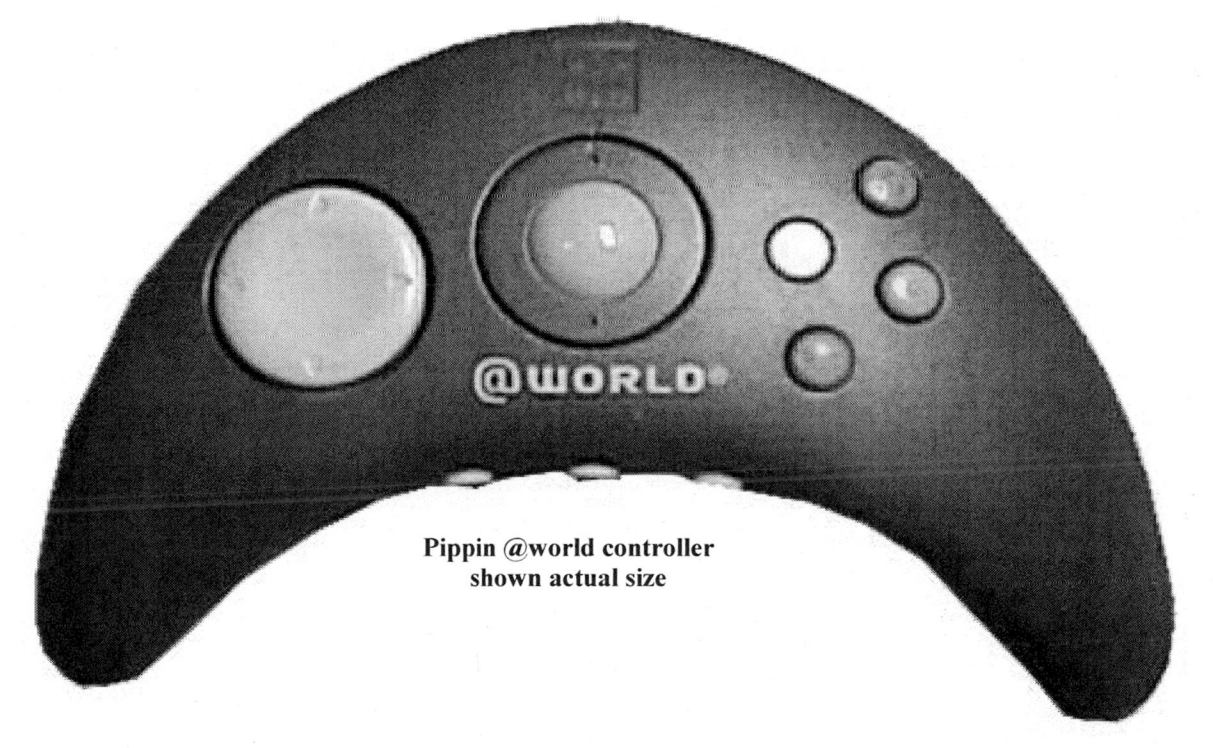

Pippin @world controller
shown actual size

How many labyrinths are in the first Zelda game on the NES?

| CineNoir | Compton's Interactive Encyclopedia | Exotic Sushi | Gus Goes to Cyberopolis |

Cool Crafts　　　　Bandai　　　8　　$50
This is a wonderful children's workshop title that offers interactive lessons for children around the ages of 5-10. This title was made under the supervision of Better Homes and Gardens, offering proof of the common American industry trying to reach a more diverse audience via multimedia titles.

CineNoir　　　　　　Bandai　　　8　　$50
This original title uses black and white film clips and footage from the 1940's to allow the creation of original stories. This is a very interesting idea for a game, but can become tedious with very limited results.

Compton's Interactive Encyclopedia
　　　　　　　　　　　Bandai　　　7　　$45
This is the 1994 version of the Compton Encyclopedia, made specifically for the Pippin, though I can make no distinction between the content of different version. Obviously the quality of the photos included are higher than those seen on other systems of the time.

Exotic Sushi　　　　Bandai　　　8　　$55
Not what most Americans were looking forward to when they bought this system, but an interesting reference regardless of the fact that few people seemed interested at the time. This interactive cookbook simply teaches the history of sushi and how to make some of the more exotic Japanese sushi dishes. This title plays in five separate languages.

Gundam Mobility Fleet 0079
　　　　　　　　　　　Bandai　　　9　　$85
This franchise is huge in Japan and has a very respectable following in the U.S. And while it has certainly aged, it is still a very sought after title by those fortunate enough to own a Pippin.

Gus Goes to Cyberopolis　Bandai　　　8　　$50
This is an edutainment title for the Pippin that teaches young children basic concepts, taught within an city environment. And while it holds no interest for gamers, it is still necessary for one wishing to complete the illusive Pippin collection…and not at all easy to find.

Gus Goes to Kooky Carnival
　　　　　　　　　　　Bandai　　　8　　$50
Another edutainment title staring Gus, this offers more of the

same skill building entertainment for young children, but is set in a circus environment.

Home Improvement 1-2-3　Bandai　　　8　　$45
A reference guide made by Home Depot, it is still unknown if this title was actually sold in Home Depots as well as computer stores. It seems unlikely however. This interactive reference offers easy to follow tips for the self-proclaimed handyman. Wouldn't a book on the subject have been easier to use though? And cheaper too! This is another example of an American company trying to reach a more mainstream audience with the use of multimedia. This title utilizes FMV sequences, and is also available in a more common Mac version.

Movioke　　　　　　Bandai　　　8　　$55
So…very…Japanese, but fun for Mystery Science Theatre fans! Similar to Karaoke, this title allows participants to speak the words of the actors onscreen. And while the U.S. public might not have been ready for this title at the time, it is one of the few titles that can entertain more than one person at a time. Actually, it seems to entertain a room full of onlookers more than the often chagrinned participants.

Mr. Potato Head Saves Veggie Valley
　　　　　　　　　　　Bandai　　　9　　$65
This title uses the once-popular Mr. Potato Head character in a short adventure to save the farm known as Veggie Valley. While this game does offer the often lacking game element of so many Pippin games, it is made for young children and will hold little, if any, interest for anyone over the age of 10. Perhaps one of the most difficult titles to find a working version of, there was at least one bad "run" of these games, where none of the copies would boot or play properly.

Pegasus Prime　　　Bandai　　　9　　$85
This is another installment of "The Journeyman Project" and offers some of the best FMV sequences available on this platform. A true game driven by interactive menus, this title should be more enjoyable than most of the non-game Pippin titles. Time travel is the key theme to this game.

Playskool Puzzles　　Bandai　　　7　　$40
This title features various puzzles that teach children basic skills in logic and problem solving.

Nine. (Eighteen if you count those found in the second quest).

Power Ranger Zeo Versus The Machine Empire
Bandai 8 $60
This is a side scrolling arcade game in which you take the role of the Power Rangers. This is one of the better titles for the system considering the fact that it actually involves game play. This title was also available in a much more common Mac version.

Racing Days Bandai 7 $40
This is a mediocre 3-D racing title that needs much improvement. Graphics are a big gritty, but the game is enjoyable with a little practice. This is the only multiplayer U.S. release for the Pippin.

Super Marathon
Bandai 8 $65
This is a direct port of the award winning first-person shooter for the Macintosh by the same name, but unfortunately it lacks a multiplayer option. Still, this is perhaps the best game available for the Pippin, and features more sound channels as the memory is upgraded. Also included on this disc is the original Marathon game. One notable problem is that this title really pushes the capabilities of the hardware, and may often become jumpy or glitchy, though only at high resolution.

Terror T.R.A.X. Bandai 8 $50
This is an interactive movie involving a Vampire theme. It was relatively popular in the early 1990's despite the fact that most interactive movies are horrible. Relatively good frame rates and decent acting make this one of the better FMV games, but not by much

HARDWARD

Pippin @world System Bandai 7 $275

Pippin @world Controller Bandai 7 $40
This controller, though easily replaced with a Macintosh compatible controller (when used with the proper adapter), has a very unique boomerang shape that is very uncomfortable for large hands. Four main buttons, two shoulder buttons and three buttons on the bottom edge of the controller make the options numerous. A directional pad is placed on the left, and a track

ball is set in the center.

Floppy Dock Bandai 10 $300
A 3.5" disk drive available for the Pippin units was made available in Japan, and tested in the U.S. with company testers, but this device is not believed to have been released in any quantity to the public. The white version can be found in Japan, and is compatible with the U.S. Pippin, but a black version has not yet been confirmed. A Zip Disk add on was also tested in Japan, and is even rare there, but was never tested in the U.S.

Keyboard/Stylist Combo Bandai 8 $90
This keyboard unit has a touch sensitive screen that allowed the user to "write" on it with a stylist. And while it is a very unique item, it is much easier to just attach a standard Macintosh keyboard and mouse to the @world.

Memory Module 2 Meg Bandai 8 $60

Memory Module 4 Meg Bandai 8 $80

Memory Module 8 Meg Bandai 9 $100

Memory Module 16 Meg Katz 9 $150
Unlike the other memory modules, this 16 meg version was only available through Katz, the company that eventually bought rights to distribute the Pippin in Europe.

Modem Bandai 5 $50
Actually made in large quantities in anticipation of the @world's acceptance, this item is actually more common than the system it is made for.

Wireless Controller Bandai 9 $100
This is a standard controller, but without the cord. Extremely difficult to find, this is the preferred controller for any Pippin system.

More information on the Pippin can be found at:
http://homepage.mac.com/pippinhistory

and

http://www.videogamebible.com

Home Improvement 1-2-3

Mr. Potato Head Saves Veggie Valley

Power Rangers Zeo Versus The Machine Empire

Super Marathon

Virtua Racing was the most expensive Genesis cart ever released in the U.S. Retail price: $100

VIS

Memorex V.I.S.
By: Andy Slaven

The Memorex Video Information System (VIS) is perhaps the most obscure system ever made for the U.S., even if it isn't the rarest. The Bandai Pippin qualifies as the rarest of all consoles, but because of that fact, its popularity among collectors is relatively high. Perhaps the VIS is so obscure because it was so bad. Or perhaps because the majority of its titles were "edutainment". But no matter how you look at it, rare or obscure, common and overt, neither or both, the fact remains that very few people actually own a Memorex VIS.

Growing up, I was always looking for the bargain video game. I wanted to get the best deal for my money. Well, this system certainly wasn't it! Sold in Radio Shack stores from 1993-1994, poor sales would quickly find it as a catalog-only item. The original price of $399 didn't seem too outrageous for this true 32-bit system. Indeed, 32-bits in 1993 was a step ahead of the competition...but as we all know, promising hardware doesn't mean anything without good games.

After the obviously poor selling season of 1994 for the system, Radio Shack sold off much of its inventory to export and discount stores. Once in these discount catalogs, the system was sold with an extra controller and some software titles. These software packages included around 20 titles, the bulk of which were interactive children's learning media. The amazing part about these catalogs was the price that they placed on this hardware/software package. Indeed, when you consider that the system had been selling (or trying to sell) for $399 only months before, it would be an amazing bargain (or so I thought) to buy this system with 20 titles for the amazingly low price of $99. This 75% reduction in price should have told the world that the system had been completely abandoned.

Due to the fact that many of these companies were located outside of the U.S., many of these "software packages" were actually 20 programs compiled onto one CD. U.S. based discount companies, not figuring this out right away, were actually matching price with these foreign companies, yet still sending out the original software with the package.

Now, having read the above, you are probably under the impression that this is one of the worst video game systems in existence. But, before you do that, you should perhaps remember other entries into the market by companies such as Fairchild (with the Channel F) and

The Sega Genesis was the preferred system of the Rosanne Show.

Commodore (with their CDTV). The VIS not great by any means, and actually is very rarely any fun, but the absolute obscurity of this system and the necessity to own one in order to call one's collection complete will drive many collectors to seek one out. Some of the software titles include Sherlock Holmes volumes 1 & 2, Links Golf, My Paint, Manhole, Learn the Guitar, Peter and the Wolf, Vampire's Coffin, and other "exciting" titles. Sadly, these titles represent some of the most interactive and game-like titles available. Perhaps the only thing more obscure than this system is reliable information about it. This section will most likely be updated quite a bit over the years to come, but to date, every known title is listed within.

Also of historical interest is the fact that this system, at its core, is a Microsoft system that Bill Gates dealt with personally. Tandy/Memorex was upset with the inclusion of a Microsoft logo (sound familiar?) within the system's code. So, after getting nowhere with John Roach, Bill Gates was brought in to give the "OK" to officially remove the logo. What was the whole dispute over? What was the logo for? It was for a product known as "Modular Windows". And in case you're not familiar with this, Modular Windows was basically the forerunner to Windows CE (the operating system used in the Dreamcast).

So, before you discount this system as one that should remain obscured in the folds of time, remember this: The VIS was Microsoft's first entry into the video game market. This has now culminated in the introduction of the Microsoft Xbox. The VIS was responsible for clearly showing that a version of Windows could be used on a console. This use of Modular Windows lead to research that showed a variant of Windows to be a viable platform to base the Sega Dreamcast upon. Oddly enough, even though Microsoft claimed differently, some IBM programs from the time will run on the VIS and visa versa. This is an interesting system to say the least, and should be documented as such.

***Note: This section contains ALL known titles produced for the Memorex V I S : not just game software. The reason that this was done is simply because this system's software library has never been documented. Future guides will likely truncate this section to omit non-game software, but it was felt that the importance of creating a complete software list was essential due to the general lack of coverage that this system receives

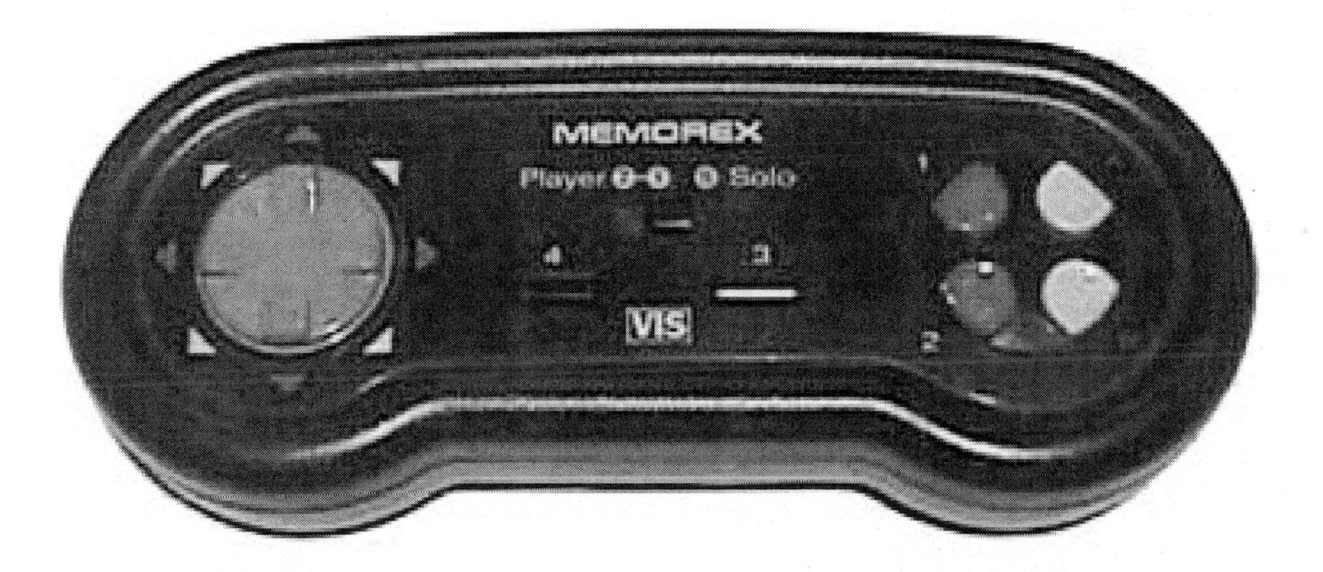

V.I.S. controller shown actual size

Atari changed the specifications of the Jaguar four times during the development of Alien Vs. Predator.

The 1992 Time Almanac	Fitness Partner	Great Lives	Henry and Mudge In The Sparkle Days

1992 Time Magazine
Compact Almanac, The   Compact   6 $12
A surprisingly complete almanac in an interactive form, this reference guide, while considered cutting edge for its time, is a good way to remember what was going on 10 years ago. Consider it a time capsule of sorts.

America's National Parks   Multicom   5 $8
A look at the national parks within the U.S., this disc relies on visual impact to relay its message. With interactive menus to guide you through different parks and some interesting photography, this should be enjoyable for anyone interested in nature.

American Heritage Illustrated
Encyclopedic Dictionary   Xiphias   4 $6
An expounded version of the American Heritage Dictionary, with illustrations and photos to help explain certain areas of interest. With an immense range of subjects and many illustrations, this antiquated reference guide is entertaining. From media such as this sprang the easily interactive format of much of the internet.

American Vista   Applied Optical Media   5 $10
Originally retailing for $80, this was certainly one of the most expensive titles available for the system. This is an introspective view of the U.S., from state to state, with photos of historically significant items, maps, topography, etc.

Americans in Space   Multicom   8 $20
Certainly one of the rarer titles for this system, and definitely the most interesting of the educational series. Americans in Space features more than one hour of video and over 500 photos chronicling America's space program. Made in 1992, only 6 years after the Challenger explosion, this title tries to instill a new sense of pride and achievement within those who have lost faith in the program. Also of note, a free mission patch of Spacelab 2, Skylab, or Apollo 11 was offered once the registration card was completed and returned. I doubt that they still honor this deal however.

Astrology Source   Multicom   6 $12
And just what type of world would we live in without the "science" of astrology? This title offers quick reference to astrological information and also includes extras such as a personality test and a matchmaker.

Atlas of U.S. Presidents
Applied Optical Media   5 $8
Certainly not a system lacking in American pride, this VIS title offers interactive information on all the Presidents through its creation. Along with each president is the First Lady, photos

taken throughout their campaigns, actual speeches recorded, political influence and wars, etc. While certainly not the topic of many social gatherings, this is a rather complete source of information on the former Presidents.

Better Homes and
Gardens: Healthy Cooking   Multicom   5 $5
Learn how to cook using less fat, calories, etc. Aside from the fact that the topic is rarely enjoyed by gamers of any station, the layout and interactivity of this title is lacking.

Better Not Get Wet,
Jesse Bear   Macmillian New Media   6 $8
This is an interactive child's storybook chronicling the exciting adventure of Jesse Bear as he plays in the dishwater, puddles, and anything else mischievous placeś he can get wet. Let the laughter begin as you...Ok, was the sarcasm thick enough for you?

Bible Lands, Bible Stories   Context   5 $8
Greatest story ever told? Well, it was until it landed on the VIS. It is an entertaining way for children to learn about the Bible, but the interactivity is low and the graphics could have been much better. Instead of teaching your kids about the bible with this title, pull out the real thing, or hand them the Video Game Bible.

Cask of Amontillado, The   Discis   4 $5
A disturbing story in writing, listening to it read to you in multiple languages can cause severe mental damage! It is a good story, and all joking aside, it is mildly entertaining to see it read to you on screen with the pictures exclusive to this version.

Compton's Multimedia
Encyclopedia VIS Edition   Compon   4 $8
The title says pretty much everything about this title. It's an interactive encyclopedia with numerous photos and illustrations.

December 24th
Macmillian New Media   5 $6
Another interactive storybook, this one engaging the most suspenseful night of childhood, Christmas Eve. If you have children that you don't want playing with your PC, this is just one of the many titles available for small children. Low levels of interaction and a fun story for kids should keep anyone under the age of 6 entertained.

Fitness Partner   Computer Directions   4 $3
This is an exercise program designed to allow you to follow the onscreen fitness instructors. The most entertaining feature about this title is the box art which features a jumping woman.

The entertaining part is the fact that she closely resembles Sigourney Weaver with an afro and blue leotard.

Great Lives   JLR   5 $5
"Do you know who created Mt. Rushmore? Or who founded the Girl Scouts? Do you know who the 'Iron Horse' of baseball is? Learn more about these American heroes in this beautifully illustrated, educational package!" I suppose the founder of the Girl Scouts has now officially been raised to the level of "hero". And all this time I thought it was Mr. Rushmore that created Mt. Rushmore. Comical graphics and dull themes make this relatively difficult-to-find title painful to watch at times.

**Henry and Mudge:
The First Book**   Macmillian New Media   4 $5
One of many interactive books for children that appears on the system, this one features a story about a boy and his dog. And while the title may hint at the fact, I can confirm that this is, in fact, the first book in the series.

**Henry and Mudge:
In the Sparkle Days**   Macmillian New Media   4 $5
Returning to the system with a winter themed title, Henry and his dog Mudge star in yet another interactive storybook for children.

**Jesse Bear, What
Will You Wear?**   Macmillian New Media   5 $8
A question that has challenged the minds of intellects for centuries: What will Jesse Bear wear? Simple interactivity with this multimedia book offers very young children to watch and read along with the narration.

Just Grandma and Me   Broderbund   6 $12
Surprisingly difficult to find, this interactive book goes one step further than offering simple interactivity with an electronic book. The environments are now interactive as well, allowing children to "explore" the illustrations within the book.

Kid-Fun   Mindplay   5 $5
Few words can be so innocent separately and so frightening when combined as the duo of "kids & karaoke". Simply put this interactive music CD into your VIS, position a child in front of the TV, and prepare to hear the wonderful music of "Cindy the Songlady" accompanied by the screamed lyrics of a child.

**Kids Can Read:
Aesop's Fables**   Discis   4 $5
One of the better titles in the "Kids Can Read" series, Aesop's Fables are even entertaining for an adult that is watching along with a child.

Kids Can Read: Cinderella   Discis   4 $5
The classic story in interactive book form. Expanded interactivity within the entire "Kids Can Read" series makes these much more than simple digital books however. Interactive photos and language lessons are often helpful for children having difficulty reading.

**Kids Can Read: Heather
Hits Her First Home Run**   Discis   4 $5
An interactive book about "Heather" and her first home run. At least the title isn't deceptive.

**Kids Can Read: A Long
Hard Day on the Ranch**   Discis   4 $5
Entertaining illustrations, voice actors, and a fun story make this one of the better interactive books for the system, although still not suitable for anyone over the age of 10.

**Kids Can Read: Moving
Gives Me a Stomache Ache**   Discis   4 $5
And if you were a veal calf, moving would make your muscles less tender and juicy. This story helps children faced with frequent moves cope with the reasons why it is necessary to relocate from time to time.

**Kids Can Read:
Mud Puddles**   Discis   4 $5
Since there really isn't anything interesting about this title itself, it might be noteworthy that the "Kids Can Read" series won the 1992 "Product of the Year" award by CD-ROM Professional Magazine.

**Kids Can Read: The
Night Before Christmas**   Discis   4 $5
Perhaps the most classic of all Christmas tales, this is an easy way to tell the story to children without having to actually read or remember it. Also, if you'd like to have some fun with this system for a change, switch the audio track to Spanish just as the kids begin to drift into sleep. They'll be dreaming of Lucus and lime-salts instead of sugar-plumbs!

**Kids Can Read:
The Paper Bag Princess**   Discis   4 $5
The "Kids Can Read" series was also awarded the 1992 "California Children's Media Award".

**Kids Can Read: Scary
Poems For Rotten Kids**   Discis   6 $15
This is really just disturbing. These poems "teach a lesson" by scaring the hell out of young children. Is your kid acting up?

Just Grandma and Me   Kid-Fun

KCR: Heather Hits her First Home Run   Links: The Challenge of Golf

VIS

The Meeting of Minds

Mosaic Magic

Mutanoid Math Challenge

My Paint

Maybe it's time to tell him a rhyming story about what horrible thing will grab him during his sleep. That should cure his questionable behavior.

Kids Can Read: The
Tale of Benjamin Bunny   Discis   4 $5
Something of note about the "Kids Can Read" series is the fact that none of their titles offer any description of the contents of the book anywhere on the package. Either one is familiar with the book's contents beforehand from an outside source, or they find out what is on the CD after they watch it. But each package boldly states, "fun!" in bold letters on the front. I suppose the marketing was geared toward getting the child to tug on mom's skirt crying until they got the interactive book.

Kids Can Read:
The Tale of Peter Rabbit   Discis   4 $5
A classic bedtime story retold with high quality illustrations and good narration.

Kids Can Read:
Thomas' Snowsuit   Discis   4 $5
Comical illustrations make even this child's story entertaining for any adult watching it with a child.

Learn To Play Guitar   Parallax   4 $4
An interactive lesson on how to play the guitar taught by James Lee Stanley. The odd thing about this title is the fact that only two songs are present. "Every Breath You Take" and "Message in a Bottle" are taught in the same fashion as they were originally arranged by the Police. I wonder if Sting knows about this.

Links: The
Challenge of Golf   Access   7 $20
A real game! That's right, not every title on the VIS is "edutainment". Playing this type of golf game on a TV was unheard of in 1992, but the VIS really was ahead of its time. While very dated and considered to be completely antiquated by today's standards, it is worth a look, and a must-have for anyone looking to collect only games for this system.

Manhole, The   Activision   6 $10
More than an interactive book, this is an interactive story geared toward children. Clicking on certain parts of the screen progress the story differently with over 600 interactive screens. A very unusual fantasy story much in the same line as Jack and the Beanstalk.

Meeting of Minds, The   JLR   5 $8
Clues are given in this game to allow the player to guess what

famous person is shrouded in secrecy. Artists, poets, scientists, etc. are among those people on the panel from which you much make your choices. This trivia game, while suitable for children, is of sufficient difficulty to make it entertaining for adults as well.

Mosaic Magic   Kinder Magic   3 $4
A paint program of sorts, this title allows the player to create and manipulate different images using a series a grids and color pallets. Very simplistic in design, it does offer a moderate level of creativity to be expressed, though a memory card is required to save any of them. Mainly marketed toward young children.

Multimedia Animals
Encyclopedia   Applied Optical Media 7 $15
Designed to show the diversity of different animal species, nearly 2000 animals are featured with photos, scientific names, behavior, etc. This is simply a database of some of the unusual animals from every part of the world. And while the information is easily found on the internet today, this was a very complete source of information on the subject for its day.

Mutanoid Math Challenge   Legacy   5 $5
Set up like a crossword puzzle, equations must be completed by inserting the correct sign or number. Not really any fun for anyone actually, it was specifically created to teach children the basics of math in a more entertaining environment than a classroom.

Mutanoid Word Challenge   Legacy   5 $5
Four difficulty levels make this more of a family oriented crossword puzzle game, but even on its most challenging level it is often simplistic and lacks any real challenge for anyone over the age of 12.

My Paint   Saddleback Graphics   7 $15
A simplified version of the popular program found on most PC's, this title is expressly for children. Offering a variety of images to manipulate with a well stocked variety of artistic tools, this is a good way for children to learn about the interactive basics necessary for the point and click interface found in most programs on any PC today.

Necklace, The   Discis   4 $5
The story, written by Guy de Maupassant, is offered by Discis Books in this interactive form. With content geared toward "Teenage+", this is one of the few digital books available for those over the age of 12. And while simplistic in design, it is certainly more fun than reading what many consider to be an often boring story.

**New Basics Electronic
Cookbook, The**   Xiphias   3 $4
Yet another cookbook for this system, this version is presented in a very professional and easy to use interface. Designed in a fashion that caters toward women, it is a useful guide on creating more elegant meals, if not a boring title.

Our House   Context   6 $12
Featuring characters from the popular comic of the same name, Our House is an interactive question and answer session designed to teach children about the different functions of an average home.

Peter and the Wolf   E Book   5 $8
The classic tale told in this digital book offers original art work and original music. While the music is about average, the images in each illustration are not very well done and interaction is minimal.

Playing With Language: Syracuse Language   4 $7
Games in English   Systems
Playing with language? This series was designed to teach the viewer the basics of the language featured on each corresponding title.

Playing With Language: Syracuse Language   4 $7
Games in French   Systems
Interactive games and puzzles keep these titles from becoming too monotonous, and learning to associate words with their visual depiction is important when learning to think in a language.

Playing With Language: Syracuse Language   5 $10
Games in German   Systems
Each title in this series originally retailed for $49.95 through Radio Shack and was among the more educational of the titles. While suited for children as young as age 4, it is still useful for anyone beginning studies in the given language.

Playing With Language: Syracuse Language   5 $12
Games in Japanese   Systems
Stressing the basics such as telling time, grammar and common expressions is the key to these often entertaining titles. Games such as "Simon Says" and bingo offer a good variety of learning techniques as well.

Playing With Language: Syracuse Language   3 $7
Games in Spanish   Systems
The most common title in this series, Games in Spanish were sold heavily in the south and in California. This title also seems to be the most extensive and well written offering more content

than other titles in the series.

Race the Clock   Mindplay   5 $8
Another puzzle game for this system, and again directed toward an audience of 3-12 year olds, this title offers the feature of completing puzzles while trying to beat the clock. Limited puzzle types reduce any replay value however, even for younger children.

Rick Ribbit   Tadpole   5 $8
A mix of children's puzzles to build basic reading and math skills. You play as Rick, a frog evidently interested in becoming more intelligent. At an original retail price of $29.95, it was one of the least expensive games for the system. But poor sales and lack of interest caused this title to be a little more difficult to come by today.

Rodney's Funscreen   Activision   4 $5
Designed for pre-schoolers, a collection of 5 games are designed to teach the most basic skills to children. A paint program, a word and math game, and two separate memory games compile the content of this title.

Sail With Columbus   Parallax   4 $6
Not only is this a documentary of Columbus's historic voyage to the "Americas", but you also get to map and make the voyage yourself to see how you fare against the explorer himself. Limited interaction, but still entertaining to a small degree.

**Secrets of Hosea
Freeman, The**   Top Ten   4 $5
You play the role of an investigator trying to unlock the century-old secret of Hosea Freeman. And while there is a lot of interaction and video, it is a poorly disguised documentary about whales. Video quality is relatively high, and if you're interested in whales then it should be enjoyable. But if you're looking for a mystery to solve on this system, stick with either of the Sherlock Holmes titles.

Search for the Sea   Multicom   5 $8
An interactive story made for children around the age of 6, this title answers basic questions such as, "Why is the sky blue?" Interaction is very limited and offers no enjoyment for anyone over the age of 10.

**Sherlock Holmes
Consulting Detective Vol. 1**   ICOM   6 $18
"The Mummy's Curse", "The Tin Soldier", and "The Mystified Murderess" are the three mysteries featured on this volume. And while the stories are the same as those found on so many other systems, this one appears to have improved video and

The Necklace   Our House

Playing With Language: Games in Japanese   Race the Clock

The SNES game Street Fighter II was the first video game to feature a 16 Meg cartridge.

VIS

Rodney's Funscreen

Sail With Columbus

The Secrets of Hosea Freeman

Sherlock Holmes Consulting Detective
Volume 1

sound. Interaction in this game is limited to choices, but a good storyline and decent actors make this one of the more enjoyable titles, and definitely suitable for adults.

Sherlock Holmes Consulting
Detective Vol. 2   ICOM   7 $25
Back with another 3 cases to solve, these are rarely seen anywhere else. "The Two Lions", "The Pilfered Paintings", and "The Murdered Munitions Magnate" are included on this installment. It seems that the video quality might actually be better than that of the first volume, but unfortunately the acting actually seems to get worse. Although sold at the same price as the first volume when released, the $70 price tag seemed a bit high for most people to buy both. And with the short lifespan of the VIS system, most people didn't get the opportunity to buy the second one. A bit more rare, and often more expensive, this title is definitely worth buying considering the almost total lack of adult games on the system.

SmartKids Challenge One   Arkeo   4 $6
Two intelligence-testing games are included in this title, "AquaLogic" and "Enigmania". AquaLogic is a reasoning game in which you must decipher the right answer by determing what can be learned by the wrong answers given. Enigmania is a jag-saw type puzzle in which random shapes are fitted to the screen for just a moment in their correct order, and then they are scrambled. Your job is to combine the pieces back to their original configuration. With random pieces used, and no picture to work from or actually form, the harder levels quickly become challenging for anyone, though the game is designed for young teens.

Stepping Stones   Compu-Teach   5 $5
Designed to be utilized by children as young as 2 years of age, the games featured are very simple development tools that teach basic reasoning and early scholastic skills. Many of the features are actually illustrations that are labeled with the corresponding word in order to teach basic vocabulary to young children.

Survey of Western Art, A   E Book   4 $4
With thousands of images detailing art from cave paintings through modern times, this is a very comprehensive study of Western art. Each piece covered is accompanied by information about the artwork itself and brief biographies of the artist that created it (assuming that the artist is known.) More information on the subject can be found on this title than anywhere on the internet, and certainly more convenient with all the work compiled on one CD.

Time Table of History:
Arts and Entertainment   Xiphias   5 $8
Covering the history of culture throughout the world, this title is a compilation of stories detailing works of art, literature and anything else considered to be of historical importance in this field of study. A very informative and comprehensive title that covers this information very well.

Time Table of History:
Business, Politics & Media   Xiphias   5 $8
What seems like a boring title at first actually becomes interesting as you move into the political aspect of this interactive database. Political leaders and their intent are discussed, world powers are evaluated, economic structures through history are examined, etc. And while it may not be the most interesting topic for everyone, it is very entertaining to see what common beliefs were included on this disc released in 1992. You might be surprised the amount of difference a decade can have on your view of history.

Time Table of History:
Science and Innovation   Xiphias   6 $15
Covering the high points of scientific research throughout history, it is easy to spend hours researching topic after topic once you get started. Presented in a straightforward fashion with word searches and a PC-style interface, navigation is very easy. The subject matter is among the most interesting of the three releases in this series, however it seems that fewer copies of this installment were made than any other, raising both the rarity and price of this interesting title.

Tell-Tale Heart, The   Discis   6 $5
Another story from Edgar Allen Poe is brought to the VIS, this time it's one of the most famous of his works. Varied amounts of interaction will keep most entertained, but the fact that this title was intended for teens and yet offers subject matter not found interesting by many of them, the rarity is a bit higher, though the demand keeps the price in check.

Title Sampler   Tandy   4 $5
This title was included with the VIS system, although it seems no box or cover art for it were made available. Instead, it was packaged in one of two ways: Inserted in a sleeve and placed within the same package as the instruction manual, or placed within a blank jewel case and simply placed on top of the packing material. It offers previews and basic information about titles that were available for the system at launch.

Vampire's Coffin, The   Sanctuary Woods   5 $8
The full name of this title is "The Awesome Adventures of Victor

Vector & Yondo, The Vampire's Coffin", but for simplicity we listed it under the volume name of "The Vampire's Coffin". An interactive cartoon that allows you to choose your character's actions via on-screen buttons. While the artwork seems promising and the screenshots show what looks like a "Dragon's Lair" experience, it is far from being that good. Still one of the better titles on the system, and designed for teens, it is playable by most with an interest in video game history. It won't, however, find its way into the hands of any gamer looking for a new experience.

Video Movie Guide 1993   Ballantine   7 $18
An encyclopedia of movies, over 12,000 in total, that rates them to help avoid renting or buying a bad movie. And while this information is readily available online, in 1993 this was a bit more difficult since the internet was hardly what it is today. Still, the title sold very poorly, and people weren't willing to buy something that was filled with what they viewed as readily available information. Still useful today, and a poor seller in 1993, these add up to a rare title for the system with a stiff price tag for something so obscure. Definitely only a title that a true collector would want.

**Vision Multimedia Bible
for the Entire Family   Candlelight   6 $15**
Beautiful illustrations decorate pages of this interactive bible. Oddly though, it is recommended for ages 5-Adult. I guess the makers assumed that children under 5 years weren't ready to learn about religion. Still, it is filled with photographs, illustrations, music, reference guides, etc. This was another poor seller with a high price tag, and is one of the more difficult titles to find for the VIS.

Wild Animals!   Optic Moon   6 $12
A series of games are used to teach children about different animals. Interactive menus are also included so that it can be used as a reference guide as well. A very limited topic kept this title from selling in any large quantity, and with no specific audience being catered to, is one of the less enjoyable titles for the system.

World Vista   Applied Optical Media   5 $8
A title with detailed maps, flags and cultural reports of countries around the world, this reference guide has quickly become dated with so many political changes in recent years. And as an obvious sign of the times, the back of the box proudly displays a map of Kuwait, obviously an area of interest in 1992. Also, a flag of Afghanistan is also displayed on the back of the box, which, had this title been released today, would most certainly not be shown in such prominent display.

HARDWARE

Memorex VIS	Tandy/Memorex	6	$40
Wireless Controller (Standard)			
	Tandy/Memorex	5	$5
Save-It Memory Card	Tandy/Memorex	7	$12

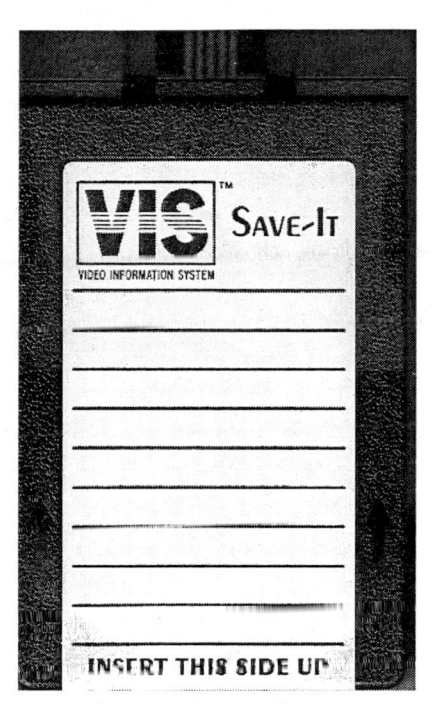

**Save-It Memory Card
shown actual size**

Sherlock Holmes Consulting Detective Volume 2   **SmartKids Challenge One**   **The Vampire's Coffin**   **Vision Multimedia Bible For the Entire Family**

The controllers released with the NES 2 system are known as "dog bone controllers."

NEC TurboGrafx-16

By: Andy Slaven

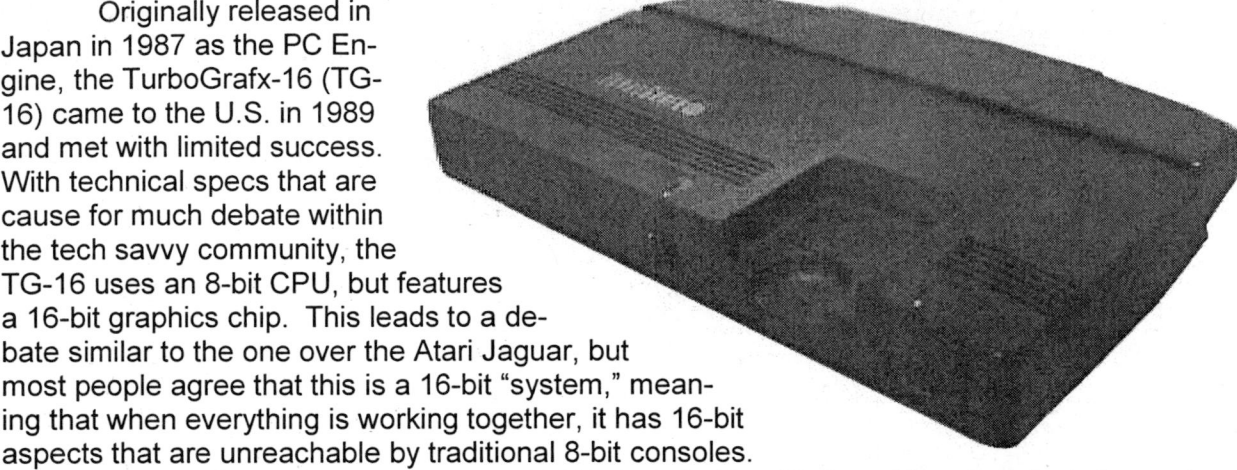

Originally released in Japan in 1987 as the PC Engine, the TurboGrafx-16 (TG-16) came to the U.S. in 1989 and met with limited success. With technical specs that are cause for much debate within the tech savvy community, the TG-16 uses an 8-bit CPU, but features a 16-bit graphics chip. This leads to a debate similar to the one over the Atari Jaguar, but most people agree that this is a 16-bit "system," meaning that when everything is working together, it has 16-bit aspects that are unreachable by traditional 8-bit consoles.

Upon its U.S. launch in August of 1989 (only in New York and Los Angeles), the system was met with moderate interest. For $190 consumers received the system, one controller and one game (Keith Courage in Alpha Zones). When the system was sold nationwide, the Turbo CD add-on was also available, but the $400 price tag was very prohibitive, making it an almost overnight failure. The TG-16 itself utilized a format known as a Hu-Card, similar in size and form to the Sega Master System cards. Since Sega's card format was never a huge success, this format was new to most U.S. gamers and offered something unique.

Perhaps even more interesting than the system itself was its advertising campaign. While average in scope, it was how these commercials were received that makes it an subject of some interest. Since 1985 saw the release of the Nintendo Entertainment System (NES), most gamers had become so loyal to Nintendo and had invested so much money in its ever-growing library that a new system seemed unthinkable. The NES had become the staple of gaming, much like the Atari 2600 had become in the years before. When commercials began airing for the TG-16, many gamers didn't really understand that this was a completely new system, but instead thought that this technology would somehow be incorporated into their NES systems. After all, who would possibly challenge the NES's dominance in the market? One commercial in particular, featuring Vigilante, barely made mention of the console itself, but instead advertised the game and showed video of the game in motion. But any confusion was short lived as the advertisements for Legendary Axe began to not only show the game in action, but also featured gamers gathered around the TG-16 system itself.

Promoting the fact that this was a 16-bit system became the main focus of NEC, and soon the Sega Genesis would step into the spotlight, also featuring 16-bit technology. Released shortly after the TG-16, the Genesis was 16-bit technology through and through, causing borderline buyers to quickly side with Sega. Both ad campaigns grew by leaps and bounds, NEC and Sega trying to best each other within the advertising market, while Nintendo simply watched and enjoyed profits from their NES software, all while waiting to unleash the Super Nintendo (SNES). All of a sudden, the U.S. was full of real video game competition. The lines were drawn, and NEC hoped that their standard games would be able to hold up against the Genesis's, and also that their Turbo CD add-on would help sway consumers to

The last SMS release was Virtua Fighter Animation in 1997 in Brazil.

their side. But it wasn't meant to be.

Having trouble securing third party developers in the U.S., the TG-16 suffered badly and never reached the market that had been hoped for. One of the most overlooked problems with the TG-16 when compared with the Genesis was the lack of three readily available action buttons. With the use of the turbo switches, gamers could actually utilize six different button functions, but it wasn't nearly as convenient as the Genesis pad that contained three action buttons. The fact that the TG-16 only had one control port was also a factor that swayed many gamers since the TurboTap was necessitated to play multi-player games. When gamers considered all of the options, the Genesis became the clear winner, and the TG-16 would be destined to run a distant second…until the SNES was released in September of 1991, at which point it would become nothing more than a niche console.

One of the most important innovations that NEC made with the TG-16, aside from the Turbo CD, is an often overlooked add-on that allowed for the system to easily hook into stereo systems for true surround sound. This add-on, known as the Turbo Booster, was plugged into the expansion port in the back of the TG-16 and replaced the area typically taken up by a large plastic shell that came standard with the system. While it had to be bought separately and wasn't cheap, this item introduced a new aspect to gaming that, until this point, had been almost completely ignored.

Many believe that the downfall of the TG-16 is due to the importance placed on graphics over game concept and game play. While this may have been a large factor in the equation, and is obvious in numerous games on the system, it is most certainly the combination of hardware limitations and a poor marketing campaign (in comparison to Sega's) that led to the ultimate demise of the system. While it is true that, overall, the system doesn't have as much to offer as the Genesis, it is still responsible for bringing the CD format and stereo sound to video game consoles. Maintaining a very loyal fan base and sporting a small but impressive library, the TG-16 is certain to live well into the 21st century as a favorite of retro-gaming fans.

TG-16

| Aero Blasters | Alien Crush | Bomberman '93 | Bonk's Revenge |

Aero Blasters   Kaneko   3 $8
A very nice side scrolling space shooter, this title features some very nice colors and detailed levels. Standard power-ups are available that increase range or separate your shots into multiple blasts, etc. Though at times, when the screen is full of enemies, occasional slowdown may occur.

Air Zonk   Hudson   3 $18
A very nice graphical effect makes this side scrolling platform shooter appear and play like a comic book. Though the very detailed graphics are nice, the rigid control and completely linear game play can make this beautiful game somewhat repetitious.

Alien Crush   Naxat   2 $8
Quite simply, this alien-based pinball game is awesome. With several side games built into the board, the action never becomes boring and the challenge level quickly increases when multiple balls are increased. This is a definite must-have for the TG-16.

Andre Panza Kick Boxing Futura-Loriciel 3 $10
While some very nice lighting effects were used in this game to give the fighting stage a true feel, this side view fighting game suffers from very rigid control and often feels like a NES game.

Ballistix   Psygnosis   2 $8
An overhead action game, this title features various rooms with puzzle elements that you must overcome. The graphics are reminiscent of The Legend of Zelda, though the goals and game play elements are completely different.

Battle Royale Incredible Technologies 2 $5
This title represents the entirety of wrestling games for the TG-16 and feature generic characters instead of licensed characters as seen in WWF games. As the name implies, you won't be fighting just one opponent, but instead will be placed in a ring with four other opponents, and no sides, so it truly becomes a melee.

Blazing Lazers   Hudson   2 $8
Pilot the Gunhed Star Fighter in this vertically scrolling shooter. With some of the best environments available for any game of this genre, the action is only made better by various weapon effects. If you are a fan of vertically scrolling space shooters, this should definitely be in your collection.

Bloody Wolf   Data East   2 $8
In this side scrolling combat shooter, you take on the role of a commando behind enemy lines and fight off wave upon wave of enemy forces. Though the game play is pretty standard fare, various cheat codes (readily available online) allow for various techniques to be used, such as a hover mode in which you

simply fly through the screen without worry of falling into any ground based traps. The game culminates in a boss fight with a warrior of unrealistic size, strength and speed, making this game very typical, but still very fun.

Bomberman   Hudson   3 $12
Strategically plant bombs in various situations to trap and destroy your onscreen enemies in this classic title. Many feel that this is one of the better incarnations of this game, though it won't support 10 players like the Saturn version.

Bomberman '93   Hudson   5 $18
An update to the original, this title increases slightly improved graphics, but keeps the same game play that made the first installment so popular.

Bonk 3: Bonk's Big Adventure
**   Hudson   6 $25**
Often overlooked, this is the third installment in the Bonk series, and though the graphical style improved over the last installment, it seems to lack the free flowing movement that made the first two so successful. Perhaps it was that after two years of advances, gamers simply expected more, but for whatever reason, this title failed to measure up to expectations, though it is still more innovative and fun than most other side scrolling platform games.

Bonk's Adventure   Hudson   1 $8
Becoming a mascot of sorts for not only the TG-16, but also for the Turbo Express, Bonk is a lovable caveman that must rescue the Princess Za from King Drool. A side scrolling platform game, this title still offers innovation in the way of attack methods and graphical design, making it one of the many "classics" to be found on this system.

Bonk's Revenge   Hudson   1 $8
The second installment to the Bonk series is considered by most to be the best of the three. With improvements over the first game, including more levels and improved graphics, this title keeps everything that made the original a success and simply makes it better.

Boxyboy   Media Rings   3 $12
Seen in various forms and sporting different names on different platforms, this box-pushing puzzle game remains fun and challenges the player to make movement decisions well in advance of the actual termination of that move. Though it certainly doesn't take a system like the TG-16 to make this type of game available, it still remains a brain teasing puzzle game.

Bravoman   Namco   3 $10
This side scrolling shooter certainly lacks any type of unique graphical style and really suffers because of it. While the con-

trol itself seems fine, it is instead the character animation that appears to make the movement choppy or stiff. The character has actually moved, though the animation simply makes it appear otherwise, making it easy to take unnecessary shots when trying to overcorrect.

Cadash   Taito   3 $15
One of Working Designs' only side scrolling adventures to date, this title became a classic quickly and features three separate characters from which to choose, each with their own attributes. Though the control can seem a bit basic at times and the characters' movements seem very stiff, this is still a solid game with RPG elements.

Champions Forever Boxing
**   Distinctive Software   3 $12**
For the time, this boxing game showed some very nice graphics, even if the characters weren't very quick to respond to control. And while the graphics have obviously aged over the past decade, this title will still impress when considering the fact that it was released in 1991. Viewed from the side and slightly above, this boxing game tries to recreate a realistic feel for boxing fans.

Chase H.Q.   Taito   3 $12
Viewed from behind the car, this game plays a lot like Out Run for the Sega Master System and sports a very similar graphical style as well. Chase down criminals and immobilize their car with a series of well placed rams.

Chew-Man-Fu   Hudson   3 $15
An overhead action/puzzle game, this title will seem a bit confusing at first before you have become use to shifting the balls and blocks onscreen, though after a short while, the rules and strategies involved will become clear, making this an addictive game once you get used to it.

China Warrior   Hudson   1 $5
A side scrolling combat game, this title gets boring very quickly. For a while, this game was advertised as one of several reasons why the Turbo Stick was nearly a necessity, though actual play showed that the standard TG-16 controller was easier to use. The graphics are nice enough, and the characters are very large for a game released in 1989, but the complete lack of enemy AI is frustrating to say the least. Wave after wave of witless enemies come strolling your way to be dispatched of as you see fit.

Cratermaze   Hudson   2 $8
An overhead view is used in this maze game featuring some creative, yet repetitive, level design. Though it can become monotonous at times, the challenge increases and something about this title makes it very addictive.

Cyber-Core   IGS   3 $12
A vertically scrolling shooter, this game lacks the detailed backgrounds and creative enemy patterns that have made others in the genre great.

Darkwing Duck   Disney   3 $12
Some cute character animations and scenarios make this title amusing at times, but overall it is a standard side scrolling platform game that wouldn't offer much enjoyment if it weren't for the use of the Disney character.

Davis Cup Tennis   Loriciel   2 $10
Finally, a two player tennis game that understands the importance of giving each player a fair view of the ball! Utilizing a horizontally split screen when in two player mode (or four player with turbotap), this title offers better graphics than most other systems could offer in 1993, and control that feels natural.

Dead Moon   Natsume   3 $12
A side scrolling space shooter, this title offers some interesting levels, though enemy design isn't very creative and often becomes repetitious, making this title mediocre at best.

Deep Blue   Pack-in Video   2 $8
This is an odd underwater shooter of sorts, relying more on strategy and proper placement over sheer firepower.

Devil's Crush   Naxat Soft   3 $15
Done in the same style as Alien Crush, this pinball game is sure to please those who have become bored with standard pinball games. Various mini-games can be unlocked, becoming increasingly challenging as your points rise. This is a definite must-have for this system.

Double Dungeons   NCS   3 $12
Viewed from the first person, this dungeon exploration game offered a nice stroke of innovative genius: A two-player mode is available so that you and a friend can play through the same dungeon at the same time. When played alone, this title is standard fare, but when played with a friend, it takes on a new element rarely seen in RPG type games, making it fun for more than just one person at a time.

Dragon Spirit   Namco   2 $8
In this vertically scrolling shooter, you take the role of a flying dragon to dispatch of various enemies over different terrain types. It is nice to play a game like this with something other than a spaceship, but other than the aspect of a dragon being used, this title is pretty average.

Dragon's Curse   Hudson   5 $25
This side scrolling adventure game is either loved or hated, though either way, it is hard to deny that this game features some colorful and detailed levels and characters.

Cadash

Chew-Man-Fu

China Warrior   Double Dungeons

A popular Shenmue advertisement consisted of two full pages and two words: Shenmue and Dreamcast.

TG-16

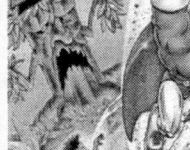

Drop Off   Falcon   Gunboat   Impossamole

Drop Off   **Data East**   **5**   **$25**
A static screen puzzle game played in similar fashion to Bust-A-Move, this title offers extremely addictive game play and requires both a quick mind and quick thumbs to make the proper move at the proper time.

Dungeon Explorer   **Hudson**   **2**   **$12**
Viewed from overhead and sporting graphics similar in style to Dragon Warrior, this title seems promising at first, but unfortunately the game play is action based, something that doesn't go well with the simple graphical style of the game. It lacks a feeling of completeness and seems as if you're playing a pre-production version of what could become a good game.

Falcon   **Spectrum Holobyte**   **5**   **$22**
Viewed from inside the cockpit, this F-16 flight simulator offers a nice HUD display and various missions that you will be briefed on. And unlike so many other flight simulators for consoles, this title offers realistic limitations on armament so missions don't become a "shoot-em-up" instead of a tactical engagement.

Fantasy Zone   **NEC**   **3**   **$12**
Featuring some of the most colorful pastel backgrounds on the system, this title is definitely eye candy, though otherwise an ordinary side scrolling shooter.

Final Lap Twin   **Namco**   **3**   **$12**
Viewed from behind the F-1 car you are driving, this title plays similarly to Pole Position, though the graphics seem a bit better and handling is much tighter. A horizontally split screen is available when playing with two people, though with such simple graphics, this really creates a very tight feeling onscreen.

Galga '90   **Namco**   **5**   **$25**
An update to the amazing arcade classic, this title features varied background and new enemies to fight against. While not as fun to play as the arcade version, much of this feeling comes from the fact that it lacks the same amount of history as the original, as well as being played at home instead of an arcade.

Ghost Manor   **TTI**   **2**   **$8**
One of many side scrolling platform games for the TG-16, this title stands alongside JJ & Jeff for the simple reason that your character sports an enormous head. Dark levels of haunted mansion will keep you busy for a while, and unique backgrounds and challenges keep this game from becoming too monotonous.

Gunboat   **NEC**   **2**   **$12**
Three separate turrets can be controlled, in addition to piloting this gunboat, with the use of the switches above the action buttons on the controller. Select your area of operation and the

armament you wish to outfit your boat with (all real weapons with different attributes) and begin your patrol upriver. Different scenarios accompany each mission and are given during a briefing before deployment. A variety of enemies will be faced along the way, including onshore enemies and other patrolling gunboats. As you fire into a crowd of enemy troops you will hear them scream in pain as they take fire, and if a grenade launcher is used, their huts will burst into flame. Very violent, though sporting graphics that may seem dated today, this title is a definite must-have for the TG-16.

Hit the Ice   **Taito**   **3**   **$15**
With the turbotap, this title will support up to four players, and offers some very nice side-view hockey action. The characters are much larger than those found on the NES at the time, though this game was released for both the Genesis and SNES in fine fashion.

Impossamole   **NEC**   **5**   **$22**
Basically the TG-16's answer to Sonic, this title was developed by Gremlin Graphics and features some interesting levels and character animations, though it remains a standard side scrolling platform game otherwise.

Jack Nicklaus Turbo Golf   **Accolade**   **3**   **$12**
This version of the game simply can't compete with its Turbo CD counterpart. The characters, while obviously meant to look realistic, take on a cartoon like feel, and the game play suffers due to easily made mistakes and unrealistic ball flight movements.

Jackie Chan's Action Kung Fu
      Hudson   **5**   **$25**
Amusing graphics that are decidedly "Chinese looking" help to make this side scrolling platform fighter very entertaining. This version supports some very nice graphical features that look refined when compared to other releases in 1992, and even surpasses many SNES games of the time.

JJ & Jeff   **Hudson**   **1**   **$5**

Keith Courage in Alpha Zones
      Hudson   **1**   **$1**
Packaged with every TG-16 system, this is definitely the most common game available for this console. Basic side scrolling platform shooting seems like an odd way to showcase this system's new technology, but though it remains a basic game, it does have its moments and can be fun when played for short periods of time.

King of Casino   **Victor**   **3**   **$12**
While this is a fun casino game in which you can travel the town in search of a new gambling spot, there is a definite problem

with the random pattern generator in card games. Frequent patterns appear, making it easy to know when you're about to win and how much you should bet. The same can be seen on roulette tables.

Klax Tengen 3 $12
This classic puzzle game that has found quite a following, though it never quite reached the famed status of Tetris. It does have very addictive game play and offers some of the best puzzle challenge around. The TG-16 version is adequate, though it offers nothing over other incarnations of this game on home consoles.

Legend of Hero Tonma Irem 3 $12
Also appearing in the arcade, this title is a basic side scrolling platform game that features average size characters and over-sized boss characters. The one fault with this 1993 release is the fact that the backgrounds have very monotonous textures, making the whole game feel like it takes place on the same level. Fun, though it could have been greatly improved.

Legendary Axe, The NEC 1 $10
One of the games used to demonstrate the TG-16's superiority over the NES, this title features some extremely large boss characters and challenging platform game play. Though, with the noted exception of occasionally large characters, this title doesn't offer much over 8-bit games of the time.

Legendary Axe II, The NEC 2 $12
Released just one year after the first installment, this title offers both improved graphics and more responsive controls. More of the same platform/fighting action awaits, though this is definitely the better of the two.

Magical Chase Quest 8 $140
Bright colors, odd characters and strange situations give this odd shooter a very "Japanese feel" not typically found in U.S. releases. Extremely difficult to find, this is the one game in the U.S. TG-16 library that will keep most from completing their collections.

Military Madness Hudson 7 $35
An oddity on the TG-16, this is a turn based strategy game featuring off-world battles with futuristic troops and weapons. Fans of the strategy genre should definitely check this title out, though those who aren't particularly fond of this type of game might find it too boring to be enjoyable.

Moto Roader NCS 3 $12
Use various vehicles with differing attributes to navigate through winding courses, viewed from overhead. Similar in style to R.C. Pro-Am, this game doesn't really show off what the TG-16 is capable of, though it remains a fun game when played in moderation.

Neutopia Hudson 3 $20
This is Hudson's answer to The Legend of Zelda. Action based overhead RPG's are definitely in abundance during the neo-classic period, though this title does a particularly nice job of it. An interesting story line, interactive characters and a large world to explore make this title a definite must-have for the TG-16.

Neutopia 2 Hudson 3 $22
This title was released two years after the first installment and really does a nice job of improving on the minor shortcomings of the first title. Improved graphics and extended play time make this superior to the first. The story line is equally compelling and is one of many reasons why this overhead action RPG is a must-have for the system.

New Adventure Island Hudson 3 $15
Played in similar style to the 1988 NES release Adventure Island, this version features improved graphics, though the game play is very similar. Fans of the series should be pleased, though it is otherwise a typical side scrolling platform game.

Night Creatures NEC 2 $5
Released in 1992, this side scrolling adventure features some very nice graphics for the time, though the character animations seem a bit choppy and control suffers because of it. Intricate backgrounds add to the eerie feeling portrayed by the game, as does the nice soundtrack.

Ninja Spirit Irem 3 $12
A very popular and fun side scrolling fighting game, this title offers some great graphics and intricate game play mechanics. Nice sound and solid control make this one of the better games on the console.

Order of the Griffon SSI/TSR 3 $18
Both a first-person RPG and an overhead RPG, this title offers both in a seamless combination that gives this title a very unique feel. Select your character class and head off to The Order of the Griffon, the local guild, so that you can fight evil.

Ordyne Namco 2 $8
This is a basic side view shooter with colorful graphics, though nothing sets it apart from the multitude of this type of game on the TG-16.

Pac-Land Namco 2 $8
Take the role of Pac-Man in this side scrolling platform game. For a while, this game reached a relatively high level of popularity, but after a while the novelty seemed to wear off, and the game fell into relative obscurity. A bit grainy in appearance, it is still nice to take the yellow pill-muncher on an adventure that breaks away from the typical Pac-Man everyone is accustomed to.

Legend of Hero Tonma   Legendary Axe II   Magical Chase   Neutopia II

TG-16

Psychosis   Side Arms   Space Harrier   Splatterhouse

Parasol Stars: The Story of Bubble Bobble III
                      Taito   4 $20
This continuation of the Bubble Bobble series offers some great levels and creative puzzles. With nice character animations and solid control, this title is what has become expected from this series.

Power Golf   Hudson   2 $8
Supporting up to two players, this golf game offers typical game play that is pretty much standard for when it was released in 1989.

Psychosis   Naxat Soft   3 $12
This is a side view shooter that offers detailed environments and quick action, but this basically makes it play as most others in this genre. Fun, but with no attributes that make it stand out from the crowd.

R-Type   Hudson   1 $8
This side scrolling space shooter has become a benchmark in the genre, and though it does offer very solid game play and interesting levels, it hasn't held up over the years. Still fun to play, even for extended periods of time, this title simply can't offer the same type of challenge of newer side scrolling shooters.

Raiden   Hudson   4 $20
It is still fun to drop quarters in this game at the arcade, and this port does a nice job of bringing the graphical and game play style home. While it is true that there are noticeable differences in every aspect of the game, the feeling of the original is maintained, making this a very fun vertically scrolling shooter.

Samurai Ghost   Namco   3 $12
A side scrolling fighting game with some outstanding graphics, the only downfall to this title is the seemingly rigid character animations that can often make precise control difficult. Released in 1992, this title really pushes the graphical capabilities of the TG-16 and offers some intricate enemies and environments.

Shockman   NCS   2 $8
A side scrolling platform shooting game, this title sports some very nice graphics and level designs, though control can seem a bit glitchy at times. Otherwise, this is a fun game, about average for the genre.

Side Arms   NEC   3 $12
Standard fare for side scrolling space shooters, this title offers weapons upgrades and multiple waves of enemy onslaughts. While considered above average by many, it really offers nothing over the rest of the entries to this genre.

Silent Debuggers   Data East   2 $8
This is a futuristic first person shooter featuring various enemies and weapons, but the monotonous hallways and confusing layout of the areas in which you explore make this game less than stellar. Even when it was first released and this genre was largely unexplored, this game was less than impressive and often resulted in boredom. Perhaps the biggest problem with this game is how easily one can become lost in the maze of corridors.

Sinistron   IGS   3 $12
This really is a good side scrolling shooter featuring both impressive level design and intricate backgrounds. The control is solid and helps make this game an impressive entry to this crowded genre.

Soldier Blade   Hudson   5 $22
Very similar in design and play to Final Soldier, this title offers substantially more. The graphics are astonishing for a vertically scrolling shooter, including some of the most impressive weapons effects seen in this type of game.

Somer Assault   Atlus   3 $12
Play as a Slinky type character in this unique platform game. This unique type of character introduces a fray of new challenges normally not seen in this type of game, allowing for movement along nearly any surface. Very innovative and fun, this game shouldn't be missed by those looking for something different.

Sonic Spike   IGS   3 $12
Viewed from the side and featuring cartoon like characters, this is a fun game, though it does not feature the realism that gamers have come to expect over the years since its release.

Space Harrier   NEC   2 $12
A very nice port of the Sega classic, this title features a hovering character that blasts away at various enemies, the most memorable of which are the level bosses that swoop in an out, demonstrating some nice pseudo 3-D effects.

Splatterhouse   Namco   1 $10
Very violent and starring a character that is very similar in appearance to Friday the 13th's Jason, this game will have you travel through various stages in a ghoul infested mansion. Made famous by its gruesome game play, this title is still fun to play and even after the challenge has worn thin, it still features about an hour of creature killing fun.

Super Star Soldier   Hudson   2 $8
Played in similar style to Galaga, this is a vertically positioned fixed screen shooter that doesn't offer much in the way of vari-

The most common game system used by American servicemen: Sony Playstation.

ety, though it can be fun for a quick game.

Super Volleyball   Video Systems   2 $8
Control one of eight preset teams or create one of your own in this lackluster volleyball game. Simple control makes it easy to play, but it lacks any real challenge and becomes tedious after only a few games.

Takin' it to the Hoop   Alcom   2 $8
This title, though offering full five-on-five teams, really has nothing to offer over the abundance of basketball games available on the NES. This 1989 release shows the progression through which the TG-16 was going during its early years, trying to perfect the capabilities of the system.

TaleSpin   Disney   4 $22
The popular Disney character comes to the TG-16 with this side scrolling platform game featuring some nice environments. The only real complaint about this title is the fact that with the intricate backgrounds found on some levels, the character can sometimes be difficult to distinguish, causing unnecessary deaths.

Tiger Road   NEC   2 $12
This side view action/fighting game features some nice characters, though they are a bit small by today's standards. The backgrounds and levels seem a bit repetitive, but overall this game offers a fun experience.

Time Cruise   Face   3 $12
A fun pinball game, this title isn't really as enjoyable as Alien Crush. Still, if you are a pinball fan, the unique board design, impossible to recreate in an actual pinball machine, should be enjoyable.

Timeball   Hudson   4 $22
An overhead puzzle game reminiscent of Gnaru for the Intellivision, this title offers greater replay due to varying level design and a constantly increasing challenge.

Tricky Kick   IGS   3 $12
An overhead action/puzzle game, this title offers some nice graphics for the genre, but fails to create the addicting game play necessary for a puzzle game to grab the public.

Turrican   Ballistix   3 $12
This side scrolling shooter takes place on Alterra, a planet supporting several human colonies. The computer that controls the environments was damaged during an earthquake and is now trying to kill the colonists. Your job is to navigate your way through 10 hostile levels in an attempt to destroy this computer, known as MORGUL.

TV Sports Basketball   Cinemaware   1 $10
A side view of the game shows that this title featured some of the most realistic looking players found anywhere in 1991. Part of a huge advertising campaign by NEC, this is one of three sports games that appear to be an attempt to grab the sports market before anyone else could.

TV Sports Football   Cinemaware   1 $10
Made very appealing by the commercials of the time that showed a football smashing through the TV screen, this title hasn't aged very well. While the graphics are better than those found on various Madden games for the Genesis, the computer doesn't seem to really know how to play the game, causing frustration at some points and disappointment at the ease of scoring at others.

TV Sports Hockey   Cinemaware   1 $10
Featuring some very nice ice-effects and a pseudo 3-D appearance, this title looks much better than other hockey games of the time, but plays about the same.

Veigues Tactical Gladiator   Victor   2 $8
This 1990 side scrolling shooter features some very large on-screen characters and detailed environments, making it stand out from so many others in this genre. Solid control and occasionally nice sound effects help bring the entire package together to make a very enjoyable game.

Victory Run   Hudson   3 $12
This 1989 release is very similar in style to Out Run and Pole Position, though it doesn't offer much in the way of graphical improvement. While this is an early release for the system, it is still a disappointing title.

Vigilante   Irem   1 $5
Used almost single-handedly to help launch the TG-16, this title was featured in commercials long before the system was actually released. Featuring graphics who's equal had never been seen on any other system, this side scrolling combat game had a style all its own. Facing numerous enemies and armed with your martial arts skill, your goal was to fight your way through parts of New York in an attempt to rescue Madonna, your girlfriend. If there is one game that epitomizes what the TG-16 was capable of upon launch, this is it. And though later games most certainly demonstrated more intense graphics and sound, this game should hold a high level of nostalgia for anyone who remembers the news of this NEC console coming to America.

World Class Baseball   Hudson   3 $10
A definite improvement over other baseball games released in 1989, this title features some early attempts at the use of depth to add realism to the game. Though the game play suffers a bit, this title still offered several nice features such as bunting, changing players and the occasional opportunity for a double, or

Takin' it to the Hoop   TaleSpin

TV Sports Football   Vigilante

TG-16

World Sports Competition

Yo Bro

even triple play.

World Court Tennis   Namco   2 $8
A 1989 release, this title offers little in the way of realism, but
instead relies on the use of cartoon-like characters and solid
control. Overall, this is a fun title, though with the availability of
so many better titles on newer systems, this game won't offer
much outside of nostalgia (assuming you owned it when it was
new.)

World Sports Competition   Hudson   3 $12
Very detailed athletes compete in various Olympic style events
in this game. Featuring both control and graphics that could not
be equaled by other systems in 1993, it is disappointing that this
game never received much recognition. This should be very
enjoyable for those who enjoyed World Class Track Meet for the
NES, but were wanting more in the way of graphical excellence.

Yo Bro   Camp California 2 $8
This is a skateboarding game with an overhead view and some
interesting enemies to confront. But what is an otherwise standard action game, this title features cover art that shares an
uncanny resemblance to that found on the NES game Wally
Bear and the NO! Gang. While unconfirmed, it seems a cer-
tainty that either both covers were created by the same artist, or
one was inspired by the other. But which inspired which is unclear since both titles were released in 1991, making any assumption misplaced at this point.

HARDWARE

TurboGrafx-16   NEC   3 $40

TurboBooster   NEC   4 $30
Used to allow for stereo sound to be utilized with the TG-16.

TurboPad   NEC   1 $10
This is the standard controller used with the TG-16.

TurboStick   NEC   2 $12
An arcade style stick with very cheap feeling buttons, this controller is helpful for some games, but certainly not to the extent
that NEC would have you believe.

TurboTap   NEC   2 $15
Play with up to four players using this device. Unfortunately,
due to the design of the TG-16, this is necessary even when
playing two-player games due to the single control port on the
console.

NEC TurboGrafx-16 Turbo CD

By: Andy Slaven

In 1989, Japan saw history in the making as the first CD-based video game console was released. Sold as an upgrade to the PC-Engine (Japanese TurboGrafx-16), the unit was known as the CD-ROM2. The ability to store huge amounts of game data on such an inexpensive format was an amazing leap for the game developing community, and NEC planned on making the most out of it.

In their attempt to capture even more of the video game market, NEC decided to market not only the PC-Engine in the U.S., but also the CD-ROM2. The PC-Engine was redesigned and renamed the "TurboGrafx 16," or TG-16 as most people began to call it. The CD-ROM2 was also redesigned, and was renamed the "Turbo CD." When new, the two systems sold for a combined price of $580, but $400 of this was the Turbo CD alone.

Due to the redesign of the TG-16 base unit, the Turbo CD had to be redesigned not only for aesthetic reasons, but also due to the fact that it would have to fit together with the TG-16. Designed to mount under and behind the TG-16, the CD player itself was actually removable. The base to which the two systems were joined would lock into place on the TG-16, and then allow the CD player portion to be removed by turning a locking knob. The CD player itself was designed so that it could be used as a portable CD player for audio discs, though carrying around a $400 CD player was a prospect that most consumers didn't care about.

During this time, the TG-16 was competing head to head with both Nintendo's NES and Sega's Genesis. These two consoles were not going to be easy to compete against, especially with the firmly rooted consumer base of Nintendo. At this point in time, the NES was king of the home video game market. Sega already had a reputation as an arcade giant and had previously released the moderately successful Sega Master System (SMS) in the U.S. But the TG-16 was something from a company that Americans just weren't familiar with. It would prove nearly impossible for NEC to get the recognition they were looking for in the U.S. market.

The TG-16 saw only a small portion of overall sales and didn't have nearly as many titles available for it as the competition. As a direct result of poor TG-16 sales, the Turbo CD unit sold dismally. It wasn't long before these units were discounted for quick sale, though even at these lower prices the units didn't sell very well. It seems that America wasn't quite ready for the Turbo CD.

Unlike Sega's future release of the Sega CD, the Turbo CD did not try to make every game into a full motion video (FMV) experience. This isn't to say that the Turbo CD didn't use

Some gamers have reported motion sickness while playing the 3DO's game Blade Force.

TG-CD

FMV, but instead used it to compliment elements of the game rather than make up the actual content of the game. Perhaps this was the case simply because the Turbo CD couldn't handle FMV as well as the Sega CD later would. Or perhaps it is because NEC wanted a higher level of interactivity within their games. Regardless of the reason, the Turbo CD has a relatively small library of games that are often questionable in quality. While it is true that some games, such as Lords of the Rising Sun, really show capabilities that would be impossible on the TG-16 alone, most games fell short of impressing anyone.

NEC's pioneering effort didn't go completely unnoticed by the public, however. RPG fans got a taste of Y's Books 1 & 2 along with Exile and Cosmic Fantasy 2. Fighting fans got to play Fighting Street, the original game in the now famous Street Fighter series. Strategy fans were treated well with the title Lords of the Rising Sun. In addition to Turbo CD games, the system could also play audio CD's via an interface that was displayed onscreen. This type of control of an audio CD was a first for American consumers, and this feature would be mimicked by almost every CD-based system to follow.

In order to allow the Turbo CD to play properly, a "system card" came packaged with the unit and plugged into the game slot of the TG-16. This card was necessary to play any Turbo CD game. Later, when the TurboDuo was released, this card could be upgraded to allow for the play of Super CD's on the original Turbo CD unit, though it was priced so that no advantage could be had by a consumer without a Turbo CD already. Later still, in Japan only, an "arcade card" was released to allow for the play of even more advanced games. While U.S. Turbo CD's won't support this type of game, the LaserActive, when properly fitted with an NEC module and the system card, can play all games perfectly.

Still, the Turbo CD had a quality that can't be quantified. Americans who purchased this system felt elite not only because they had paid $400 for the unit, but also because they were playing games unlike anyone else could. The system has a "Japanese feel" to it, almost as if it wasn't intended for the U.S. market, and this is something that a very hardcore fan base has held on to for years. Even today, TurboGrafx fans are among the most fanatical about their systems, second only to the Neo-Geo community.

This system, though a total failure in the U.S., is still very entertaining to play from time to time. Though the introduction of the TurboDuo (which will play all Turbo CD games) makes this unit obsolete even for retro-gamers, the TurboGrafx Turbo CD was the first CD-based video game console ever released.

***Note: TurboGrafx Turbo CD games came in a jewel case that were inside of boxes. Prices are for games complete in the jewel case with instructions, but do not account for the inclusion of the cardboard box. The standard addition of 20% of the original price should be applied to games that are in their original jewel case AND box.

A typical NES cartridge contains 28 ridges on the front and back.

| Cosmic Fantasy 2 | Exile | Fighting Street | It Came From the Desert |

Addams Family   NEC   3 $8
This side scrolling adventure places you in control of Tully Alford, the Addams Family's lawyer. Your goal in this game is to gain access to the house, through the graveyard, and into the underground passageways in order to recover the fortune that lies within. While the game can be fun, it is obvious that the Turbo CD is not being used to its full potential. Sometimes frustrating control will have your character do exactly what you didn't want him to, and grain and glitches often appear onscreen for no apparent reason.

Buster Brothers   Hudson Soft   5 $15
This is a variation of sorts of the classic game Asteroids. Instead of controlling a spaceship, you control one of the Buster brothers, and instead of shooting asteroids, you're shooting bouncing balls. When shot, the balls split, and those pieces must be split again before you can finally destroy the numerous pieces that you have created. Varied power-ups and assorted enemies offer this game more variety than Asteroids ever had, plus the graphics are done very nicely. Simple in concept, and often difficult in execution, this game is best played by two people. Excellent control, graphics and sound make this a very fun installment to the Turbo CD library.

Cosmic Fantasy 2   Working Designs   4 $15
This Working Designs title for the Turbo CD is absolutely amazing and one of the "must-have" games for this system. A classic RPG with animated cut scenes and free roaming capabilities make this game not only entertaining, but challenging. The voice actors in this game are top notch and quite a pleasant surprise for a game from this time period. You are only allowed to save twice however, making your choices during the game all that more important. Graphics and sound are amazing, and control is very simple and easy to understand.

Exile   Working Designs   3 $12
An action RPG with various perspectives, this game features towns and villages portrayed in a 3/4 isometric view, while action sequences are displayed in a side scrolling format. Animated cut scenes are accompanied by voice actors that do a nice job, but occasionally the animation becomes very grainy and occasionally freezes. Magic use is extremely limited in this game and you must rely on physical weapons to do most of the work in this game. While it is entertaining on the whole, it is extremely easy and very short. This might be a nice break for RPG gamers looking for something new, but it could have been improved in quite a few areas.

Fighting Street   NEC   4 $22
Street Fighter 2 is perhaps the best known fighting game of all time. It spawned a revolution that has seen hundreds of variants and clones. But it seems odd that most gamers never stopped to question the number "2" in the title. Indeed, Fighting Street was the game that began it all (actually, it was named Street Fighter in the arcades, and the name changed for its home release). You can choose to play as Ryu or Ken in your quest to beat 0 opponents, culminating in a fight with Sagat, the reigning champion. The graphics are admittedly grainy at times, and the control often seems a bit blocky, but there is no denying that this game is the forerunner to one of the most influential games of all time. This game was also released under the original title "Street Fighter" for the PC (DOS), Amiga and Atari ST, though this is the only video game console that received a port. And just in case you are interested, the ten opponents that you will face off against in this game are: Adon, Birdie, Eagle, Geki, Gen, Joe, Lee, Mike, Retsu and Sagat.

Final Zone II   NEC   4 $12
This is a vertical shooting game in which you control 5 different characters that change from level to level. On several levels you will actually be able to change the character to one you choose, but even though each character has their own weapons and attributes, you'll be just as good with one as you are with the next. Solid control and average graphics make this a fun game to play. There are cinematic cut scenes between levels which were included, no doubt, to show the consumer exactly why they paid all that money for a Turbo CD system.

It Came From The Desert   NEC   4 $12
This is a very odd game with several different types of action throughout. There is a straightforward side scrolling portion in which you avoid giant oncoming ants by jumping over them, or by shooting them. Also, a portion of the game involves an odd FMV sequence in which you must shoot all the ants before they devour the flesh of whatever character has been captured at that particular time. This portion of the game is a prime example of early attempts to utilize the CD technology. Heavy "clusters" form in the digitized graphics and it often becomes difficult to see exactly what you are shooting at. With your friend tied to the ground and the ants coming, it is humorous to see what happens when a large chunk of that person's flesh is eaten. A giant gap is left in their body, clean to the bone. And even with these injuries, if the person is successfully saved, they stand up, brush off, and act as if they had suffered no injuries. There are different endings, most notable is the tragic ending if you don't beat the game. Also, "Sea of Love" is performed by Chris Issak, though I've never seen this song available on any album. Also, a notably bad portion of the game involves a very long speech by a blind sax player. To make matters worse, he seems to be playing nothing but rotating scales that can really become annoying quickly. Overall this title is fun to play for very short periods of time, but can quickly become frustrating due to poor video quality and boring action sequences.

81

The TurboCD was the first system to use CD technology for video games.

TG-CD

J.B. Harold Murder Club NEC 6 $25

More than 25 characters comprise over 3 hours of speech in this digitized game. Unlike an interactive movie, the majority of this game uses digitized still frame images of the character you are speaking with. You control J.B. Harold, a private investigator trying to solve the murder of a man named Bill Robbins. Of course Bill had a list of people who wanted him dead that was a mile long, so sifting through all the information can be tricky at times. While the package declares that this game is suitable for players 12 years and older, it is doubtful that anyone that young could really appreciate the depth that this game offers. Not to say that it can't be solved by anyone 12 years old, just that there is so much information to read through, and so many characters to deal with that it might not hold the attention of anyone but the most die hard mystery fans. This is a decent title that can be played with friends since the person with the controller doesn't control so many actions as choices. It is definitely recommended that you keep notes while playing this game however, as it is easy to lose track of who's who.

Jack Nicklaus Turbo Golf Accolade 3 $8

Digitized players are used in this early attempt to make golf games resemble real life. The graphics actually turn out a bit blocky and an attempt at textures makes this game resemble something that the NES could have supported. Control is easy enough to get used to, and the courses are about par for the genre, no pun intended. Up to four people can play at once, making this more enjoyable than golf games that don't offer multi-player support. Interestingly, the back cover has Jack Nicklaus's photo with a quote directly beneath stating, "I designed my golf game with one goal in mind…", as if Jack himself programmed this game.

Last Alert NEC 4 $15

Featuring graphics similar in style to Metal Gear for the NES, Last Resort allows for a selection of various weapons in this action game. Played from an overhead view, your job will be to infiltrate the enemy fortress and, well, save the world…what else? Cut scenes will progress the story along after you have completed a level and prepare you for the next mission. The environments in this game, while colorful, lack a "crisp" feel that is necessary in this genre. Some levels seem to lack any depth at all and could easily have been produced by a lesser 8-bit system. Control is intuitive and the sound is decent. Though there are several areas that could have been worked on, this title should be enjoyable for those who want a quick game of shooting everything. The save feature is supported, so you can play until you become bored, and then pick up your saved game when you have the time.

Lords of the Rising Sun NEC

A strategy game that takes place during the feudal period of

Japan, this title should be entertaining for both history buffs and fans of strategy. Designed in a way reminiscent of Defender of the Crown, there is more animation and interaction in the course of this game, though your ultimate goal is to unify (read: conquer) all of Japan. You can choose between three separate characters, each with his own storyline and varying degrees of difficulty. Political maneuvers are part of this game, as is the use of Ninjas to assassinate the leaders of opposing forces. When attacking a garrison, the amount of time you are allotted is determined by how many men you have under your command at the time. The period in which you must successfully find the center of the garrison is determined by a sun passing overhead. Once night falls, if you have not reached the center, your attack is brought to an unsuccessful conclusion. But by far, the most amazing part of this game is the imaginatively drawn opening sequences. Instead of using animation, still frames were used and a "pan and scan" technique was used to lay out the story. The voice actor used to narrate the opening sequences is flawless and really sets the mood for this enthralling game. By today's standards, the opening sequence and subsequent game play may seem substandard, but to have played this game when it was first released was an amazing experience.

Magical Dinosaur Tour NEC 3 $5

Not a game at all, but instead an interactive tour of different dinosaur populated panoramas, this title offers information on all aspects of various dinosaur species. Animations will allow you to view what dinosaurs might have looked like in motion. You are guided through this virtual tour by a small purple dinosaur, though navigation is simple enough. Definitely targeted toward younger children, this title offers no game play of any type and should only be picked up by collectors.

Monster Lair NEC 4 $12

Fourteen levels of mutated monsters make this side scrolling platform game entertaining and occasionally challenging. The graphics are very colorful with sharp edges. This is not a typical early CD game at all. Instead of relying on FMV, this title relies on solid control, nice graphics and quality sound to deliver a fun gaming experience.

Sherlock Holmes: Consulting Detective
  NEC 3 $8

Seeming available on every CD-based game platform ever created, you will control Sherlock in his quest to solve three mysteries. The FMV sequences, though acted out adequately, often show signs of digital degradation and begin to "clump" and freeze form time to time. This game almost requires that you take notes, though it does have an in-game "note pad" that records essential names and information…but this doesn't keep track of your thoughts and suspicions. Also included with the game is a series of reduced-size newspapers from the same time period as the game. This is a very fun addition to the

J.B. Harold Murder Club   Last Alert

Lords of the Rising Sun   Monster Lair

Can you name the Super Mario Bros. trick made famous by "The Game Handler" one-handed controller?

| Valis II | Valis III | Y's Book 1 & II | Y's III: Wanders From Y's |

game, and they are actually used from time to time when looking for different clues. It really adds a lot to the experience and makes the game more enjoyable when played with onlookers.

Valis II   **NEC**   **3**   **$10**
The second installment in the very popular Valis series, this side scrolling adventure game has you facing off against the evil King Magus. Featuring six levels and some very impressive graphics, this installment is a very nice addition to the series, though most agree that Valis 3 is much better. While available on several platforms, this version has very clean looking graphics and the addition of cut scenes. The environments in this game are among the best found on the system, and though they can often seem repetitious, the still have a very polished feel to them.

Valis III   **NEC**   **4**   **$12**
Once again taking the role of Yuko, you must use the Valis sword in this game to destroy Ramses, the lord of the spirit world. This installment allows you to transform into different characters in order to take control of their various capabilities. For instance, Char uses a bladed whip and Vernal uses a "death cube" that is thrown at enemies. This title contains nine levels of diverse environments that are all nicely done. Control is very solid, and the cut scenes are especially good looking.

Vasteel   **Working Designs** **3**   **$12**
A strategy game at heart, this title also offers some very interesting fighting sequences when a confrontation takes place. The best part of this game is the option to play with a friend in a head to head strategy duel. Very nice graphics accompany this title and voice actors comprise over 90 minutes of speech. With 4 different endings and the ability to play in multi-player mode, this game offers an extremely high replay value.

Y's Book I & II   **NEC**   **3**   **$18**
An extremely popular RPG series both in Japan and the U.S., this title offers complete versions of the first two games. The game play is amazing and the storyline is among the best in the genre. The back of the box does a nice job detailing some of the highlights, so I will simply list them here. 24 minutes of digitized speech, 14 bosses, 150 items, 70 maps, over 20 minutes of animation and 43 music tracks. Definitely a "must-have" for this system!

Y's III: Wanderers From Y's NEC   **6**   **$30**
The Y's series continues with this amazing installment. Side scrolling action and RPG elements are mixed perfectly in this game. Featuring yet another compelling storyline and a large world to explore (divided into 5 major sections), this game is yet another "must-have" for the Turbo CD. The only real disappointment in this game is the fact that the graphics often seem

uninspired in certain areas, but in others they are amazing. This lack of consistency takes a little bit away from the overall experience, but should be among the favorites of any RPG player.

HARDWARE

TurboGrafx Turbo CD   **NEC**   **4**   **$45**
The Turbo CD is most commonly referred to simply as the TurboGrafx CD, even on the cases of most the games. This item is rarely found alone, but instead is usually attached to a TG-16. Just like any CD-based system, the lens is often out of alignment on system that have been treated roughly. This price should include the system's unique power supply and a system card of some sort, but at least one version of the card must be present. If it is not included with the CD player, deduct its appropriate value from the total price.

System Card 1   **NEC**   **4**   **$15**
This is the first system card available for the system and is necessary to play CD-ROM games in your Turbo CD. Since they were included with the system itself, they can often be difficult to find by themselves.

System Card 2   **NEC**   **5**   **$25**
This system card allows for the use of Super CD's (TurboDuo titles) on your Turbo CD system. These were made available after the release of the TurboDuo in the U.S. to allow owners of a Turbo CD system to upgrade instead of buying a new system.

DUO

NEC/TTI TurboDuo

By: Andy Slaven

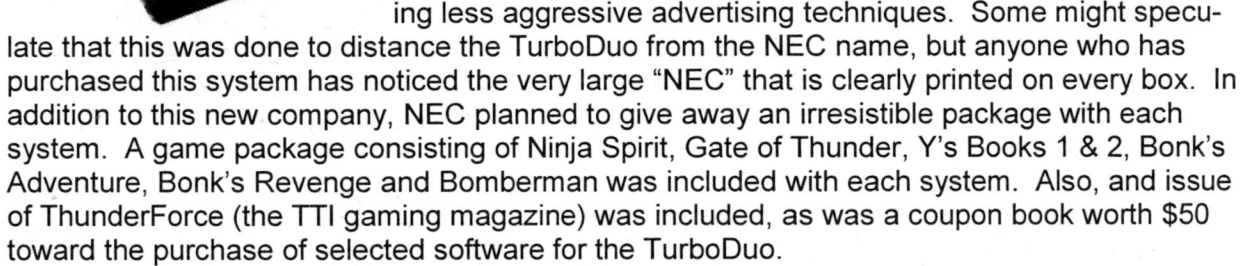

The TurboDuo, released in October of 1992, represents NEC's final entry to the U.S. video game console market. With an original release price of $299, and NEC's shaky history of U.S. console releases, something had to be done to help swoon the American gamer. First off, NEC formed Turbo Technologies Incorporated with Hudson Soft in an attempt to appeal to the average U.S. gamer by using less aggressive advertising techniques. Some might speculate that this was done to distance the TurboDuo from the NEC name, but anyone who has purchased this system has noticed the very large "NEC" that is clearly printed on every box. In addition to this new company, NEC planned to give away an irresistible package with each system. A game package consisting of Ninja Spirit, Gate of Thunder, Y's Books 1 & 2, Bonk's Adventure, Bonk's Revenge and Bomberman was included with each system. Also, and issue of ThunderForce (the TTI gaming magazine) was included, as was a coupon book worth $50 toward the purchase of selected software for the TurboDuo.

Oddly enough, the system still didn't sell very well, and part of the reason is probably due not only to the public's skeptical view of NEC, but also because of the appearance that this system, right from the start, was almost pleading for attention. Had the system been sold for a reduced price and only included one or two games, things might have turned out differently. As was the case with the ill-fated TurboCD, NEC simply didn't know how to market a console to the American consumer.

Several things stand out as obvious flaws with the system that might have scared away potential consumers. This system was not compatible with existing TurboGrafx controllers even though it was compatible with the games. As with the TG-16, the system only had one control port, necessitating the DuoTap accessory to play games with more than one person. Aside from the SuperCD format that the TurboDuo could play exclusively, the system didn't offer much in the way of improvement over the TurboCD. One attempt to promote the system to TurboCD owners was made with the announcement of an unusual peripheral, a cable designed to allow the TurboDuo to function as a CD-ROM for standard PC's. Little interest in this device quickly saw TTI's retraction of this item from its lineup, and once again, the TurboDuo offered no reason for TurboCD owners to upgrade. Do not misunderstand the SuperCD format to be something that was a minor improvement or enhancement; it was a truly new format that only the TurboDuo could take advantage of. But trying to explain this to consumers who had paid $400 for a TurboCD system and were let down by a meager game library was going to be a difficult task. Ultimately, TTI was unable to convince TurboCD owners to upgrade, adding to the losses that this system would create for both NEC and TTI.

What is the fastest car in the 3DO's game The Need for Speed?

While this console may not have dazzled consumers in 1992, it is now one of the most sought after U.S. consoles around. The ability to play TurboGrafx-16 HuCards, TurboCD's and the new SuperCD format designed specifically for the TurboDuo truly make this a versatile system. Faster access times make playing some of the more complex TurboCD games more enjoyable, and the graphical power of the TurboDuo is evident in several of the releases on SuperCD format.

Due to poor sales of the system, only a relatively small library of games was ever released. Of these games, most are high quality, and the system sports some little known, but awesome RPG titles. As a product of poor sales, not only is the system difficult to find, and expensive when it is, but the games are also difficult to find. Even the most common games for this system can demand what many people would consider to be an unreasonable price.

While the U.S. release of the TurboDuo was less than spectacular, its Japanese release was one of great success. The Japanese market would see several varieties of this system, a battery backup unit, and an LCD screen that could be attached to the system for portable play. Because of this success in Japan, the TurboDuo's library of Japanese games is far superior in both quality and quantity to that of its U.S. counterpart. Some very interesting titles can be imported for this system, though it should be noted that since cinematic scenes were all the rage at this point, many Japanese games progress their story with the use of Japanese dialog, making them incomprehensible by the average U.S. gamer.

Because of the failure of the TG-16, TurboCD, and now the TurboDuo, NEC decided not to bring the PC-FX to the U.S. This system (listed in the Import Systems section) had the potential to compete with, and defeat the Sony Playstation, but without a U.S. launch NEC would be forced to compete within Japan only. The SuperGrafx, once slated for a U.S. release, was kept within Japan as well. The TurboDuo, without a doubt, had the potential to be a successful system within the U.S., but due to poor marketing and a market unwilling to take a chance on another system from NEC, the system would fail for reasons other than its own merits (much as the Sega Dreamcast would).

One of the best looking systems around, and the ability to play three separate formats of games, the TurboDuo should be in the collection of any serious gamer. The TurboDuo remains the system of choice for TG-16 fans due to its versatility. Though the price can be a bit steep, the system has a quality library with several title unique to the system, and some of the best RPG's around.

DUO

Camp California

Cotton: Fantastic Night Dreams

Dragon Slayer: The Legend of Heroes

Gate of Thunder

4-in-1   TTI   3 $12
A pack-in title for the TurboDuo, this CD features Bonk's Adventure, Bonk's Revenge, Bomberman and Gate of Thunder, though Bomberman must be accessed by pressing a specific button sequence at the title screen (Up, Right, Down, Left, II.)

Beyond Shadowgate   TTI   5 $35
One of the best looking titles for the Duo, this was not only a late release, but a well refined one at that. Making use of menu driven action and a direction pad controlled character works nicely for this game and allows for a feel similar to that of the first King's Quest game, though obviously more fluid. Fans of medieval action games should be pleased with this title.

Bonk 3: Bonk's Big Adventure CD
    Hudson Soft   5 $30
A continuation of the series was inevitable, and this platform game offers both aural and graphical improvements over the TG-16 installments. Fans of the series will be impressed, while everyone else will simply see this as yet another platform game from Hudson Soft.

Camp California   Camp California   5 $18
Choose one of several animal characters, each with special powers, at the beginning of each side scrolling platform level in which you are tasked with cleaning up trash. Playing heavily on the ecology preservation trend of the time, this title doesn't offer much fun for today's gamer.

Cotton: Fantastic Night Dreams
    TTI   6 $25
Take the role of a young witch known as Cotton in this side scrolling shooter. Interesting environments and nice level design made this part of a very popular series in Japan, but this title remains the sole proof of the series' existence in the U.S.

Dragon Slayer: The Legend of Heroes
    Hudson Soft   5 $20
While the Duo's library might be small, it is outstanding games such as this that make it stand out as being one of quality. An overhead RPG interlaced with cinematic cut scenes, this title should be a favorite of RPG fans that enjoy the Dragon Warrior series. Of course, the graphics, while simple in concept, are much improved over those found in the Dragon Warrior series. The cinematic sequences are done well and add to the story instead of interrupting it as is often the case in newer games.

Dungeon Explorer II   Hudson Soft   7 $90
The story line is the most basic seen in RPG's, save the princess from the leader of a horde of monsters, but the game really stands out as one of the best RPG's of its day. Overhead action, cinematic sequences, great story progression and intricate areas to explore all come together to make this an outstanding

title. Excellence and scarcity combined make this an expensive title to track down however, turning the average gamer away.

Dungeon Master: Theron's Quest
    TTI   4 $20
Take on the "Cult of Deaths" in this first person point-and-click RPG in order to secure the Seven Great Treasures that were taken from the monks at the Ya-Brodin monastery. While this is a fun game and offers some impressive visuals, the game can become tedious if you are not familiar with this type of interface.

Dynastic Hero, The   Hudson Soft   4 $18
A very sharp graphical style is evident in this side scrolling platform game's backgrounds and environments, though the game play remains simple in concept. Cinematic cut scenes are used in various places to progress the story and explain how your task is to defeat the wicked Drillkor Empire. This title is fun for short periods, but hardly shows what the Duo is capable of.

Exile Wicked Phenomenon   Working Designs   4 $20
Overhead action is used in this title, along with short cinemas that are used to progress the story. One of many RPG's from Working Designs, this title doesn't live up to the complexity that has come to be expected from this company, but is hardly a slouch. What might be considered an average-at-best Working Designs title still stands out as an above average RPG by anyone else's standards.

Forgotten Worlds   NEC   5 $20
Battle through 9 intricate levels in this scrolling shooter that really shows off the Duo's capability to handle large numbers of onscreen characters. Nice character animations and smooth control really help this game, though in the end, many might find this type of game play repetitive and uninspired.

Gate of Thunder   Hudson Soft   4 $15
A side scrolling space shooter, this title is fun and features some nice animations and several detailed levels, but fails to impress on the whole. While this game might be fun for small periods of time, it can quickly become monotonous for all but the most hardcore side scrolling shooter fans.

Godzilla   TTI   5 $22
Take on one of 16 classic monsters from the Godzilla movie series in this fighting game. Released in 1993, this title was what Godzilla fans were really looking for, not the strategy based Godzilla games on the NES. While the environments aren't overly impressive, the monsters within the game contain enough character to carry this title. Control is a bit choppy, but then again, so was the original Godzilla.

Hawiian Island Girls   Excite Software Corp.   8 $70
An adult title that doesn't offer any game elements, but instead

What was its top speed without cheat codes?

offers photos of bikini clad models of Hawaii. This is one of only two titles of this kind for the TurboDuo that were released in the U.S. Technically a TurboCD game, this title was marketed specifically for the TurboDuo, and as such is listed in this section.

John Madden Duo CD Football
| | TTI | 4 | $12 |

Local Girls of Hawaii   Excite Software   8 $70
This title, like its counterpart, is technically a TurboCD title, but due to the cover which expressly states that it is for use with the TurboDuo, this title is listed here. Retailing for $89.99 when it was first released, this title sold very poorly even when it could be found.

Loom   TTI   4 $15
This is a graphic adventure in which you take on the role of Bobbin Threadbare, an apprentice in the Guild of Weavers. Learn different combinations of notes as you progress through the game in order to "weave" spells through music in an attempt to...wait for it...save the world.

Lords of Thunder   Hudson Soft   4 $18
Perhaps the best game for the Duo, this side scrolling shooter really shows off the system's ability to maintain a constant frame rate even while the screen is swamped in multiple characters. While the graphics are certainly nice, it is the fluid control that makes this game stand out as a must-have for the Duo.

Might and Magic III: Isles of Terra
| | TTI | 6 | $33 |

An outstanding first person RPG adventure with amazing graphics and unusually addictive game play, this title is a must-have for any RPG fan. Control your party through various environments, all of which are extremely detailed, and take on various creatures and enemies in classic RPG fashion. With the ability to control up to eight characters within your party, this title offers some situations that will call for unique strategic skills as well as brute force.

Prince of Persia   TTI   4 $18
Seemingly available on every system ever made, this is a nice version of the now-classic side scrolling platform game. The original version of this game, first released on the PC (DOS) was one of the first that used real human movements to model the character movements after. While this title does offer nice graphics and solid game play, it really doesn't show off the Duo's capabilities due to its overall simplicity.

Riot Zone   TTI   4 $15
With some of the most comically bad cover art, not much was expected of this game, and it didn't deliver anything special to be sure. Take the role of either Hawk or the mohawk-sporting

Tony as you fight through various enemies on your quest to save Hawk's girlfriend. The final fight is between you and Dragon Zone, though you will probably be glad that the game is over instead of being proud of beating it.

Shadow of the Beast   TTI   4 $22
Undoubtedly featuring some of the nicest graphical effects seen in a side scrolling adventure game, this title is full of "eye candy". Take the role of a man transformed into a creature and track down your nemesis for a final showdown. While the level designs aren't really that inspired, the backgrounds used in some of them are simply amazing. Just look at the detail put into every tree or into the decidedly large boss characters that you will fight along the way. Vibrant colors and a soundtrack of only the highest caliber were used to make this a very enjoyable game.

Shape Shifter   TTI   4 $18
This is a side scrolling adventure in which you are trying to save the land of Krelion. You have the ability to change your character's shape and take on the attributes of the character you change into. While the graphics certainly aren't much to look at today, and few could tell the difference between this title and any other side scroller of its day, this game made use of a very wide color pallet and intricate level design. When this game was first released, few others had even come close to matching its graphical style, though it seems to have gone unnoticed by most gamers. Also featured in this game are several cinematic sequences, though the animation is a bit too much like cartoons to match the dark story well.

Sherlock Holmes: Consulting Detective Volume 2
| | TTI | 4 | $18 |

Take the role of Sherlock Holmes himself as you try to solve three mysteries: Two Lions, The Pilfered Paintings, and The Murdered Munitions Magnate. In this, the best home console version of the follow up to Volume 1. Apparently this title was originally slated for release on the Turbo CD, but it was moved to the Duo due to lack of sales of the Turbo CD system and to help bulk up the small Duo library. Though available on several other systems, this game is best known as a Duo title.

Sim Earth: The Living Planet
| | TTI | 4 | $18 |

Considered by many to be the best incarnation of this game for a home console, this title built upon the popularity of the earlier Sim City phenomenon. Treating Earth itself as a living entity that must be taken care of, this title will require that you treat the ecosystem as a whole, and not just minor parts. Watch as creatures evolve, and make sure that they have a habitable planet to inhabit.

Loom   Might and Magic III: Isles of Terra   Shape Shifter   Sherlock Holmes: Consulting Detective Volume 2

Super Air Zonk Hudson Soft 6 $45
A nice side scrolling adventure game starring none other than Air Zonk himself. In a continuing attempt to form a more solid mascot for the NEC system (after what NEC considered a failure by Bonk), this title was released for the Duo, but would be the only one. Perhaps if the system had lived longer, more Air Zonk titles would have been released, but this simply wasn't to be. This is basically an expansion of the first Air Zonk game, and only features four new levels and music that seems a bit odd for this type of game. Nice backgrounds are used in this game, though both level designs and enemy character animations are a bit dull.

SydMead's Terraforming TTI 5 $20
The name might compel you to believe that this is some sort of intricate simulation on how to convert a harsh planet for use by humans, but instead is one of several side scrolling shooters for the system. Intricate backgrounds that feature some advanced scrolling and shading techniques make this game very enjoyable, as do the detailed enemy ships.

HARDWARE

TurboDuo TTI 3 $140

DuoPad Controller TTI 2 $12

DuoTap TTI 2 $15
This device allows up to 5 controllers to be hooked up at once, facilitation multiplayer games.

Duo Adaptor TTI 3 $18
This allows for the use of TG-16 controllers to be used on the TurboDuo.

Nintendo Entertainment System
By: Andy Slaven

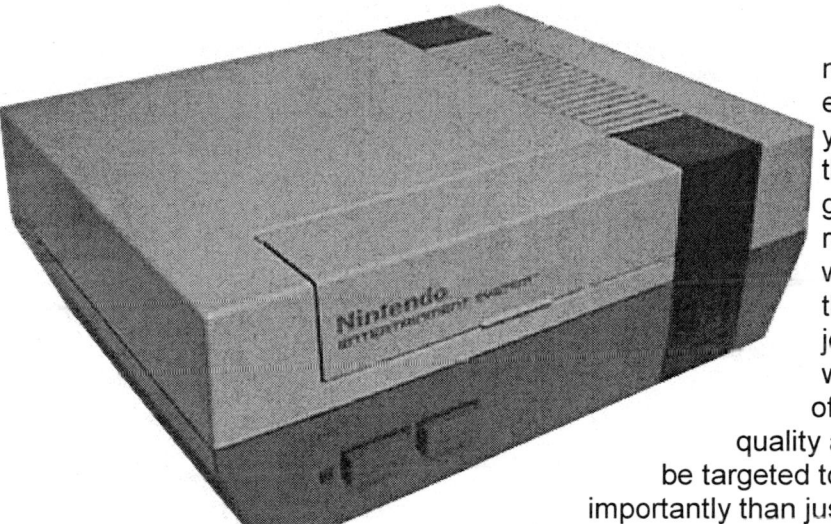

The Nintendo Entertainment System (NES) defined an entire generation and nearly 20 years later it still ranks among the favorite systems of many gamers. This system would redefine the way video games were played and what people thought of them forever. The joystick was gone, replaced with a game pad, games were of superior graphical and aural quality and the system seemed to truly be targeted toward entire families. More importantly than just entertaining the masses however, the NES was almost single handedly responsible for breathing life back into the U.S. video game market after the near total video game crash of 1984. Nintendo was virtually unknown in the U.S. before NES swooped in to save the world from a future of refurbished Intellivisions.

Released in 1983 in Japan, the Famicom (Family Computer) was Nintendo's second foray into the video game market (the first being a dedicated pong type system.) This system featured hardwired controllers with a directional pad on the left and two buttons on the right, with select and start buttons in the center. The system itself was small and durable, and accepted 60 pin cartridges about the size of those later seen on the Sega Genesis. Making record sales in Japan, Nintendo considered bringing the system to the U.S. and originally showed the Nintendo Advanced Video System (NAVS) at the Consumer Electronics Show in 1984. But the U.S. market wasn't ready for another video game console so soon after the crash (or rather in the middle of it.) Nintendo rethought the idea and consulted Atari for help in distributing the system in the U.S. The agreement would allow Atari total distribution rights outside of Japan, keeping a share of each system sold. The world was very close to seeing an "Atari Entertainment System", but a twist of fate would change this agreement, and as a result, the world of Video Games.

Atari was struggling in the post-crash industry at this point, relying heavily on the sales of its computer line, and trying their best to resurrect their stake in the video game market. The one thing they had in their favor was the highly sought after characters in their game library. One of these Characters was Donkey Kong (owned by Nintendo, but licensed exclusively to Atari for home computer use). Seeing a demonstration of Donkey Kong on the Coleco Adam outraged Atari executives, thinking that Nintendo had somehow broken their agreement concerning the Donkey Kong franchise. In reality, Coleco had created this title for the Adam under the pretext that since the Adam accepted cartridges, it was a video game console and not a home computer. Both Nintendo and Atari were embarrassed by the incident, but having felt betrayed, Atari had begun plans to resurrect an old game console project that would later be

The 3DO's Snow Job was the first game to feature internet surfing as part of the gameplay.

released as the Atari 7800.

Due to the delays caused by this fiasco, Atari had not yet signed an agreement to market the NES worldwide. As a result, Nintendo now had a chance to view previously unavailable quarterly reports from Atari, showing that the company was in far more serious shape than had previously been thought. Nintendo quickly backed out of the deal and decided to market the system without the aid of Atari. But this wasn't going to be an easy task, as Nintendo soon discovered from the unwillingness of U.S. companies to market a video game console during a time when the industry was thought to be dead.

Nintendo quickly changed strategies and introduced the Robotic Operating Buddy (R.O.B.) This accessory to the NES was actually used as the main selling point for the system, stating that the NES itself was necessary to make this toy work. R.O.B. was accompanied by a game called Gyromite that was used in tandem with the robot via onscreen interaction. In addition to R.O.B., the system also included the Zapper light gun, though this was not the first incarnation of the light gun for video games. Test marketed in New York City only, the system quickly showed potential buyers that the NES was most certainly worth investing in, and quickly became one of the best selling game consoles of all time.

One game in particular stands out more than any other on the NES, Super Mario Bros. The character, originally dubbed Jump Man, is rumored to have received his name due to a striking resemblance to a janitor by the same name that worked at Nintendo's offices. This game is often credited with starting the side scrolling platform genre, of which you will seen numerous examples in this section. Featuring not only entertaining play and solid graphics, this title offered game assisting "Easter Eggs", unlike previous secrets that were merely entertaining, but with no real purpose. Then, along came other groundbreaking games such as The Legend of Zelda and Final Fantasy, both of which would continue in various forms until present day.

As time went on, R.O.B. was eventually dropped from the NES package entirely and has now become somewhat difficult to find complete. Later versions of the NES would be sold with another gimmicky accessory known as the Powerpad. This allowed gamers to run on the mat and control various movements of onscreen characters. This was part of Nintendo's strategy to market the system as a family oriented toy that not only entertained, but would also provide exercise. Dance Aerobics was a Bandai release targeted toward girls, while the pack-in game, World Class Track Meet, was targeted toward the fathers and sons within perspective families. The NES was really becoming the staple of video game players across the country.

One thing that helped to ensure the NES's success was Nintendo's tyrannical contract agreement that game developers were required to agree to. This agreement basically kept any developer that made video games for the NES from making any game for any other competing console. For instance, if a company were making "Game X" for the NES, they wouldn't even be allowed to make "Game Y" for another platform. This is the main reason for the failure of the technically superior Sega Master System, and even for the antiquated-before-release

Here's a tip for you PowerPad newbies: Use your hands instead of your feet.

Atari 7800.

     With a library of well over 1000 titles worldwide, and nearly 800 domestic releases (more if you include Sachen releases), the NES was never short of games to be played. Several companies found a way to work around Nintendo's lockout chip however, and after numerous lawsuits to try and stop this type of publication, a flood of shoddy games were released in the wake. Tengen is perhaps the most famous of these companies with its highly sought after Tetris release. Tengen eventually signed a licensing agreement with Nintendo, though other companies such as Color Dreams, American Video Entertainment, Wisdom Tree and Camerica would never sign on with Nintendo. All of these companies would suffer multiple lawsuits from Nintendo, with the notable exception of Wisdom Tree. Many believe that Nintendo feared the stigma associated with suing a company that only made games of a religious nature, but whatever the reason, this company was allowed to continue production of their games unabated.

     In 1993 Nintendo released the Nintendo Entertainment System 2, a.k.a. the NES Top Loader for $49.99 in an effort to continue profits seen from software sales. These systems have proven to be more reliable, though they often cause vertical lines to be overlaid onscreen during certain games, though they are almost a necessity for using an adapter to play import titles from Japan. This system was discontinued in 1994 and remains one of the most desirable pieces of NES hardware available.

     There is no denying that the NES is one of the most influential game systems ever released. With one of the largest user bases ever seen and a huge library of quality games, the Nintendo Entertainment System not only revitalized the U.S. gaming market, but also marks the beginning of the Neo-Classic era.

Nintendo was one of the world's largest consumers of silicon when making the N64.

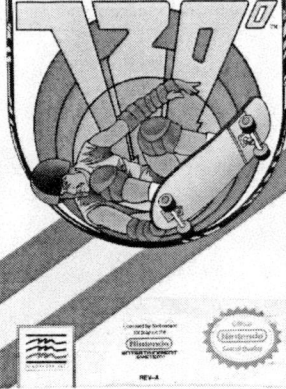

| 1943 | 6-in-1 (Caltron) | 720° | Adventures of Lolo 2 |

10-Yard Fight   Nintendo   1 $2
Basic graphics and simple control make this a good game for those not wanting a lot of strategy to get in the way of playing football.

1942   Capcom   2 $3
A solid vertical scrolling game, this game places you in a Spitfire as you wipe out wave after wave of enemy planes.

1943: The Battle of Midway
                                 Capcom   2 $3
Very similar to "1942", this title offers the same solid control and enjoyment as the first.

3-D Worldrunner   Acclaim   2 $3
Very similar in both style and performance to Sega's Space Harrier, the notable exception is, of course, the fact that you run in this game instead of hovering/flying. Also, press the select button during play and put on a pair of 3-D glasses for a true 3-D effect.

6-in-1   Caltron   6 $25
This title contains Adam & Eve, Balloon Monster, Bookyman, Cosmos Cop, Magic Carpet 1001 and Porter.

6-in-1   Myraid   7 $30
Identical to the Caltron version, this is actually a relabeled version of surplus cartridges, but is slightly more difficult to find.

720°   Mindscape   2 $3
While the control can take a little practice to get used to, this title offers some fun but simple skateboarding action. Skate or Die is a much better game however.

8Eyes   Taxan   2 $4
Set in a gothic style future, this side scrolling adventure game offers some very intricate background graphics and complex level designs.

Abadox: The Deadly Inner War
                                 Milton Bradley 2 $4
This scrolling space shooter actually shifts from side scrolling to vertically scrolling over 6 levels. Standard play and numerous power-ups keep the game interesting, if not a bit easy.

Action 52   Active Entertainment 7 $30
This game was originally sold for $200 and contains 52 games of questionable quality.

Adams Family, The   Ocean   3 $7
A side scrolling platform game, this title is standard fare, but with the addition of the characters from The Adams Family.

Addams Family: Pugsley's Scaventer Hunt, The
                                 Ocean   5 $10
This side scrolling adventure features some nice graphical effects that show an attempt at adding depth to an otherwise flat game.

Adventure Island   Hudson   1 $5
Colorful graphics and nice level design helped to make this side scrolling adventure very popular.

Adventure Island II   Hudson   3 $8
Similar to the first, updated levels are used in addition to a new story line.

Adventure Island III   Hudson   3 $10
Much improved over the first two, the graphics in this installment are very nice, though your character is still a bit on the small side.

Adventures in the Magic Kingdom
                                 Capcom   5 $12

Adventures of Bayou Billy, The
                                 Konami   1 $5
Side scrolling adventure, racing, and light gun shooting games are all included in this adventure title. Decent graphics and nice sound made this game stand out when it was released, as did its $70 price.

Adventures of Dino Riki, The
                                 Hudson   1 $2
Played in the same style as Ikari Warriors, this game has simple levels and control.

Adventures of Lolo, The   HAL America   3 $8
Creative puzzles and great level design make this entire series one of the best around. Adventure elements are used to help progress the story, instead of simply solving puzzle after puzzle.

Adventures of Lolo II, The   HAL America   4 $12
This continuation of the series is pretty much the same as the first, but with new level designs.

Adventures of Lolo III, The HAL America   5 $18
A new world map design adds even more of an adventure ele-

The TG-16 does not have a power light, but instead an orange sticker that becomes visible when the system is turned on.

ment to this game since it allows for the completion of levels in the order you choose. Still a puzzle game at heart however, this title won't disappoint fans of the first two installments.

Adventures of Rad Gravity, The
Activision 4 $5

This is a substandard platform game featuring very dark graphics and comically bad character animations.

Adventures of Rocky & Bullwinkle and Friends, The
T*HQ 4 $5

A side scrolling platform game based on the cartoon by the same name, this title allows you to fly when playing as Rocky and to attack with your horns when playing Bullwinkle. The graphics in this game are unique in that they are very colorful and look to have been hand drawn, but with an intentional lack of detail.

Adventures of Tom Sawyer
Seta 4 $3

From what I remember, the book didn't have any dragons in it, but this atrocious game does. Horrible graphics, sound and control make this one side scrolling platform game to avoid!

After Burner
Tengen 3 $5

This port of the popular arcade game fails to impress, though still offers solid arcade style fighter jet combat.

Air Fortress
HAL America 3 $5

One of many side scrolling space shooters for the NES, this is pretty average all around with the exception that certain areas will allow you to leave your ship, similar in style to the game play found in Blaster Master, but certainly not as much fun.

Airwolf
Acclaim 3 $5

In 1984, the world was treated to a TV series named Airwolf and this game is Acclaim's translation for the NES. Combat sequences are done in first-person mode, though various segments are viewed from overhead. Unfortunately for fans of the show, this game fails to deliver the same amount of action the show did, though the theme music made the journey to the NES nicely.

Al Uncer Jr. Turbo Racing
Data East 3 $5

This is a very enjoyable F-1 racing game, though the graphics haven't aged well at all. It should be worth your time if you really enjoy the genre however.

Alfred Chicken
Mindscape 4 $7

Nice colorful graphics, expansive levels, and unique characters make this one of the better platform games for the NES, though a bit unusual. You are able to fly for a limited distance, and each level is finished by popping all the balloons.

Alien 3
LJN 4 $5

Creative level design and a dark feel help this game stay true to the film from which it was inspired, not to mention the often creepy soundtrack that can really help set the mood of the game.

Alien Syndrome
Tengen 2 $5

With an overhead perspective and large areas to explore in this shooter, this game seemed promising. However, problems with control, lackluster graphics, dismal sound and uninspired game play make this a title that most will dislike.

All-Pro Basketball
Vic Tokai 2 $2

This is a dated basketball game with fictional teams and dunk scenes similar to those seen in Double Dribble.

Alpha Mission
SNK 2 $3

This is an average vertically scrolling shooter with interesting level designs, though a monotonous color pallet.

Amagon
American Sammy 2 $3

This average platform game features 6 levels and the ability to upgrade your character to the more powerful and resiliant Megagon.

American Gladiators
GameTek 4 $7

Based on the TV show from the 1990's, this is a collection of modern gladiatorial sports.

Anticipation
Nintendo 2 $3

The classic board game is brought to the NES in this less than exciting title.

Arch Rivals
Acclaim 2 $7

This basketball game is a favorite among NES gamers due to the fact that it often turns into a fighting game. With an emphasis on "dirty play" and nice graphics, this title was well received and features two on two play.

Archon
Activision 3 $7

An interesting title, this game is a mixture of both traditional chess and overhead action sequences. With a more active role in the game than that seen in Battle Chess, but lower quality

Adventures of Tom Sawyer

Airwolf

After Burner

Archon

A game console version of the Commodore 64 was released, but only in Europe.

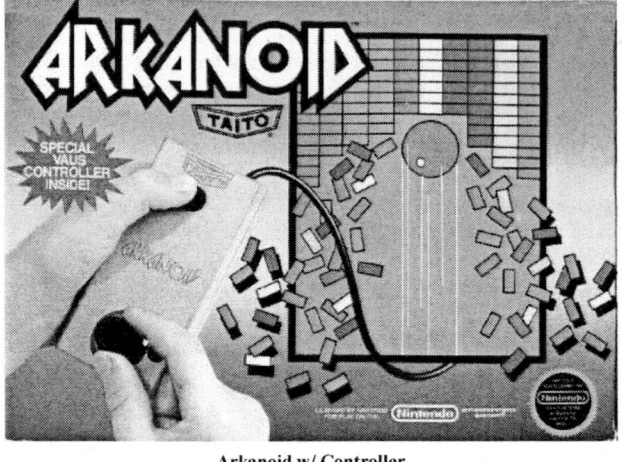

Arkanoid w/ Controller   Athletic World   Baby Boomer

animations, this game is an interesting and entertaining title that is worth a shot.

Arkanoid   Taito   4 $30*
Basically another rendition of the game Breakout, this title was packaged with a special controller that is often difficult to find. Due to the included controller, the outer box for this game is also much larger than a typical NES game would have. *The price listed includes the special Arkanoid controller valued at around $20.

Arkista's Ring   American Sammy 4 $10
Often overlooked, this overhead action/adventure RPG is a very good game. Taking an active role in your character's actions separates this title from traditional RPG's such as Dragon Warrior, but instead plays more like The Legend of Zelda.

Astyanax   Jaleco   2 $5
A graphical treat for the NES, this side/vertically scrolling adventure features 12 levels and some of the largest onscreen characters for the system. Great colors and smooth character animations add to this tit's appeal, as does the choice of weapons and magic.

Athena   SNK   2 $4
You take the role of the goddess Athena in her quest for a new life in this platform game has a very Japanese feel.

Athletic World   Bandai   2 $4
A collection of sporting events that must be played with the Power Pad, this game is identical to that of Stadium Events. This is the much more common version of the two, though the only real differences are the label and title screen…and a few hundred dollars at least.

Attack of the Killer Tomatoes
                        T*HQ   4 $8
The common belief is that this game is based on the 1978 film by the same name, but it is actually based on the cartoon series released on FOX in 1991. This title offers a visually dark experience and graphics that are surprisingly good for a game with such a comical name.

Baby Boomer   Color Dreams 4 $5
The ability to use the Zapper is odd for this game considering the fact that it was Color Dreams' first entry to the NES game market. The goal is to protect an infant from various creatures by shooting them. While not a huge success by any means, this is the best game released by Color Dreams and is very entertaining.

Back to the Future   LJN   1 $1
What could have been a very cool game turned out to be a disappointment in the form of this vertically scrolling game. Uninspired game play, boring mini-games, repetitive level design and a general lack of fun make this game an absolute dud.

Back to the Future II & III LJN   2 $2
It has been a while since I have watched the movies, but at what point was he warped into a strange world filled with mythical beasts that he must avoid in platform filled, side scrolling levels? Actually supposed to be taking place in the "alternate 1985" created in BTTF II, this game has absolutely no resemblance to any of the movies.

Bad Dudes   Data East   1 $4
This side scrolling fighter is actually a port from the arcade version, but the NES was unable to recreate the graphics necessary to make this game very enjoyable. Instead, problems with the control become evident as the NES struggles to keep up with the inputted commands. The game is difficult due to technical problems, not level or enemy design.

Bad News Baseball   Tecmo   3 $5
Fictional teams and characters detract from the feeling of a baseball simulation, and the graphics are so dated that replay of this game is strictly for the enjoyment of seeing how primitive NES games could be.

Bad Street Brawler   Mattel   3 $4
A horrible color pallet is the first notable feature in this game, though bad level design and repetitious play will quickly get your attention as well. This is a side scrolling fighting game in which you stand alone against the world and must duke it out with every person on the street. Sounds a lot like a trip to New Jersey.

Balloon Fight   Nintendo   3 $5
Fly around the screen affixed to balloons in a duel of sorts. Entertaining game play and good control make this title a lot of fun when played in moderation.

Bandai Golf Challenge Pebble Beach
                        Bandai   3 $5
An average golf game for the time with standard cartoon-like graphics and uninspired courses.

Bandit Kings of Ancient China
                    Koei   5 $12
Hexagonal movement fields are used in this quality strategy game that takes place, oddly enough, in ancient China.

Barbie   Hi-Tech Expressions   4 $5
Part of an attempt to get more girls interested in the NES, this puzzle/platform game was released in 1991. Certainly holding little interest for the average gamer, it isn't really isn't a bad game, but instead is one with content too "girlie" for the average player.

Bard's Tale, The   FCI   4 $12
A first-person RPG, this is one of the best in the genre. Available in many formats, the NES version is admittedly a bit weak, but certainly remains a great game. Released in 1991, the complex story line, intriguing characters and nicely portrayed graphics ensure that this title will remain a gamers' favorite for another decade.

Barker Bill's Trick Shooting
                    Nintendo   3 $3
This fun shooting title uses the Zapper light gun, though it can quickly get old if you're used to newer shooting games.

Base Wars: Cyber Stadium Series
                    Ultra   3 $5
This odd baseball game features a 3-D effect and robotic players for an interesting game experience.

Baseball   Nintendo   1 $1
Baseball at its most basic level, concentration on good control makes this an arcade style baseball experience, though the graphics are notably simple.

Baseball Simulator 1000   Culture Brain   3 $5
The word "simulator" seems to be tossed around carelessly in this situation, as the graphics and control are anything but realistic. Changing fields do improve this title a bit, and while not really bad, it doesn't stand out as being exceptional, especially considering the fact that it was released in 1990.

Baseball Stars   SNK   2 $5
This is the best baseball game available on the NES, hands down. With scrolling field effects and a sense of how big the field actually is, this title really stands out, even overshadowing its sequel.

Baseball Stars II   Romstar   4 $8
More options are available over this game's predecessor, though the very solid feel and scope of the first game lost something over the 3 year period it took to release this game. In all fairness, this game is very fun, and some might say that its even better than the first installment, but the fact that this title offered so little over the first version and took 3 years to make really detract from what should have been a much better game.

Bases Loaded   Jaleco   1 $1
A touch of realism and a 132 game season make this first installment of the long running series a solid, but graphically flawed game.

Bases Loaded II: Second Season
                    Jaleco   1 $2
The improvement to this game over the first installment is absolutely staggering. Taking a nearly 3-D aspect, this title doesn't look like a typical NES game, though it doesn't play as well as the superior Baseball Stars.

Bases Loaded 3   Jaleco
(See "Ryne Sandberg Plays Bases Loaded 3)

Bases Loaded 4   Jaleco   4 $5
The addition of some well placed shading effects really help this title, though it can't make up for the often unresponsive control of some of the field positions. Still very fun, and one of the best looking baseball games available for the NES, had this series continued past this 1993 release, there is no telling how advanced the series could have become.

Batman   Sunsoft   1 $2
This side scrolling fighter was released in 1990 during the period when the Tim Burton film had an insanely tight grip around the world's imagination.

Batman Returns   Konami   4 $5
This is a side scrolling fighting based on the Dark Night, and in the glow of his movie fame.

Batman: Return of the Joker
                    Sunsoft   3 $5
This side scrolling platform game doesn't offer much innovation, but was popular after its 1991 release.

Battle Chess   Data East   4 $8
The graphic effects that made this game so popular on the PC are lacking on the NES version, though it can still offer a chal-

Bandit Kings of Ancient China

Baseball Stars

Bases Loaded   Battle Chess

40% thought it was the Sony Playstation!

| Battle Tank | Bible Buffet | Blades of Steel | The Black Bass |

lenging game of chess.

Battle of Olympus　　Broderbund　3　$5
This side scrolling RPG plays very similarly to the action sequences of Zelda II and is definitely overlooked by most retro-gamers. This title is a lot of fun and offers a relatively high challenge.

Battleship　　Mindscape　4　$8
The classic board game is brought to the NES in this solid, but simple appearance.

Battle Tank　　Absolute　4　$5

Battletoads　　Tradewest　1　$4
Nice graphics and sound compliment this enjoyable game featuring your favorite fighting frogs…er…toads.

Battletoads & Double Dragon: The Ultimate Team
　　Tradewest　5　$12

Bee 52　　Camerica　4　$7
This side scrolling shooter has surprisingly nice graphics for a Camerica game, and features your character (a working bee) as she protects the hive.

Bettlejuice　　LJN　3　$7
A unique graphical style helps this game, but it remains a simple side scrolling platform game of little interest to most gamers. Still, this title should hold a bit of interest for fans of Tim Burton movies.

Best of the Best: Championship Karate
　　Electro Brain　5　$10
This 2-D fighting game, based on the martial arts movie, offers some unusual lighting effects, but substandard control.

Bible Adventures　　Wisdom Tree　4　$8
This religious game is available in two cartridge variations, the most common version is black, with a slightly more scarce blue version.

Bible Buffet　　Wisdom Tree　6　$12
A collection of religious games by Wisdom Tree, this title is becoming more difficult to find in good shape.

Bigfoot　　Acclaim　3　$5
Simple but enjoyable, this title features head to head monster truck racing over rugged tracks and cars.

Bignose Freaks Out　　Camerica　6　$12
Better than the first installment to this series (below), the largest improvements are not only in the graphical style, but also in the use of a skateboard within the game.

Bignose the Caveman　　Camerica　4　$7
Nice vibrant colors and great background animations make this side scrolling platform game very enjoyable.

Bill & Ted's Excellent Video Game Adventure
　　LJN　3　$3
This isometric adventure is based on the strangely popular movie and features amazingly detailed and colorful graphics.

Bill Elliot's NASCAR Challenge
　　Konami　3　$3
The use of real NASCAR tracks is a nice feature in this 1991 title. Solid control is nice, but an overall lack of realism makes this title playable only be diehard racing fans.

Bionic Commando　　Capcom　2　$8
A bionic arm is the key to this game's unique feel and original game play. Amazing level design and the inability to jump both require that the use of this arm is mastered quickly. Various weapons and upgrades can be collected, adding to the variation found within this game, and the inability to save makes this a very difficult game since it will require hours of constant game play to complete.

Black Bass, The　　Hot-B　4　$8
An early attempt in this growing genre, this game's graphics and sound are very basic but still offer an addictive challenge. It might be fun to play if for no other reason than to see how far the genre has come.

Blackjack　　AVE　7　$18
It's blackjack and it's on the NES. And that might have been all that was said if it weren't for the options available on this game. It is set up to allow for simulation of various situations, such as number of decks used. This seems a bit unusual, but with the reputation AVE had at the time, this could have been intended as a card counting teacher, though there is no proof of this.

Blades of Steel　　Konami　1　$1
This hockey game was made popular by the fact that you can get into fist fights with your opponents in the game. A solid hockey game at heart, this feature just adds to the appeal of the game.

96

Blaster Master Sunsoft 1 $5
Platform driving, shooting and both overhead and side scrolling adventure all take place in this amazing game. Difficult to learn at first, a little practice will almost certainly add this title to anyone's "favorites" list.

Blue Marlin, The Hot-B 5 $15
Three years after the release of The Black Bass, this title shows amazing improvement and features saltwater fishing from the back of a trolling yacht.

Blues Brothers, The Titus 5 $10
Based on the characters from SNL, this is a nice side scrolling platform game featuring accurate control and comical story line.

Bo Jackson Baseball Data East 3 $3
Once upon a time, Bo Jackson was known for being able to play any sport well...then came the multiple injuries and this horrible game. Menu driven game play and baseball should never be combined, as this game proves adequately.

Bomberman Hudson 2 $8
Great levels and intense action have made this title a favorite across multiple systems. Power-ups and various ability enhancements can be picked up when portions of the levels are destroyed, adding a lot of variation.

Bomberman II Hudson 5 $15
As with most sequels in this series, regardless of system, this title expands on the solid game play that made the first so popular. The varied abilities of different bombs and various level designs keep this game challenging.

Bonk's Adventure Hudson 6 $15
Made famous by his popular games on NEC consoles, Bonk makes his way to the NES in this hard to find platform game. Great graphics, unique levels and a great feeling of fun accompany this game.

Boulder Dash JVC 5 $10
This is a nice puzzle game with a lot of replay value and interesting levels.

Boy and His Blob, A Absolute 2 $3
Graphically dark, this is an average platform adventure game without much in the way of an interesting story line.

Bram Stoker's Dracula Sony Imagesoft 5 $8
Dark graphics and themes make this title very entertaining for horror game fans, though it is presented in a side scrolling style much like Castlevania.

Break Time: The National Poor Tour
FCI 5 $8
Average for a pool game of the time, this should be enjoyable to billiards fans, but average gamers might want to look for a more modern pool game offering more precise control and smoother graphics.

BreakThru Data East 2 $4
This 1987 release is a side scrolling driving/shooting game with repetitious levels and game play, though still fun in small amounts.

Bubble Bath Babes Panesian 9 $175
One of three adult titles from Panesian, this title is the most desired of the three. Offering nude women as an incentive to buy the game, these were typically rented and were distributed in a hard snap case instead of a cardboard box.

Bubble Bobble Taito 1 $5
Addictive play and charismatic characters make this puzzle/platform game a favorite of many. The game play itself is reminiscent of Mario Brothers (not Super Mario Brothers).

Bubble Bobble Part 2 Taito 6 $20
Nicely improved graphics and great backgrounds simply enhance the same fun experience of the first title in this franchise.

Bucky O'Hare Konami 4 $8
Playing the roll of an outer space rabbit, you must jump and shoot your way across five separate planets in order to rescue your friends in this graphically stunning game.

Bugs Bunny Birthday Blowout, The
Seika 4 $5
This side scrolling platform game resembles a version of SMB 3 that simply wasn't finished. Problems with the controls can often cause frustration to set in.

Bugs Bunny Crazy Castle, The
Seika 4 $4
A "stairway platformer", this title features Bugs through 60 levels of various difficulty but similar graphical style.

The Blue Marlin

Bomberman II

Boulder Dash

Bubble Bath Babes

The Intellivision does not use a joystick, but instead features a directional disc very similar to a directional pad.

NES

California Games

Casino Kid

Castlequest

Castlevania

Bump 'N Jump   Vic Tokai   4 $7
This vertical racing shooter offers a unique feel. It is very enjoyable to see this updated version of a classic.

Burai Fighter   Taxan   3 $3
Don't expect too much from this questionable scrolling screen adventure. Graphics that are reminiscent of Deathbots make this a tough title to like, especially once the below average control is experienced.

Burgertime   Data East   3 $3
A remake of the classic that so many video gamers grew up on, this title offers improved graphics and very solid control. The object, of course, is to complete the hamburgers on each stage without being crushed or killed.

Cabal   Milton Bradley   3 $2
Not only must you accurately place shots, you must also keep your character from receiving fire in this over-the-shoulder shooter. This game would have been much better had there been more control types on the NES, but only one directional pad was available, so this wasn't an option.

Caesars Palace   Virgin   4 $8
Various casino games litter this title with amusing, though often frustrating game play. It seems that patterns would occasionally form that would either be consistently unfair, or uncommonly fruitful.

California Games   Milton Bradley   2 $4
Six games are combined to form this title, none of which are stellar, but all of them typically Californian.

Capcom's Gold Medal Challenge '92
                      Capcom   3 $4
This is a very nice compilation of Olympic games featuring solid control and a sense of overall fairness.

Captain America and the Avengers
                      Data East   4 $7

Captain Comic   Color Dreams   4 $7
The distinctive blue case will give away this game in a lineup, this title offers eight separate levels of mediocre quality.

Captain Planet and the Planeteers
                      Mindscape   5 $8
As if a cartoon teaching liberal misinformation about the importance of recycling wasn't enough, both a comic book and this game were made to manipulate the minds of susceptible children. Using a technique similar to that of "Earth Day", which offered children a day out of classes as an incentive to participate, this game was given a flashy box and a promise of entertaining game play. This was a tool intended to coax children into wanting to learn about recycling and the importance of fighting back against evil conservatives that had plans of dominating the Earth by actually producing garbage for the sole intent of littering it across the world, apparently. One small problem kept this idea from polluting America's youth, however, it is absolutely horrible.

Captain Skyhawk   Milton Bradley   1 $1
Vertically scrolling shooters are often compared to this game, which offers solid control and a good number of onscreen enemies at any given time. Unlike other shooters on the NES however, this title features a very innovative 3-D effect achieved with lighting effects and contour lines.

Casino Kid   Sofel   4 $7
Take the role of a gambler who is simply trying to make a buck. Try and meet specified dollar amounts in order to advance within the ranks of other gamblers, though nothing more is ever made of this aspect. Fun and simple casino action makes this title fun a quick game.

Casino Kid 2   Sofel   5 $12
A more expansive version of the first game, this title is significantly more difficult to find than the first installment.

Castelian   Traffix   4 $5
Little known but fun to play, this side scrolling platform game has standard graphics and control but offers a unique experience due to its relative lack of popularity after its 1991 release.

Castle of Deceit   Bunch Games   4 $5
Showcasing decidedly nice cover art, this platform game is, as is often the case with Color Dreams games, mediocre at best.

Castle of Dragon   Seta   4 $5
Bland side scrolling hand to hand combat becomes very monotonous after defeating hundreds of mindless and reactionless enemies.

Castlequest   Nexoft   4 $5
Basically a platform puzzler, this game suffers from primitive looking graphics and repetitive game play.

Castlevania   Konami   1 $5
This the original game that so many others have come to be judged by. A sinister story line coupled with dark graphics and solid control make this vampire story/game one to remember and a definite must-have.

Castlevania II: Simon's Quest
             Konami   1 $7
Graphical improvements and a new story line are just parts of this game, making it notably better than the first.

Castlevania III: Dracula's Curse
             Konami   1 $8
Notably improved graphics mark the most obvious improvement to this installment, which is actually a prequel to the first installment.

Caveman Games   Data East   4 $8
Surprisingly fun, this title offers an Olympic style experience with primitive games that often result in killing the competitor. This title is a must-have, and is definitely more fun when played with friends in the multi-player mode.

Challenge of the Dragon   Color Dreams   6 $10
A typical entry from Color Dreams, this side scrolling fighting game suffers from substandard graphics and control.

Championship Bowling   Romstar   4 $5
An improvement over Bowling as seen on the Atari VCS, but this title still doesn't have the right feel necessary to make a bowling game a success. Not quite a simulation, and not quite an arcade style game, falling in the middle is a bad place for a game like this.

Championship Pool   Mindscape   4 $8
Overhead perspectives were common for pool games released in the early 1990's, though the physics used in this title make the shots very difficult, and often it seems as if the CPU is cheating.

Cheetahmen II   Active Entertainment   8 $40
A lot of confusion surrounds the release of this game; but basically it was going to be released, then cancelled. The stock was later purchased and sold in limited quantities. It is very difficult to find in any resale shop, though a steady stream of sealed copies is available through online auction sites.

Chessmaster, The   Hi-Tech Expressions   4 $8
The classic strategy game features 16 different levels of diffi-

culty and standard control.

Chiller   AGC   5 $10
Featuring horrible graphics and bad sound, this Zapper game isn't much fun, though it is actually a port of an arcade game known for its violence.

Chip 'n Dale Rescue Rangers
             Capcom   1 $2
Based on the cartoon series, this is your average kids game, spiced up a bit to improve its appeal to older kids. Nice colors help the graphics in this title quite a bit.

Chip 'n Dale Rescue Rangers 2
             Capcom   5 $12
More of the same with improved level design and new music.

Chubby Cherub   Bandai   4 $5
This unexciting side scrolling platform game looks and plays like a bad version of SMB.

Circus Caper   Toho   4 $8
A side scrolling adventure to find your kidnapped adventure, this title takes you through various parts of the circus and some very creative levels.

City Connection   Jaleco   4 $6
An odd racing game that utilized platforms and monotonous levels, the action takes place on a side scrolling screen and should be tried at least once.

Clash at Demonhead   Vic Tokai   3 $5
Nice graphics make this side scrolling platform adventure more enjoyable, though at heart it is an average game with little creativity.

Classic Concentration   Gametek   4 $8
Based on the game show from the 1980's, and also available on the C64, this is a simple puzzle game requiring…you guessed it…concentration.

Cliffhanger   Sony Imagesoft   5 $6
If you liked the movie, see a psychiatrist. This game is absolutely horrible. A side scrolling adventure of sorts, unresponsive controls and staggeringly bad graphics are the highlights of this title.

Clu Clu Land   Nintendo   4 $8
A basic puzzle game with multiple levels, nice graphics, sound

Championship Bowling   Cheetahmen II

Chiller   Chip 'n Dale Rescue Rangers

The RCA Studio II has no controllers at all, but instead uses two number pads attached to the console.

NES

Contra

Cybernoid: The Fighting Machine

Cance Aerobics

Darkman

and control make this title very enjoyable.

Cobra Command   Data East   3 $4
Helicopters and side scrolling shooters were just meant for each other, though this title is still average. A unique graphical style and interesting choice of colors give this game an unnecessarily dark feel however.

Cobra Triangle   Nintendo   2 $4
Isometric boat racing is a great idea and is pulled off nicely in all 25 levels of this game.

Code Name: Viper   Capcom   1 $3
Some very nice graphics are used in this side scrolling platform shooter. With backgrounds reminiscent of both Contra and Golgo 13, this 1990 release is a nice game to have.

Color a Dinosaur   Virgin   6 $15
Color dinosaurs in this paint program with no game elements.

Commando   Capcom   1 $5
Ikari Warriors is better in both appearance and in execution than this vertically scrolling shooting game, , though that isn't to say this game isn't fun.

Conan: The Mysteries of Time
    Mindscape   4 $3
Bad...just bad. Platform gaming at its worst, honestly.

Conflict   Vic Tokai   4 $8
Hexagonal field movement is incorporated into this turn based war strategy simulation.

Conquest of the Crystal Palace
    Asmik   3 $4
Interesting game play breaks up what would otherwise be a repetitive side scrolling game with average graphics.

Contra   Konami   1 $8
This game defines the NES for many people. Take the role of Ace and Gary of "Blue Oyster" to defeat the "vile Red Falcon" in one of the greatest platform games ever made. Interlaced with over-the-shoulder game play on two levels and a notably different vertical level on stage 3, this title offers little challenge to the experienced gamer, but never seems to grow old either. And when you've beaten the game, prepare for one of video game history's greatest lines: "Congratulations! You've destroyed the vile Red Falcon and saved the universe. Consider yourself a hero." Oh, and incase you forgot...Up Up Down Down Left

Right Left Right B A (select for 2 players) Start.

Contra Force   Konami   5 $10
Not originally intended as a Contra title, this game was labeled as such in an effort to make this 1992 release sell better. Five stages done poorly just don't do justice to the great Contra series.

Cool World   Ocean   5 $10
A side scrolling platform game with horrible color and questionable control, this title is best avoided.

Cowboy Kid   Romstar   6 $15
This is an action/adventure RPG of sorts. Set in the old west, this game's overhead view and direct action sequences should make this fun for anyone who enjoys the old west.

Crash 'n the Boys Street Challenge
    American Technos   5 $12
Olympic style games are played on the streets in this "tough guy" game.

Crystal Mines   Color Dreams   4 $8
Control a robot as he digs through levels reminiscent of those found in the classic game Dig Dug.

Crystalis   SNK   3 $8
An often overlooked action RPG, this title is almost certain to please fans of Zelda and other similar games.

Cyberball   Jaleco   5 $8
Robotic football is featured in this title, though it isn't very good due to poor graphics and sluggish control.

Cybernoid: The Fighting Machine
    Acclaim   1 $2

Dance Aerobics   Nintendo   3 $3
Designed as part of a kids health drive by Nintendo, this was a poor seller and doesn't offer much in the way of entertainment, but instead a simple exercise for kids to follow using the power pad.

Danny Sullivan's Indy Heat
    Tradewest   4 $4
Play with up to four people in this overhead racing game. With competitive friends, this title can quickly become very fun, though it will quickly prove boring if played in single player mode.

Want to create a video game for a current console? About 60% of your studies will be devoted to physics!

Darkman   Ocean   4 $7
Proving that absolutely any movie can have a video game made for it and still resemble nothing from the big screen, Darkman isn't really bad as you might expect, but instead features nice graphics, solid control and some genuinely fun levels.

Darkwing Duck   Capcom   4 $8
Based on the mildly popular and often amusing cartoon, this is an example of a game intended for children that instead found more of an older teen audience.

Dash Galaxy in the Alien Asylum
         Data East   3 $5
This puzzle game offers unique action elements and a shifting perspective that keeps the game entertaining, if not necessarily challenging.

Day Dreamin' Davey   HAL America   5 $10
You might find yourself daydreaming while playing this overhead action game with varied, yet boring levels.

Days of Thunder   Mindscape   3 $5
Stock car racing is portrayed in this game, showing off a good attempt at graphical innovation. The notable lack of Tom Cruise's acting makes this title enjoyable as well.

Deadly Towers   Broderbund   3 $5
They're tall…they're dangerous…they're "Deadly Towers". Seemingly unable to coax your enemy, Rubas, to a more evenly matched area such as "Swiss Plains" or "Monotonously Rolling, Yet Neutral Foothills", you must face your enemy on his own turf. Varied levels with color saturated backgrounds keep this action RPG entertaining.

Death Race   AGC   5 $10
Based on the cult movie by the same name, this overhead racing game is played by running over as many enemies as possible, though it is notable that the enemies aren't actually humans as this would have caused too much controversy in 1991.

Deathbots   AVE   5 $5
An absolutely awful game, this title was featured in the VGB column known as "Avoid Like Typhoid." Redundant game play, stiff and unresponsive controls, endless enemies that simply don't react in any discernable way, doors that won't open, sound that makes players nauseous, and many other flaws in this game make it one of the worst available for the NES.

Defender II   HAL America   4 $8
An update to the classic, this is a side scrolling space shooter with nice control and infinite replay value.

Defender of the Crown   Ultra   3 $8
Available on quite a few other systems, the NES version is where a large portion of America's youth became familiar with this title. Great strategic game play and various action sequences keep this game enjoyable even after it has been beaten. Try to unite England once and for all.

Defenders of Dynatron City
         JVC   4 $5
This is an average side scrolling combat game with decent graphics and adequate control, though nothing seems notable about the game.

Déjà Vu   Seika   3 $8
Waking to find that you don't know who you are can be very disturbing and is the premise for this first person graphic adventure. Available on other systems, this version is fun, but lacking in certain areas considering its PC roots.

Demon Sword   Taito   3 $4
Fast side scrolling action make this title stand out from slower games of its day, especially considering that it was made in 1990.

Desert Commander   Seika   3 $5
This is an overhead strategy game that is very enjoyable, though it can become monotonous if played too often.

Destination Earth Star   Acclaim   3 $5
With both first person space shooting action and side scrolling sequences, this title should have been above average, but instead is a disappointment due to unresponsive controls and undue difficulty.

Destiny of an Emperor   Capcom   4 $8
All too often ignored, this RPG offers a strategy engine unique to the NES. Command representatives of various armies in China around 150 A.D. in this challenging and fun title.

Dick Tracey   Bandai   3 $5
A resurgence in the classic comic strip character was seen after the movie was released, and this side scrolling platform game/driving game is just one of the many ways people were cashing in. The actual game play isn't very good, the graphics are average at best and the control seems flawed.

Dash Galaxy in the Alien Asylum   **Days of Thunder**   **déjà Vu**   **Demon Sword**

Add the first two numbers for the vertical position.

NES

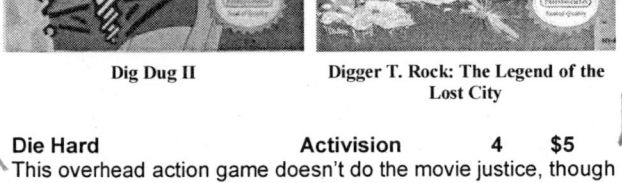

| Dig Dug II | Digger T. Rock: The Legend of the Lost City | Dirty Harry: The War Against Drugs | Donkey Kong Jr. |

Die Hard   Activision   4 $5
This overhead action game doesn't do the movie justice, though it is about average in both control and graphics.

Dig Dug II: Trouble in Paradise
                Bandai   5 $10
A change in game play from the classic first installment and inexcusably bad graphics make this title disappointing for fans of the original.

Digger T. Rock: The Legend of the Lost City
                Milton Bradley   5 $8
An above average side scrolling platform game, this title does suffer from color saturation on most levels that can make long periods of play difficult.

Dirty Harry: The War Against Drugs
                Mindscape   4 $5
You made someone's day if you paid good money for this title. Featuring horrible controls and quickly produced graphics, this title really has nothing to offer.

Donkey Kong   Nintendo   3 $8
The classic comes to the NES with improved graphics and control.

Donkey Kong 3   Nintendo   3 $7
An updated version of the original, this title offers the same game play and style.

Donkey Kong Classics   Nintendo   4 $10
This title is a compilation of both Donkey Kong and Donkey Kong Jr.

Donky Kong Jr.   Nintendo   3 $8
More complex game play makes this title more challenging than that of his dad's.

Donkey Kong Jr. Math   Nintendo   5 $12
Hey, I have an idea! We could take something kids love (Donkey Kong) and combine it with something kids hate (Math) and when we put them together we'll have a title that won't appeal to anyone!

Double Dare   GameTek   4 $4
Does Mark Summers know about this?

Double Dragon   Tradewest   1 $5
Many complain that the reduced control response and rushed graphical style make this version of the original a complete disappointment when compared to the great arcade game.

Double Dragon II: The Revenge
                Acclaim   1 $8
Many improvements were made to this installment, making it the best of the three on the NES.

Double Dragon III: The Sacred Stone
                Acclaim   2 $5
Perhaps expectations were too high, but this side scrolling fighter is disappointing when compared to the second installment.

Double Dribble   Konami   1 $5
Made famous by its amazing (though black and white) dunk scenes that were better than any other of the time, playing this game today will reveal that those same dunk scenes are pathetically animated and only offer about 3 frames of animation. More comical than disappointing, this common game is still a favorite among many retro-gamers.

Double Strike   AVE   5 $10
A side scrolling shooter with comical graphics, this title might be fun for young children.

Dr. Chaos   FCI   3 $3
Uninspired graphics and average control make this side scrolling adventure little fun to play.

Dr. Jekyll & Mr. Hyde   Bandai   3 $3
With the occasional screen showing some nice graphical qualities, the entire game isn't a pain to watch, but the lack of any good story and fumbling controls are enough to make it a frustrating game to play.

Dr. Mario   Nintendo   1 $7
This is similar to playing Tetris, but with colorful pills instead. Parental groups were upset with Nintendo at their choice of content, since many parents disagreed with the use of medicine in the game. Nintendo basically told these groups that they could bite the "Big N" and kept producing this title (which parents bought for their children anyway).

Dragon Fighter   Sofel   4 $7
Like in Altered Beast, you have the ability to turn into a dragon in this side scrolling adventure game.

Use the last number for the horizontal.

Dragon Power   Bandai   3 $5
This adventure game stars a monkey type character in uninspired game play that could have easily been improved. This title isn't worth the time, though it is notable that it was originally intended to be a Dragon Ball Z release.

Dragon Spirit: The New Legend
    Bandai   4 $8
Take the role of a flying dragon as you shoot your way through everything in this vertically scrolling shooter game.

Dragon Warrior   Nintendo   1 $5
Given away with subscriptions to Nintendo Power for a while, this title is extremely common, but still remains one of the best RPG's ever made. An expansive environment, multiple objectives, tons of objects, weapons and enemies, and quite a few interactive non-playing characters help this game stand up against the ravages of time. And while the graphics are notably dated by today's standards, the other wonderful aspects of this game remain to elevate it to the top games of all time.

Dragon Warrior II   Enix   5 $25
The ability to control multiple characters is added to this installment in the series and proves to make this RPG very entertaining and challenging. Also, the character class is introduced in this installment.

Dragon Warrior III   Enix   5 $25
Multiple character control is back in this title, along with a more customizable class system. Again, an amazing story line drives this adventure filled with random encounters and turn based combat.

Dragon Warrior IV   Enix   6 $40
Follow five separate story lines in this, the most expansive installment on the NES. An incredibly detailed story drives this RPG far beyond what was expected, making it not only one of the best for the NES, but for any home console. It is also becoming very difficult to find, especially boxed.

Dragon's Lair   Sony Imagesoft   4 $8
The NES obviously can't reproduce the graphics seen in the arcade version of this classic game, nor could it even try. Instead of being some sort of bad version of an animated title, this is actually a side scrolling adventure. Unfortunately, this idea wasn't carried out very well, and the difficult level is possibly even greater than that of the LD version. This game was supposed to offer freedom of movement and control, though in reality you will see that Dirk rarely follows your commands on time, often resulting in a lost life. Though the graphics are very nice, it is a shame that this game and its controls couldn't have been refined a bit more.

Duck Hunt   Nintendo   1 $1
This simple but fun Zapper game that finds you either hunting ducks, or shooting skeet. The only problem with this game is the fact that you aren't allowed to shoot your dog when he raises up to laugh at your misses (though a version like this can be found for emulation on the internet.)

Duck Tales   Capcom   3 $5
This is an average game staring the characters made famous by the cartoon of the same name.

Duck Tales 2   Capcom   5 $12

Dudes With Attitude   AVE   5 $10
Surprisingly, this puzzle game from AVE isn't all that bad, though there are many other puzzle games with better game play.

Dungeon Magic: Sword of the Elements
    Taito   3 $4
A nice first-person RPG, this title lacks the same appeal as the more popular Bard's Tale, though it is still a great game if this genre interests you.

Dusty Diamond's All-Star Softball
    Broderbund   5 $10
With the graphical limitations of the NES, it is obvious that the use of the term "softball" instead of "baseball" was an attempt to make this game stand apart. However, the use of creatively designed characters also makes this game different from others, and the emphasis on fun instead of realism is really what makes this title stand out.

Dynowarz: The Destruction of Spondylus
    Bandai   3 $5
One of many average side scrolling platform games, this one can quickly become monotonous without the benefit of frequent background changes.

Early Years: King of Kings, The
    Wisdom Tree   6 $20
This game sports a label that features one of the wise men jumping out of the label riding a camel. This is the least common version and it is felt that the label was changed due to the

Dragon Spirit: The New Legend

Dragon Warrior II

Dragon's Lair

Dudes With Attitude

In order to reduce costs, the SNES 2 has no power light, nor does it have an eject button.

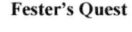

| Family Feud | Fantasy Zone | Fester's Quest | Felex the Cat |

apparent "super hero" look of the wise man featured. This is the same game as "King of Kings: The Early Years", except this label clearly shows that this version is titled "The Early Years: King of Kings".

Elevator Action   Taito   3 $5
The classic game is brought to the NES in fine fashion, though most seem to prefer the C64 version when given the choice.

Eliminator Boat Duel   Electro Brain   3 $5
An overhead boat racing game with nicely drawn courses, this unique combination is a nice break from vertical and horizontal scrolling games.

Excitebike   Nintendo   1 $5
Solid control and fun courses make this game a classic that must be played on the NES.

Exodus: Journey to the Promised Land
    Wisdom Tree   4 $8
Play as Moses in this Crystal Mines clone in your quest through 100 levels. While a blatant rip-off of Crystal Mines, Wisdom Tree dodged a lot of lawsuits due to the religious nature of the company.

F-117A Stealth Fighter   Microprose   5 $10
This is an early attempt at a console flight simulation that features some new graphical techniques, though overall it plays a little below average, even by the standards of a NES flight game.

F-15 City War   AVE   4 $6
This is a bad pseudo 3-D flight game through narrow streets featuring repetitive enemies.

F-15 Strike Eagle   Microprose   5 $10
Much better than F-15 City War, this title is played from within the cockpit and includes the bombing of Baghdad.

Family Feud   GameTek   3 $5
The game show comes to the NES, though replay is limited to a finite number of surveys.

Fantastic Adventures of Dizzy
    Camerica   4 $5
Take the role of Dizzy the Egg in his quest to collect 100 stars and rescue his girlfriend.

Fantasy Zone   Tengen   3 $3
Gaudy pastel colors are a staple in this side scrolling shooter.

Faria   Nexoft   4 $8
This overhead action RPG features graphics of a lesser quality than Dragon Warrior, though it is still a sizable adventure similar in style to The Legend of Zelda.

Faxanadu   Nintendo   1 $5
Multiple weapons and items are used in this action/adventure RPG that relies heavily on side scrolling action. Nice graphics and an interesting story raise it above mediocrity, though not by much.

Felix the Cat   Hudson   5 $10
A nice side scrolling platform game featuring Felix from the comic strip (and wall clock) fame, this title offers nice control and decent graphics.

Ferrari Grand Prix Challenge
    Acclaim   4 $7
Race on 16 different tracks in this game which looks and feels a lot like the arcade classic Pole Position 2.

Fester's Quest   Sunsoft   1 $1
Proof that the use of a popular TV character doesn't always result in a fun game, this overhead adventure lacks a feel of quality that is necessary for a game to be enjoyable.

Final Fantasy   Nintendo   3 $12
Made by Square Soft in an attempt to compete against Enix's Dragon Warrior, this title would eventually spawn numerous sequels and branching story lines. Considered by many to be the best RPG ever made, there is no doubt that this title still offers a good challenge and amazing replay value. Traditional in style, this game uses a turn-based battle system, numerous weapons and magic. Very few games can even come close to matching the greatness of this game, though the graphics in this game haven't held up even as well as those in the equally antiquated Dragon Warrior.

Fire Hawk   Camerica   3 $3
Released by Camerica, this title is one of only a few to feature a silver case, and is very easy to spot in large piles of games as they are often stored at flea markets.

Fire 'N Ice   Tecmo   6 $18
Gaining popularity very recently, this difficult to find game is a

The Pioneer LaserActive system can't play any games right out of the box. Additional modules must be purchased.

fun and challenging fixed screen puzzle.

Fisher Price: Firehouse Rescue
GameTek   4
$5
This child's game features several styles of play to help teach motor skills, and mainly to keep children glued to the TV while their parents were occupied.

Fisher Price: I Can Remember
GameTek   4 $5
More basic than the title listed above, this game is an edutainment title meant for very young children.

Fisher Price: Perfect Fit   GameTek   4 $5
Basic educational puzzled are featured in this game.

Fist of the North Star   Taxan   3 $5
Based on the very popular anime movie by the same name, this game features side scrolling fighting action with graphics that could have been improved.

Flight of the Intruder   Mindscape   4 $8
Viewed from within the cockpit, this is a nice flight simulation based on the 1990 film by the same name.

Flinstones: Surprise at Dinosaur Peak, The
Taito   7 $20
This side scrolling platform game features some very nice graphics and enjoyable characters from the Hanna Barbara cartoon.

Flinstones: The Rescue of Dino and Hoppy
Taito   4 $5
Again, very nice graphics grace this Flinstones title.

Flying Dragon: The Secret Scroll
Culture Brain   3 $7
This side scrolling fighting game features lackluster graphics and often irritating control.

Flying Warriors   Culture Brain   3 $5
Featuring some very bland levels without any creative backgrounds, this side scrolling fighting game is about average, though it does have accurate control.

Formula 1: Built to Win   Seta   4 $8
Played similarly to Pole Position 2, this game features nicer graphics and solid control.

Frankenstein: The Monster Returns
Bandai   4 $5
Very nice backgrounds help hide the control problems found in this game that features no similarities to Mary Shelly's classic character.

Freedom Force   Sunsoft   3 $4
This two player Zapper game lacks originality and becomes one of many gun games to fall into a repetitious state after only a few games.

Friday the 13th   LJN   2 $2
A horrible translation of the horror movies of the same name, this title is played in an adventure style with several areas and multiple characters…but still very bad.

Fun House   Hi-Tech Expressions   3 $4
The overhead action in this game is loosely based on the kids game show from 1988.

G.I. Joe: A Real American Hero
Taxan   5 $10
Featuring characters from the comic book/toy line, this platform game is fun, though it doesn't stand out from others in the genre.

G.I. Joe: The Atlantis Factor
Capcom   4 $5
More of the same, this title features solid game play on par with other platform games from the early 1990's.

Galactic Crusader   Bunch Games   4 $8
This is a vertically scrolling space shooter that plays horribly!

Galga   Bandai   2 $10
The original arcade masterpiece comes home in a decent yet flawed version of the classic.

Galaxy 5000   Activision   5 $10
An odd racing game, this title features some very unique futuristic tracks and solid control.

Gargoyle's Quest II: The Demon Darkness
Capcom   4 $8
Average overhead action is used in this colorful though often boring quest game.

Friday the 13th   G.I. Joe: A Real American   Galactic Crusader   Gauntlet

One 3D fighting game was created for the PC-FX, but was never released.

NES

Ghoul School

Ghosts 'n Goblins

Goal!

Gauntlet   Tengen   1 $2
Both licensed and unlicensed versions exist of this classic arcade adventure game, though neither is notably rarer than the other.

Gauntlet II   Mindscape   2 $4
Many improvements are featured in this installment, though the graphics are obviously dated by today's standards.

Gemfire   Koei   4 $8
This complex strategy game features colorful graphics and numerous options, making it a title with high replay value.

Genghis Khan   Koei   4 $10
Turn based action is used in this strategy game featuring the Mongol leader.

George Foreman's KO Boxing
    Acclaim   4 $7
Played in the same style as Mike Tyson's Punch-Out!!, this game lacks the creative characters and responsive control that made said game so famous.

Ghostbusters   Activision   3 $3
Different styles of difficult to understand game play make this title far less entertaining than the movie.

Ghostbusters II   Activision   3 $4
More of the same from Activision, this title has at least one entertaining driving style game within it.

Ghosts 'n Goblins   Capcom   2 $5
Solid side scrolling action and creatively dark levels made this one of the most popular games for the NES in 1986.

Ghoul School   Electro Brain   4 $7

Gilligan's Island   Bandai   4 $5

Goal!   Jaleco   2 $3
Horrible field graphics and an isometric view make this title a little difficult to get used to.

Goal! Two   Jaleco   3 $5
With toned down colors and improved control, this title is a bit better than its predecessor.

Godzilla 2: War of the Monsters
    Toho   5 $10

More options than the first installment and a new movement system make this better than the first. The new price was a staggering $70!

Godzilla: Monster of Monsters!
    Toho   4 $8
This is a hexagonal moving strategy game based on the popular Japanese character.

Golf   Nintendo   1 $2
Golf at its most basic, simple control and graphics make this an easy title to play.

Golf Grand Slam   Atlus   5 $10
Nice graphics make this game look really nice, but unfortunately the control is a bit off, severely reducing the amount of fun that this game can offer.

Golgo 13: Top Secret Episode
    Vic Tokai   2 $10
This side scrolling adventure is very challenging and very enthralling. Taking the role of Duke Togo, a.k.a. Golgo 13, you are known as "the man with the custom M-16". Based on a very popular graphic novel series in Japan, this game offers a title suitable for teens and adults, and even features a silhouetted, yet brief, love scene that helps you regain health. Numerous and long levels, coupled with varied modes of game play ranging from air combat scenes to water scenes to first person mazes make this one of the best action games available on the NES.

Goonies II, The   Konami   3 $5
Sequel to the Japanese only release "The Goonies", this adventure game has a strong following in the U.S. Now, if they'll just make a sequel to the movie.

Gotcha!   LJN   3 $4
An entertaining Zapper game, it will take a bit of practice to get used to this game's style, though it remains challenging even after a lot of practice.

Gradius   Konami   2 $4
Very popular after its 1986 release, this is a solid side scrolling space shooter.

Great Waldo Search, The   T*HQ   4 $8
Find Waldo, a letter and his dog in this title, inspired by the popular book series.

106

A Zelda title, known as Ura Zelda, was slated for release on the 64DD, but never made it.

Greg Norman's Golf Power Virgin   4 $7
Up to four players can play this simple golf game.

Gremlins 2: The New Batch
                    Sunsoft   3 $4
Based loosely on the movie, this title offers overhead action with nice graphics and control.

Guardian Legend, The   Broderbund   3 $5
Both overhead action sequences and vertically scrolling shooting sequences are included in this game, though it doesn't do an outstanding job with either. Average at best, the fact that the action sequences are different is enough to keep it interesting.

Guerilla War   SNK   2 $5
Similar in style to Ikari Warriors, this title offers a jungle environment and lots of shooting action.

Gumshoe   Nintendo   4 $7
A large variety of targets and objectives are made available in this Zapper game.

Gun*Nac   Asciiware   4 $8
Featuring some very interesting enemies and creative levels, this often underrated vertical shooter should definitely be played at least once.

Gun Smoke   Capcom   3 $5
Vertical shooting action is the basis for this substandard old west game.

Gyromite   Nintendo   1 $5
The original NES game that utilizes R.O.B., this title can be very difficult if actually using the robot and not cheating. Be on the lookout for heavier versions of this game, early versions contained a Famicom game that was connected to a 72 pin converter. This can be taken out and used to play Famicom games on your NES!

Gyrus   Ultra   3 $5
Based on the arcade game, this title plays similarly to Galga.

Harlem Globetrotters   GameTek   5 $8
Stick with Double Dribble, really. Just because this title features the famous basketball players' names, it doesn't mean it has any of their charm.

Hatris   Bullet-Proof   6 $15
Stack various style hats in the same game play fashion of Tetris

in this 1991 release.

Heavy Barrel   Data East   2 $4
Overhead action is featured in this shooter that plays similarly to Ikari Warriors, without the strict vertically scrolling limitations.

Heavy Shreddin'   Parker Brothers   3 $4
An early entry to the snowboarding genre, this title is entertaining, though hardly delivers the type of thrill felt in newer games of this type.

Heroes of the Lance   FCI   3 $5
A horrible adventure game based on the awesome Dragon Lance novels, this title has slow controls, an unintuitive interface, and often boring play.

High Speed   Tradewest   4 $8
A pinball simulation, this game does a good job of recreating the fell of a pinball machine, though notably two dimensional.

Hillsfar   FCI   5 $12
This game really lacks a good sense of direction, and as a result becomes a collection of pointless tasks and challenges. What could have been a decent RPG was turned into a poor action game because of rushed production.

Hogan's Alley   Nintendo   1 $5
A very fun Zapper game, released in 1985, this title is impressive and features human shaped targets popping up in random configurations.

Hollywood Squares   GameTek   4 $8
Does anybody remember what Shadow Stevens was famous for anyway?

Home Alone   T*HQ   2 $3
Quickly produced in the wake created by the popular movie, this is a side scrolling platform game of questionable quality.

Home Alone 2: Lost in New York
                    T*HQ   4 $7
Occasionally nice graphics are the only thing about this title that isn't completely horrible. Avoid this platform game unless you absolutely must have every NES game made.

Hook   Sony Imagesoft   4 $7
Very nice backgrounds and graphical effects are used in this Peter Pan game that features side scrolling action.

Gumshoe

Hogan's Alley

Hollywood Squares

Hot Slots

The CD-i features 3 Zelda titles. That's more than any other home console to date.

NES

Hudson Hawk	**Image Fight**	
		Impossible Mission II (AVE)	**Impossible Mission II (SEI)**

Hoops Jaleco 2 $3
This is a surprisingly nice looking basketball game for the NES that features some interesting camera angle effects, though the action quickly becomes boring with predictable opponent movements.

Hot Slots Panesian 9 $140
One of the three Panesian releases, this is the least desirable of the three, though still highly sought after and expensive.

Hudson Hawk Sony Imagesoft 4 $6
An interesting platform puzzle game based on the movie of the same name, this title suffers from control problems making it nearly as unplayable as the movie was unwatchable.

Hunt for Red October, The
Hi-Tech Expressions 3 $5
Side scrolling action isn't the best way to try and recreate the action and suspense of the movie, making this title a bit disappointing.

Hydlide FCI 1 $1
An overhead action/adventure game with RPG elements, this game is despised by many, and found interestingly addictive by just as many others. Similar in look and feel to a poorly played Dragon Warrior, this title should at least be given a chance.

Ice Climber Nintendo 3 $4
There are 32 mountains (levels) to clear in this fun fixed screen puzzle game.

Ice Hockey Nintendo 1 $2
Very simple graphics make the control limitations of this overhead, horizontally scrolling hockey game easy to get used to and create a fun experience.

Ikari Warriors SNK 1 $5
Vertical shooting and various weapons upgrades make this game a classic that must be played on the NES. Just a tip though, when you lose all your lives, press A B B A and Start... you should come right back, though this won't work on the last level.

Ikari Warriors II: Victory Road
SNK 2 $5
Improvements that didn't change the original formula make this title as enjoyable as the first.

Ikari Warriors III: The Rescue

SNK 3 $7
Featuring the best graphics by far in the series, this game does a good job of retaining that non-quantifiable virtue that makes this an Ikari Warriors title.

Image Fight Irem 4 $6
Vertically scrolling action is used in this space shooter of average quality.

Immortal, The EA 4 $8
An isometric RPG, this title received a lot of press upon its release due to great game play and the rarely used isometric perspective.

Impossible Mission II AVE 4 $8
This adventure game should most certainly not be confused with the far superior version from SEI (below).

Impossible Mission II SEI 6 $10
A very interesting adventure game taking place within some very nicely illustrated building layouts make this title superior even to the C64 version.

Incredible Crash Dummies, The
LJN 4 $7
Control Spin and Slick, the two dummies featured in commercials during the 1990's in this side scrolling platform game with poor control and uninspired levels.

Indiana Jones and the Last Crusade
Taito 4 $8
Several styles of game play are used in this game which follows the story line seen in the movie by the same name.

Indiana Jones and the Last Crusade
Ubi Soft 6 $12
Completely different from the Taito version, this title simply isn't as much fun and features platform action that is often plagued with control problems.

Indiana Jones and the Temple of Doom
Mindscape 3 $5

Indiana Jones and the Temple of Doom
Tengen 2 $3
This is simply a horrible game featuring archaic graphics and overly simple controls that become difficult due to inaccuracies and often encountered fatal flaws.

The Atari Jaguar CD is known as "the football" by collectors.

Infiltrator   Mindscape   2 $4
Several styles of game play are implemented in this attack helicopter game of decent graphic and control design.

Iron Tank   SNK   3 $4
Vertically scrolling tank action reminiscent of those found in Ikari Warriors made this game popular in 1988, though it is often overlooked.

IronSword: Wizards & Warriors II
         Acclaim   2 $5
Simply great control and action make this side scrolling adventure game a lot of fun to play, even for extended periods of time.

Isolated Warrior   NTVIC   3 $5
This shooting game features pseudo isometric perspective closer to the vertical than the horizontal, and displays some nice graphics as well.

Jack Nicklaus' Greatest 18 Holes of Major Championship Golf   Konami   3 $3
An average attempt at a golf simulation by 1990 standards, this title obviously relied on the inclusion of the golf great's name.

Jackal   Konami   2 $5
Overhead jeep shooting action became very popular after this release. An interesting note about this game is the fact that VG&CE magazine mistakenly listed the 30 man cheat code for Contra under this title's heading.

Jackie Chan's Action Kung Fu
         Hudson   4 $8
Made before his fame was apparent to the U.S., this title is fun to own if for no other reason than to see the seriousness that the creators tried to display in the cover art.

James Bond Jr.   T*HQ   4 $0
Graphically dark, this title offers some innovative platform stages and great action.

Jaws   LJN   2 $4
Perhaps I'm biased toward this game simply because of the fact that I tried my best as a kid to understand it and play it well, but the rest of the world seems to hate this game. It can become very frustrating due to the confusion of what exactly is expected. It is fun to shove the strobe down Jaws' throat, but it never seemed to do any good.

Jeopardy!   GameTek   3 $4
Like most Jeopardy video games, this title will become easier as the questions begin to repeat themselves.

Jeopardy! 25th Silver Anniversary Edition
         GameTek   3 $4
An updated version of the original, this is a fun game, though not much different than the first.

Jeopardy! Jr. Edition   GameTek   3 $5
Simply Jeopardy for a younger audience.

Jetsons: Cogswell's Caper, The
         Taito   5 $10

Jimmy Connors Tennis   Ubi Soft   6 $15
This basic tennis game is fun, though very simple. Two good players can engage in some very long volleys with little practice.

Joe & Mac   Data East   3 $8
Very nice graphics can not save a game from horrible controls and glitch filled game play.

John Elway's Quarterback   Tradewest   2 $3
The players in this game are absolutely miniscule, though the field does look nice and a play's moving formation are easy to see in the distant overhead view. Stick with Tecmo Bowl.

Jordan vs. Bird: One on One
         Milton Bradley   3 $5
One on one basketball in this game features two of the game's greats, and even allows for a slam dunk contest.

Joshua: The Battle of Jericho
         Wisdom Tree   4 $8
The unofficial sequel to Exodus, it only makes sense that Joshua would follow in the footsteps of Moses. 100 levels of puzzle game play are featured in this title.

Journey to Silius   Sunsoft   3 $5
This is one of many average side scrolling shooters for the NES, though this title does feature solid control and a very cool looking sky.

Joust   HAL America   4 $7
The classic returns on the NES in this 1988 release featuring solid game play and control.

IronSword: Wizards & Warriors II   Jack Nicklaus' Greatest 18 Holes of Major Championship Golf   Jackal   Jordan vs. Bird: One on One

More counterfeit copies of Metal Slug exist for the Neo-Geo AES than do the real cartridge.

Kabuki Quantum Fighter   **Kid Kool and the Quest for the Seven Wonder Herbs**   **King's Quest V**   **Klax**

Jungle Book   Virgin   6 $15
Based on the Disney classic, this title offers nice colors and some interesting graphics with average game play.

Jurassic Park   Ocean   5 $12
Very nice graphics are featured in this overhead dinosaur filled game based loosely on the movie.

Kabuki Quantum Fighter   HAL America   4 $8
A little known, but fun to play title, this 1990 release uses side scrolling platform levels throughout.

Karate Champ   Data East   3 $5
While true to the arcade classic, it just doesn't feel right without two joysticks to control your characters.

Karate Kid, The   LJN   3 $4
This title certainly doesn't do the film justice, featuring inadequate side scrolling sequences and barely useable fighting controls.

Karnov   Data East   3 $5
A horizontal platform shooter, this title features an unusually chubby main character.

Kick Master   Taito   4 $7
Detailed background graphics and character animations make this side scrolling fighter better than most.

Kickle Cubicle   Irem   4 $10
Simple to learn, this puzzle game is addictive and challenging.

Kid Icarus   Nintendo   3 $7
Creative level design and solid controls made this 1987 release one of the best sellers of the year.

Kid Klown in Night Mayor World
    Kemco   6 $15
Very odd color combinations add to the strange feel of this platform game.

Kid Kool and the Quest for the Sevan Wonder Herbs
    Vic Tokai   4 $7
Sparse backgrounds and uncreative levels keep this game squarely within the limits of mediocrity.

Kid Niki: Radical Ninja   Data East   2 $4
Ported from the little known arcade release, Kid Niki features a strange graphical quality that makes the levels appear to be

drawn by hand, and in crayon.

King Neptune's Adventure   Color Dreams   6 $15
Featuring some very unique and creative levels with beautiful backgrounds, it is a shame that this title couldn't feature more solid game play. Instead, it becomes just another side scrolling shooter with questionable control.

King of Kings: The Early Years
    Wisdom Tree   5 $10
Available in three separate cartridge formats, this version actually has two variations that share the same label art. This shows the three wise men with Mary and Joseph looking over Jesus, but one's case is blue, while the other is black.

King's Knight   Square   3 $5
Overhead action scenes really accentuate how poorly the characters were animated, and also making control a very difficult proposition.

Kings of the Beach   Ultra   3 $4
This is a nice beach volleyball title with solid control and challenging opponents.

King's Quest V   Konami   5 $15
The amazingly popular PC text-based graphic adventure makes a great appearance on the NES, but instead of having to type, you simply select words from the available list in order to form verb-noun combinations. Being in the right place and forming the right combination will cause an action to take place on-screen in this early-style RPG.

Kirby's Adventure   Nintendo   3 $7
Released in 1993, this side scrolling platform game features some very nice graphics and addictive game play.

Kiwi Kraze   Taito   5 $10
Monotonous backgrounds and colors make this otherwise average platform game repetitious, and overall, a substandard game.

Klash Ball   Sofel   4 $8
This is a futuristic rendition of what the future holds for the combined sports of basketball, soccer and hockey.

Klax   Tengen   4 $8
The best way to describe this game is as a 3-D version of Tetris, and while very fun, it lacks the simplicity that made Tetris so popular.

Knight Rider   Acclaim   3 $4
Played from inside the car's "cockpit", this title has some very blocky graphics and features both racing and shooting.

Krazy Kreatures   AVE   5 $10
Involving the alignment and proper placement of different animals, this game of poor graphic quality can actually be addictive for a while, until frustration sets in.

Krion Conquest, The   Vic Tokai   5 $10
This platform game features some very nice character animation, but poor level design and bland backgrounds.

Krusty's Fun House   Acclaim   4 $5
An overhead action game featuring puzzle elements, this game is based on Krusty the Clown from The Simpsons.

Kung Fu   Nintendo   1 $1
Repetitive side scrolling fighting was fun in 1985, but has not aged well, as this game clearly shows.

Kung-Fu Heroes   Culture Brain   3 $0
A very addictive two player game, take the role of one of the kung-fu brothers to team up and clean level after level of increasing challenges. Viewed from the top down, this title does support single player action, but it isn't nearly as fun.

L'Empereur   Koei   5 $15
This is a nicely done two dimensional strategy game with multiple options and good replay value.

Laser Invasion   Ultra   5 $10
This is an average Zapper game that offers some difficult to hit targets and nice environments.

Last Action Hero   Sony Imagesoft   4 $8
Side scrolling fighting is featured in this movie translation, but the characters are too small and the control is too inaccurate to really enjoy the game

Last Ninja, The   Jaleco   4 $8
Based in Manhattan, this game has you take the role of a banished ninja in your adventure to find and destroy those responsible for your exile.

Last Starfighter, The   Mindscape   3 $4
Based on the amazing sci-fi film by the same name, this title does not feature the awesome graphics seen in the movie's

arcade game, but instead side scrolling shooter action.

Lee Trevino's Fighting Golf
     SNK   3 $3
This title suffers from poor course design, bad control and sub par graphics.

Legacy of the Wizard   Broderbund   3 $5
Interesting levels keep this side scrolling adventure game from becoming repetitive.

Legend of the Ghost Lion   Kemco   4 $8
Featuring classic turn based encounters and a standard overhead adventure mode, this game is far too often overlooked.

Legend of Kage   Taito   2 $5
Though popular upon its 1987 release, this side scrolling hack and slash adventure has lost a lot of its appeal due to uncreative levels.

Legend of Zelda, The (gold)
     Nintendo   1 $8
Possibly the most popular game of all time, you must take the role of Link in search for 8 pieces of the triforce so that they can be joined to give entrance to Death Mountain, the home of Ganon. Some very innovative features were introduced to overhead action gaming with this title, and even today this game remains one of the most played action RPG's on any console. And just when you think the game is beaten, a second quest will begin that features increased difficulty and completely new locations and labyrinth layouts. This title is a definite must-have for the NES.

Legend of Zelda, The (gray)
     Nintendo   3 $10
Sold toward the end of the NES lifecycle, this is identical in content to the gold version, but is made of gray plastic instead and features a new box design.

Legendary Wings   Capcom   3 $5
This 1988 vertical shooter features some interesting level designs that keep the game interesting, though the control seems a bit too touchy at times.

Legends of the Diamond   Bandai   4 $7
Very nice graphics are used in this 1992 baseball release, though control while on defense seems a bit complicated and often unresponsive.

Last Action Hero   **Lee Trevino's Fighting Golf**   **The Legend of Zelda**   **Life Force**

The Atari XEGS uses pastel colors for its function buttons.

NES

The Lone Ranger

The Magic of Scheherazade

Magician

MagMax

Lemmings	Sunsoft	4	$8

A platform based puzzle game, save as many lemmings as you can with the use of specially skilled working lemmings. Fun and addicting, there are plenty of levels to keep you entertained.

Lethal Weapon	Ocean	5	$10

This side scrolling shooter features areas from multiple installments of the movie, not just the first one, keeping an otherwise average game enjoyable.

Life Force	Konami	2	$5

A great side scrolling space shooter, this title offers some nice graphics and very good control.

Linus Spacehead's Cosmic Crusade

	Camerica	4	$8

Pastel colors and nicely designed areas are used in this unique graphic adventure, using multiple views instead of the typically stagnate first-person view.

Little League Baseball Championship Series

	SNK	4	$8

Really, with the graphical capabilities of the NES, doesn't it seem a bit odd to try and make a game that can actually be distinguished from any other baseball game? A nice title nonetheless, there is little that separates this game from any other.

Little Mermaid, The	Capcom	3	$4

Little Nemo: The Dream Master

	Capcom	3	$5

There are some really nice graphic and lighting effects in this side scrolling adventure.

Little Ninja Brothers	Culture Brain	4	$8

Played much like Kung-Fu Heroes, this title offers a more expansive scope of play and is more of an adventure than a simple action game.

Little Samson	Taito	6	$20

Great graphics and level design compliment the solid control in this hard to find and very fun platform game.

Lode Runner	Broderbund	3	$5

Simple graphics and game play are featured in this remake of the Apple II classic.

Lone Ranger, The	Konami	4	$7

Play the masked man in this title featuring various game play modes, including enjoyable overhead adventure type areas.

Loopz	Mindscape	5	$12

This is a simple but entertaining puzzle game, and for a change it isn't just another Tetris clone.

Low G Man: The Low Gravity Man

	Taxan	3	$4

This is a side scrolling adventure that offers the gimmick of being able to jump nearly twice the height of the typical game screen, opening many possibilities for new challenges and puzzles to be implemented into the levels.

Lunar Pool	FCI	3	$5

Offering various table sizes and shapes in this futuristic pool game keeps a classic game interesting.

M.C. Kids	Virgin	3	$5

The only thing that stands out about this game is the fact that it is a McDonald's restaurant advertisement wrapped up in a side scrolling platform game for the NES.

Mach Rider	Nintendo	3	$5

A forward scrolling motorcycle game, this title features various levels, each with a unique look and feel.

Mad Max	Mindscape	3	$5

Based on the movie, this title features driving combat scenarios where destruction of your enemy is the only goal.

Mafat Conspiracy, The	Vic Tokai	4	$8

The sequel to Golgo 13, this title lacks the appeal of the original and instead is replaced with the typical three life game style.

Magic Darts	Romstar	4	$8

Simply a game of darts, it is really hard to go wrong with something like this, though you can hardly get the feel for a game of darts by pressing buttons. This title is nice, but it is much easier just to set up a real dart board.

Magic Johnson's Fast Break

	Tradewest	3	$3

Released in 1990, this is one of several two on two basketball games for the NES with few unique features to distinguish it from others.

Magic of Scheherazade, The

	Culture Brain	4	$8

A company known as Songbird is still producing new games for the Atari Jaguar and the Atari Lynx.

The unpronounceable name of this game is part of the reason it never caught on, though this 1990 title features some appeal considering its similarities to the Legend of Zelda and its overhead action/adventure RPG style.

Magician   Taxan   5 $10
This is a magical side scrolling action/adventure RPG with some nice graphical effects and decent control, though some of the action sequences seem to falter a bit due to slow reaction time on the part of the character, not the player.

MagMax   FCI   3 $4
This side scrolling vehicle shooter is hardly anything new, though instead of simply flying in space, you are actually on the surface of the planet.

Major League Baseball   LJN   1 $2
For a 1988 release, this game isn't really all that bad, though there are better baseball games for the NES.

Maniac Mansion   Jaleco   3 $10
Taking on a nearly cult status, this is a graphic adventure in which you choose one of several characters to explore the mansion. Don't forget to microwave any small mammals you come across!

Mappy-Land   Taxan   4 $8
Graphically dismal and offering little above other side scrolling platform games, this game just isn't much fun to play.

Marble Madness   Milton Bradley   3 $8
Control the path of a rolling marble through tunnels, over ramps, around holes and complete difficult challenges in this must-have title. Neither amazingly complex in concept or execution, the simple fact that this title's makers remembered that games were supposed to be fun makes this one of the best games available for the NES.

Mario Brothers   Nintendo   3 $5
Not to be confused with SMB, this is a port of the Atari VCS game.

Mario is Missing!   Mindscape   5 $10
Designed as an educational title, this game was developed by Radical Entertainment, not Nintendo. Featuring Super Mario World type graphics, this should still be a bit entertaining, though not nearly as much as other Mario titles.

Mario's Time Machine   Mindscape   6 $15
More education from Mario, this title (also developed by Radical Entertainment) is meant to help teach about history in addition to being fun.

Master Chu and the Drunkard Hu
    Color Dreams   4 $8
One of Color Dreams' worst entries, this title offers decent graphics but completely frustrating graphics and bland level design.

Maxi-15   AVE   7 $30
Fifteen games (bad games) in one, this AVE release is becoming more difficult to find.

MechaNized Attack   SNK   3 $4
This Zapper title offers some nice graphics and interesting level design.

Mega Man   Capcom   4 $18
Starting a series that would become this popular was something that Capcom was doubtful to expect. The unique experience found in this platform adventure is amazing and still a favorite among many gamers.

Mega Man 2   Capcom   2 $15
Considered the best in the series by many, once you beat Woodman, you're nearly unstopable!

Mega Man 3   Capcom   3 $10
Improvements and expansions continue throughout the series, each becoming more graphically tuned, though with the success of the second installment, it was very difficult to actually improve much else.

Mega Man 4   Capcom   4 $12

Mega Man 5   Capcom   5 $15

Mega Man 6   Nintendo   5 $20
After Capcom had stopped releasing games for the NES, Nintendo stepped in to publish this game for them.

Menace Beach   Color Dreams   7 $20
This is a side scrolling skate board platform game that isn't nearly as good as T&C 2, but is still entertaining.

Mendel Palace   Hudson   4 $8
This is a fixed screen puzzle game featuring the most basic of

| Mappy-Land | Marble Madness | Mega Man 2 | Metal Fighter |

Certain Genesis games are larger than others, though the internals are identical to those of other carts.

| Metal Gear | Mig 29 Soviet Fighter | Mike Tyson's Punch-Out!! | Monopoly |

graphics, but addicting game play. Moving floor tiles will redirect the characters onscreen, which you must manipulate in order to clear each level of play.

Mermaids of Atlantis   AVE   6 $20
This is an edited version of Bubble Bath Babes that doesn't feature any nudity, but instead has mermaids. The game play is the same as BBB, though more options are now available.

Metal Fighter   Color Dreams   4 $8

Metal Gear   Ultra   1 $10
What would later become a game franchise that captured the imagination of the world, this is the game that started it all (in the U.S.) While the original was released on the MSX system in Japan, American gamers were treated with an often comically translated version. Stealth is emphasized instead of force, cunning and tactical thinking are necessary to complete this masterpiece of a game.

Metal Mech   Jaleco   4 $8
An early mech game, this title is actually a side scrolling platform game.

Metal Storm   Irem   4 $8
Fly through colorful levels in this horizontally scrolling shooter as you face wave after wave of oncoming enemies.

Metroid   Nintendo   1 $10
Considered by many to be the best platform game on the NES, this game has you take the role of Samus as she clears stage after stage in this amazing futuristic shooter.

Michael Andretti's World GP
    American Sammy   3 $5
Fourteen real F-1 racers are featured in this otherwise standard Grand Prix racer.

Mickey Mousecapade   Capcom   3 $5
A side scrolling platform game, this one is surprisingly disappointing due to poor level design and substandard graphics.

Mickey's Adventures in Numberland
    Hi-Tech Expressions   5 $10
Learn about numbers with the help of Mickey in this edutainment title staring the famous rat.

Mickey's Safari in Letterland
    Hi-Tech Expressions   5 $10

The rat is back, and this time to teach children about letters. Yay!

Micro Machines   Camerica   5 $15
This is just an awesome overhead track racer. Based around the concept of those tiny toy cars everyone used to buy during the late 1980's, this game features both nice graphics and control, and stands out as one of the most enjoyable racers for the NES.

Mig 29 Soviet Fighter   Camerica   4 $8
This is a vertically scrolling shooter that features really nice box art but substandard in-game graphics.

Might & Magic: Secret of the Inner Sanctum
    American Sammy   6 $18
Mighty Bomb Jack   Tecmo   4 $8
This is a platform game, though not a side scrolling one, in which you must clear each level of the pyramid before he can progress to the next in his search for points, coins and bombs.

Mighty Final Fight   Capcom   5 $10
A colorful yet graphically challenged side scrolling fighting game, this should be entertaining, but is hardly on par with those found on the next generation of systems.

Mike Tyson's Punch-Out!!   Nintendo   2 $8
One of the best games for the system, this is an absolute must-have. Play as Mac in your rise through the ranks in this over-the-shoulder boxing game. Featuring very unique opponents, you must learn their patters and habits in order to best them in this boxing game. And finally, face off against the girlie-voiced ear biter himself, Iron Mike.

Millipede   HAL America   4 $8
The classic comes to the NES, with nice graphics and solid control.

Milon's Secret Castle   Hudson   2 $4
This is a standard side scrolling platform game with occasionally nice graphics and easy control.

Mission Cobra   Bunch   4 $8
The sparse levels make this vertically scrolling shooter abysmal.

Mission: Impossible   Ultra   3 $5
This is an overhead action game based loosely on the TV series, not the movie.

A SNES was dropped from a height of 22 feet onto cement. While the case shattered, the system still functioned! Don't try this though!

Monopoly Parker Brothers 3 $5
The board game comes to the NES in a very good way. Nice graphics and the fun of the original are all wrapped up in a package that doesn't allow you to accidentally swallow a pewter top hat and F-1 car while trying to impress friends.

Monster in My Pocket Konami 4 $8
A fun side scroller, not much really stands out about this game except the fact that it is based on the toy line from 1991.

Monster Party Bandai 3 $7
Travel through 8 dark levels in this side scrolling Dark World, armed only with your baseball bat.

Monster Truck Rally INTV 5 $10
A shifting isometric track view and some very nice graphics help this title stand out, as does the fact that it is published and developed by the company that was making the Intellivision system.

Moon Ranger Bunch Games 3 $5
This is a typical futuristic side scrolling shooter game. Though the backgrounds can occasionally look nice, nothing really stands out about the average game play and control.

Motor City Patrol Matchbox 4 $8
An overhead driving game that offers solid control and some interesting city streets to drive down, monotony will eventually set in due to a lack of variation and any real challenge.

Ms. Pac-Man Namco 7 $25
One of the most loved arcade games of all time comes to the NES true to form from Namco.

Ms. Pac-Man Tengen 5 $20
Tengen decided to improve a classic, but instead of butchering the original, they left the arcade version intact as one of the many options available. This version offers maze variation options, as well as speed and difficulty options.

M.U.L.E. Mindscape 3 $8
Multiple Use Labor Elements, or "M.U.L.E." is an economic game set in the future that deals with space mining farming and energy production. If you enjoy economic theory and think that the Laffer Curve is a good party theme, then this title might be enjoyable.

Muppet Adventure: Chaos at the Carnival
  Hi-Tech Expressions 4 $8

M.U.S.C.L.E. Bandai 3 $3
A simple wrestling game, this title is based on those strange orange rubber toys that were popular for a while in the U.S.

Mutant Virus, The American Softworks 5 $8
Carefully placed shots will keep the virus in the center of the room from growing outside of its allotted area, but enough misses will soon see not only the end of level advancement, but your death as well.

Mystery Quest Taxan 3 $5
Generic level design and graphical style make this bland side scrolling platform boring, even for this genre.

NARC Acclaim 3 $4
This side scrolling shooter was actually noted for its excessive violence after its 1990 release.

NES Open Tournament Golf
  Nintendo 3 $4
Simple and fun gameplay make this an entertaining golf game, even for very young gamers.

NES Play Action Football Nintendo 2 $3
Stick with Tecmo Bowl, even over this nice 1990 release from Nintendo.

NFL Football LJN 2 $4
Standard graphics and easy controls make this a simple game to play, yet it can't compete with Tecmo Bowl's appeal.

Nigel Mansell's World Championship Racing
  GameTek 5 $10
Probably the best F-1 racing game for the NES, this title is played from within the car's cockpit and gives a decent feeling of speed.

Nightmare on Elm Street, A
  LJN 3 $5
Graphically dark and based on the series of horror movies, this title worried parents a bit when it was released, but bland platform action quickly showed it to be just another of so many side scrolling adventure games.

Nightshade Ultra 3 $5
A side view graphic adventure dealing with a dark criminal investigation, this title is often overlooked, but should definitely be played by both mystery fans and those who enjoy graphic ad-

Ms. Pac-Man (Tengen)

Mystery Quest

NES Play Action Football   Nightshade

The Nintendo 64 was originally going to be named the Ultra 64.

North and South   Operation Secret Storm   Operation Wolf   Pac-Man

ventures.

Ninja Crusaders   American Sammy   4 $7
A side scrolling fighting game featuring wave after wave of enemies, this just shows that the word "ninja" was all too popular in
the late 1980's. Not a very good game at all, this title suffers
from major controller inaccuracies.

Ninja Gaiden   Tecmo   1 $5
Introducing the moving still frame cut scene, this title stands out
in history for other reasons as well, namely the awesome side
scrolling adventure with great control and attacks.

Ninja Gaiden II: The Dark Sword of Chaos
                        Tecmo   3 $7
Expanding its popularity, this series would continue to grow with
quality games such as this title.

Ninja Gaiden III: The Ancient Ship of Doom
                        Tecmo   3 $7
Coming to a culmination with the introduction of this title, the
game had never looked better, nor featured such solid control
and enthralling music.

Ninja Kid   Bandai   3 $5
Resembling a SMB game instead of that of a Ninja's world, this
title offers a lot of platform jumping, even for a side scrolling
adventure.

Nintendo World Championships 1990 (Gold)
                        Nintendo   10 $5500
26 of these carts were made and given to winners of a Nintendo
Power contest. Aside from the gold color of the cart and the
label itself, this game is identical to the gray version listed below. By far, this is the rarest and most expensive NES game
every distributed.

Nintendo World Championships 1990 (Gray)
                        Nintendo   10 $1800
Known as the NWC cart, only 90 of the gray version were ever
made. These were given to finalists in the 1990 Nintendo World
Championships and feature SMB, Rad Racer and Tetris. The
game itself has a black and white label and a "dip switch" on the
top used for disabling the timer function that would limit game
play to 6 minutes. The games had different rules than those
normally found within the games however. SMB requires simply
that 50 coins be collected, at which point the game will switch to
Rad Racer. This title requires that the first level be completed
before moving on to Tetris, which actually does play like the

normal version, with the exception of the time limit (controlled by
the dip switch).

Nintendo World Cup   Nintendo   3 $4
A nice soccer game with large characters and solid control, this
is one of the better in the genre.

Nobunaga's Ambition   Koei   3 $7
This awesome strategy game is one of the best in the genre for
the NES, and even allows you to sell your wives.

Nobunaga's Ambition II   Koei   6 $15
Both a continuation and an improvement, this title is both collectable and enjoyable.

North and South   Seika   5 $10
This is a hard to find strategy game based on the Civil War and
can often become very complicated for those uninitiated to strategy games.

Operation Secret Storm   Color Dreams   6 $10
Shoddy graphics are used in this side scrolling fighting game.

Operation Wolf   Taito   1 $4
Side scrolling characters necessitate a nice shot to their head in
this Zapper game. Changing environments and often difficult
boss characters make this a great port of the arcade title.
Though it isn't quite the same without a recoiling Uzi in your
hands, as in the arcade version, this title shouldn't be missed by
anyone looking to relive a few hours of their childhood.

Orb-3D   Hi-Tech Expressions   3 $5
One of the truly unique puzzle games for the NES, an interesting 3-D concept and challenging game play make this a fun title.

Othello   Acclaim   3 $5
An ancient game is brought into the electronic age without the
need to keep a bunch of black and white pebbles laying around
the living room. Now available on nearly every PC in the world,
this game holds little interest for anyone other than NES collectors.

Overlord   Virgin   4 $8
Fight against the evil Rom in this strategy game with action
elements.

P'radikus Conflict   Color Dreams   4 $8
A space shooter done much in the same fashion of Space War!,
but with notably improved graphics, though still very simple.

116

Pac-Man   Namco   4 $12
One of the most known names in video game history is brought to the NES intact.

Pac-Man   Tengen   4 $15
Available in both licensed and unlicensed form, this title is better than the Namco version due to Tengen's attention to detail and various options.

Pac-Mania   Tengen   6 $25
A change in camera angle and pseudo 3-D effects accompany Pac-Man in this 1991 release from Tengen, in addition to a new ghost named Funky.

Palamedes   Hot-B   5 $10
A very fun puzzle game featuring the use of dominos and their speedy but accurate placement.

Panic Restaurant   Taito   4 $8
Fill the shoes of Cookie the Chef as he fights off crazed food that has come to life in this side scrolling adventure game.

Paperboy   Mindscape   2 $5
An arcade favorite, this title makes a decent appearance on the NES, though not nearly as detailed as the arcade version.

Paperboy 2   Mindscape   4 $8
Updates to the original and the same control style and accuracy make this a fun title to own if you liked the first installment.

Peek-A-Boo Poker   Panesian   9 $150
One of the three Panesian releases, this title is highly sought after and is extremely difficult to find. Featuring a simple poker game and the ability to see partially nude women, this game never saw any real mainstream press after its 1991 release, unless it was to criticize the game.

Pesterminator   Color Dreams   4 $8
This is a bad side scrolling platform game with jagged graphics and poor control.

Peter Pan & the Pirates   T*HQ   4 $8

Phantom Fighter   FCI   3 $5
Very choppy movements make the control in this game difficult to get used to, and the graphics and sound are average at best.

Pictionary: The Game of Video Quick Draw

LJN   4 $8
The classic board game is included in this title as are four additional miniature games, making for a nice party game among older gamers.

Pinball   Nintendo   2 $4
Simple graphics are fine for this 1985 release since it offers accurate control.

Pinball Quest   Jaleco   4 $8
Play through six levels (pinball machines) in order to save the Princess Bali in this fun pinball simulation.

Pinbot   Nintendo   4 $8
Actually a conversion of the pinball machine by the same name, this is a relatively good version with solid control and good ball physics.

Pipe Dream   Bullet Proof   5 $12
Viewed from the top down, this is a Tetris-like game viewed from a different angle. You must find the proper configuration of the pipe pieces in order to clear each stage.

Pirates!   Ultra   5 $10
Take the side of the pirates in sea battles, sea to land battles and even hand to hand battles in this action/adventure RPG.

Platoon   Sunsoft   2 $5
Based on the war movie by the same name, this title features one of the most memorable first levels in game history, and even some first-person tunnel and open field fire fights. A very fun game if you're able to find your way past the first stage.

Pool of Radiance   FCI   5 $12
While the graphics are often found to be lacking, a solid story and game play allow this first person RPG to stand out as one of the better titles on the NES. Also available for the C64, the NES simply lacked the capability of producing the same sound quality, but made a good attempt.

Popeye   Nintendo   3 $5
This is a static screen platform game played much in the same fashion as Mario Brothers (not SMB).

P.O.W. – Prisoners of War   SNK   2 $4
Unlike most other side scrolling fighting shooter games, this one has a nice character of its own and is very enjoyable. Later, games like Bloody Wolf would imitate this style.

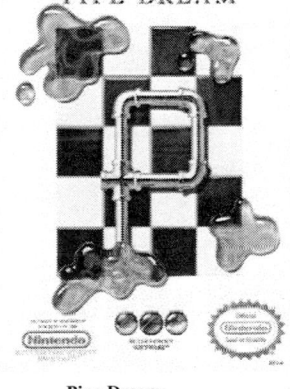

Peek-A-Boo Poker   Pipe Dream   Platoon   Power Punch II

While the Atari 7800 had several light gun games, no light gun was ever made specifically for the system.

NES

Pyramid

Quattro Adventure

Rad Racer

Rainbow Islands

Power Blade   Taito   3 $5
Use a special boomerang for your main weapon in this futuristic side scrolling shooter. With nice graphics and control, this title is fun, even for those burned out on platform games.

Power Blade 2   Taito   4 $8
A small step backward, this title's levels are much darker and take away a portion of the enjoyment of the first title's superior graphics.

Power Punch II   American Softworks   4 $8
This 1992 boxing release has inexcusably bad graphics and horrible control.

Predator   Activision   3 $4
This platform game bears no resemblance to the movie and features levels and characters so dark it is often difficult to properly control the onscreen action.

Prince of Persia   Virgin   4 $8
The popular platform makes a nice appearance on the NES with good graphical style, though the control seems a bit sluggish.

Princess Tomato in the Salad Kingdom
    Hudson   5 $10
This is a first-person graphic adventure with an odd story line and nice graphics.

Pro Sport Hockey   Jaleco   5 $10

Pro Wrestling   Nintendo   1 $3
A very early and very basic title, this 1987 release really offers no special features, but simply solid control.

Punch-Out!!   Nintendo   3 $8
This is the same game as "Mike Tyson's Punch-Out!!", but features Mr. Dream instead of Mike.

Punisher, The   LJN   4 $8
This 1991 release tried to capitalize on the popularity of The Punisher at that time, but even then it was seen as a bad platform game with poor control.

Puss 'n Boots: Pero's Great Adventure
    Electro Brain   4 $7
Use multiple weapons and vehicles to get through seven stages of this platform game, though how a cat can drive is beyond me. Perhaps he knows Toonces.

Puzzle   AVE   5 $10
This is basically one of those 16-square, 15 piece puzzles where the pieces must be rearranged to form pictures such as The Statue of Liberty and a tiger.

Puzznic   Taito   6 $15
This 1990 release is actually a port of the arcade puzzle game, and does a nice job of reproducing the quality of the original.

Pyramid   AVE   5 $10
A sort of Tetris copy, this title features very simplistic graphics, even for the falling block genre. It is still fun and addicting, though it is more difficult to find than Tetris.

Q*Bert   Ultra   4 $7
That bouncing orange straw faced guy named Q*Bert comes to the NES in a pretty good translation. The graphics are nice and it retains the feel of the original.

Qix   Taito   7 $20
A very popular puzzle game, you must complete the construction of shapes without making contact with a virus, watch your time, clear the levels, and avoid working yourself into a spiral.

Quattro Adventure   Camerica   4 $7
This title features Boomerang Kid, Linus Spacehead, Super Robin Hood and Treasure Island Dizzy.

Quattro Arcade   Camerica   6 $12
This title features CJ's Elephant Antics, F16 Renegade, Go! Dizzy Go! and Stunt Buggies.

Quattro Sports   Camerica   3 $5
This title features Baseball Pros, BMX Simulator, Pro Tennis and Soccer Simulator.

Race America   Absolute   6 $12
This is a side view racing game with repetitive game play.

Racket Attack   Jaleco   3 $4
The distant view of the court makes this tennis title difficult to play.

Rad Racer   Nintendo   2 $4
Very similar in appearance and feel to Out Run, this title offers the choice of two cars and is viewed from inside the cockpit.

Rad Racer II   Square   4 $8
Slightly improved graphics and the fact that the same successful

Platoon for the NES features a "morale" meter at the bottom of the screen.

game design was kept from the first game ensured that this 1990 release would be a success.

Rad Racket Deluxe Tennis II   AVE   6 $15
This is an average tennis game with decent graphics for an AVE cart, though control could have certainly been improved since the characters seem to move very slowly at times.

Raid 2020   Color Dreams   3 $5
Featuring a unique graphical effect that causes all the characters to appear to have real depth, this Color Dreams title is surprisingly good looking, though full of control problems.

Raid on Bungeling Bay   Broderbund   4 $8
Destroy the ultimate weapon being created at Bungling bay with a variety of weapons in this overhead shooting action game.

Rainbow Islands   Taito   5 $12
Help Bubby through various levels by creating and climbing rainbows in an attempt to defeat Krabo.

Rally Bike   Romstar   5 $10
A vertical racer in the same spirit as Spy Hunter, this game features a motorcycle for the entire game.

Rambo   Acclaim   2 $3
I'm almost certain that Rambo never wore flaming red pants in any of the movies, but he sure does in this side scrolling platform game. Surprisingly, this title isn't all that bad, and actually has some high points such as solid control and nice backgrounds. "Rambo...what mean expendable?"

Rampage   Data East   3 $5
Take the role of one of two monsters in your quest to cause the most property damage. As an added bonus, you get to eat people right out of the buildings you are climbing on. Inspired by the building climbing scene in King Kong, this game is a good stress reliever and will find you causing death and destruction in every imaginable city.

Rampart   Jaleco   4 $8
This 1992 release is a port of the arcade original and features puzzle like strategy decision based around maintaining defenses for your castle and proper placement of weaponry. A unique idea that offers a lot of fun, this title is available for numerous systems.

RBI Baseball   Tengen   2 $4
Made in both licensed and unlicensed forms, this 1987 release features comical looking players and control that feels a bit clumsy.

RBI Baseball 2   Tengen   2 $4
Three years after the first installment, this title shows great graphical improvement as well as a much more solid control element.

RBI Baseball 3   Tengen   3 $5
Improvements continued, though as a tradeoff for these better looking graphics, you're going to have to be willing to accept seemingly reduced defensive control. The players just don't move right and frustration can set in quickly trying to chase after a ball that isn't even moving.

R.C. Pro-AM   Nintendo   2 $3
This overhead curving track racing game offers simple control and a lot of replay.

R.C. Pro-Am II   Tradewest   5 $10
Released four years after the first version, this title features more of the same fun game play and cleaner looking edges on all of the graphics, making it look much sharper.

Remote Control   Hi-Tech Expressions   3 $4
A game show based on the short lived MTV program, this title should be proof that a station named "Music Television" should at least, on occasion, play music.

Ren & Stimpy Show: Buckaroo$, The   T*HQ   4 $8
This side scrolling shooter/platform game features mundane levels, but fun game play.

Renegade   Taito   2 $4
In this street fighting melee, you simply fight everyone you come across in areas such as the subway station and narrow alleys.

Rescue: The Embassy Mission   Seika   3 $5
Rescue hostages in the embassy taken prisoner by terrorists via several types of game play in this title that emphasizes both stealth and firepower.

Ring King   Data East   3 $4
Released in 1987, this title features small characters and poor control.

Rampage   R.C. Pro-AM   River City Ransom   RoadBlasters

Soccer is the most common sport portrayed in European video games.

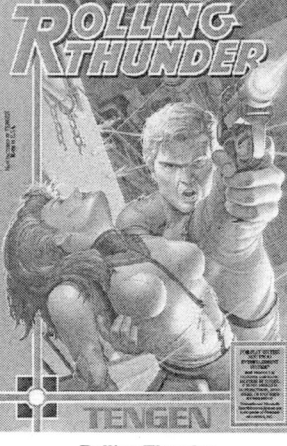

Robin Hood: Prince of Thieves   The Rocketeer   Rolling Thunder   Rygar

River City Ransom   American Technos   3 $8
This side scrolling fighting game is one of the most popular in the genre for the NES and often demands a high price.

Road Runner   Tengen   5 $10
Try and avoid being caught by Wile E. Coyote as he chases you through multiple levels using all sorts of gadgets to level the playing ground.

RoadBlasters   Mindscape   3 $5
Fifty levels and various weapons highlight this racing combat title, ported from the arcade classic.

Robin Hood: Prince of Thieves
**   Virgin   3 $5**
An overhead action/adventure RPG, this title is loosely based on the 1991 movie and features the silhouette of Kevin Costner on the cover.

RoboCop   Data East   2 $4
Unrefined looking graphics scar an otherwise enjoyable platform shooting game based on the movie.

RoboCop 2   Data East   3 $5
With great improvements to the graphics in this installment, this is the best in the series.

RoboCop 3   Ocean   4 $8
Graphically much darker than the other two titles, this game also suffers from sluggish control and is the worst in the series.

Robodemons   Color Dreams   4 $8
This horizontally scrolling shooter features very basic levels and enemies that attack in predictable patters, making this an unenjoyable title.

RoboWarrior   Jaleco   2 $3
With an overhead view similar to the action scenes in Blaster Master, this game is enjoyable and easy to control, all while maintaining a good level of difficulty.

Rock 'n Ball   NTVIC   4 $8
A simple pinball simulation, this title features seven separate tables, though most are relatively simple.

Rocket Ranger   Seika   3 $5
Fight your way through various levels in search of parts that you need for the construction of your rocket pack so that you can confront the invading alien force known as the Leutonians.

Rocketeer, The   Bandai   3 $4
Based on the movie of the same name, this title features side scrolling fighting action with solid control and some unique level designs.

Rockin' Kats   Atlus   4 $8
Simple levels and uninspired graphics are common in this game, but it remains fun after a little practice using your extendable boxing glove.

Roger Clemens' MVP Baseball
**   LJN   3 $4**
Some very nice pseudo 3-D graphics and nice camera angles add a real sense of depth to this complex baseball simulation.

Rollerball   HAL America   4 $8
One of many pinball simulations on the NES, this title offers solid control, though the graphics are lacking for a title released in 1990.

Rollerblade Racer   Hi-Tech Expressions   5 $10
Race through the streets in this rollerblade title that unfortunately has a very sensitive control scheme, causing many unnecessary falls.

Rollergames   Ultra   3 $5
Try to infiltrate V.I.P.E.R. headquarters by putting on a pair of roller skates and racing through multi-directional streets in this entertaining, yet occasionally monotonous game.

Rolling Thunder   Tengen   3 $4
Fight through ten levels of enemies in an attempt to rescue a fellow Rolling Thunder agent named Leila in this side scrolling action shooter. The characters within this game are uncharacteristically thin, obviously an over anxious attempt to make them look more lifelike, unlike other games with chubby characters when this game was released in 1989.

Romance of the Three Kingdoms
**   Koei   3 $8**
This intricate strategy RPG takes place in ancient China and remains a favorite of retro-gamers.

Romance of the Three Kindoms II
**   Koei   5 $15**
Released in 1991, two years after the first installment, this title features more complex strategy and a continuing story line.

There are more NES clone systems than any other type.

Roundball: 2 on 2 Challenge
Mindscape 4 $8
Ridiculously simple graphics make this title look like something from the Atari 5200, hardly a 1992 NES release.

Rush 'n Attack Konami 2 $4
Really nice backgrounds liven up this side scrolling fighting arcade port, released in 1987 when the world was still scared of the Russian threat.

Rygar Tecmo 2 $5
Some of the most creative levels and very solid game play make this side scrolling platform game really stand out in the genre, as well as making it a must-have for the NES.

Ryne Sandberg Plays Bases Loaded 3
Jaleco 2 $4
More graphical improvements and game play updates mark this installment's entry to the NES library. Ryne Sandberg's name was added to the title in an attempt to improve lagging sales of the series.

S.C.A.T. Special Cybernetic Attack Team
Natsume 3 $5
A very good side scrolling platform shooter, this graphically dark adventure is a lot of fun

Secret Scout Color Dreams 7 $20
A typical Color Dreams platform game, this title features less than stellar graphics and questionable control.

Section Z Capcom 2 $4
This side scrolling shooter features some very nice level design and a vibrant color pallet.

Seicross FCI 2 $4
A very unique graphical style helps this side scrolling motorcycle combat racer different from anything else on the NES.

Sesame Street 123 Hi-Tech Expressions 3 $3
A child's game that teaches numbers with the popular Sesame Street characters.

Sesame Street ABC Hi-Tech Expressions 3 $3
More of the same with letters.

Sesame Street ABC/123
Hi-Tech Expressions 5 $10
After they milked you for two carts, they sell the more economi-

cal version containing both games.

Sesame Street: Big Bird's Hide & Speak
Hi-Tech Expressions 4 $8
This child's game features Big Bird and several other characters from the TV series.

Sesame Street: Countdown
Hi-Tech Expressions 5 $10
This edutainment title featuring characters from the TV series to teach children basic math skills.

Shadow of the Ninja Natsume 4 $8
A very dark platform game, this title features a nice combination of dark levels and very interesting background images.

Shadowgate Seika 3 $7
An outstanding first-person graphic adventure, this title features both a great story line and intuitive controls.

Shatterhand Jaleco 3 $4
Take the role of Hermann as you fight through seven levels of side scrolling action in an attempt to defeat the organization known as Metal Command.

Shingen the Ruler Hot-B 4 $8
This strategy game takes place in feudal Japan and offers a good story line and complex options.

Shinobi Tengen 3 $5
The ever popular Ninja makes an appearance on the NES in this side scrolling platform game. The debate rages on as to which title is better, this title or Ninja Gaiden, though both are definitely worth owning.

Shockwave AGC 4 $8
A nice puzzle game from American Game Cartridges with often addicting game play, though not on the same level as Tetris.

Shooting Range Bandai 4 $8
This Zapper title is set in a carnival type atmosphere with a shooting range set up for winning prizes, but small targets and uninteresting variety keep this title from standing out.

Short Order/Egg-Splode! Nintendo 5 $10
Two games on one cartridge, this Powerpad only title is the only one made by Nintendo and offers variety not seen in other games such as Dance Aerobics.

Shingen the Ruler

Short Order/Egg-Splode!

Side Pocket

Silent Assault

The Famicom features controllers that cannot be detached from the system.

Skull & Crossbones

SkyKid

Smash TV

Solar Jetman: Hunt for the Golden Warship

Side Picket   **Data East**   4 $8
An overhead perspective is used in this 1987 release with decent geometry and simple controls, though a lack of variety reduce replay value.

Silent Assault   **Color Dreams**   4 $8
Extremely dark graphics and simple graphics are featured in this, another sub par Color Dreams side scrolling shooter.

Silent Service   **Ultra**   2 $4
Take control of a submarine in this simulation featuring a large area of the ocean to maneuver in.

Silkworm   **American Sammy**   3 $4
This 1990 helicopter game features simple side scrolling action and some very simple graphics.

Silver Surfer   **Virgin**   3 $5
Take control of the comic book hero in this overhead adventure that features some very sharp and creative level designs.

Simpsons: Bartman Meets Radioactive Man, The
           Acclaim   4 $8
Simply put, the poor control of this game ruins what should have been a very entertaining title. Side scrolling levels featuring some nice colors and detail are showcased in this otherwise disappointing title.

Simspons: Bart vs. the Space Mutants, The
           Acclaim   2 $4
This, the best of the Simpsons titles on the NES, is a side scrolling adventure with five levels in which you must stop invading Space Mutants.

Simpsons: Bart vs. the World, The
           Acclaim   3 $5
Featuring several types of game play, this title matches Bart against Mr. Burns and his evil henchmen. The control is still a bit lacking, though noticeably better than Bartman Meets Radioactive Man.

Skate or Die   **Ultra**   1 $4
With several types of skateboarding events to compete in, this title lacks great graphics, but more than makes up for it with fun levels and challenging control. Also, seeing the skate shop owner with his blue mohawk is reason enough to play the game.

Skate or Die 2: The Search for Double Trouble
           EA   4 $8

A side scrolling platform game, this title adds the feature of a story in which you are trying to earn money to build a new half-pipe and the permit to build it.

Ski or Die   **Ultra**   3 $5
Choose different events in this snowboard version of the popular Skate or Die series including the halfpipe and trick slope.

Skull & Crossbones   **Tengen**   4 $8
Fight your way through various levels in this Pirate inspired side scrolling fighting game.

Sky Shark   **Taito**   2 $4
A vertical airplane shooter, Sky Shark is often considered to have very responsive control and addictive game play, though the graphics are very remedial and resemble something that might be seen on an Intellivision.

SkyKid   **Sunsoft**   4 $8
This side scrolling airplane shooter sports very basic graphics, but controls nicely, making it moderately entertaining.

Slalom   **Nintendo**   3 $5
A 1986 release, this title really doesn't demonstrate what the NES is capable of, and seemingly unfair control makes this game frustrating.

Smash TV   **Acclaim**   3 $4
Pick up various weapons to defend yourself with in this futuristic game show in which the only goal is to survive.

Snake Rattle 'n Roll   **Nintendo**   3 $5
Play the role of a snake moving through isometric levels featuring very nice colors and sharp graphics. Eat enough balls and you will gain the required amount of weight to tip the scales and progress to the next level.

Snake's Revenge   **Ultra**   3 $5
This game simply does not live up to the Metal Gear name, and as such was officially dropped form the chronology of the Metal Gear saga...though the story line in Metal Gear Solid 2 makes the most recent installment equally embarrassing for Hideo Kojima. Did anyone other than "gaming snobs" even claim to understand that game's (or should I say movie's) plot? Way to ruin an otherwise awesome game.

Snoopy's Silly Sports Spectacular
           Kemco   4 $8
This title not only features the popular Peanuts character and

The first game to feature openly gay characters was Fear Effect for the PSX. They were lesbians.

some of his friends, but also includes several entertaining events such as a sack race and plate balancing.

Snow Brothers   Capcom   5 $12
A fun combat game similar in style to Mario Brothers (not SMB), with a boss character after every 10 levels. Fun graphics and responsive control make this a very fun game to play, especially with a friend.

Soccer   Nintendo   1 $3
Easy-to-learn controls and basic game play are part of what make this game enjoyable, but the lack of any complex strategy may make it less fun for hardcore fans of the sport.

Solar Jetman: Hunt for the Golden Warship
                        Tradewest   3 $4
This is a nice side scrolling space shooter with numerous enemies and challenging levels.

Solitaire   AVE   7 $20
Play the classic card game on your NES, though why a game this simple was made for a system as advanced as the NES is a mystery.

Solomon's Key   Tecmo   3 $5
This is an overhead action puzzle game that is both addicting and frustrating, but it will certainly demand a few hours of your time once you start a game.

Solstice   Sony Imagesoft   2 $4
This action/adventure game features an isometric view and very solid control to complement the nice graphical style.

Space Shuttle Project   Absolute   5 $12
A space shuttle maintenance title of sorts, this game is somewhat of a simulation that tasks you with keeping the shuttle safe and functioning seamlessly.

Spelunker   Broderbund   3 $4
Explore deep and dark caves in your search for treasure in this entertaining platform game.

Spider-Man: Return of the Sinister Six
                        LJN   4 $8
Take control of Spidey in this side scrolling platform game in an attempt to rid the world of some of the most sinister villians.

Spiritual Warfare   Wisdom Tree   4 $8
Best described as a Zelda clone with biblical overtones, this is

often considered to be the best of the Wisdom Tree games, and is also available for the Genesis.

Spot   Virgin   3 $4
This platform game features the once popular Spot character, straight off of 7-Up cans.

Spy Hunter   Sunsoft   2 $4
The classic vertically scrolling drive and shoot game looks nice and plays well on the NES.

Spy vs. Spy   Seika   3 $5
This game is criticized by many for simplistic game play and the fatal flaw that allows for guaranteed victory every time you play against the computer (by waiting for the CPU to leave the stage and punching him before he finishes...stealing his victory.) This title does offer some fun game play when played in two player mode however.

Sqoon   Irem   4 $8
An underwater adventure with graphics that closely resemble the water levels of SMB, this game is entertaining only for a little while, at which point it becomes tedious.

Stack-Up   Nintendo   6 $55*
Very difficult to find complete, this title used R.O.B. to stack blocks in tandem with the onscreen game. *Price includes complete set of blocks.

Stadium Events   Bandai   10 $350
Actual release numbers are unknown, though this is perhaps the rarest NES game ever produced. Test marketed the northeast U.S., and later renamed "Athletic World", Stadium Events is the crown jewel to any NES collector's collection. More common European versions are often available online, but the two can be easily distinguished with a simple glance. While the artwork in the same the U.S. version has a date on the bottom right corner of the box, while the European version has a letter (typically "B").

Stanley: The Search for Dr. Livingston
                        Electro Brain   4 $8
Travel to Africa in 1870 on your search for Dr. Livingston and to discover the answer to the mystery of the Lost Temple.

Star Force   Tecmo   3 $4
A vertical scrolling space shooter, this title is heavy on geometric shapes and full of various enemies that fill 24 levels of action.

Solomon's Key   Space Shuttle Project   Star Trek 25th Anniversary   Star Tropics: A Test of Human Courage

The character used to promote the Sega Saturn in Japan, Sega Man, was killed while deflecting a missile into outer space.

NES

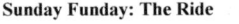

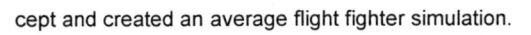

| Strider | Stunt Kids | Sunday Funday: The Ride | Super Glove Ball |

Star Soldier   Taxan   3 $4
Very similar in both control and appearance to Star Force, this title lacks the intricate levels that made Star Force so much fun to play.

Star Trek: 25th Anniversary
                          Ultra   4 $12
Disappointing for fans of the show, this title doesn't offer the same captive entertainment that made the show successful.

Star Trek: The Next Generation
                          Absolute   5 $20
As with seemingly every Star Trek console game, this title disappoints and fails to deliver the Star Trek feel.

Star Tropics: A Test of Human Courage
                          Nintendo   2 $4
Take the role of Mike Jones in this overhead action/adventure RPG that has generated a very large fan base. With game play similar to that of Zelda, and a good mixture of action and RPG elements, it is no wonder why this game is so good.

Star Voyager   Acclaim   3 $4
Both navigate and fight in this first-person space shooter. Added difficulty elements such as the necessity to refuel add to this game's appeal.

Star Wars   JVC   4 $12
With some of the best in-cockpit flight scenes available on the NES, this title quickly pleased fans of the movies, but continued on to offer adventure and vertically scrolling speeder levels as well.

Star Wars: The Empire Strikes Back
                          JVC   4 $12
Following the story line found within the second Star Wars movie (or is it the 5th?), you will play through various levels based on the different planets and locations seen in the corresponding movie.

Starship Hector   Hudson   3 $4
Falling between Star Soldier and Star Force in quality, this is a nice vertical space shooter offering the occasionally nice background and a good level of difficulty.

Stealth ATF   Activision   3 $5
Isn't the point of having the world's most sophisticated stealth aircraft to be able to fly a mission without getting into a dogfight? Evidently the makers of this game didn't understand that con-

cept and created an average flight fighter simulation.

Stinger   Konami   3 $5
This side scrolling shooter simply does not have the graphics necessary to make it enjoyable. And while graphics aren't everything in a game, average game play and a low level of difficulty simply aren't enough to compensate.

Street Cop   Bandai   5 $10
Track down and arrest offending criminals in this sub standard side scrolling action game.

Street Fighter 2010: The Final Fight
                          Capcom   4 $8
Whoever made the decision to star Ken in this side scrolling platform game is probably digging ditches somewhere in the bowels of Tokyo at this point. Having seemingly nothing to do with the actual Street Fighter series as we know it, this is a futuristic title that sees Ken placed in an enforcer role, basically killing everyone in site. The goal is to avenge the death of a colleague named Troy and to take back the technology that was stolen from him. Very difficult not only because of design, but also because Ken does not react quickly enough to controller inputs, causing unnecessary deaths. Fortunately, there is an unlimited supply of continues.

Strider   Capcom   2 $4
One of the best known and loved side scrolling platform games for the NES, Strider is best known in this game for having the trademark arc of light when he attacks. Nice levels and a dark element make this title stand out as being better than most, and a must-have for the NES.

Stunt Kids   Camerica   6 $18
A basic motocross game by Camerica, while not particularly bad, this title fails to impress, especially coming from the makers of the Game Genie.

Sunday Funday: The Ride   Wisdom Tree   6 $15
This is basically a hack of Color Dreams' Menace Beach, though being of a religious nature this title certainly doesn't show your girlfriend chained to a wall in shredded clothing. This title holds the title as the last NES game ever released in the U.S.

Super C   Konami   2 $5
Not quite what the original Contra was, this title has better control, graphics and sound, but lacks a non-quantifiable quality that make gamers prefer the original. Perhaps it is because the

Coke, Pepsi, and 7-Up have all had video games released featuring either their name in the title, or the soft drink's mascot.

only code for this game gives 10 lives instead of 30.

Super Cars — Electro Brain — 5 — $10
Driving some of the world's most expensive cars is a nice idea, but unfortunately the NES wasn't able to pull it off, as this racing game shows.

Super Dodge Ball — Sony Imagesoft — 3 — $5
Still a favorite of many, this title offers several playing fields for the unlikely international sport of dodge ball. Especially fun when you thump someone in the head with a fast mover, this title should be tried by everyone at least once.

Super Glove Ball — Mattel — 3 — $5
Designed to work well with the Power Glove, this is a sort of 3-D handball game and plays relatively well...unless you actually try to use the Power Glove.

Super Jeopardy! — GameTek — 4 — $8
Simply another installment to the series, this version was released in 1991.

Super Mario Bros. — Nintendo — 1 — $1
The game that changed the world, this side scrolling platform game was unlike anything any other home console had ever seen. Inventing a new genre, and rarely matched in creativity, this title remains a fun challenge for millions of gamers.

Super Mario Bros./Duck Hunt
Nintendo — 1 — $1
Simply a combination of SMB and Duck Hunt on one cartridge.

Super Mario Bros./Duck Hunt/World Class Track Meet
Nintendo — 1 — $3
The games in this compilation are identical to those found on their respective carts, and this cart was a pack-in title for the NES Power Pad set. And no, regardless of what people on internet auction sites might say, this is NOT a rare game.

Super Mario Bros. 2 — Nintendo — 1 — $3
With a choice of Mario, Luigi, or Princess Toadstool, this title grabbed the attention of the American public and remains a favorite of many gamers to date.

Super Mario Bros. 3 — Nintendo — 1 — $3
Perhaps the most common game ever made, estimates place production numbers above 17 million. Featured in the advertisement...um...movie titled The Wizard, this game is a very fun platform game improving upon the first two installments with additional features and power-ups. There is no excuse not to own this game.

Super Off-Road — Tradewest — 3 — $4

Super Pitfall — Activision — 3 — $5
It's certainly not super and it barely qualifies as Pitfall. Honestly, avoid this title unless it is needed for your collection.

Super Spike V'Ball — Nintendo — 3 — $5
Nice graphics highlight this beach volleyball, as does the solid control. This is the beach volleyball game of choice on the NES.

Super Spike V'Ball/Nintendo World Cup
Nintendo — 3 — $7
This is a combination of the two mentioned titles with no changes to either.

Super Sprint — Tengen — 3 — $4
Overhead winding tracks are used in this racing game, but instead of the screen shifting, the tracks are miniscule and contained on one screen. It's miniaturized fun.

Super Spy Hunter — Sunsoft — 4 — $8
An update to the original, this title features improved graphics and a real feeling of speed. This racing/shooting game is played in a vertically scrolling fashion.

Super Team Games — Nintendo — 3 — $5
Various outdoor sports are played in this rustic track and field game.

Superman — Seika — 4 — $8
Based on the story from Superman II, this side scrolling adventure just isn't a lot of fun due to graphical and control disappointments, and the look of freedom within the game.

Swamp Thing — T*HQ — 4 — $0
While the cult movie from which this title draws its inspiration had its good moments, this game does not. Boring platform action with generic looking backgrounds and bad character animations are key in making this title uninteresting.

Sword Master — Activision — 5 — $10
This is an average side scrolling hack and slash, released in 1992.

Super Mario Bros. 3

Super Spike V'Ball

Superman

Tagin' Dragon

In Custer's Revenge for the Atari 2600, your objective is to avoid falling arrows so that you may rape an Indian woman tied to a post.

NES

Tecmo Super Bowl

Tecmo World Wrestling

Teenage Mutant Ninja Turtles

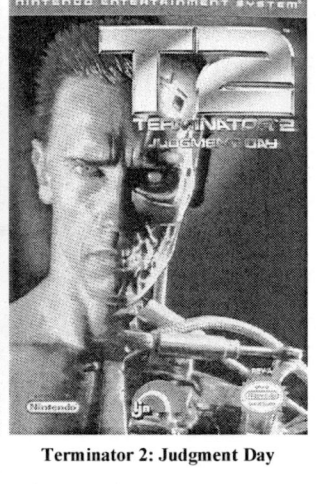
Terminator 2: Judgment Day

Swords and Serpents Acclaim 4 $10
Travel through a 16 level dungeon in this first person graphic adventure. This game is very fun and offers a very sinister feel through the use of sparse, but well placed sound effects.

T&C Surf Designs: Wood & Water Rage
LJN 1 $4
Several sports grace this game, and though a bit difficult at first, the surfing section can become VERY addictive.

T&C II: Thrilla's Surfari LJN 4 $8
Wow, where did this surprisingly good title come from? Completely unlike its predecessor, this is actually an adventure game with some really incredible graphics, though it seems a bit odd that skateboard ramps and tracks have been laid through the African jungles. Very fun and addictive, tracks, rivers, waterfalls and other challenges will keep this game entertaining through every level.

Taboo: The Sixth Sense Tradewest 3 $5
Definitely an odd entry into the NES market, this title is actually a computerized tarot card reader that acts like a magic eight ball of sorts, providing an answer to any question you pose to the "game".

Tagin' Dragon Bunch Games 5 $12
This is a re-release of the Sachen game Colorful Dragon.

Tag Team Wrestling Data East 2 $3
A distant view of the ring makes this 1986 wrestling simulation very difficult to see or enjoy playing.

TaleSpin Capcom 4 $8
Featuring the cartoon character of the same name, an altered version of this title was also available on the TG-16.

Target: Renegade Taito 3 $5
This is an average street fighting game with side scrolling action, though the graphics just don't seem advanced enough to properly portray this type of game.

Tecmo Baseball Tecmo 3 $4
While their football game is considered to be a stroke of genius, Tecmo's baseball entry to the NES market is average at best.

Tecmo Bowl Tecmo 1 $5
Considered by most to be the best football game on the NES, this title is much more fun when played with multiple people.

Tecmo NBA Basketball Tecmo 3 $4
Playing similarly to most other basketball games on the NES, this title features nice control and average graphics and sound.

Tecmo Cup Soccer Game Tecmo 5 $10
The mandatory soccer entry for Tecmo turned out to be very engaging with very detailed aspects of the sport implemented into the actual game elements itself.

Tecmo Super Bowl Tecmo 2 $5
The portion of people that don't consider Tecmo Bowl to be the best football game on the NES consider this game to hold that title. More intricate plays and a slightly angled view of the playing filed add new depth to the strategic elements of the sport, though many felt that the appeal of the first installment was its simple approach to the game.

Tecmo World Wrestling Tecmo 2 $4
Professional wrestling is bad enough, but generic wrestling is nearly as bad as being forced to watch that Mexican midget wrestling hour that comes on late night TV. Not particularly bad as far as game play is concerned, the lack of any real personalities in this game is what makes it suffer.

Teenage Mutant Ninja Turtles
Ultra 2 $3
This side scrolling fighting game stars the TMNT gang of embarrassingly popularity and was featured in the movie "The Wizard" with Fred Savage. Of course, Lucas with his dorky sidekicks and aluminum cased power glove were also in the movie, so it isn't saying much.

Teenage Mutant Ninja Turtles II: The Arcade Game
Ultra 2 $4
This port of the awesome arcade game didn't lose too much in the translation and remains fun if you can get over controlling the turtles. Of course, if you're playing this game, you might have a dinner plate photo button of Donnie still pinned to your rhinestone denim jacket.

Teenage Mutant Ninja Turtles III: The Manhattan Project
Ultra 3 $5
Honestly, this is a fun game with some nice graphics. Released in 1992, the NES was in full stride and games like this kept it popular long past its prime.

Teenage Mutant Ninja Turtles: Tournament Fighters
Konami 6 $15

The creator of the GameBoy, Gumpei Yokoi, was killed after a minor car accident. When he stepped out of his car, he was run over.

One of the few 2-D fighting games on the NES to actually pull off the challenge of making the characters both recognizable and playable, this title is pretty impressive considering the graphical limitations of the NES's hardware. Also, this game has some of the best looking box art for the system.

Tennis   Nintendo   1 $3
Simple and easy, the way Nintendo planned it. This title was released in 1985, so don't expect graphical perfection, but it got the job done and created a fun tennis game.

Terminator   Mindscape   4 $8
A decent side scrolling adventure game, this title is based loosely around the movie plot, though the action in this game is mild compared to that found in the movie.

Terminator 2: Judgement Day
   Acclaim   3 $5

Terra Cresta   Vic Tokai   4 $8
While this vertical shooter looks bad and often becomes tedious, the game itself plays relatively well, though it is not nearly as responsive as the arcade version from which it was ported.

Tetris   Nintendo   1 $5
The classic falling block game is great on the NES, but this version isn't nearly as good as the Tengen version.

Tetris   Tengen   6 $40
This much talked about game isn't nearly as rare as most assume. With a two player option, this version is definitely superior to that of the Nintendo produced version. Recalled due to a lawsuit filed by Nintendo, this game received a lot of hype that has increased its desirability and price, though it is sure to decrease in value as people begin to realize that it isn't the gem they originally thought it was.

Tetris 2   Nintendo   3 $7
New features were added to this title over the original, probably due to the apparent preference people had for the superior Tetris version that Tengen had made.

Three Stooges, The   Activision   4 $8
Multiple play modes are used in this title that features one of the most memorable scenes in NES game history, the famed pie fight taking place across an expansive room.

Thunder & Lightning   Romstar   5 $10

Thunderbirds   Activision   4 $8
In this vertical scrolling flight simulation, you take control of war planes trying to stop the invading alien by the name of Hood. Average on the whole, this game doesn't stand out for much other than a silly story.

Thundercade   American Sammy   3 $4
Using a specially equipped war bike, shoot your way through multiple levels of vertically scrolling scenery, and don't forget to pick up power-ups along the way to change the functions and capabilities of your bike.

Tiger-Heli   Acclaim   3 $5
An overhead view and numerous waves of enemies make this vertically scrolling helicopter shooting game a favorite among retro-gamers.

Tiles of Fate   AVE   4 $10
No system would be complete without this classic Chinese tile game featuring basic cursor control, simple graphics, and a definite challenge.

Time Lord   Milton Bradley   3 $4
The Earth is under attack from an invading planet, and there is only one sensible option, to lightly outfit a single man with sparse armament and send him to meet the alien scourge face to face in an attempt to kill them one by one. Thank goodness video game designers aren't in charge of national defense! Collect 5 orbs from five different time periods so that the invading force can be repelled.

Times of Lore   Toho   4 $8
The choice of three separate adventurers is a nice option, but a stagnate story line and a very generic feel to the whole experience really make this game less than it should have been. With an overhead view, similar to Zelda this action/adventure RPG actually has moments of graphical genius, but at other times shows the programmers' carelessness when the character becomes almost invisible in certain areas due to excessive outlines.

Tiny Toon Adventures   Konami   3 $4
This average side scrolling platform game features characters from the popular cartoon series, though the graphics simply don't do them justice. Regardless of its shortcomings however, this title still remains a favorite for fans of the show, and those who remember wasting countless hours of their life trying to beat their friends' scores.

Tetris (Tengen)

Tiger-Heli

Tiles of Fate

To The Earth

The Sega Dreamcast was released on 9/9/99.

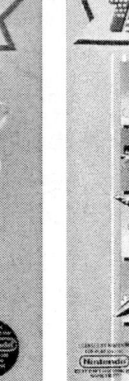

Top Gun	Track & Field	Track & Field II	Treasure Master

Tiny Toon Adventures 2: Trouble in Wackyland
Konami   4 $8
Some nice innovations have been added to this platform game, though the control seems to suffer a bit.

Tiny Toon Adventures Cartoon Workshop
Konami   5 $10
This is not a game, but instead an art program that allows for the manipulation of existing work and the creation of new works.

To the Earth   Nintendo   3 $4
Zapper games are typically a little on the bland side, but this title offers some very nice targets and some great locations including Uranus. (*snicker*) A nice story line accompanies this game, telling of the invading alien force an the importance placed on your mission, and the difficulty quickly mounts as ships begin to move more quickly and erratically.

Toki   Taito   4 $8
An average platformer at best, this title features obstacles that are obviously placed for no other reason than to necessitate a button press. This is pretty annoying to be honest, and detracts from the game instead of adding to it.

Tom & Jerry   Hi-Tech Expressions   4 $7
Some really nice animations are included in this video game translation of the cartoon. The characters look true to life and control nicely as well in the game's side scrolling platform levels.

Tombs & Treasure   Infocom   4 $8
This is a fun graphic adventure with a very mysterious feel to the whole story. Played in the same fashion as Déjà Vu, first-person perspective will add some realism to this text and graphic adventure.

Toobin'   Tengen   4 $7
A nice original idea, this is actually a racing game placing you squarely into an inner tube that is moving quickly down a cluttered river. Supporting a very fun two player option, this is somewhat of an obstacle course on the river.

Top Gun   Konami   1 $3
A nice attempt at recreating the feel and action from the movie, this title remains fun, though the graphics may not be what you remember.

Top Gun: The Second Mission
Konami   3 $5
Featuring head to head dogfights with a friend, this title has more replay value than the first.

Top Player's Tennis   Asmik   3 $4
Featuring four player simultaneous support and a good view of the court, this is one of the better tennis titles for the nes.

Totally Rad   Jaleco   3 $5
It was 1991 and saying things like "Totally Rad" were actually considered to be hip and swell by golly. This game features a notably purple motif and standard side scrolling platform action, though it must be bought if for no other reason than to get a chuckle in from time to time…Not! (Ok, if you didn't pick up on the sarcasm, please re-read that overview in a pre-Matrix Keanu Reeves voice and it should become clear.)

Total Recall   Acclaim   3 $4
This side scrolling adventure game may show an occasional resemblance to the movie, but this is just your standard platform game with a popular movie title affixed.

Touchdown Fever   SNK   4 $8
Diagnosed incorrectly as the bubonic plague during the middle ages, thousands of football fans suffering from this strange fever were needlessly coated in lye and tossed into mass graves. This football game features vertically scrolling action and very small characters, though the game play is still solid and easy enough to control.

Toxic Crusaders   Bandai   4 $8
A game for fans of Troma only, the characters found within were actually featured in their own cartoon as well as the questionable cult films.

Track & Field   Konami   1 $4
Basic control is used to play this fun game featuring Olympic style track and field events.

Track and Field II   Konami   2 $5
Improvements to the original and some new events make this the preferred of the two titles, though they're both fun.

Treasure Master   American Softworks   5 $10
Take the role of Scooter as he undertakes this side scrolling adventure for treasure foretold in his dreams.

TROG!   Acclaim   4 $8
This is a static screen puzzle/maze game that was first released in the arcades, then on the NES in 1991.

Some late TG-16 releases were sold in a box, but contained no jewel case.

Trojan   Capcom   2 $4
This side scrolling hack and slash fighter is entertaining and features a variety of levels (seven in total) that you will pass through on your way to kill the evil king. Power-ups can be found along the way that allow for different attributes such as your attack and your jumping power to be increased.

Trolls on Treasure Island   AVE   6 $15
Remember the rubber dolls with the fuzzy hair? Well, this title features the little guys in a puzzle game that is honestly more annoying than it is fun or addicting.

Twin Cobra   American Sammy   2 $4
This is a vertically scrolling helicopter shooter featuring blasé graphics but responsive control. If you're looking for this type of game, try Tiger Heli instead.

Twin Eagle   Romstar   3 $5
Five varied stages of changing landscapes/oceanscapes are used in this vertically scrolling helicopter shooter. Again, Tiger Heli is the preferred choice for this genre, but this game doesn't stand out as being especially bad.

Ultima: Exodus   FCI   3 $5
Form parties and explore this vast land from an overhead view in this 1989 RPG. This title does not fit into the lineage of the computer titles, but instead is a completely separate quest.

Ultima: Quest of the Avatar
     FCI   4 $12
Played in the same style as the first Ultima release on the NES, this title is actually a translation of Ultima 4.

Ultima: Warriors of Destiny
     FCI   5 $18
The last Ultima release on the NES, this title offers some very nice graphical enhancements and remains a favorite of many fans of this series.

Ultimate Air Combat   Activision   5 $10
An average entry to the flight simulation genre on this system, the NES simply did not have the capability to carry out the look and feel the designer obviously intended for this often choppy title.

Ultimate Basketball   American Sammy   3 $4
Featuring disappointing graphics by today's standards, this 1990 release had some nice size characters for its day and a good color pallet as well. Control is solid, though this title offers nothing to really make it stand out from the other basketball games for the NES.

Ultimate League Soccer   AVE   6 $12
Substandard control and graphics make this soccer game one of many that failed to deliver.

Ultimate Stuntman   Camerica   3 $5
On a quest to save your girlfriend, you take the role of the Ultimate Stuntman through various types of stages, including horizontally scrolling fighting levels.

Uncharted Waters   Koei   5 $10
An action/adventure RPG on the high seas, this title is best played on the SNES or Genesis.

Uncanny X-Men, The   LJN   3 $7
An overhead action game, this title simply can't do the comic book characters justice due to control limitations, though it is entertaining to actually play some of your favorite X-Men.

Uninvited   Seika   4 $8
A first person graphic adventure, this title takes you through spooky situations, though better sound would have greatly improved the mood effects that the graphics struggled to produce.

Untouchables, The   Ocean   3 $5
Based on the movie of the same name, this title features several types of game play, including overhead shooting, horizontally scrolling segments, driving, and other types of game play.

Urban Champion   Nintendo   2 $3
This 1986 release shows that the NES simply was not ready for 2-D head to head fighting games. Though it can be amusing at times, it simply lacks the type of precision control necessary to make this genre enjoyable.

Vegas Dream   HAL America   4 $10
This is one of several gambling games for the NES, and while average at best, it is certainly better than the Sachen releases.

Venice Beach Volleyball   AVE   6 $12
A few customizable options set this title aside from other volleyball titles, though as is typical with AVE, the graphics and play mechanics suffer throughout.

Vice: Project Doom   American Sammy   3 $5
Played in the same style as Spy Hunter, this is a vertically scrolling racing/shooting game that relies on your horizontal

Uninvited   Vegas Dream

Videomation   Wally Bear and the NO! Gamn

The Atari 5200 originally retailed for $330.

NES

| Who Framed Roger Rabbit | Whomp 'Em | Widget | Willow |

movement prowess. This game can really cause some blisters.

Videomation T*HQ 5 $10
This is a poorly designed drawing program with no game elements.

Vindicators Tengen 3 $5
A vertically scrolling space shooter, this title offers some nice levels and solid control, though the sound could have been improved.

Volleyball Nintendo 2 $3
Played on a hard court, this title features international level competition, but you will be handicapped with poor control and collision detection that doesn't seem to be very accurate, causing many lost points.

Wacky Races Atlus 5 $10
This side scrolling kart racing game features some very nice levels and graphics.

Wall Street Kid Sofel 3 $5
Play the stock market and learn a little bit about the process in this simplified gaming version of Wall Street.

Wally Bear and the NO! Gang
AVE 6 $15
A game to make Nancy Reagan proud, this side scrolling game features a strong anti-drug theme.

Wario's Woods Nintendo 4 $8
This is a colorful Tetris style puzzle game with a background featuring…the woods.

Wayne Gretzky Hockey T*HQ 3 $5
An average hockey game, this title can't stand out in a field filled with quality versions of the same game.

Wayne's World T*HQ 4 $8
This basic hockey is little different than others in the genre on the NES, but does include The Great One himself.

WCW: World Championship Wrestling
FCI 1 $3
Basic graphics and control toss this wrestling title squarely in with every other wrestling game for the NES.

Werewolf: The Last Warrior
Data East 3 $4

Basic side scrolling fighting is featured in this game with a dark feel and repetitive levels.

Wheel of Fortune GameTek 3 $5
The game show is played in simple fashion, and limited game play is caused the small number of solvable puzzles, though it does feature some nicely drawn cartoon like players.

Wheel of Fortune: Family Edition
GameTek 3 $5
This is basically an update to the first installment, with over 1000 new puzzles.

Wheel of Fortune Featuring Vanna White
GameTek 4 $8
More of the same, but with the lovely Vanna.

Wheel of Fortune: Junior Edition
GameTek 3 $5
Played in the same style as the other three versions, this game features simpler puzzles suitable for younger players.

Where in Time is Carmen Sandiego?
Konami 5 $8
Also available on the Genesis, this game is very informative and relies on the use of a dictionary to find where Carmen has gone to next. Technically a point and click adventure game, this title could easily be classified as edutainment simply because something might accidentally be learned while playing.

Where's Waldo? T*HQ 4 $8
Look for Waldo in large crowds, guide him through a dark cave, and help him escape a confusing subway layout in this 1991 release based on the fame of the Where's Waldo? book series.

Who Framed Roger Rabbit
LJN 3 $5
Based on the entertaining movie, this is an action/adventure game that features some nice graphics and an entertaining story line.

Whomp 'Em Jaleco 4 $8
This is an above average side scrolling adventure features nice control and graphics, though is one of many on the NES and does not stand out as being much different from the crowd.

Widget Atlus 5 $10
A side scrolling adventure, this game features a small purple character from which this game gets its title.

The N64 is the preferred game system in the HBO series The Sopranos.

Wild Gunman   Nintendo   3 $5
A Zapper title, this game is a port of the arcade game by the same name. You can choose to fight one on one, or to shoot at multiple people at once in the gang mode.

Willow   Capcom   3 $7
A very fun action/adventure RPG that is often forgotten, it was based on the movie by the same name and was released in 1989.

Win, Lose or Draw   Hi-Tech Expressions   3 $4
A difficult concept to pull off on the NES, at least there is an excuse for this game's poor game play.

Winter Games   Acclaim   3 $5
Average game play and control make this an enjoyable title for fans of the Winter Olympics.

Wizardry: Knight of Diamonds – The Second Scenario
     Asciiware   5 $15
While this sequel isn't quite as good as the first, it is still an awesome first person RPG with heavy text and a good story line. This title was probably intended for older audiences.

Wizardry: Proving Grounds of the Mad Overlord
     Asciiware   3 $7
A text heavy first person adventure/RPG, this title is often confused with its sequel, though this is the better of the two.

Wizards & Warriors   Acclaim   2 $4
A very popular 1987 side scrolling release, this title is very entertaining and features some creative level designs.

Wizards and Warriors III: Kuros' Visions of Power
     Acclaim   3 $5
Released in 1991, this title shows some nice graphical improvements over the last installment, and still features the same addictive platform game play.

Wolverine   Acclaim   4 $7
This side scroller/vertical scroller features Wolverine of X-Men fame, though it hardly does the character justice.

World Champ   Romstar   5 $10
This 1991 release from Romstar can't even compare to the fun in Punch-Out!!, but is still a nice attempt at boxing innovation halfway through the NES's lifecycle.

World Class Track Meet   Nintendo   1 $2
Simple track and field events are played in this Powerpad title.

World Games   Milton Bradley   3 $5
Various cultural sports from around the world are featured in this entertaining title. Where else can you ride a bull and Sumo wrestle within minutes of each other?

Wrath of the Black Manta   Taito   2 $4
This is a side scrolling fighter with average graphics and lousy control.

Wrecking Crew   Nintendo   3 $5
Take the role of Mario as he goes from site to site destroying the work being done by various construction workers.

Wurm: Journey to the Center of the Earth
     Asmik   3 $5
Side scrolling shooter, first person vehicle shooter and adventure game are all rolled into one in this entertaining and underrated title.

WWf King of the Ring   LJN   5 $10
At least this wrestling title offers characters that actually look like people, but other than that, it is identical to the other WWF titles for this system.

WWF Wrestlemania   Acclaim   1 $3
Simple graphics and control make this game truly boring, considering the nature of a sport that is supposed to be exciting.

WWF Wrestlemania Challenge
     LJN   3 $3
This is basically the same game as above, with a different name.

WWF Wrestlemania Steel Cage Challenge
     Acclaim   3 $4
Not surprisingly, a simple camera shift is all that seems to be different in this title. The NES really milked the WWF titles.

Xenophobe   Sunsoft   3 $5
Bad color selections and repetitive game play make this platform game just another entry into a crowded genre of superior titles.

Xevious   Bandai   3 $5
This is a fun vertically scrolling space shooter featuring some nice levels and an average challenge.

Wurm: Journey to the Center of the Earth   Yoshi

Yoshi's Cookie   Zanac

Nintendo Power Gloves are still used in virtual reality research.

Zelda II: The Adventures of Link

Zoda's Revenge: Star Tropics II

The Fantastic Adventures of Dizzy

Linus Spacehead's Cosmic Crusade

Xexyz Hudson 3 $4
1990 saw the release of this nice looking side scrolling platform game that features adequate control and sound to be entertaining.

Yo! Noid Capcom 4 $7
Remember this guy from the Dominos Pizza ads? Well, evidently someone from Capcom really liked the character, because he stars in this horrible side scrolling adventure game with colorful graphics and awful control.

Yoshi Nintendo 3 $5
One of several Tetris clones, the usual color pallet and background changes accompany this title.

Yoshi's Cookie Nintendo 3 $5
Still a falling block game, instead of shapes, this title relies on the shifting order of the dropped objects to make matches and clear levels.

Young Indiana Jones Chronicles, The
Jaleco 5 $12
This 1992 release shows adequate graphics and game play, but this title should have been much better considering the quality of the movie from which it was inspired.

Zanac FCI 3 $5
Later the name of a prescription drug, this title is an overhead space shooter with very nice control, though the levels become repetitive quickly.

Zelda II: The Adventures of Link (gold)
Nintendo 1 $8
Replacing the overhead action view from the first installment with an overworld map and side scrolling action scenes, this title is either loved or hated. Experience has shown, however, that those who once despised the game will eventually come to appreciate its engaging story line and intricate world.

Zelda II: The Adventures of Link (gray)
Nintendo 3 $3

Zen: Intergalactic Ninja
Konami 4 $8
Kidnapped as a child and taught the arts of the Ninja on another planet, this game features standard side scrolling action in addition to isometric game play and vertical stages as well. A nice title to try out, it falls short of being a must-have.

Zoda's Revenge: Star Tropics II
Nintendo 3 $5

Zombie Nation Meldac 4 $8
An uninspired platform shooter in which you must take on droves of zombies, this title is average at best.

ALADDIN CARTS

These carts are for use with the Aladdin Deck enhancer only. They are much smaller than normal NES carts and were packaged in hanging box-packs instead of standard boxes.

Bignose Freaks Out	Camerica	6	$15
Dizzy the Adventurer	Camerica	6	$15
Fantastic Adventures of Dizzy	Camerica	6	$15
Linus Spacehead's Cosmic Crusade	Camerica	6	$20
Micro Machines	Camerica	6	$20
Quattro Adventure	Camerica	6	$10
Quattro Sports	Camerica	6	$10

SACHEN GAMES

Sachen released a total of 60 games that are compatible with the NES, but it is still unclear as to the actual distribution practices of the company, and if these games were ever officially released in the U.S. They have been included in this guide separately to reflect the feeling by many that they should not be considered domestic releases. However, it is commonly felt that these games were brought into the country in large enough quantities by resellers to justify their classification as U.S. games. Perhaps the most compelling evidence is the fact that these games, in NTSC format (Japan and U.S. TV format), utilize a cartridge that is incompatible with Japanese Famicom systems, leaving the U.S. and Canada. With Canada as an unlikely market for such a marketing scheme, it is almost certain that these games were intended to be sold in the U.S. either officially or unofficially, but certainly with the approval of Sachen. These games should be considered to have a rarity of "6", though firm prices have yet to be set for these titles. Normally a price of around $20 per game is considered reasonable, though the inclusion of a box should add around 30%-40% of this price.

Only a few copies of the Amiga CDTV game Indiana Jones and the Last Crusade are known to exist, yet the game WAS officially released.

Auto-Upturn   Sachen
This odd puzzle games features a strange combination of characters.

Bingo 75   Sachen
This is an adult gambling title with a spice of nudity, but not much fun

Challenge of the Dragon   Sachen
Color Dreams made a game with the same name, though the two are completely separate games. This title is similar in fashion and appearance to Double Dragon.

Chess Academy   Sachen
This is an adult version of Chinese Checkers with occasional nudity.

Chinese Checkers   Sachen
Another version of Chinese Checkers, this title offers different graphics than Chess Academy, though the rules of the game are the same.

Colorful Dragon   Sachen
This is the same as Bunch Game's Tagin' Dragon.

Cosmocop   Sachen
This title requires the Zapper accessory.

Dancing Blocks   Sachen

Final Combat   Sachen
This is a basic shooting game at heart with little to offer.

Gaiapolis   Sachen
The home version of a mildly popular arcade game released in Japan by Konami, this title is not believed to have ever included a box.

Galactic Crusader   Sachen
This title was later released by Bunch Games.

Great Wall, The   Sachen
One of many puzzle games from Sachen.

Happy Pairs   Sachen
A tile game similar in execution to that of the child's game "memory".

Hell Fighter   Sachen
This is a basic platform game.

Hidden Chinese Chess   Sachen
This is the forerunner to Chess Academy and does not contain nudity, as the later title would.

Honey Peach   Sachen
Roshambo and nudity never went together so well!

Jovial Race   Sachen
This is a Rally-X clone.

Jurassic Boy   Sachen
This Sonic the Hedgehog clone is riddled with control problems and graphical glitches.

Little Red Hood   Sachen
Leave it to Sachen to take a famous childhood story an turn it into one of their games.

Locksmith   Sachen

Lucky Bingo   Sachen
This gambling game actually has "Lucky Bingo" on the label, but the game itself seems to be titled "Lucky 777".

Magic Cube   Sachen
Yet another puzzle game by Sachen, that borrowed ideas from more popular puzzle games of the time.

Magical Mathematics   Sachen

Mahjong Trap   Sachen
Mahjong and nudity go together like peanut butter and antifreeze, as this game adequately illustrates.

Mahjong World, The   Sachen
An eternally popular inspiration for Asian video games, Sachen made sure that the NES had its share.

Master Chu and the Drunkard Hu
Sachen
This title was later released by Color Dreams.

Metal Fighter   Sachen
This title was later released by Color Dreams.

Challenge of the Dragon   Cosmo Cop

Jovial Race   Jurassic Boy

The SMS 2 has no slot for games made in the card format.

| Magical Mathematics | Olympic I.Q. | Poker III | Thunder Blaster Man |

Millionaire Sachen
This is simply a Monopoly clone.

Olympic I.Q. Sachen

Penguin and Seal, The Sachen
One of several title that were later released by HES, this was converted to an Australian released named "Arctic Adventure".

Pipe V Sachen
Re-released by HES as Pipemania.

Poker II Sachen
A sequel to "The World of Card Games", this title includes Max 2, Ghost-Buster, 99 and Change Around.

Poker III Sachen
An RPG of sorts, taking place within a casino. This title is considered to be the best Sachen game made.

Popo Team Sachen
This is a clone of the game "Anteater".

Pyramid Sachen
This title was later released by AVE.

Pyramid II Sachen
This title was not re-released and contains both a story line and a two player mode.

Q-Boy Sachen
This Kirby's Adventure clone allows you to switch the overall graphical style to that of Super Mario Brothers by pushing the select button while the game is paused.

Rockball Sachen
This is a strategy game involving the proper placement of rocks.

Sidewinder Sachen
Released by Color Dreams as Mission Cobra.

Silent Assault Sachen
This title was later released by Color Dreams.

Silver Eagle Sachen
This is simply a bad stealth/action game.

Strategist Sachen
An odd turn-based strategy game, this title relies on the use of

cards to determine victory.

Street Heroes Sachen
This title is also available from Sachen on the Game Boy.

Super Cartridge Version 1 - 4 in 1 Sachen
Bingo 75, Lucky 777, Honey Peach and Chess Academy. (No box released)

Super Cartridge Version 2 - 10 in 1 Sachen
The same games contained on The World of Card Games and Poker II, with some exclusive additional. (No box released)

Super Cartridge Version 3 - 8 in 1 Sachen
Jovial Race, Little Red Hood, Twin Eagle, Silent Assault, Super Pang, and Mine Sweeper. (No box released)

Super Cartridge Version 4 - 6 in 1 Sachen
Master Chu and the Drunkard Hu, Metal Fighter, Galactic Crusader, Auto-Upturn, Magic Cube and Super Pang 2. (No box released)

Super Cartridge Version 5 - 7 in 1 Sachen
Penguin and Seal, Middle School English, Pyramid, Magical Mathematics, Strategist, Olympic I.Q. and Chinese Checkers. (No box released)

Super Cartridge Version 6 - 6 in 1 Sachen
Colorful Dragon, Pyramid II, Pipe V, Millionaire, Dancing Blocks and Locksmith. (No box released)

Super Cartridge Version 7 - 4 in 1 Sachen
Sidewinder, Happy Pairs, Tasac and Silver Eagle. (No box released)

Super Cartridge Version 8 - 4 in 1 Sachen
Final Combat, Worm Visitor, Frog Adventure and Magical Tower. (No box released)

Go, a recent release for the CD-i is actually centuries older than its more popular cousin Othello.

Super Cartridge Version 9 - 3 in 1
Sachen
Challenge of the Dragon, Rockball and Popo Team. (No box released)

Super Pang   **Sachen**
This is an unlicensed version of Buster Bros.

Super Pang II   **Sachen**
This is an unlicensed version of Super Buster Bros.

Taiwan Mahjong   **Sachen**
You really never can have enough mahjong.

Tasac   **Sachen**
This is an entertaining overhead shooter.

Thunder Blaster Man   **Sachen**
The label reads "Thunder Blaster Man, but the title screen reads "Rockman X". This title is not believed to have ever been released with a box.

Tough Cop   **Sachen**
The Zapper is required for this shooting title.

Twin Eagle   **Sachen**
This title was later released as Double Strike by AVE.

World of Card Games, The   Sachen
Omnibus Hearts, Fan Tan, Chinese Rummy and The Clock are featured on this game which is actually the first installment in the "Poker" series by Sachen.

HARDWARE

NES   **Nintendo**   **1**   **$15**
Often referred to as the "toaster" version of the NES, it is very common to come across this system in the wild, but much harder to find one that doesn't suffer from "blinking." The contacts uses to connect the cartridge to the NES are made of copper and are subject to quick corrosion. The typical solution of blowing into a cartridge that wouldn't work (as most of us are guilty of doing) caused moisture to remain on these copper contacts after the game was removed, promoting ever quicker corrosion to occur.

NES 2   **Nintendo**   **5**   **$75**
This is the toploading model sold from 1993-1994.

Alladin Deck Enhancer   **Camerica**   **6**   **$35**
This is an unlicensed item that inserts into the cartridge slot of the NES and facilitates the use of specially made cartridges from Camerica, though only 7 games were ever made.

Dog Bone Controller   **Nintendo**   **4**   **$10**
Sold with the NES 2, this controller is rounded and more comfortable for long periods of play, though it is a bit small for adult hands.

Game Genie   **Galoob**   **1**   **$5**
A device used to unlock game cheats, it is worthless without the code book.

NES Advantage   **Nintendo**   **1**   **$7**
The joystick of choice for the NES, this controller suffers from a very cheap feel, though it offers features such as slow motion and rapid fire.

NES Controller   **Nintendo**   **1**   **$2**
The standard controller packaged with every front loading NES.

NES Four Score   **Nintendo**   **1**   **$5**
A device used to facilitate the use of four controllers per control port.

Power Glove   **Mattel**   **4**   **$20**
Worthless without the screen calibrators, this was worn on the hand and controls onscreen movements via IR signal, though the responsiveness is poor. If you want to see just how ridiculous this thing can look in the hands of a professional, watch The Wizard with Fred Savage and marvel at Lucus as he has his lackeys open the custom case containing the almighty Power Glove!

Powerpad   **Nintendo**   **2**   **$3**
Sold with the NES for a while and bundled with World Class Track Meet, those that have used it remember pounding the ground with their fists instead of trying to beat Rabbit or Cheetah by actually running in place.

R.O.B.   **Nintendo**   **4**   **$25**
Becoming more difficult to find complete, this little guy was sold with the original NES package.

U-Force   **Nintendo**   **5**   **$15**
This is a touch-free controller that translates your hand movements to the onscreen characters (poorly).

Zapper   **Nintendo**   **1**   **$3**
The standard light gun for the NES, it comes in both gray and day-glow orange (due to toy gun laws), though neither is rarer than the other.

Video games generate more revenues than any other entertainment media, save movies.

SNES

Super Nintendo

By: Lucus Barnes, Charlie Reneke, Michael Collins, & Andy Slaven

Many gamers still refer to the days that the Sega Genesis and Nintendo Super NES battled it out as the best years of gaming. The year gamers first got their button-hungry fingers on Nintendo's new console was 1991, and from then on, games would be changed forever.

The Super Nintendo was one heck of a machine at the time of its release, with a 16-bit processor and a half of a megabit of video RAM. Programmers could choose from a palette of well over 32,000 colors and display 256 on-screen at any given time. All of this power also meant that the system had the ability to display multiple layers of graphics, all independent from one another. The SNES blew away the systems of the previous generation, like the NES and SMS. Though sheer power doesn't always equal quality, the SNES did at least allow programmers to have more freedom in what they do -- make games.

Originally, the designers of the SNES wanted to make the new system backward-compatible with NES cartridges. As we all know, though, this never happened. The reason? Quite simply, it would have cost too much. By Nintendo's estimates, the console would have cost an additional $75, and this obviously would not do. A converter cartridge much like the Super GameBoy could have been released, but this unfortunately never happened.

In the days of the NES, Nintendo had all sorts of policies and restrictions for third-party developers. In a nutshell, a company that made a game for Nintendo could not make a game for anybody else, even if it was a different game altogether. When the SNES was released (at the price of $199.99), it had a long way to get to the top. The Genesis had already been released and established a firm foothold in the market. As in the Nintendo tradition, there were only a handful of games available at release, though several of them were of very high quality. To compensate for the lack of games, Nintendo altered some of their policies towards third-parties, and the games began to come out more steadily.

Nintendo has always believed in the power of multiplayer gaming, with four controller ports on their Nintendo 64 and GameCube, and two different multi-tap units available for their NES. Though the SNES did not have four controller ports built in to the unit, there was a muti-tap available after its release, so up to five players could play a game at a time. Sadly, this wasn't used as much as it could have been.

The SNES's controller is arguably one of the best ever, because of how revolutionary and how comfortable it was. The controller was the first to introduce "shoulder" buttons, labeled 'R' and 'L,' one on each shoulder of the controller. It also changed the main button area of video game controllers, by placing four buttons, rather than two (like the NES or SMS) or three (like the Genesis). Today, both of this innovations are standards on video game controllers. Some may argue that the SNES controller is a little bit small for older gamers, but it isn't too small to handle. All in all, the folks at Nintendo knew what they were doing when they designed it.

Several additional peripherals were released for the Super NES, and two of these stand out as particularly special: the Super Scope and the mouse. The Super Scope was released relatively soon after the SNES's American debut, and is essentially an extremely gaudy light gun. Today, a gun like this would never be released, because it is shaped like a bazooka with a gun sight and shoulder rest. Several games were released for it, and the pack-in game was Super Scope 6. As stated previously, the other optional controller for the SNES that is of special note is the mouse, which was originally released with Mario Paint. Mario Paint is probably the best example of mouse usage for the system, but a few other games used it including Civilization and Lemmings 2: The Tribes.

Before the release of the Nintendo 64 in 1996, Nintendo released a second model of the Super Nintendo. It was smaller and had a more attractive, streamlined look. It too was designed to be too rounded for a drink to be placed on it (as was the first model SNES), to prevent spills and therefore ruined consoles. (This had been a problem with the NES.) Though the second model SNES isn't impossible to find, it didn't see the same level of production that the first model did, and is therefore more difficult to find at a reasonable price, unfortunately.

Several of the SNES's games were mentioned above, but a few more deserve special note, because their characters have become household names. Super Mario World is arguably the best Mario game to date, and certainly the best at the time it came out. If Mario fans still couldn't get enough, they could play Super Mario All-Stars, which was a compilation of the American Super Mario Bros. series and the true Super Mario Bros. 2, dubbed the "Lost Levels." Super Metroid was also an incredible update to a classic NES game, and games like Mario Kart and F-Zero revolutionized the way racing games were made and played.

As mentioned earlier, the NES adaptor for the SNES never became a reality. Fortunately, though, something else did: the Super GameBoy. It was capable of playing black and white GameBoy games in color on the SNES. The unit picked colors for each game automatically, and usually picked a nice combination. Still, gamers had the option of changing colors around, which was a nice feature. The ability to play all of one's GameBoy games on a TV screen was incredible, and the Super GameBoy was a huge success.

Though the console wars of today are certainly interesting and very competitive, many will still look back upon the 16-bit wars on the Genesis and Super Nintendo with nostalgia. The battle between the two consoles was a fierce one, and even today, gamers debate as to which one came out on top. In the end, there really is no clear cut winner, but the both were still wonderful consoles, and the SNES will always rank amongst the best of the best.

SNES

A.S.P. Air Strike Patrol

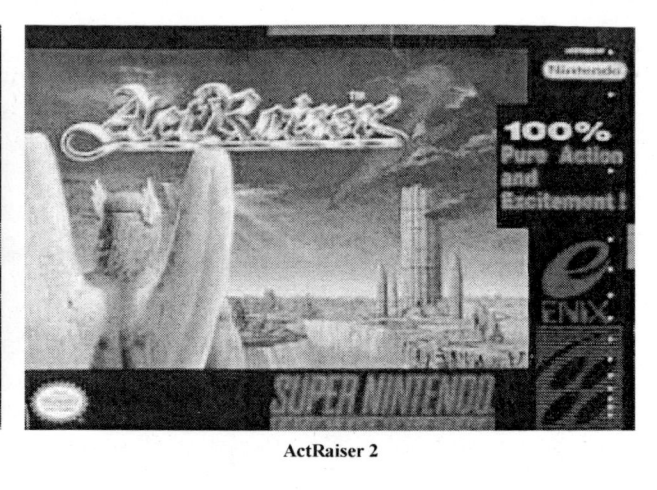

ActRaiser 2

3 Ninjas Kick Back   Sony   6 $20
This is a side scrolling fighting game loosely based on the kid's movie by the same name. While it does involve a lot of fighting, the seriousness of this title (or rather lack thereof) makes it evident that it was intended for children.

7th Saga, The   Enix   3 $10
An overhead RPG, this title offers seven different characters, each with their own story line. The interesting part of this situation is the fact that the six characters that you didn't choose become competitors of sorts that you can either oppose or join forces with. Nice music and a classic feel help make this a very entertaining game, though it is extremely difficult to build up your character's attributes.

A.S.P. Air Strike Patrol   Seta   3 $5
An action oriented flight game, real planes are used along with real armament, and each mission is preceded by a mission briefing accompanied by terrain maps.

Aaahh!!! Real Monsters   Viacom   4 $7
Based on the 1993 Nickelodeon series of the same name, this title is a side scrolling adventure with nice graphical effects and comical situations involving the main characters. Definitely designed for kids, this title might also be enjoyable for those that watched the show.

ABC Monday Night Football
                     Data East   4 $6
This is an unlicensed football game with few options and minimal features. Though the graphics are a bit above average, the lack of any real depth makes this a below average football game.

ACME Animation Factory   Sunsoft   4 $4
This is a paint program that features the Looney Tunes characters and offers no real game play aspects. Aside from the painting aspect, limited music making abilities have been included to help keep things interesting.

ActRaiser   Enix   2 $8
Often criticized as being too easy, this title features both world building strategy and side scrolling action. The overall feel of the game is one of intrigue and offers an enjoyable experience. This game offers six levels that are each broken into two action sequences for every strategy sequence. Actraiser is often credited as having one of the best soundtracks ever for a video game, amazing considering it's an SNES game.

ActRaiser 2   Enix   4 $12
Discontinuing the strategy aspect of the first installment, this game is a side scrolling action title featuring a winged warrior as the main character. While the levels are very detailed and offer some intricate environments through which you must fight, the character animations seem to be a bit choppy, and as a result the control seems to suffer a bit.

Addams Family, The   Ocean   3 $5
A side scrolling adventure game, this title obviously features characters from the TV series and movie, and while the rooms of the mansion are often impressively designed, the game play itself becomes repetitious and probably won't hold much interest for serious gamers.

Addams Family, The: Pugsley's Scavenger Hunt
                     Ocean   3 $5
Side scrolling platform action is used in this title, which happens to have the best graphics of all three Adams Family games on the SNES. Entertaining for a while, this title can become frustrating quickly, though not from an excessive difficulty, but rather a lack of difficulty.

Addams Family Values   Ocean   2 $4
Take the role of Fester as you search for Pubert, who was kidnapped by his nanny. Viewed from overhead and containing both action and RPG elements, this title will have more appeal than either of the other two Adams Family games.

Adventures of Batman & Robin
                     Konami   4 $8
With pretty much every villain that Batman ever faced in this game, it will certainly add a variety that many other Batman titles were lacking. This is a side scrolling fighting game with extremely nice graphics for a SNES title. Some of the backgrounds used are as impressive as games that were released only a few years back, yet this title was released in 1994. Any Batman fan should own this game, period.

Adventures of Dr. Franken
                     Hect   3 $5
Play the role of Franky, an updated (and "cool") version of Frankenstein's monster, and travel the world in this platform game. The story: Your girlfriend didn't have a passport, so instead of simply getting one, you decide to take her body apart and send the pieces to the U.S. Unfortunately for your girlfriend, Bitsy, the packages were all lost in the mail and wound up in 20 separate countries all over the world. Now you must track them down and put them all back together if you want to see her again. Normally, that type of story would seem very

Jaguar fans say it is decidedly so, but the debate still has no clear "winner."

creepy, but this is a lighthearted game that features a low learning curve and hardly anything that is disturbing.

Adventures of Kid Kleets, The
Ocean 4 $10
This 1994 release is a continuation of the Soccer Kid title that can be found on several platforms. Side scrolling action is actually made fun again by using a soccer ball as your weapon against various enemies.

Adventures of Rocky and Bullwinkle and Friends
THQ 5 $15
An adventure game with both side scrolling action and mountain climbing, this title offers up the two famous characters in this graphically unique game. While the game itself is average at best, the background images used are done in the same style as the cartoon, adding a lot of character to this title.

Adventures of Yogi Bear, The
GameTek 6 $22
The graphics might convey the look and feel of the simplistic cartoon quite well, but the simplicity continues on in the game play department as well, making this side-scrolling action game an experience best left to the kiddies.

Aero Fighters
Video System 3 $12
This is a vertically scrolling fighter jet shooter, very similar in style to Raiden. Various weapons upgrades will improve your firepower, and you must face both air and ground targets. This is a good game for a "quick fix", but probably won't keep you interested for too long as most of the levels are very similar to each other.

Aero The Acro-bat
Sunsoft 2 $5
Taking place in a circus environment, your job is to make your way through various levels by any means possible, including being shot out of a cannon, using tightropes, and other circus style events. All of this is to help bring down a formerly employed clown...and everybody hates clowns.

Aero The Acro-bat 2
Sunsoft 4 $10
Slight improvements to control and graphics are featured in this sequel, though it is played in basically the same way and features the same style side scrolling action.

Aerobiz
KOEI 3 $8
An airline simulator, instead of flying the planes, you organize the purchasing and flight plans of the aircraft. What seems like a simple task at first can quickly become a very challenging game considering the level of strategy that your competitors will use.

Aerobiz Supersonic
KOEI 4 $15
A continuation of the first game, but this title features the ability to use certain supersonic aircraft once enough money has been earned. A bit more difficult than the first, in higher demand, and much preferred of the two, this title is often difficult to find, though not impossible.

Air Calvary
Cybersoft 3 $6
Helicopter simulations were becoming more popular around the time this 1994 release was made, and this game seems to be a bit rushed. The graphics and action are arcade style rather than a real simulation, but each mission is preceded by a briefing and features various types of military targets, air and ground, that must be destroyed.

Al Unser Jr's Road to the Top
Mindscape 4 $10
Taking a break from all the NASCAR and F-1 games, this title features go-kart racing. Featuring some nice scaling to recreate the feel of speed within a 3-D environment. The control seems to be just right, giving the feel of driving an overpowered, underweight vehicle.

Aladdin
Capcom 2 $4
While not quite as gorgeous as the fantastic-looking Genesis game (which featured some innovation programming techniques), this otherwise sold and enjoyable platform game is backed by lush visuals, great sound, and solid game play.

Alfred Chicken
Mindscape 3 $7
Take control of Alfred in a search for the kidnapped Billy and his brothers. Search out and destroy the Meka Chickens through various platform filled levels in this entertaining and lighthearted game.

Alien 3
Acclaim 2 $5
The movie only featured one alien (if you don't count the one in her chest), but the video game features hordes of them. But don't let this little oversight take anything away from this great game, because it really shouldn't be missed. While it is a standard platform shooter, this title features some very impressive environments (through six stages) and the soundtrack is well used in order to create a feeling of both suspense and excitement throughout. If the movies interested you at all, or if you are just a fan of platform shooters, this title should definitely be played.

Alien vs. Predator
Activision 4 $15
This is NOT the same game as the highly acclaimed Atari Jaguar title, but instead is an average side scrolling fighting game. Taking the role of the Predator, you will fight through various

Adventures of Yogi Bear

Aerobiz

The original Atari 2600 featured 6 switches, while later versions only contain 4.

SNES

Animaniacs

Arcana

platform filled levels against decidedly weak aliens. While the graphics are done nicely, the sheer power of these two types of beasts simply wasn't portrayed well, and as such this is just one of many side scrolling action games.

American Gladiators   GameTek   2 $5
Compete against four gladiators in seven events based on those seen in the TV show of the same name. Occasionally fun to play, this title is great entertainment for those who remember the TV series and are looking for some nostalgia. Unfortunately, Nitro isn't one of the characters that you can smack around in the jousting event.

American Tail, An: Fievel Goes West
**   Hudson Soft   6 $22**
Based around the story seen in the movie by the same name, this is a side scrolling platform game designed to entertain both young children and early teens. The level of challenge involved is a bit low however, featuring only five levels.

Andre Agassi Tennis   Tek Magik   4 $10
Back in 1993, Andre Agassi had lots of hair, and was seen as a "Tennis Rebel" (try to squeeze that term into a conversation while keeping a straight face.) And just like the player himself, this game has not aged well. While the overall appearance is nice enough, racket control is poor, the speed necessary to make a return simply isn't present, and the inability to get into the proper position quickly enough all add up to what many feel is a huge disappointment. And the game is really bad too.

Animaniacs   Konami   2 $5
This is a side scrolling platform adventure featuring the popular characters from the Animaniacs cartoon series. Both the graphics and control are nice, and the difficulty is enough to challenge any age group. A bit above average all around, though it will appeal mainly to fans of the TV series.

Arcade's Greatest: Atari Collection 1
**   Midway   4 $12**
Featuring Asteroids, Battlezone, Centipede, Missle Command, Super Breakout and Tempest, this collection is sure to please classic gaming fans.

Arcana   Halken   5 $18
A little known RPG, this title uses an overhead map screen for travel, and first person windows for interaction. While certainly not well known, and not of the same caliber as many other RPG's on the SNES, this game should still be played by RPG fans looking for a new experience.

Arcus Odyssey   Renovation   5 $15
Take control of one of the four available characters in order to traverse 8 levels of dungeon in this isometric adventure game. While otherwise average, this title features two player simultaneous play, and becomes much more fun when played with a friend.

Ardy Lightfoot   Titus   5 $16
This side scrolling platform game features some very nice graphics and detailed environments. Character animations and control are both very smooth and help make this title a fun gaming experience.

Arkanoid: Doh it Again   Nintendo   4 $10
The classic NES game is brought to the SNES with improved graphics, though the rules of the game are the same. Break as many blocks as possible by keeping the ball in play. If you are confused after reading the instruction manual, find a Pong cabinet and read the two sentences of instruction and you'll understand perfectly.

Art of Fighting   Takara   3 $8
This port of the Neo-Geo title is a head-to-head fighter with adequate graphics and control, though the characters are considerably smaller than those featured in the original version.

Axelay   Konami   3 $5
This space shooter not only features nice graphics and sound, but very solid control and extremely addictive game play. Similar in style to Gradius, this game should keep any shooter fans busy for a long time and shouldn't be too difficult to find.

B.O.B.   Electronic Arts   3 $7
Guide the robot known as B.O.B. through 45 levels in this side scrolling platform game. New abilities and weapons can be collected along the way to make the tougher levels more realistic to beat.

Ballz   Accolade   3 $7
A nice variation on the typical 2-D fighting game, this title features characters consisting entirely of spheres, held together by some unknown force. The control is about average, as are the graphics, but this concept was new at the time and a welcome change.

Barbie Super Model   Hi Tech   5 $10
Featuring several types of game play, including driving sequences and side scrolling action sequences, this game simply does not offer anything that would interest the average gamer. Certainly designed for young girls, it is doubtful that this game

The average U.S. highschool graduate has spent about 11,000 hours in school, and about 3,000 hours playing video games.

will find its way into the collections of anyone but the most hard-core collectors.

Barbie Vacation Adventure
| | Hi Tech | 5 | $12 |

Again featuring several types of game play, this title seems to have been created for girls in their early teens, though still not enjoyable for the average gamer.

Barkley: Shut Up and Jam!
| | Accolade | 2 | $5 |

Using a side view, this street-based basketball game is a bit lacking in overall quality. While the graphics are about average, the control simply isn't solid, making this a frustrating game to play.

Bass Masters Classic   Malibu Games   3 $7
The object is simple: Catch as many bass as possible in order to have the highest total weight. With various tournaments to enter and very detailed variables such as weather conditions, season, region, etc., this title was impressive upon its release. Though it has since been surpassed by other fishing games in terms of realism, this is still a fun title to play from time to time.

Bass Masters Classic: Pro Edition
| | Electronic Arts | 3 | $12 |

All around improvements were made over the standard version of Bass Masters in order to create this game. Larger lakes have been added, more tackle is available, better graphics and sound, real fishing "personalities" are included, and a difficulty setting are all included in this game.

Bassin's Black Bass   Hot-B   4 $8
Enter the amateur tournament and progress through the competition until you reach your final challenge at the Bassin' World Championship. This is a fun game and features an over-the-shoulder view while fishing. Though it isn't on the same level as the Bass Masters Classic I'L listed above, this title was enjoyable upon its 1994 release and is still fun for some quick fishing.

Batman Forever   Acclaim   4 $8
With both Batman and Robin as selectable characters, this game had a lot of promise, but the very rigid control made this game a bit difficult to play.

Batman Returns   Konami   2 $4
Much better than Batman Forever, both the graphics and control are well done in this title, featuring both side scrolling fighting sequences and one driving level.

Battle Blaze   American Sammy   7 $40
While the characters can often look nice in this game, the very rigid control and unresponsive characters make this 2-D fighting game one to avoid.

Battle Cars   Namco   4 $10
Using scaling techniques to portray a behind-the-car viewpoint, this is an average racer at best in that you must try to destroy your opponents with various weapons. While it can be entertaining for short periods of time, nothing makes this title stand out from all the other racer/shooters around.

Battle Clash   Nintendo   4 $8
Designed to work with the SuperScope, this is nothing more than target practice on various monsters that will jump into view and move around. It is fun for a while, but the poor design of the SuperScope (really, what were they thinking?) will make this game seem a bit childish after a while.

Battle Grand Prix   Hudson Soft   6 $20
This is an average F-1 racing game that doesn't offer anything innovative, though fans of racing games might want to try it at least once.

Battletoads & Double Dragon
| | Tradewest | 3 | $10 |

An unlikely tag-team, this game features characters from two popular series at the time in an entertaining side scrolling fighter. This title will be very entertaining for both fans of the genre and for fans of either series.

Battletoads in Battlemaniacs
| | Tradewest | 3 | $10 |

This side scrolling fighting game features some nice character designs and animations, though the levels can become a bit monotonous.

Bazooka Blitzkreig   Bandai America   4 $8
Designed for use with the SuperScope, this title features some of the best action seen on this type of SNES game. Viewed from the first person, and guided through levels, you must shoot pretty much everything in your way. It plays similarly to Operation Wolf and other scrolling FPS's.

Beauty and the Beast   Hudson Soft   4 $8
This is a rather bland and often lazy-feeling action/platform game based on the Disney animated film.

Bebe's Kids   Motown Software   6 $25
An interesting piece of gaming history, this is one of only two titles released by Motown Software. Made in an attempt to

Barbie Super Model

Beethoven: The Ultimate Canine Caper!

Aiwa made a boom-box for distribution in China that also plays Sega CD games.

SNES

Best of the Best Championship Karate

The Blues Brothers

appeal to the black population, the characters are all black, and have names like Lashawn and Kahlil, and the music used in the game is even hip-hop. The game itself is a side scrolling fighter with very poor control and mediocre graphics, but might be of interest for its historical significance. Often named one of the worst video games ever made.

Beethoven: The Ultimate Canine Caper!
Hi Tech   5 $15
This is a side scrolling platform game featuring characters from the Beethoven movie series (a group of dogs.) Unresponsive controls and horrid character animations help make this dreadful game nearly as bad as the movies it was based upon.

Best of the Best: Championship Karate
Electro Brain   4 $8
Utilizing some nice lighting effects, and graphics that were greatly improved over the NES release two years earlier, this would be a fun fighting game if it weren't for the repetitive feel of every single match.

Big Sky Trooper   LucasArts   4 $8
A very odd action RPG, this title features comical situations as you try and destroy the aliens who have declared war against everyone on the earth. There are over 100 worlds that must be explored, making this a game that won't be solved quickly, though the "cheese factor" can be a bit too high to play for extended periods of time.

Biker Mice from Mars   Konami   6 $22
No, this isn't a joke, it really is the title of a video game. And what's worse, it was actually a cartoon series at one point. In a world filled with Teenage Mutant Ninja Turtles and Adolescent Radioactive Black Belt Hamsters, a few biker mice from Mars weren't going to cause too much of a stir, and as such this game is exclusive to the SNES. Racing your bike through a selection of 30 courses and against varying opponents will be much easier once you learn how to take them out of the running with various weapons. Viewed from an isometric viewpoint, this title offers a unique experience all around and becomes more enjoyable after some practice has been put into it.

Bill Laimbeer's Combat Basketball
Hudson Soft   2 $4
Viewed from overhead and featuring futuristic cyborg opponents, this title offers something a bit different, though overall it is a substandard basketball game.

Bill Walsh College Football
Electronic Arts   3 $10

While an average football game when regarding game play, this game offers the chance to challenge some of the greatest college football teams of all time with the college teams of 1993. A good concept that is executed nicely and should be a treat for college football fans.

BioMetal   Activision   6 $18
This side scrolling shooter is often considered to be a bad game, but it has some nice weapons systems and interesting backgrounds on certain levels. While it isn't overly addictive, you will probably find yourself wanting to finish "just one more level" from time to time.

Blackthorne   Interplay   5 $12
In this platform game you will play Kyle Blackthorne as he returns home to get revenge on those that killed his family. In addition to all the action typically associated with this type of game, puzzles solving will also play a role in this game.

BlaZeon: The Bio-Cyborg Challenge
Atlus   5 $12
A side scrolling space shooter, this title simply lacks the graphics and control that should be found on a game of this type on a system with the capabilities of the SNES.

Blues Brothers, The   Titus   6 $25
This side scrolling platform game stars the characters created by Saturday Night Live, trekking through 35 levels of increasing difficulty in order to get to their first paying job as musicians. While the characters are American icons, it doesn't save this game from becoming repetitive.

Boogerman: A Pick and Flick Adventure
Interplay   5 $12
If you thought that Conker's Bad Fur Day was the first Nintendo game to be based on gross bodily functions, then you should take a look at this side scrolling platform game. Featuring a gas attack and the ability to fling mucus at your enemies, this title was obviously meant to sell based on shock value alone.

Boxing Legends of the Ring
Electro Brain   4 $12
Graphics like these were simply unthinkable for a cartridge based system in 1993, but this game manages to recreate realistic looking boxers. Viewed from behind the shoulder, this boxing game is very enjoyable, though the control seems to be a bit too slow at times.

Brain Lord   Enix   4 $12
This is a fun RPG with an overhead view and decent graphics in

Nearly 150,000,000 Americans play video games.

which you will lead Remeer in his quest to find the lost Dragons. Along the way you will find 9 ferries that will aid you by bestowing special abilities such as new forms of attack and healing.

Brainies   Titus   4 $8
An interesting puzzle game, this title features 100 levels of overhead puzzle action. Lead the fuzzy creatures known as Brainies to the appropriately colored pad, but be careful of dangerous obstacles that stand in your way. The levels become increasingly difficult and will be extremely challenging toward the end of the game.

Bram Stoker's Dracula   Sony Imagesoft   4 $7
Featuring some very nice levels and a large amount of detail, this title suffers from poor control.

Brandish   KOEI   6 $28
An often overlooked action RPG, this game includes some very difficult mazes, numerous spells and items, and numerous enemies of all types. Though not quite as much fun as the better known RPG's for the SNES, this title should still please those that have already played everything else and are looking for something new.

Brawl Brothers   Jaleco   3 $8
Choose from five playable characters in this game, and fight your way through various levels in a fashion very similar to that of Final Fight.

BreakThru!   Spectrum Holobyte   5 $15
Best played with the mouse controller, this title was created by Alexev Pajitnov, the creator of Tetris. Selecting blocks that are in groups will cause that cluster to disappear, forming new block configurations as others fill their place. Once you have a large cluster of blocks of the same color, you can take them all out of the equation with a single click. Very fun and addictive, this title still fails to match Tetris's game play.

Breath of Fire   Square   3 $18
Often overlooked by the average gamer, this title is a favorite of hardcore RPG fans, and offers top notch gameplay all around. From a brilliant story line to an innovative battle engine, this game is definitely worth playing, even with the often steep price.

Breath of Fire II   Capcom   4 $25
By far the better of the two BoF games released on the SNES, some feel that this title even bests the amazing Final Fantasy 3. Superb graphics, excellent story and well designed characters help make this one of the best RPG's available for the SNES, but like its predecessor, often overlooked for the better known Final Fantasy 3.

Brett Hull Hockey   Accolade   3 $5
A respectable hockey title, this game is licensed by the NHLPA and features over 600 actual NHL players.

Brett Hull Hockey '95   Accolade   3 $7
Released two years after the original, this title features upgraded graphics that are impressive for a SNES game, and the control seems to have improved as well.

Bronkie the Bronchiasaurus
**   Raya Systems   7 $35**
Don't play this game without an inhaler! Designed to teach children the importance of understanding their asthma problems, this game features easily beaten side scrolling platform levels. The graphics certainly wouldn't be considered impressive by anyone, though it is interesting to play a game with a topic as odd as this one.

Brunswick World Tournament of Champions
**   THQ   2 $5**
While no video game can recreate the years of grueling physical training, strict diet, and the spiritual cleansing necessary to become a pro bowler...ahem...this game does feature a nice recreation of the sport. Various types of balls can be chosen for both primary and spare positions, and different styles of tournaments are available to keep things a bit more interesting than simply playing 10 frames.

Brutal: Paws of Fury   Cybersoft   4 $8
This Street Fighter II clone features some nice backgrounds, fluid character animations, and a very fast and solid fighting engine. This baby moves fast!

Bubsy II   Accolade   4 $6
While some of the levels show that a lot of work went into certain graphical aspects of the game, this title simply isn't any fun. Being a side scrolling platform game, the one thing a game in this genre can't afford to suffer from is control problems, and they're abundant in this game. The audio tracks also seem to be added as an afterthought and really detract from what is left of this horrible game.

Bubsy in Claws Encounter of the Furred Kind
**   Accolade   3 $5**
Better than its sequel, this side scrolling platform game still lacks what it takes to stand out as being a good game, and slips, unnoticed, between the cracks of the video game world's floor.

Boogerman: A Pick and Flick Adventure

Bubsy II

The Bally Astrocade was featured in National Lampoon's Vacation, as was an Apple IIe.

SNES

California Games II

Captain Novolin

Bugs Bunny Rabbit Rampage
Sunsoft 4 $10
An entertaining side scrolling platform adventure starring everyone's favorite cartoon rabbit (as if there were so many), this game has 10 levels and some nice graphical effects such as being "painted" into a new area.

Bulls vs. Blazers and the NBA Playoffs
Electronic Arts 2 $5
Viewed from side court, this game not only features the two titled teams, but all 14 teams that made it to the 1992 NBA playoffs. The graphics are nice and the sound effects are done well, creating an impressive environment for a game released a decade ago. A glitch in the game allows players to hit a three pointer just pass the half-court line every time.

Bust-A-Move
Taito 5 $20
As addictive as any other version of this game, the rules are simple to understand and the challenge quickly increases as the levels progress. Connecting three balloons of the same color cause the cluster to disappear, along with any other balloons that are supported by that structure. This is one of the few games to challenge Tetris as the best puzzle game of all time.

C2: Judgement Clay
Interplay 4 $8
This is the sequel to Clayfighter, and offers not only graphical and control improvements, but also contains twice as many playable combatants.

Cacoma Knight in Bizyland
Seta 4 $8
Awesome update to the puzzle classic Qix, but with power-ups and more bad guys to deal with.

Cal Ripken Jr. Baseball Mindscape 4 $8
With nice graphics, easily controllable characters, and a variety of stadiums to play in, this is a fun baseball game.

California Games II Hect 5 $12
The events featured in this title include bodysurfing, snowboarding, jet skiing, water skiing, and several others. The graphics are a bit below average, and the control could have used quite a bit of work. Overall, this feels like a NES game.

Cannondale Cup American Softworks 5 $12
This is pretty much the same game as Road Rash, but this time around you are on a bicycle. Set in an off-road bike tournament, the rules go out the window once the race begins, and you will need to fight your way to the finish line.

Captain America and the Avengers
Mindscape 3 $5
Arcade style side scrolling combat is the staple of this title. Featuring the four characters that make up the Avengers, this title should be enjoyable for comic book fans, and for those that remember the original release in the arcade.

Captain Commando Capcom 6 $20
A side scrolling fighting game, this title offers four unique characters to choose from: Mummy Commando, Captain Commando, Ninja Commando, and Baby Commando.

Captain Novolin Raya Systems 7 $35
A very interesting title, though not because of game play. This game was designed to teach diabetic children the importance of regulating their blood sugar. A side scrolling platform game, the action is repetitive and overly easy, though some of the enemies are interestingly disguised as various sugary foods. Limited in distribution, strictly as a learning aid, this game is difficult to find, and the box is even more difficult to come across.

Carrier Aces Cybersoft 4 $8
This is a prop plane war game viewed from behind the plane and features both two player action and pre-mission briefings.

Casper Natsume 6 $22
This side view/free roaming adventure game features some nice graphical effects and enjoyable game play. Notably, this is a completely different game than the 3DO version of Casper.

Castlevania Dracula X Konami 5 $35
The original PC Engine CD (our TG-16) game is a simply amazing and highly sought-after addition to the Castlevania series, but the SNES port is surprisingly bad. The graphics and sound effects just don't compare. Regardless, this game's pedigree and low production run keep it in high demand.

Champions World Class Soccer
Acclaim 3 $5
While the control and game play are about average, the viewpoint is so far away from the field that the players are miniscule.

Championship Pool Mindscape 3 $5
An overhead view pool game, there are various types of pool games that can be played, and the geometry seems to be very accurate in this game.

Championship Soccer '94 Sony Imagesoft 4 $6
While graphics aren't the most important part of video games, it is still unacceptable to have graphics this archaic on a 1994

The never-released Atari 2700 was simply an Atari 2600 in a new case, and featuring wireless controllers.

SNES release. The players resemble ants on the field, and while control is accurate, it is too difficult to make precise movements due to the size of the players.

Chavez   **American Softworks 4 $10**
Named after the boxing great, this game is about average, though it does offer some nice graphics. The one major complaint with this game is the speed at which your character reacts to the controls. The speed necessary to win a boxing match seems to be missing from time to time.

Chavez II   **American Softworks 6 $20**
Graphical and control improvements were both made, and while the players are still a bit faster, it still seems as if there is a delay between control input and character reaction.

Chessmaster, The   **Software Toolworks 3 $5**
A great way to burn some extra time, this title features the classic game of chess, and offers both an adequate challenge for different player levels, but also looks nice.

Chester Cheetah: Too Cool to Fool
                Kaneko   4 $8
This, the first Chester Cheetah game for the SNES was released in 1992 and features side scrolling action in your quest to recover your lost scooter

Chester Cheetah: Wild Wild Quest
                Kaneko   5 $12
About average as side scrolling games go, this title features the lovable Cheetos mascot, though he was starting to be overused at this point.

Choplifter 3   **Beam Software 4 $8**
This helicopter combat game features arcade style action and improved graphics over its predecessors.

Chrono Trigger   **Square   4 $60**
Often heralded as the quintessential RPG, and rarely rivaled by any other, this game is becoming increasingly difficult to find due to the fact that so many RPG fans are buying them at every chance they get. Utilizing time travel as a key element within the game itself and featuring a free roaming adventure/RPG style, this game is an absolute must-have for every SNES owner, though the price is often prohibitive. Puzzles and small side events will keep you interested even during periods of frustration when the correct path is not always obvious.

Chuck Rock   **Sony Imagesoft 3 $5**
The SNES version of this game features some nice colors and sharp graphics, and the characters seem to control nicely, making it an above average platformer.

ClayFighter   **Interplay   3 $5**
Featuring characters of clay, this fighting title offered something new in the crowded world of fighting games. Seeing moderate success, it would spawn several sequels over a variety of video game consoles.

ClayFighter: Tournament Edition
                Interplay   9 $120
This is a Blockbuster Video exclusive version of Clay Fighter with more options and levels plus an extra character or two. Keep an eye for this one, it's quite the rarity.

Claymates   **Interplay   4 $8**
This is a side scroller featuring a variety of claymation characters, each with their own special moves.

Cliffhanger   **Sony Imagesoft 3 $5**
This is an interesting variation of a side scrolling brawler, where you must climb mountains and build fires to stay alive in this game based on the hit movie.

Clue   **Parker Brothers 3 $5**
This is a fantastic adaptation of timeless board game with lots of options to make each solution harder to solve. For example, on the more difficult settings you only learn which room weapons are in which rooms as opposed to being told which weapons/rooms/characters are not part of the answer. Clue has replay value that soars through the roof.

College Football USA '97 **Electronic Arts 3 $5**
Another Football game from EA Sports that uses the Madden engine with a college theme.

College Slam   **Acclaim   4 $6**
This is simply NBA Jam with better graphics and college teams.

Combatribes, The   **Technos Japan 3 $6**
Help save New York City in this Double Dragon style brawler.

Congo's Caper   **Data East   4 $8**
This game features 35 levels of simple platform action designed for a younger audience.

Contra III: The Alien Wars Konami   2 $8
Amazing graphics and solid control help make this one of the best Contra titles ever made. With both side scrolling action and overhead sequences, this game features enough variation to keep anyone interested. And the boss characters, large and detailed, round out this title, making it a must-have for your

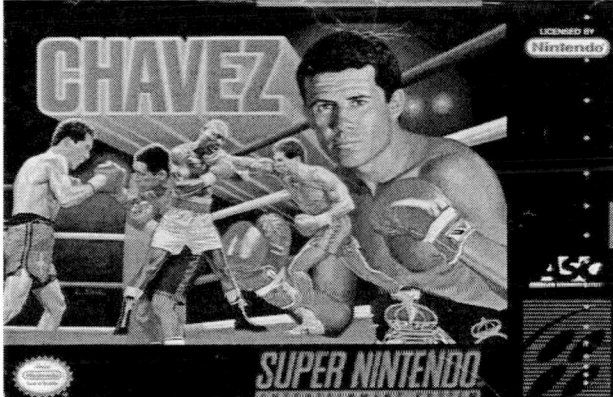

Chavez

Chrono Trigger

Early Intellivisions often overheated, especially when used on the carpet.

SNES

Congo's Caper

Cool World

SNES library.

Cool Spot   Virgin   3 $5
Guide the 7-Up mascot through this average platform jumping adventure.

Cool World   Ocean   4 $8
This game is based on the Brad Pitt animated/live action movie.

Cutthroat Island   LJN   4 $8
Based on the movie that was the single biggest box office flop in history. Cutthroat Island lets players choose either a sword slashing quest or a punchy-kicky brawler in this game that lives up to the moves hype. That is to say, it doesn't.

Cybernator   Konami   3 $5
Take control of a giant robot that features a wide variety of ammo in this running and shooting side scroller.

Cyberspin   Takara   6 $22
This is a futuristic style overhead racing game with embarrassing graphics.

D-Force   Asmik   4 $8
This is a vertically scrolling shooter with solid control, but inferior graphics.

Daffy Duck: The Marvin Missions
    Sunsoft   4 $10
Based on the classic cartoon "Duck Dodgers in the 24th and a Half Century," you play as Daffy Duck who must rescue intergalactic ambassadors from the hands of Marvin the Martian. Stale platform action and shamefully dull graphics make this one of the worst Looney Tune games on the SNES.

Darius Twin   Taito   2 $5
This is an incredibly difficult shooting game with an overwhelming enemy count.

David Crane's Amazing Tennis
    Absolute   3 $5
This is a stale tennis game by the creator of Pitfall!

Death and Return of Superman
    Sunsoft   5 $15
Based on the popular comic series where Superman died at the hands of the soulless killing machine Doomsday. Standard punch and kick Final Fight clone but with the added bonus of five different Supermen to control.

Demolition Man   Acclaim   4 $8
Game Play switches from an overhead run and gun to a platform jumping shooter in this mediocre game based on the hit movie.

Demon's Crest   Capcom   4 $8
A sequel to the popular series of Gargoyal games by Capcom, Demon's Crest is a side scrolling platformer with Castlevania flavor and incredible graphics. Horrible sales for Demon Crest was enough to drive the final stake in this underrated series.

Dennis the Menace   Ocean   4 $8
This is a boring side scroller that is based on the movie and not the comic strip.

Desert Strike: Return to the Gulf
    Electronic Arts   3 $5
Take the controls of a helicopter and wipe out our Middle Eastern enemies in this free roaming overhead shooting game.

Dino City   Irem   4 $8
This side scrolling platform game features six levels in which you will ride on the back of a dinosaur to defeat the Neanderthal Rockeys and save DinoCity.

Dirt Trax FX   Acclaim   4 $8
While impressive upon its release, this polygon based motocross title has aged poorly and the graphics are nostalgic at best.

Donkey Kong Country   Nintendo   1 $5
This title is a ground breaking platform adventure that was the first ever fully rendered video game. Instead of stopping at state of the art graphics, Nintendo put together an incredible quest that sees players guide Donkey Kong and Diddy through 50 levels. Donkey Kong Country was the best selling Super NES game and is thusly the most common.

Donkey Kong Country 2: Diddy's Kong Quest
    Nintendo   2 $8
One of the hardest SNES platform games, Donkey Kong has been kidnapped and now Diddy Kong and his girl friend Dixie must rescue him. The graphics were vastly improved over the previous Donkey Kong Country, a feat nobody thought possible. Finding all the hidden objects is still a great way to test your video game skills.

Donkey Kong Country 3: Dixie Kong's Double Trouble
    Nintendo   2 $8
The series was getting stale by the third entry where both Don-

The Colecovision can play Atari 2600 games with the proper adapter.

key Kong and Diddy have been captured. Dixie had her dopey brother use a variety of special attacks to navigate another fifty levels of fully rendered eye candy.

Doom   Tradewest   3 $5
Regardless of the FX chip residing inside the cart, the SNES simply isn't capable of handling the graphics necessary to make this game look good. On an interesting side note, this cart contains a metal pin just inside the opening of the cartridge that can become hung on the internals of your SNES, and upon removal can actually damage the system. It is rare that this actually happens, but it warrants a look inside your Doom cart to see if the pin is bent or protrudes unduly.

Doomsday Warrior   Renovation Products   3 $5
Choose from seven characters in this head-to-head fighting game. The environments are pretty simple, but the fighters are detailed and control relatively well.

Double Dragon V: The Shadow Falls
            Tradewest   4 $10
This 2-D fighting game features 10 selectable characters from the Double Dragon franchise, and plays relatively well for a SNES fighting game.

Dragon: The Bruce Lee Story
            Acclaim   4 $8
A fighting game based on characters from the movie by the same name, this game can be entertaining, though the moves are overly simple and the graphics are obviously dated. It won't take more than an hour or so to beat the game, and as such has very little replay value.

Dragon's Lair   Data East   4 $8
Platform action game featuring Dirk the Daring in this title based very loosely on the arcade laser disc classic.

Drakkhen   Kemco   3 $5
While the graphics aren't very impressive, this is still a solid early-release RPG using an action window and menu driven game play.

Drakkhen 2: Dragon View   Kemco   5 $15
Changing styles from the first installment of this RPG series, this title is more action oriented and is viewed in the third-person.

Dream TV   Traffix Entertainment   6 $18
This is a poorly designed and executed action game with very below average graphics and sound. You'll spend a lot of time just wandering around.

Dungeon Master   JVC   4 $10
Also available for the Atari ST line, this is an average first-person RPG.

EarthBound   Nintendo   2 $5
This is a surreal RPG where aliens are invading the Earth. As Ness, you face off against Retro Hippies, Spiteful Crows, and various other strange enemies. Earthbound, known as "Mother" in Japan, was heavily hyped by Nintendo. Ads for the game featured the most foul smelling scratch & sniff stickers on the planet, which had hilarious results. Nintendo packaged Earthbound in an oversized box so that they could include a full sized players guide with it. Many parents thought the box was oversized because the game included a device that would leak the foul smelling odors from the scratch & sniff ads into your room. As a result, some kids were denied the right to play this classic over the fear that the house would smell bad because of it. The whole "Smell-o-Vision" thing has become an urban legend among gamers.

Earthworm Jim   Playmates   2 $4
Take the role of Jim himself in this platform adventure. Featuring some very nice character animations and gorgeous levels, this title has become a favorite among many gamers.

Earthworm Jim 2   Playmates   3 $5
More of the same high quality game play is featured in this sequel that features small graphical improvements and maintains a high level of control.

Eek! The Cat   Ocean   5 $12
Featuring the character Eek from the TV show by the same name, this side scrolling platform game has some nicely detailed levels, though the game itself is a bit too simple for serious gamers.

Elite Soccer   GameTek   1 $0
This is a solid soccer title that offers numerous types of game play, and even offers an indoor field to play on.

Emmitt Smith Football   JVC   2 $4
Not able to stand on its own merits as a game, Emmit Smith's name was added to this substandard title in an attempt to make it more competitive with the Madden series.

Equinox: Solstice II   Sony Imagesoft   3 $8
An awesome isometric RPG, this title should please fans of the first Solstice title as well as those new to the series.

ESPN Baseball Tonight   Sony Imagesoft   3 $4
Released in 1994, this baseball title should have been refined a

Doom

Doomsday Warrior

The Amiga CDTV originally retailed for $999.

SNES

Eye of the Beholder

Faceball 2000

bit more, but instead player control is often difficult, and the graphics and sound could have both been improved.

ESPN Basketball   Sony Imagesoft   3 $4
This is an average basketball sim with respectable graphics and sound but a rather slow game engine.

ESPN Hangtime '95   Sony Imagesoft   3 $4

ESPN National Hockey Night
           Sony Imagesoft   3 $4

ESPN Speed World   Sony Imagesoft   4 $6
This stock car racing game features a viewpoint from behind the car, and while it controls relatively well is a simple game overall.

ESPN Sunday Night NFL   Sony Imagesoft   3 $4
Released in 1994, this game features all AFC and NFC teams are present, though no real players names are used.

EVO: The Search for Eden   Enix   4 $8
This wildly underrated (and highly original) action/RPG is based completely on the concept of human evolution… you start the game off as a fish and work your way up. How you proceed from there is entirely up to you.

Exertainment: Mountain Bike Rally
           Life Fitness   8 $35
Designed as part of a fitness plan, and used with a special exer-cycle, this is a mountain biking game that can be controlled by using the exercycle attachment. These weren't very popular at all, and the bike was prohibitively expensive. As more collectors are made aware of these titles and the desire for them is in-creased, the price will almost certainly increase as well.

Exertainment: Project Manager
           Life Fitness   8 $40
Instead of offering a specific type of game, this title offered exer-cise programs designed for different functions such as raising your heart rate, burning fat, etc.

Exertainment: Speed Racer
           Life Fitness   8 $35

Extra Innings   Sony Imagesoft   2 $4
This average baseball game looks and feels like a glorified NES game.

Eye of the Beholder   Capcom   4 $10
Create a party of four characters, and take the lead as Paladin-

son in an attempt to destroy the evil creature known as Xana-thar. Control your character with a first person perspective through the tunnels beneath the city of Waterdeep. This is an entertaining game that should be played by any action/ adventure RPG fan.

F1 Pole Position   UBI Soft   4 $6
The graphics and sound of this F1 racer are up to the usual SNES standards, but the wretched gameplay and top-down view renders the game virtually unplayable.

F1 Pole Position 2   Human Entertainment   4 $8

F1 ROC: Race of Champions
           Seta   4 $8
This title features some of the worst graphics seen in any F1 game.

F1 ROC II   Seta   5 $12
Released two years after its predecessor, this version has better graphics and control, though is still not very impressive.

Faceball 2000   Bullet-Proof Software   4 $8
Pretty much the same game that can be found as freeware online, your job is to take down your opponents, that just hap-pen to be large faces. While this game is fun for a few minutes, it can quickly become repetitive as the levels, though different in design, still feel the same throughout.

Family Dog   Malibu Games   5 $12
Platform jumping game based on the once popular primetime cartoon character. Incredibly bad game but also quite rare.

Family Feud   GameTek   4 $8
Based on the TV show by the same name, this title will probably bore most gamers, though it should be entertaining for those old enough to remember the original game show.

Fatal Fury   Takara   3 $5
This port of the classic Neo-Geo fighter doesn't quite make the grade… the selection of fighters is poor and the fighting engine is very shallow.

Fatal Fury 2   Takara   3 $5
Quite an improvement over the original game, Fatal Fury 2 fea-tures a much deeper and satisfying game engine and seems to be a clone of Street Fighter II.

Fatal Fury: Special   Takara   5 $15
The third and final Fatal Fury game for the SNES is better than

The RDI Halcyon only had two games released for it.

the previous games in several key areas... the character selection is much better, the graphics are improved, and the gameplay has been enhanced and perfected.

Fido Dido Kaneko 6 $20
This 1993 side scrolling platform game is only available for the SNES and Genesis, though this version looks better.

FIFA Soccer '96 Electronic Arts 3 $5
Improvements abound in this yearly update to the perennial favorite, but the game engine is still inferior to the Genesis port.

FIFA '97: Gold Edition Electronic Arts 4 $6

FIFA '98: Road to the World Cup
Electronic Arts 4 $6
The SNES finally got out from behind the shadow of the Genesis for the final FIFA release on the console. The game engine moves at a solid pace, and the graphics and soundtrack are very nice.

FIFA International Soccer Electronic Arts 3 $5
EA's series of superlative soccer games made a solid appearance on the SNES, but the first few installments lagged behind their Genesis counterparts in the crucial area of game speed.

Fighter's History Data East 4 $8
This otherwise below-average 2D fighter actually represents an important milestone in gaming history. It was the first real Street Fighter II clone, and Capcom sued Data East because of the two games' similarities. The courts ruled in favor of Data East, forever opening the door for other companies to release their own fighting games without fear of reprisal.

Final Fantasy II Square 3 $30
This glorious continuation of the now-classic NES game reeks of imagination and quality... rarely do RPG's get any better than this. The graphics aren't much to shout about, but the experience is unforgettable.

Final Fantasy III Square 2 $40
Most Final Fantasy Fans will tell you that this is the best Final Fantasy ever made. Most RPG fans will tell you that this is the best RPG ever made. And yes, there are even those that would say it is the best video game ever made. Originally released as Final Fantasy 6 in Japan, this title has become extremely desirable, though it isn't actually that difficult to find, just expensive. If you have never played any of the Final Fantasy games, this should definitely be the one to try out. An if you are looking for a way to entertain yourself for 40-50 hours, this is a nice way to do it.

Final Fantasy Mystic Quest
Square 2 $8
While some might complain that this installment in the Final Fantasy series is too simple, it still remains a fun RPG that should be entertaining for most gamers.

Final Fight Capcom 1 $2
Side-scrolling action/fighters were once a popular gaming genre, but they have fallen on hard times as of late. Whatever the case, the SNES port of this arcade favorite is nearly perfect.

Final Fight 2 Capcom 3 $8
This sequel to the popular scrolling fighter is an SNES exclusive and features more characters and levels, plus enhanced graphics and sound.

Final Fight 3 Capcom 4 $10
Capcom ended the series' run on the SNES in fine style, providing gamers with more of the brutal side-scrolling fighting action they had grown accustomed to. The graphics and game play are better than the already-good prequels, and this the largest and longest-lasting of the three games.

Final Fight Guy Capcom 8 $50
A Blockbuster Video exclusive title that is extremely hard to find in the open market. Final Fight Guy is a remake of the original brawler but with one new selectable character and a different variety of bad guys.

Firepower 2000 Sunsoft 4 $8
This is an excellent vertical shooter featuring tank or helicopter control, a cool 2-player mode, great graphics, and a wonderful soundtrack.

Firestriker Hect 5 $12
This interesting and highly unusual take on the standard Break-out formula is entertaining at first, but the game play wears thin after a while.

First Samurai Kemco 5 $12
This is a mediocre side-scrolling fighter with unremarkable graphics and a convoluted storyline involving a Samurai warrior and time travel.

Flashback: Quest for Identity
U.S. Gold 3 $6
Search for your identity in this adventure game, featuring some very nice graphics that utilize color and depth in a totally new way. Available for several systems, this title is best played on either the SNES or Atari Jaguar.

SNES

F-Zero

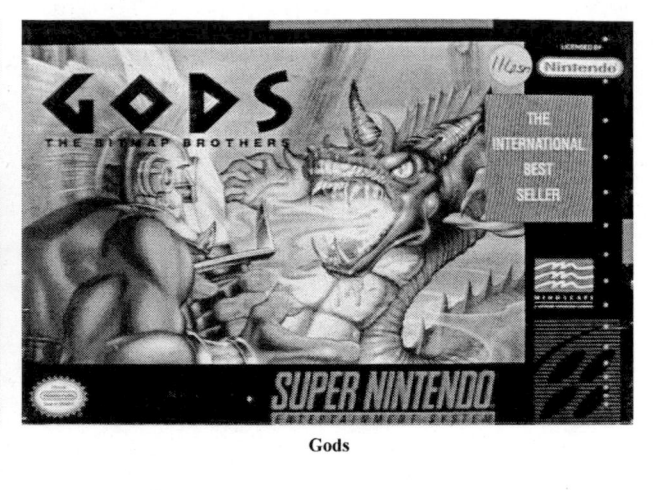

Gods

Flintstones, The   Ocean   4 $8
This 1995 side scrolling platform game features some very detailed graphics and fun gameplay.

Flintstones: Treasure of Sierra Madrock
     Taito   4 $8
Released in 1994, this title features the cartoon characters from the series, and not those from the movie on which the above game (The Flintstones) would be based.

Football Fury   American Sammy   3 $5
A side angle makes it difficult to execute intricate plays, and this game quickly becomes a time killer with no satisfaction.

Foreman for Real   Acclaim   4 $6
Some very nice graphics are used in this 1995 boxing release, though the characters are difficult to control at times, making it an often frustrating game.

Frank Thomas Big Hurt Baseball
     Acclaim   2 $4
With nice graphics and decent control, this is a very playable baseball game.

Frantic Flea   GameTek   4 $8
Featuring extremely colorful backgrounds, this side scrolling platform game actually appears to have been hand drawn in certain areas.

Frogger   Majesco   4 $8
One of the last Super Nintendo releases, this port of the classic arcade game is surprisingly poor (especially when compared to the Genesis version, which was also released by Majesco around the same time.) The visuals are substandard, the gameplay doesn't feel quite right, and the music is nearly nonexistent.

Full Throttle Racing   Game Tek   5 $10

Fun 'N' Games   Tradewest   5 $12
Edutainment and entertainment don't go together where adults are involved, so save this one for the kids.

F-Zero   Nintendo   1 $2
This first generation racer amazed gamers with its smooth "mode 7" graphics, incredibly tight and intuitive control, glorious soundtrack, and cool futuristic design. Many of us still consider F-Zero to rank among the top racers ever made, and it's a real shame that the SNES sequel was a Japan-only treat. Thankfully, the N64 and GBA updates are nearly as good as the origi-

nal, and still offer endless hours of racing fun.

Gemfire   KOEI   3 $6
Unlike many of Koei's strategy games, Gemfire isn't set in a particular historical period... it's set in a fantasy world instead. Otherwise, the game is as deep and enjoyable as any Koei title.

Gengis Khan II: Clan of Grey Wolf
     KOEI   3 $12
While not quite up to the level of the Romance of the 3 Kingdoms series, this deep simulation nevertheless manages to provide great entertainment with its blend of strategy-based gameplay and historical fact.

George Foreman's KO Boxing
     Acclaim   3 $5
The aging heavyweight has hawked more than just grills and mufflers... he also has his own mediocre boxing sim to sell to the unsuspecting masses.

Ghoul Patrol   LucasArts   5 $12
This is a rare sequel to Zombies ate my Neighbors that features more zombie busting action with a larger variety of weapons.

Goal!   Jaleco   3 $4
This soccer game sports some nice features and adequate graphics, making it a close competitor with the FIFA line of games on the SNES.

Gods   Mindscape   3 $5
While the game play is both solid and fun, the level designs become repetitive quickly.

Goof Troop   Capcom   5 $12
This excellent little action/puzzle game is a departure from many of the Disney licensed platform games released for the SNES. The game engine is a fairly close adaptation of the battle sequences from the NES classic Star Tropics.

GP-1   Atlus   3 $6
Similar in feel and style to Sega's Hang-On, this motorcycle racing game gives both the feeling of speed and of tight control through various tracks.

GP-1 Part II   Atlus   4 $8
While the graphics have actually taken a step down in this release, control was improved a bit to give more of a realistic feel to the game.

The standard controllers for both the Memorex VIS and the Amiga CDTV are wireless.

Gradius III Konami 2 $6
The Gradius games aren't among the best horizontal shooters ever made, but they're still better than half the games out there. The graphics are a bit sad in part 3, but the soundtrack and control are quite good.

Great Circus Mystery: Starring Mickey and Minnie
Capcom 3 $8
Lush graphics, a lovely soundtrack, excellent control, and ingenious level design all conspire to make this platform game a winner.

Great Waldo Search THQ 4 $6
Just like pet rocks, the Where's Waldo fad is nearly nonexistent these days. While those who grew up on the book series might find this title entertaining, it is an overall disappointment. Stick with the books if you must find Waldo.

GunForce Irem 4 $8

Hagane Hudson Soft 6 $18
This is a fairly average action/platform game with some admittedly stunning graphics and a lovely soundtrack.

HammerLock Wrestling Jaleco 4 $6
Wrestling games are an acquired taste, but had had como difficulty acquiring the taste of this bland and poorly designed wrestling title.

Hardball III Accolade 2 $4
This Hardball series laid groundwork most of today's favorite baseball sims. Many of the features we take for granted in baseball games were introduced, including the first-person home plate view and the deeper, less arcade-style gameplay.

Harley's Humongous Adventure
Hi Tech 4 $8

Harvest Moon Natsume 4 $12
This gentle series of RPG's has a small but loyal fan based that seems to have grown in recent years. Whatever the case, if farming and animal husbandry are your thing, here you go!

Head-On Soccer U.S. Gold 4 $8
Not quite arcade-style action, not quite full-on simulation, Head-On Soccer walks the line between the two and mostly succeeds with its simple yet gameplay-oriented approach to the soccer genre.

Hit the Ice Taito 3 $5
This is a port of the popular arcade hockey game. It's not on the

same level as any of EA's hockey games, but it's good for a quick fix of arcade-style action.

Hole-In-One Golf Natsume 2 $4
This early golf simulation features some surprisingly nice graphics and good game play.

Home Alone THQ 3 $5
This bad platform game is based on the popular movie series. It is full of bad humor and irritatingly cheap gameplay.

Home Alone 2: Lost in New York
THQ 2 $4
This is yet another bad platform game based on the popular movie franchise.

Home Improvement Absolute 4 $8
This platform action game is based on the popular TV series staring Tim Allen.

Hook Sony Imagesoft 3 $5
Like the ultimately dreadful movie that spawned it, this licensed game has some cute bits but the whole package is less than the sum of its parts.

Hunt for Red October Hi Tech 3 $5
The excellent movie may have been a bit hard to follow if you didn't pay close attention, but this mission-based shooter is fairly easy to get into, even if it is difficult to beat.

Hurricanes U.S. Gold 4 $8
Take control of various soccer team members as they travel through several side scrolling platform levels. The detail in the environments is amazing, and this title was only released for the SNES.

Hyper V-Ball Video System 3 $5

HyperZone Halken 2 $4
Part Space Harrier, part F-Zero, this futuristic shooter sports some impressive graphics and level design, but the gameplay is rather shallow and it ends all too quickly.

Ignition Factor Jaleco 4 $8
How many firefighting games can you name off the top of your head? Here's another one to add to your list. Unfortunately, the intriguing concept of this action/platform game is plagued with design and control issues.

Illusion of Gaia Nintendo 2 $10
This is an incredibly long and draw out action/RPG. The action

Harvest Moon

Home Improvement

The first "easter egg" was found in the game Adventure for the Atari 2600. It was an invisible dot that led to a room with the maker's name.

SNES

Inindo: Way of the Ninja

The Jetsons: Invasion of the Planet Pirates

elements, although few and far between, are very much like Legend of Zelda and make the 80+ hour epic somewhat enjoyable. Look out for a hilariously melodramatic scene where a pig commits suicide to feed starving villagers.

Imperium   **Vic Tokai**   5 $12
This vertically scrolling shooting game features nice detail, but can suffer from slowdown from time to time.

Incantation   **Titus**   4 $8

Incredible Crash Test Dummies
                    LJN   4 $8
This is a substandard and slow-moving platform game starring Vince and Larry, the Crash Test Dummies that were once popular due to some public safety announcements but have since disappeared.

Incredible Hulk   **U.S. Gold**   3 $5
Bruce Banner's mean green alter ego has received a bad reputation in the video gaming world, and this substandard action/fighting game certainly doesn't to anything to improve his reputation.

Indiana Jones' Greatest Adventures
                    LucasArts   3 $6
This is a difficult platform game that recreates scenes from the popular movie trilogy. In addition to the side scrolling action, there are some special events, like riding the mine cart from the Temple of Doom.

Inindo: Way of the Ninja   **KOEI**   3 $6
Koei has carved a niche for by developing great strategy games steeped in historical fact. Unfortunately, Inindo is not one of their best efforts (but it's still an entertaining game.)

Inspector Gadget   **Hudson Soft**   4 $10
You should know what to expect from a game bearing the Inspector Gadget license, and you get it in spades… colorful graphics combined with standard platform game action.

International Superstar Soccer
                    Konami   4 $6

International Superstar Soccer Deluxe
                    Konami   4 $6
One of the better soccer titles on the SNES, ISSD manages to impress even jaded sports fans with its blend of lush graphics and spot-on control.

International Tennis Tour   **Taito**   4 $5

Itchy & Scratchy Game   **Acclaim**   4 $6
This wacky title (based on the violent cartoons of the sick cat and mouse duo) isn't much of a game but it is just bizarre enough to be fun.

Izzy's Quest for the Olympic Rings
                    U.S. Gold   3 $5
This is a dull platform game bearing the likeness of Izzy, Atlanta's uninspiring mascot for the 1996 Summer Games.

Jack Nicklaus Golf   **Tradewest**   4 $6
This really is a fun golf game, and features both detailed players and accurate courses, plus the added bonus of being the official game of the Golden Bear himself.

James Bond Jr.   **THQ**   4 $8
This installment to the series offers improved sound, graphics and control over the NES version, but still remains an average side scrolling platform game at heart.

Jammit!   **GTE Entertainment**   2 $2

Jeopardy!   **GameTek**   2 $3
Based on the TV show of the same name, this game should entertain until the same questions begin to cycle back through the rotation. This is a common problem found on games of this sort, and every console version of this game exhibits this flaw.

Jeopardy! Deluxe Edition   **GameTek**   2 $3
More clues and questions in this, an expanded version of the popular game show title.

Jeopardy! Sports Edition   **GameTek**   2 $3
As the title implies, this is Jeopardy with the key subject being sports.

Jetsons: Invasion of the Planet Pirates, The
                    Taito   5 $12
Take control of George Jetson in this side scrolling platform adventure in which you must complete 9 levels in order to save the world.

Jim Power: Lost Dimension in 3-D
                    Electro Brain   5 $12
It's best that this game stay buried and forgotten right where it is. The graphics and game play of this mediocre 3-D style shooter will leave you under whelmed.

Three versions of the Neo-Geo CD were released in Japan, but only one made it to the U.S.

Jimmy Connors Pro Tennis Tour
UBI Soft   4 $6
This highly regarded tennis simulation allows you to play as Jimmy Connnors (there are no other characters to select) and progress up the tournament ladder. The graphics and control and near perfect.

Jimmy Houston's Bass Tournament USA
American Sammy   4 $8

Joe & Mac   Data East   2 $4
Average platformer that follows a pair of cavemen who battle dinosaurs. The incredible graphics left players in awe when it was first released.

Joe & Mac 2: Lost in the Tropics
Data East   2 $4
This sequel offers more of the same dino fighting action with a larger variety of weapons.

John Madden Football   Electronic Arts   1 $1
The first of many football games featuring the likeness of the legendary football coach. The Madden series is still alive and well to this day because of the success of this first title which had an amazing playbook and a realistic feel that other football games didn't offer.

John Madden Football '93   Electronic Arts   1 $1
Follow up to the original features a larger playbook and a wide variety of options.

Judge Dredd   Acclaim   2 $4
This movie-based action/platform game is better than you'd expect.

Jungle Book   Virgin   4 $8
This is yet another beautiful and well-designed platform game sporting a Disney movie license.

Jungle Strike   Electronic Arts   3 $5
This cool helicopter shooter features the same cool graphics, sound, and tough gameplay found in all the Strike games.

Jurassic Park   Ocean   2 $4
Combining overhead and first person shooting, Jurassic Park is a fairly enjoyable adaptation of the popular movie. Jurassic Park was one of the few games that support the SNES house.

Jurassic Park 2: The Chaos Continues
Ocean   3 $5
The frenetic shooting action continues in this excellent but overly challenging sequel featuring beautiful graphics and a rousing soundtrack.

Justice League Task Force
Acclaim   4 $8
This is disappointingly average fighting game featuring a select group of superhero characters. We remember looking forward to this title with great anticipation, but Acclaim dropped the ball and delivered a mediocre and shallow fighter unworthy of its license.

Kablooey   Kemco   3 $5
This addictive shooter/puzzle game is presented from an isometric perspective. Nothing about the game is particularly noteworthy, but it's more than the sum of its parts.

Kawasaki Caribbean Challenge
GameTek   4 $8

Kawasaki Superbike Challenge
Time Warner Interactive   4 $8
A bit better than the average motorcycle racing game, this title offers a good sense of control when making turns.

Ken Griffey Jr. Presents Major League Baseball
Nintendo   2 $3
The CEO of Nintendo of America went out and bought the Seattle Mariners, then used their most popular star to drive up sales of this sour baseball game that features all the big league teams without the big league players. The MLBPA wouldn't lend their license to the title, and as a result the only real professional in the game is Griffey himself.

Ken Griffey Jr.'s Winning Run
Nintendo   3 $5
Like the original Ken Griffey title, Winning Run was not supported by the Major League Baseball Players Association and thusly had no real players except Junior himself. Amazing graphics and sound make this one of the best baseball games ever made, but the baseball strike drove away some potential buyers who were fed up with America's pastime.

Kendo Rage   Seta   4 $8
This bizarre little action game features a colorful cast of characters and a very Japanese feel to it. The boss characters and humor are a welcome departure from the norm, but the challenge ramps up a bit too fast for some gamers.

Kid Klown in Crazy Chase
Kemco   4 $8
A strange three-quarter perspective is the only glaring problem in this simple action-adventure title.

Kawasaki Caribbean Challenge

King Arthur's World

Japanese controllers are typically smaller than those in the U.S. since hands are larger in the U.S. (on average)

SNES

Killer Instinct

Knights of the Round

Killer Instinct   Nintendo   1 $2
When this title was released in the arcades, crowds would gather to see the smoothly animated characters within. Long and complex combination moves were utilized during game play, and nobody ever thought that this title would make it to the SNES. Though it doesn't look as flashy or play as well as the arcade version, it was still nice to be able to bring this title home to the SNES.

King Arthur & the Knights of Justice
                                Enix   6 $22
Based on a rather unpopular and mostly ignored cartoon series, this is a dreadful attempt at an RPG seems unfinished and underdeveloped.

King Arthur's World   Jaleco   4 $8
This is a Lemmings style action puzzler with a medieval theme.

King of Dragons   Capcom   4 $8
This is a rather dated side-scrolling action game ported from an equally dated arcade game. The RPG elements add a refreshing change of pace, though.

King of the Monsters   Takara   3 $5
As with all Neo-Geo games, this title simply can't compare to the original, though the control seems to be about right. A high learning curve will keep most gamers from becoming addicted to this fighting game, though it becomes very enjoyable after the special moves have been learned.

King of the Monsters 2   Takara   3 $5
With less playable characters than the first, and little graphical improvement, this title just isn't as good as the first, though it is often felt that this installment has a better control scheme.

Kirby Super Star   Nintendo   2 $6
Kirby is one of Nintendo's cutest (and some would say most irritating) corporate characters. Regardless of your feelings for the little cloud, the simple yet entertaining game play of this action game will entertain both children and adults alike.

Kirby's Avalanche   Nintendo   3 $8
The classic puzzle game Puyo Pop with Kirby characters. Kirby's Avalanche is considered one of the best versions of it ever made. The game is also known as Dr. Robotnik's Mean Bean Machine on the Sega Genesis.

Kirby's Dream Course   Nintendo   3 $8
Incredibly fun golf game that is among the most underrated games for the systems. Dream Course combines Golf with puzzle elements and a variety of enemies and hazards to make one of the most innovative games ever made.

Kirby's Dream Land 3   Nintendo   4 $10
The last of the Kirby games for the SNES, Dream Land 3 continues the series tradition of simple yet addictive action combined with colorful graphics and overly cute characters.

Knights of the Round   Capcom   5 $18
This is a better-than-expected side-scrolling fighter (ported from an arcade game) featuring lovely graphics and sound plus some great level design.

Krusty's Super Fun House   Acclaim   3 $5
This Lemmings clone plays well enough but doesn't do much with its great Simpsons source material.

Lagoon   Kemco   3 $6
An old fashioned Action-RPG, you play as a child of the light who must discover who has been making the waters of the land muddy. The graphics were ground breaking when this was released in 1991, and they still hold up well today. The game controls fairly well, although there are some frustrating jumps at various times in the game. Although not too rare, it's worth picking up if you're a fan of genre.

Lamborghini - American Challenge
                                Titus   4 $7
Not one of the better SNES racers, Lamborghini AC suffers from poorly designed courses, mediocre graphics, and a lack of innovation all around.

Last Action Hero   Sony Imagesoft   3 $5
Proving that any big movie, good or bad, success or failure can be made into a game, Sony presents us with Last Action Hero. The flick was a disaster critically and commercially, which technically could make this title one of the most accurate games based on a movie ever. The graphics are horrible even by NES standards, and the play control makes the game nearly impossible. If you're not trying to put together a complete Super NES library, then avoid this game at all costs.

Lawnmower Man   THQ   3 $5
Based on the science fiction movie, you control a scientist trying to stop his out of control human experiment.

Legend   Seika   4 $10
A Final Fight style brawler with a fantasy twist. Legend has a very slow pace and a lack of variety that will become boring

The Star Fox wingman, Falco Lambardi was named after the French actor Carlo Lombardi.

really quick if you're not into the side-scrolling beat 'um ups.

Legend of Mystical Ninja   Konami   2 $5
One of the better games on the system, Legend of the Mystical Ninja combines elements of overhead RPGs with platform action to make an unique hybrid. As Goemon and Ebisamaru, you set out to rescue the Princess using your martial arts skills. With an anime look and hilarious dialog, the storyline stays fresh and always challenging. A fairly common classic that no SNES collector should be without.

**Legend of Zelda: A Link to the Past, The
                          Nintendo   1 $5**
Easily one of the best titles for the SNES, this game is a necessity for any SNES owner, and very easy to come by. Featuring game play that is similar to The Legend of Zelda, and greatly improved graphics, this title builds upon the first installment's success, and still manages to branch out into new directions. Featuring an enormous overworld map and expansive dungeons, this game was large to begin with, but the inclusion of the Dark World makes the game twice as big as originally perceived. Transporting back and forth from the Light World to the Dark World eventually becomes an easy task, though in the beginning it is difficult to find passage even once. Creative boss characters, extensive environment interaction, a great story with plenty of twists, challenging puzzles, and the overhead view that helped make the first installment of this series a success are all intact and make this title one of the greatest action/RPG's ever created.

Lemmings   Sunsoft   2 $5
An action/puzzle game featuring the mindless lemmings as those that you both control and protect, you must utilize various abilities of different lemmings to help them find safe passage to the end of each level.

Lemmings 2: The Tribes   Psychosis   4 $10
The follow up to Lemmings which features more challenging puzzles and new abilities for the suicidal little characters.

Lester the Unlikely   Hect   4 $10
This is a mediocre platform game that follows the adventures of a nerd who must do battle with pirates. Lester is Horrible in just about every category possible, especially play control. Only hardcore SNES collectors should seek out this one.

Lethal Enforcers   Konami   3 $5
A digitized shooter, this game is also available on the Genesis, though the graphics and game play are about the same.

Lethal Weapon   Ocean   5 $12

Based on the hit series of movies, you shoot the bad guys and save the day, though this isn't nearly as entertaining as its celluloid counterpart.

Liberty or Death   KOEI   4 $15
Yet another strategy game by Koei, this one focuses on the Revolutionary War. Choose between England or the Americans and wage war against your enemies in this almost RISK style title. Be prepared for a long session when you sit down to play this one.

Lion King   Virgin   2 $5
Based on the hit movie, you control Simba as he tries to dethrone his evil uncle Scar and reclaim the throne. The Lion King is simply a great game that recreates many memorable scenes from the movie, such as the stampede. It's also not just another platform game. In addition to the standard running and jumping action, there are several logic puzzles spread throughout the game. Although the controls can be difficult to master, players of any age can enjoy this beautiful game.

Lock On   Vic Tokai   4 $10

Looney Tunes B-Ball   Sunsoft   4 $10
This is a fun cartoon clone of NBA Jam. Choose two Looney Tunes who will use standard ACME gags to beat up their opponents in a game of basketball.

**Lord of the Rings, The: Volume 1
                          Interplay   4 $22**
Based on the best selling novels, 'Rings is a pretty bland action-RPG that was created mostly for diehard fans of the saga. Players will be pleased that many of the memorable scenes have been recreated in the game. The price of this game has climbed slightly since the release of the first Lord of the Rings movie.

Lost Vikings   Interplay   3 $5
Take control of three Vikings, each with different abilities, and lead them back to their homeland in this Lemming inspired puzzler.

Lost Vikings 2   Interplay   3 $7
Rehash of the surprise hit with a few new features and additional moves for the three mindless Vikings.

**Lufia and the Fortress of Doom
                          Taito   3 $12**
One of the most popular SNES games, you take the roll of a knight sent to protect a neighboring kingdom from a monster. The graphics aren't very pretty but the gripping storyline and

The Legend of Zelda: A Link to the Past   Looney Tunes B-Ball

Every third party game maker for the NES was sued by Nintendo, except Wisdom Tree. Suing a religious company would have looked too bad.

SNES

MTV's Beavis and Butthead

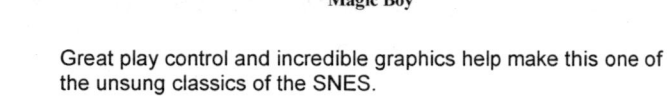

Magic Boy

fast paced action will keep you coming in this RPG classic.

Lufia II: Rise of the Sinistrals

| | Natsume | 3 | $25 |

This follow up to Fortress of Doom features better graphics and a more engaging cast of characters. Lufia II is universally praised as one of the best RPGs of all time. Complete copies have been known to bring in $75 dollars on various auction sites.

MTV's Beavis and Butthead

| | Viacom | 3 | $3 |

Based on the hit show, but minus anything entertaining, you guide the decidedly un-PC in a quest to take pictures of themselves doing cool things so that they can get into a concert. As fun as that sounds, the controls are totally unresponsive, rendering the game useless.

Madden NFL '94 Electronic Arts 2 $3
Yet another lineup in the Madden series, this time with a larger playbook and improved AI.

Madden NFL '95 Electronic Arts 2 $3
Yet another lineup in the Madden series, this time with a larger playbook and improved AI. And no, you didn't just read that description for Madden '94.

Madden NFL '96 Electronic Arts 2 $3
It's like Madden '95, except with a different label. Oh, and a larger playbook and improved AI.

Madden NFL '97 Electronic Arts 2 $3
Second verse, same as the first! It's like Madden '96 except with a larger playbook and improved AI.

Madden NFL '98 Electronic Arts 3 $3
The last Madden game on the Super NES is slightly the rarest of the bunch, but it should still be pretty easy to locate.

Magic Boy JVC 4 $8
Guide a young magician through this platform action game.

Magic Sword Capcom 3 $5
Sword wielding platformer where you control a knight trying to stop evil forces from obtaining a magical orb.

Magical Quest starring Mickey Mouse

| | Capcom | 3 | $5 |

Incredible action platformer where you must lead Mickey on a quest to save Pluto from the always abusive clutches of Pete.

Great play control and incredible graphics help make this one of the unsung classics of the SNES.

Mario Is Missing! Software Toolworks 3 $6
In this "Edutainment" game, you guide Luigi on a quest around various countries to find Mario in this take of the "Carmen Sandiego" series. The younger audience it's aimed at might not respond well to this sometimes boring geography game. It's far more common then it's NES counterpart.

Mario Paint Nintendo 1 $2
Painting on the SNES would become a reality with this title, though not overly interesting. Featuring a mouse and matching mouse pad, this "game" was actually in high demand for a short period of time, though today both the game and mouse can be found with relative ease. And while not overly expensive, the mouse pad is actually the most difficult part of this title to come across, having often been thrown away by gamers after the enjoyment of this title was gone.

Mario's Early Year: Fun with Letters

| | Software Toolworks | 5 | $12 |

Designed for a younger audience, the Mario's Early Years series are pretty collectable, if not all that fun to play.

Mario's Early Year: Fun with Numbers

| | Software Toolworks | 5 | $12 |

Yet another game that was made for the wee ones, but collectable for grown ups, this game will help the rug rats learn to count.

Mario's Early Year: Pre-School

| | Software Toolworks | 5 | $12 |

One of the better games of the series, little kids should have fun solving problems with Mario. Pre-School is the rarest of the Mario's Early Years trilogy.

Mario's Time Machine

| | Software Toolworks | 4 | $12 |

First they ripped off Where in the World is Carmen Sandiego, and then Software Toolworks stole the not as popular "Where in Time is Carmen Sandiego." It's not a bad game, but it's not a great way for kids to learn their history either.

Mark Davis' The Fishing Master

| | Natsume | 4 | $8 |

It's a tired and true fishing game featuring cable TV host Mark Davis.

Can you name the three most recognized video game characters?

Marvel Super Heroes: War of the Gems
Capcom   3 $5
Double Dragon/Street Fighter hybrid where you control of popular super heroes such as Spiderman or the Hulk and fight off villains. Each character has their own attributes and special abilities, but like any beat um up, it grows old quickly.

Mary Shelley's Frankenstein
Sony Imagesoft   4 $8

Mask, The   Electronic Arts   3 $5
Based on the popular Jim Carrey movie and not the one that stars Cher, Mask is a standard side scrolling action game.

Math Blaster   Davidson & Associates   6 $18
Based on the PC title of the same name, Math Blaster is a educational game under the guise of a quest to stop aliens. It's one of the rarer games for the SNES, so if you see one, get it.

Maui Mallard in Cold Shadow
Nintendo   4 $8
This was a sleeper hit for the SNES where you take control of a Donald Duck like character and navigate nine worlds in this absolutely huge side scroller. Be ready for a challenge.

Mecarobot Golf   Toho   3 $5
Have you ever wished you could play golf using robots? If so, this is the game for you.

MechWarrior   Activision   3 $6
A port of the popular PC series, you do battle with other robots using various fighting tactics in this simulation game.

MechWarrior 3050   Activision   4 $10
This is a sequel of sorts to MechWarrior with more options and a wider variety of mechs.

Mega Man 7   Capcom   3 $18
A return to it's NES style roots, Mega Man 7 places the Blue Bomber against a new field of robot bosses. Although not rare, the game is highly sought after and the price reflects that.

Mega Man Soccer   Capcom   3 $6
A very strange sports game, you control various characters from the original NES Mega Man in what would otherwise be a standard soccer game. Each character can launch a special attack that can potentially disable an opponent for a short period of time. The ability to customize teams is a plus, but overall the game grows old rather quick.

Mega Man X   Capcom   1 $10
The first Mega Man game on the SNES, X brings more features to the series then it's NES cousins with the ability to upgrade your weapons. Additionally, you face off against giant robotic animals at the end of each level instead of a bunch of guys who's last name is "Man." Great graphics and sound plus accurate controls make this a must own for any gamer.

Mega Man X2   Capcom   2 $40
Like the original Mega Man X except with better graphics and slightly less challenging bosses. Still, Mega Man X2 is a must own for SNES owners.

Mega Man X3   Capcom   3 $50
Like any Mega Man game before it, you kill the bosses, take their weapon, and then kill the next boss with it. Rinse and repeat. Actually, you can't go wrong with Mega Man, so if you like the series, of course pick this one up. It's slightly harder to find then Mega Man X2, but shouldn't require that much searching.

Metal Combat-Falcon's Revenge
Nintendo   3 $5
A totally bland Super Scope game that shows why the oversized Zapper was such a bust. If your arm hasn't gone numb five minutes into this game, then the swarms of enemies that have little variety will cause your brain to go numb.

Metal Marines   Namco   5 $12
In this real time strategy game you must build up an army of mechs to defeat the rival army.

Metal Morph   FCI   5 $15
Action Side Scrolling with a futuristic setting.

Metal Warriors   Konami   4 $8
This is a platform based shooting game where you face off against hordes of giant robots.

Michael Andretti's Indy Car Challenge
Bullet-Proof Software   3 $4
This is a Pole Position style racing game featuring Indy circuit star Michael Andretti.

Michael Jordan in Chaos in the Windy City
Electronic Arts   4 $6
It might be Michael Jordan, but it's not a basketball game. Instead, you guide the basketball hero through side scrolling levels and fight bad guys with basketballs made of fire and ice. The concept was bad but the game is pretty decent.

The Mask

Mega Man X2

SNES

Micro Machines

Ms. Pac-Man

Mickey Mania: Timeless Adventures of Mickey Mouse
Sony Imagesoft   3 $6
Incredible graphics and sound are the foundation for Mickey Mania, where you must guide the popular character through his classic cartoons. From Steamboat Willy to the Mad Doctor, all of Mickey's memorable cartoons are recreated here. The game is pretty challenging, so much that it might be a turn off to some gamers. Additionally, Mickey Mania features some insanely long load times for a cart based game, but it's still worth checking out.

Mickey's Ultimate Challenge
Hi Tech   4 $10
The name is a bit misleading, as Mickey's Ultimate Challenge is strictly an educational game. The game tests children's memory and logic, but it's hardly a challenge at all. As far as educational games go, it's one of the better ones produced for the SNES.

Micro Machines   Ocean   4 $10
Choose from a variety of vehicles and race through 28 different tracks in this RC Pro Am style game. This game cartridge is notably different than other Genesis cartridges as it is tapered toward the top.

Might and Magic II   Sammy   4 $15
You will either love or hate this first person RPG adventure, and this title's merits are often debated among gamers.

Might and Magic III: Isles of Terra
FCI   6 $22
A poor conversion of the PC hit, you lead a band of adventurers on a quest to find the remains of a dead explorer, and while it could have been improved it is still an enjoyable title.

Mighty Morphin' Power Rangers
Bandai   3 $5
Totally forgettable brawler where you assume the roles of the Power Rangers as they battle space aliens that all seem to look the same. Like the TV Show, the climax is a fight between your giant robot and a giant monster.

Mighty Morphin' Power Rangers - Fighting Edition
Bandai   3 $5
Using popular characters and robots from the series, players brawl in the pretty tame fighting game.

Mighty Morphin' Power Rangers - The Movie
Bandai   3 $5
Help the Rangers fight off Ivan Ooze in yet another punch and kick brawler with bland graphics.

MLBPA Baseball   Electronic Arts   2 $4
This is simply a standard EA Sports baseball game.

Mohawk and Headphone Jack
Black Pearl   6 $30
Poorly designed platformer that features a rotating camera angle. The camera trick makes avoiding some of the bad guys impossible, in what would otherwise be a decent game. Get it for it's rarity, not for the game.

Monopoly   Parker Brothers   3 $5
The classic board game with a little more flash, at least you can't accidentally choke while trying to prove to your friends that you can fit 20 hotels in your mouth at once.

Mortal Kombat   Acclaim   2 $4
This game was the only one at the time with the ability to stand up against the nearly unchecked power of Street Fighter 2, and when it was brought to home consoles it was a great day for gaming. But just in case you don't remember the controversy surrounding this title, it was considered one of the most gruesome video games ever released. During the porting process, this version lost all the blood, which was replaced with white "sweat". While this version plays better than the Genesis version, it just didn't seem to be Mortal Kombat without it. The debate rages still today as to which version is better, though in recent years gamers have become desensitized to gore in video games, an now rarely notice its inclusion or omission. Due to this fact, most retro-gamers consider this to be the superior version, while hardcore fighting game fans still insist on the blood being in place, and choose the Genesis version. While it may seem a trivial thing today, Nintendo's choice not to offend parents with the inclusion of so much gore in their games was a vital turning point that would eventually lead most gamers to consider Nintendo a "kiddie" company.

Mortal Kombat II   Acclaim   2 $4
Considered to be the best in the series by many, this title obviously lost a bit of its graphical superiority in the conversion to the home console, but it remains a fun game to play.

Mortal Kombat 3   Tradewest   2 $4
The kombat kontinued, although this time the results weren't as good. The addition of the "Run" button was the only new feature in this series which was starting to show it's age at this point.

Mr. Do!   Electronic Arts   4 $8
Based on the classic arcade hit of the same name, this remake

158

is as enjoyable as the original with bright graphics and sharp controls.

Mr. Nutz — Ocean — 5 — $12
This is a side scrolling adventure featuring a loveable squirrel that had no problem finding work before Conker ruined their reputation as foul mouthed drunks.

Ms. Pac-Man — Tradewest — 3 — $10
This is a remake of the arcade mega hit but with some special features added to keep the game from growing dull.

Musya — Seta — 4 — $8
This is a side scrolling Castlevania clone with great graphics but unresponsive play control.

Mutant Chronicles: Doom Troopers
Playmates — 4 — $8
This gory Contra clone is based on the popular pen and paper RPG series.

Natsume Championship Wrestling
Natsume — 4 — $6
This is an unresponsive professional wrestling game. Don't expect any big stars to be show up in this one.

NBA All-Star Challenge — Acclaim — 2 — $3
This is a poorly designed basketball variety game that features one star from each 1992 NBA team in games of One-on-One, H-O-R-S-E, and three point shootout. Despite all the features, it grows old fast.

NBA Give 'N Go — Konami — 3 — $5
Based on the arcade hit, this port is hampered by it's sluggish frame rate and bad camera angle.

NBA Hang Time — Tradewest — 4 — $6
A turbo charged version of NBA Jam that was a late SNES release and rare compared to most other NBA games.

NBA Jam — Acclaim — 2 — $3
Based on the Arcade super hit, Jam is a two-on-two basketball game with no rules and gravity busting dunks. Of note: two versions of NBA Jam are known to exist. One version contains Charles Barkley of the Phoenix Suns, who later got his own game and had to be taken out, so in later versions he was replaced by Dan Majerle. As of now, it is unknown if one version is rarer then the other.

NBA Jam Tournament Edition
Acclaim — 2 — $4

This is an update to the original NBA Jam that features more players on each team and the addition of 'hot spots' on the court that are worth more points then a normal basket.

NBA Live '95 — Electronic Arts — 2 — $3
Like NBA Showdown except with improved graphics and AI.

NBA Live '96 — Electronic Arts — 2 — $3
Like NBA Live '95 except with improved graphics and AI, and a new feature or two thrown in.

NBA Live '97 — Electronic Arts — 2 — $3
This is yet another update to the series of NBA Live games and contains slightly updated graphics and control.

NBA Live '98 — Electronic Arts — 3 — $4
Like Madden '98, NBA Live '98 was the last of the popular series for the SNES.

NBA Showdown — Electronic Arts — 2 — $3
This follow up to Bulls vs. Blazers features every NBA team, better graphics, and more signature moves.

NCAA Basketball — Nintendo — 1 — $2
Popular college basketball game that was heavily hyped by Nintendo, you choose from a variety of colleges and try to win the championship.

NCAA Final Four Basketball
Mindscape — 3 — $4
Guide your team to the National Championship in this five on five basketball game.

NCAA Football — Mindscape — 3 — $4
Select your favorite college team and take them to the championship.

Nowman Haas' Indy Car Racing
Acclaim — 4 — $6
This is standard racing fare, but still enjoyable.

NFL Football — Konami — 2 — $3
Choose a professional football team and take them to the Super Bowl. Depending on who you ask, NFL Football either has the best playbook ever or the worst.

NFL Quarterback Club — LJN — 2 — $3
The first of the popular series of football games that kept getting worse with each passing installment.

NBA Live '96

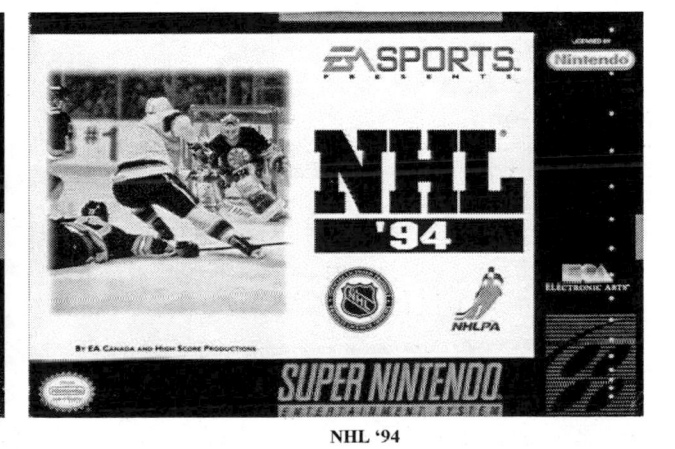

NHL '94

The arcade game Karate Champ was featured in the movie Blood Sport.

SNES

NHLPA Hockey '93

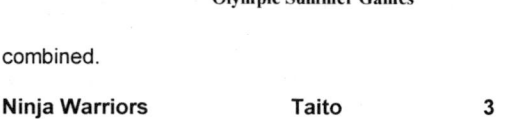

Olympic Summer Games

NFL Quarterback Club '96   Acclaim   3 $4
This follow up features more plays but slightly less responsive controls.

NHL '94   Electronic Arts   2 $3
Professional Hockey game by EA Sports, this one set to the 1994 rosters.

NHL '95   Electronic Arts   2 $3
Professional Hockey game by EA Sports, this one set to the 1995 rosters.

NHL '96   Electronic Arts   2 $3
Professional Hockey game by EA Sports, this one set to the 1996 rosters.

NHL '97   Electronic Arts   2 $3
Professional Hockey game by EA Sports, this one set to the 1997 rosters.

NHL '98   Electronic Arts   3 $4
Professional Hockey game by EA Sports, this one set to the 1898 rosters. If you were paying attention, you will have noticed I put down 1898 instead of 1998. Clever you. You will also have noticed that NHL '98, like all other entrees made by EA that year, is slightly the rarest entry in it's series.

NHL Stanley Cup   Nintendo   2 $3
Nintendo takes a shot, pun intended, at hockey with this unexceptional high sticking game.

NHLPA Hockey '93   Electronic Arts   2 $3
Before they dropped the dopey "PA" part of it, NHLPA is basically just another entry into the popular series of hockey games by EA Sports.

Nicklodeon GUTS   Viacom   4 $6
Based on the hit children's game show, you take on various physical challenges and try to score more points then your opponents. It's a lot like a kiddie version of American Gladiators, and it's not a bad game.

Nigel Mansell's World Championship Racing
**   GameTek   3 $5**
This bland racing title makes use of a bland racing 'star.'

Ninja Gaiden Trilogy   Tecmo   5 $30
Containing all three of the original Ninja Gaiden titles, this game is one of the most sought after titles for the SNES and often demands a price that is actually greater than the original three

combined.

Ninja Warriors   Taito   3 $5

No Escape   Sony Imagesoft   4 $10
This game is loosely based on the film by the same name, the object is still the same: stay alive and find a way out of Absolom.

No Fear Racing, Kyle Petty's
**   TradeWest   4 $8**
Racing game featuring a driver named Kyle Petty. We do our homework at Video Game Bible.

Nobunaga's Ambition   KOEI   5 $18
Remake of the popular series of NES war simulation games.

Nobunaga's Ambition: Lord of Darkness
**   KOEI   6 $25**

Nolan Ryan Baseball   Romstar   3 $5
The legendary pitcher is the featured star of this disappointing baseball game.

Nosferatu   Seta   3 $6
A series of delays annoyed fans who couldn't wait to get their hands on the Castlevania style platformer. The game is considered by many to be not worth hype it received.

Obitus   Bullet-Proof Software   5 $15
Third person Role Playing Game that was also released on the Commodore Amiga.

Ogre Battle: The March of the Black Queen
**   Enix   6 $50**
One of the most sought after SNES games, with complete copies known to go for over a hundred dollars. It's a standard strategy/RPG with an innovate battle system and a variety of characters.

Olympic Summer Games
**   Electronic Arts   3 $5**
Compete different Olympic events, including archery, skeet, javelin, and seven other track and field competitions.

On the Ball   Taito   3 $5
Guide a ball through a maze in this one player action puzzler.

Operation Europe: Path to Victory
**   KOEI   4 $8**
Another simulation game by KOEI, this one set during World

In the movie The Wizard, what NES game kept the father up all night playing?

War 2. Also released on the Genesis.

Operation Logic Bomb   Jaleco   4 $8
This overhead shooting game is similar to Commando or Ikari Warriors.

Operation Thunderbolt   Taito   4 $8
Designed for use with the Super Scope, you take out the bad guys as the Scope gives you arthritis of the neck.

Oscar   Titus   6 $20
A tried and true action platformer that is extremely hard to come by.

Out of This World   Interplay   3 $5
Great scenery and suspenseful scenarios help this game stand out from others of the time, though fans of action games might become bored after only a short period of time.

Out to Lunch   Mindscape   7 $28
You play as a chef who has to recover the food that escaped from his fridge. This rare game would make a nice addition to any SNES collection.

Outlander   Mindscape   3 $4
You drive around in a car, then get out and walk around while shooting people. Maybe not the most politically correct game, but fun nonetheless.

Pac-Attack   Namco   5 $18
A Tetris style action puzzler that was not well received by fans of the genre nor the most devote Pac-fans.

Pac-In-Time   Namco   7 $45
This is an extremely hard to find platform jumper centered around everyone's favorite dot eating hero.

Pac-Man 2: The New Adventures   Namco   2 $6
One of the most original games for the system. Pac-Man has a mind of his own so you must use a slingshot to guide him through various puzzles in this genre-less adventure. Throughout the game, Pac-Man's facial expressions change to reflect his mood. Sometimes, it's fun just to see how fast you can make him angry by launching rocks at him with your slingshot.

Pacific Theater of Operations   KOEI   4 $12
Being a Koei game, a war simulation should be expected. This time, it's Japan vs. the Allied forces featuring scenarios like Pearl Harbor.

Pacific Theater of Operations II   KOEI   6 $22
This is the follow up to PTO, it's still Japan vs. the Allied Forces in war simulation.

Packy & Marlon   Raya Systems   5 $12

Pagemaster   Fox Interactive   4 $8
This is a platform jumper based on the Macaulay Culkin movie of the same name.

Paladin's Quest   Enix   4 $10
This is a mediocre RPG that features one of the most awkward battle systems ever invented. RPG fans will want to check it out, but everyone else will want to avoid it.

Paperboy 2   Mindscape   3 $5
This is the sequel to the popular arcade game, and does a nice job of keeping the same feel that made the original so much fun. Unfortunately, not enough is different to make it stand out from the first installment. Still, this is the only version on the SNES and is worth a look if you enjoyed the original.

Peace Keepers, The   Jaleco   4 $8

Pebble Beach Golf Links   T & E Soft   3 $5

PGA European Tour   Electronic Arts   4 $8
An odd choice for a state side release, Euro Tour is basically the same as all other EA golf games except with a different lineup of professional golfers and popular European courses.

PGA Tour '96   Electronic Arts   3 $5
This is an update to the original PGA Golf that features more pros and more courses.

PGA Tour Golf   Electronic Arts   2 $4
Digitized graphics and a variety of courses are featured in EA's first golf game for the SNES.

Phalanx: Enforce Fighter A-144   Kemco   3 $5
This shooting game is famous for it's hordes of enemies and it's bizarre box artwork.

Phantom 2040   Viacom   4 $8
This platform game is based on the popular comic character.

Pieces   Atlus   7 $35
Making use of the SNES Mouse, Pieces is one of the rarest and

PGA European Tour

The Peace Keepers

SNES

Populous

Power Rangers Zeo: Battle Racers

most innovative games on the Super NES. Put together a jig-saw puzzle in this fast paced action game that up to five players can enjoy.

Pilotwings   Nintendo   2 $6
The original version of what would later become a small sensation on the N64, this title offers mission based flight using various vehicles to propel you through the skies. While certainly not as detailed as the N64 version, or even as much fun for that matter, it remains a great game that can be played for hours on end.

Pinball Dreams   GameTek   3 $5
Horrible physics ruin the multiple boards of pinball action this game could have offered.

Pink Goes to Hollywood: Pink Panther in
           Tec Magik   4 $10
The popular cartoon character makes a jump to video games in this side scrolling platform game.

Pinocchio   Nintendo   5 $12
Action platformer based on the Disney movie, you control Pinocchio in his quest to become a real boy.

Pirates of Darkwater   Sunsoft   4 $10
Poorly designed Double Dragon clone based on the popular comic book and TV series.

Pit Fighter   THQ   2 $4
What once awed crowds in the arcade now appears to be a simple game featuring less than impressive digitized characters. Choose between three generic characters, one with strength, one with speed, and one balanced fighter. Aside from the digitized graphics featured in this game, the ability to utilize weapons from the crowd was a new feature to fighting games. Considered a groundbreaking title upon its release, it was eventually lost in a veritable sea of fighting games, most notably the Mortal Kombat series.

Pitfall: The Mayan Adventure
           Activision   2 $4
This is a fairly average platformer that makes use of colorful graphics but is sorely lacking in play control. You guide Pitfall Harry through dense jungles, solving the occasional puzzle. The Atari 2600 classic Pitfall! is hidden in this update.

Plok!   Tradewest   2 $4
You guide Plok the Cloak through various levels, throwing your arms and legs and enemies in this neat twist on the platform

genre. The graphics are very colorful but the game sometimes lacks in variety.

Pocky & Rocky   Natsume   3 $5
This is a popular shooting game in which you choose between Pocky the boy or Rocky the raccoon. The overhead perspective makes this game feel like Ikari Warriors at times.

Pocky & Rocky 2   Natsume   5 $12
Hard to find sequel of the popular shooting game.

Populous   Acclaim   2 $3
The original "god game", this title enables the player to manipulate land, call disasters upon your opponent's followers, and rally your own worshipers into a final Armageddon showdown. Once the first basic levels have been cleared, more interesting and unusual levels will become available, including such oddities as "Cake World". Interestingly enough, this title didn't bring too much negative attention from religious groups of the time, who were obviously more interested in fighting against violence in video games, not blasphemy.

Porky Pig's Haunted Holiday
           Acclaim/Sunsoft   3 $5
As expected with all Sunsoft Looney Tunes games, cartoon like graphics help support an otherwise bland platform game.

Power Instinct   Atlus   5 $12
Yet another disappointing Final Fight clone on the Super NES. At least this one is rare.

Power Moves   Kaneko   3 $5
This is a very poor Street Fighter 2 clone featuring an unresponsive control system.

Power Piggs of the Dark Ages
           Titus   5 $15
Fairly standard platformer with innovative graphics.

Power Rangers Zeo: Battle Racers
           Bandai   4 $6
Have you ever said to yourself, "Man, those Power Ranger games were just so great, but what they really need to do is make a racing game featuring our favorite spandex wearing super heroes!" If you have, then this is the game for you.

Prehistorik Man   Titus   4 $8
Guide the title character on a quest to save his villiage from Dinosaurs in this 2-D Platformer.

Ms. Pac-Man has been adopted as a mascot for the fight against breast cancer.

Primal Rage
                    Time Warner Interactive   2 $4

One of the few fighting games of the time to offer any real variety, Primal Rage features prehistoric beasts dueling in one-on-one fighting matches, often ending in the gruesome death of your opponent. The SNES version of this game doesn't do the arcade version justice, though no system of the time was capable of reproducing such large characters and fluid motion as was seen in the original.

Prince of Persia   Konami   3 $8

Available on numerous platforms, this version is among the most playable simply because of the accurate control that keeps you from needlessly dying simply because of a miscalculated jump. Certainly nothing groundbreaking, but a nice platform title.

Prince of Persia 2: The Shadow and the Flame
                              Titus   5 $12

This follow up to Prince of Persia offers little in the way of innovation.

Pro Quarterback   Tradewest   2 $4

Yet another football game on the Super NES with nothing to really distinguish itself from any other pigskin game on the system.

Pro Sport Hockey   Jaleco   3 $4

Push-Over   Ocean   5 $12

It's a version of Domino Rally for the Super NES. You control an ant that must arrange the dominos and then topple them over to reach the next level. Push-Over features a wide variety of dominos but this has to be one of the most boring games for the system.

Q*Bert 3   NTVIC   4 $10

There's not a whole lot of innovation to the classic series, but Q*Bert still loves to hop from square to square while avoiding villains

Race Drivin'   THQ   4 $8

This is a nice port of the popular arcade driving game by the same name.

Radical Rex   Activision   4 $10

Raiden Trad   Electro Brain   3 $5

A very enjoyable version of Raiden, this game remains one of the most enjoyable vertically scrolling shooters for any system.

Rampart   Electronic Arts   3 $5

Port of the PC war simulation game of the same name.

Ranma 1/2 Hard Battle   Hect   4 $10

Based on the popular anime series from Japan, take the role of various characters from this show in one-on-one battles. Unique characters and nice graphics help this title past the one hurdle of often rigid control.

Rap Jam: Volume One   Motown Software 6 $15

Horrible basketball game featuring dopey "music" from rap icons. Terrible, but quite rare, so keep an eye out for it.

Realm   Titus   5 $12

While the levels are obviously detailed and a lot of work went into the graphics involved, the game itself is an average side scrolling platform shooter.

Redline F-1 Racer   Absolute   4 $8

Relief Pitcher   Left Field Entertainment   4 $6

Ren & Stimpy Show, The: Buckaroo$!
                              THQ   3 $5

Released in 1993, this side scrolling platform game quickly becomes boring and is just more of the same repetitive movements over and over.

Ren & Stimpy Show, The: Fire Dogs
                              THQ   4 $6

Released in 1994, this game really shows that it was rushed through production simply in order to capitalize on the character names while they were still popular.

Ren & Stimpy Show, The: Time Warp
                              THQ   3 $5

Ren & Stimpy Show, The: Veediots!
                              THQ   3 $5

Trapped in the TV set, you must control both Ren and Stimpy through 4 levels in order to escape from this mediocre side scrolling platform game.

Revolution X   Acclaim   3 $5

Based on the popular arcade game, you can use the Super Scope to help save the band Aerosmith in this extremely bland shooting game. The graphics are very poor and like any shooting game, there is no variety.

Q*Bert 3

3DO's unreleased M2 system was originally slated to be a cartridge console. This would've been an industry first, going from CD to cart.

SNES

Riddick Bowe Boxing

Rocky Rodent

Rex Ronan: Experimental Surgeon
                                  Raya Systems   5 $15

Riddick Bowe Boxing   Beam Software   4 $6
One time heavyweight champion of the world Riddick Bowe
lends his likeness to this otherwise average boxing game. One
has to wonder whether or not Bowe threw this game in the trash
can just like he did his title belt.

Rise of the Phoenix   KOEI   4 $8
Often overlooked for the more popular Romance of the Three
Kingdoms series, this title is also a strategy game based in
ancient China, and will require military skill in order to complete
the tasks ahead. You will lead your army to victory, though
don't expect to do this on your first try.

Rise of the Robots   Acclaim   4 $6
Fight through various robotic opponents within a factory that has
suffered severe damage, causing the robots inside to become
vicious killers. The only problem with this game, and it is a big
one, is the fact that control is so stiff that it almost makes the
game unplayable. Eventually, this game will only be won by
repeating an effective move over and over until your opponent is
drained of life. Though later opponents can be difficult, it is not
a result of good character design or advanced AI, but instead is
simply a result of not being able to adequately control your
movements.

Rival Turf   Jaleco   2 $4
This is simply an unoriginal 2-D brawler.

Road Riot 4WD   THQ   3 $5

Road Runner's Death Valley Rally
                                  Sunsoft   3 $5
Incredible graphics are the lure in this average platformer. You
guide the Road Runner through platform jumping levels while
trying to avoid the always hungry Wile E Coyote. The graphics
look just like the popular Warner Bros cartoons, but the controls
are unresponsive.

Robotrek   Enix   4 $8

RoboCop 3   Ocean   3 $5
The sequels to the movie should have never been made, and
certainly no games should be made for these, but they were.
This side scrolling platform game plays and feels a lot like E-
Swat for the Genesis.

RoboCop vs. Terminator   Virgin   3 $5

Taking two movie franchises and combing them is an obvious
attempt to squeeze more money out of the market, and this
game is no exception. Actually based on the Dark Horse comic
book by the same name, this is simply another platform shooter
that happens to feature our favorite onscreen robots. And if you
are lucky enough to have the box to this game, you already
know that it is made of hard molded plastic and is among the
best boxes ever made for any video game.

Rock 'N Roll Racing   Interplay   4 $8

Rocketeer   IGS   4 $8
Based on the movie, you control an unlikely hero who must
keep his experimental helmet out of the hands of spies. Pretty
good graphics but poor play control bog down this standard
action title.

Rocko's Modern Life: Spunky's Dangerous Day
                                  Viacom   3 $5
An average side scrolling platform, the characters and enemies
within this gave have a very cartoon like appearance, making it
more entertaining for children.

Rocky Rodent   Irem   5 $15
The detailed levels and overall fun of this title make it very enjoyable. The graphical style is unique and resembles old Italian
movies from time to time.

Roger Clemens' MVP Baseball
                                  LJN   3 $4

Romance of the Three Kingdoms II
                                  KOEI   4 $15
Continuing the series from the original NES game, this title remains an excellent strategy simulation and shouldn't disappoint
fans of the first game.

Romance of the Three Kingdoms III: Dragon of Destiny
                                  KOEI   4 $15
While all the games in this series are of high quality, the level of
detail continues to increase with each installment. The maps
used in this version are evidence of this, as are the ever increasing options that are added to the games.

Romance of the Three Kingdoms IV: Wall of Fire
                                  KOEI   5 $20
By far the best looking title in the series, this game features very
solid game play as well. This title was also made available on
the PSX and Saturn, though the Saturn version often stands out
as the best.

The Panasonic 3DO originally retailed for $700.

RPM Racing	Interplay	3	$5

R-Type III: The Third Lightning
Jaleco 4 $10
R-Type has become synonymous with side scrolling space shooters, perhaps even more than earlier titles such as Vanguard, and this title continues the tradition of making an addictive and fun side scrolling shooter. Simple and to the point, and featuring some nice environments, this title is a lot of fun.

Run Saber Atlus 4 $8
A side scrolling fighting game, this 1993 title really doesn't stand out as being exceptional in any area, but level design was interesting and even incorporated a few vertical movement areas.

Samurai Showdown Takara 5 $12
The Neo-Geo classic is brought to the SNES in an adequate version, though it simply cannot compare to the original. If you really want to play this game the way it was meant to be played, the only options are Neo-Geo AES or MVS units. The characters in the SNES version are much smaller than the original, and the control simply isn't as responsive as it should be.

Saturday Night Slam Masters
Capcom 4 $6

Scooby-Doo Mystery Acclaim 3 $5
Catch the bad guys in this nifty (if a tad bit easy) mystery-side scrolling game based on the TV show.

SeaQuest: DSV Malibu Games 4 $8
Poorly designed game based on the short lived NBC series.

Secret of Evermore Square 3 $15
More of a spin-off then a sequel to Secret of Mana featuring a boy and his dog in a surreal nightmare world. Breath taking graphics and one of the best sound tracks ever aren't enough to save this from being one of Square's worst games ever

Secret of Mana Square 2 $28
A cross between the Legend of Zelda and Final Fantasy, Secret of Mana remains a popular and sought after RPG to this day. Guide three youngsters in a quest to restore balance to the world. Fantastic graphics and an engaging plot make Mana a timeless classic.

Secret of the Stars Tecmo 5 $15
Incredibly boring RPG with poor graphics and terrible dialog.

Shadowrun Data East 3 $5
Unsettling action-RPG where you play as a man with a computer in his brain who awakes in a morgue without any memory. The awesome plot makes this a must own title that was based on the popular pen and paper RPG.

Shanghai II: Dragon's Fire Activision 5 $12
The classic tile-matching game with some extra features added.

Shaq Fu Electronic Arts 3 $5
Considered by many to be the worst game ever made, this fighting title was actually the first appearance of Shaq in any home video game; surprising considering the numerous basketball game franchises that would have loved to attach his name to their series.

Shien's Revenge Vic Tokai 4 $8
This is a first person action-shooter where you control a ninja in his quest to rescue his girlfriend. Because really, that's all expert martial artists do with their time. Just watch any Jean Claude Van Dam movie.

Side Pocket Data East 4 $8
This billiards game is similar to Data East's original Side Pocket for the NES.

SimAnt Maxis 5 $12
The ever-expanding sim series branches out into one of the most interesting and addictive titles in the series. Build and maintain a working ant colony, keeping the queen safe and trying to keep the colony productive. If you are a fan of simulation games, this title should offer enough variation to be a refreshing break from so many others such as SimCity.

SimCity Nintendo 1 $3
Based on the PC hit, you take over as the mayor of a city who must do what is asked of him to make his town's population rise. It's up to you to build power lines, roads, railroad tracks, zoos, sports stadiums, airports, and whatever else your city will need to become a Megaopolis.

SimCity 2000 Electronic Arts 4 $8
A more futuristic sim City with extra features and a wider variety of building to make.

SimEarth FCI 3 $5
It's Sim City with a slightly bigger setting.

Simpsons: Bart's Nightmare
Acclaim 2 $4
This is yet another Simpsons game. Bart has actually written a

Saturday Night Slam Masters

Scooby-Doo Mystery

Plug in a keyboard, and the Atari XEGS starts up in Atari BASIC. Take it out, and the system starts with a game.

SNES

Snow White in Happily Ever After

Spindizzy Worlds

good term paper, but he then loses it in a nightmare world. Although Bart's Nightmare features a wide variety of gameplay, poor controls ultimately ruin the fun.

Simpsons: Virtual Bart   Acclaim   3 $5

Follow up to Bart's Nightmare, Virtual Bart offers a better variety of gameplay and sharper graphics. Easily one of the better Simpsons games out there.

Sink or Swim   Vic Tokai   6 $22
Action-Puzzler with a Titanic theme. Rescue passengers from a sinking ship.

Skul Jagger: Revolt of the Westicans
   American Softworks   3 $5
Fight pirates in this forgettable sword swinging platform game.

Skyblazer   Sony Imagesoft   4 $8
A mix of platform and brawling action where you must free a sorceress from an evil warlord.

Smart Ball   Sony Imagesoft   4 $8
Platform adventure where you control a prince turned into a jelly bean.

Snow White: Happily Ever After
   American Softworks   7 $30
Mediocre platform game that is not based on the Disney movie. Good luck finding it.

Soldiers of Fortune   Spectrum Holobyte   3 $5
Overhead shooter where you choose from one of six mercenaries to stop an evil baron from conquering Europe.

Sonic Blast Man   Taito   3 $5
This is a very bad Final Fight clone where punches are useless and the bad guys all look a little too similar.

Sonic Blast Man 2   Taito   5 $12
Only slightly better sequel to Sonic Blast Man that just happens to be rare.

S.O.S.   Vic Tokai   4 $8

Soul Blazer   Enix   3 $5
This is an action RPG with a slow paced storyline and a lack of variety to keep things fresh.

Space Ace   Absolute   4 $8
Platformer loosely based on the arcade Laser Disc anti-classic.

Space Football: One on One
   Traffix Entertainment   4 $8

Space Invaders   Nintendo   2 $4
The all time classic arcade game sports some added features and updated graphics.

Space Megaforce   Toho   5 $12
Frantic space shooter featuring hordes of enemies and a large variety of weapons.

Spanky's Quest   Natsume   3 $5
Take control of a monkey and bust some bad guys in this Bubble Bobble style action game.

Sparkster   Konami   4 $8
Sequel to the popular Genesis game Rocket Knight Adventure with a large variety of action elements and innovative level design.

Spectre   Cybersoft   6 $18
Strange vertical shooting game with terrible graphics.

Speed Racer   Accolade   4 $8
Mario Kart style combat racing game featuring the popular anime character.

Speedy Gonzales: Los Gatos Bandidos
   Acclaim   4 $8
Somewhat awkward play controls make this one of the weaker Looney Tunes games on the Super NES.

Spider-Man   LJN   3 $5
Action adventure where Spidey takes on just about every villain he's ever faced off against in this game based on the animated Fox series.

Spider-Man and the X-Men: Arcade's Revenge
   Acclaim   3 $5
Platform action staring popular characters from Marvel Comics. The actions shifts from hero to hero although Spiderman is the most commonly used character.

Spindizzy Worlds   ASCII   5 $12
Bad play control spoils the potential of this exploration puzzler.

Originally designed to be worn on the head, the Virtual Boy design was changed for fear of gamers walking into traffic while playing.

Sports Illustrated Championship Football & Baseball
Malibu Games   4 $6

Star Fox   Nintendo   2 $5
This is one of the first U.S. titles that caused lines to form outside of video game stores. Featuring 3-D polygon based graphics, gamers across the country were anxious to see the full potential of the SNES. While it was an impressive title upon its release, by today's standards it is very simplistic and extremely rough looking. The closest any other game came to reproducing the feel of this title is Guardian, for the Amiga CD32. Unfortunately for those who bought this game based on graphics alone, the title features a very linear flight path, severely limiting the amount of replay that can be tolerated, though various paths can be chosen to reach the final objective. Overall, however, this title should still be fun for those interested in gaming history, and want to see early 3-D graphics on a home console.

Star Fox Super Wekend: The Offcial Star Fox Competition
Nintendo   10 $120
One of the holy grails of Super NES collecting, less then 300 of these were made as part of a traveling road show to showcase Star Fox. Players would race to score points in an attempt to be crowned National Champion of Star Fox. People who won the cart via the tournament will likely be unwilling to part with their copies, and the few that have ended up in collectors hands will bring home a few thousand dollars in the open market.

Star Trek: Deep Space Nine: Crossroads of Time
Playmates   3 $6

Star Trek: Starfleet Academy Starship Bridge Simulator
Interplay   3 $6

Star Trek: The Next Generation
Spectrum Holobyte   3 $6

Stargate   Acclaim   0 $0
Side scrolling platform/shooter based on the popular movie.

Steel Talons   Left Field Entertainment   4 $8

Sterling Sharpe: End 2 End Jaleco   4 $8
Football game featuring some very poor play control and a terrible play book.

Stone Protectors   Kemco   3 $5
Side scroller based on the popular line of Troll dolls.

Street Combat   Irem   4 $8

Street Fighter Alpha II   Nintendo   4 $8
The rarest Street Fighter game on the Super NES, SF Alpha 2 is prequel of sorts to the popular series. Unlike previous entrees, the Super NES simply couldn't recreate the visuals found in the arcade version.

Street Fighter II Turbo: Hyper Fighting
Capcom   2 $4
Think of SF2 Turbo as a DVD special edition. It's still the same Street Fighter but with improved graphics and adjustable speed settings. Additionally, the four boss characters from the original Street Fighter 2 are now selectable characters. SF2 Turbo is considered one of the best games for the SNES.

Street Fighter II: The World Warriors
Capcom   1 $3
A major hit that was a Super Nintendo exclusive at the time, Street Fighter 2 practically saved the machine from the Sega Genesis. Based on the arcade mega sensation, you choose from one of eight characters and then brawl your way through eleven other fighters or against a second player. Street Fighter 2 is still the measuring stick for which all fighting games are compared to. Capcom was able to make the SNES version a near perfect port, with arcade quality graphics and sound. The Super NES controller's six buttons were a key factor in landing the title as an exclusive to the system.

Street Hockey '95   GTE Entertainment   4 $6

Street Racer   UBI Soft   4 $8
Above average Mario Kart clone with eight characters and a variety of settings.

Strike Gunner: S.T.G.   NTVIC   4 $8
Stop aliens from invading the Earth in this fun and fast paced shooter.

Stunt Race FX   Nintendo   3 $5
Super FX chip based racing game with poor play control and glitchy graphics.

Sunset Riders   Konami   4 $8
This is an underrated platform shooting game with cowboys avoiding stampedes and taking on outlaws.

Super Adventure Island Hudson Soft   2 $8
This is the sequel to the popular NES action series follows Master Higgins as he tries to save his girlfriend from an evil witch doctor. Awkward jumping and stale gameplay take are annoyances in this otherwise enjoyable title.

Star Fox

Street Fighter II Turbo

Zangief, from Street Fighter II, supposedly wrestled bears to train for his matches.

SNES

Super Bomberman 2

Super Conflict

Super Adventure Island II   Hudson Soft   3 $8
Yet another sequel in the Adventure Island series, this one with a few more game play elements and better play control.

Super Aquatic Games   Seika   5 $10
Various water themed events hosted by forgotten mascot James Pond.

Super Baseball 2020   Tradewest   3 $5
Yet another Baseball game on the Super NES.

Super Baseball Simulator 1,000
**   Culture Brain   4 $5**
Remake of the of Baseball Simulator 1,000 for the NES.

Super Bases Loaded   Jaleco   2 $4
An update to the popular series of NES baseball games.

Super Bases Loaded 2   Jaleco   2 $4
This is the sequel to the update of the popular series of NES baseball games.

Super Bases Loaded 3: License to Steal
**   Jaleco   3 $5**
This is the sequel to the sequel of the update to the popular series of NES baseball games. Try saying that three times fast.

Super Batter Up   Namco   3 $5
Namco's semi-popular baseball game for the SNES.

Super Battleship   Mindscape   3 $5
A conversion of the timeless board game, with some war themed backdrops.

Super Battletank: War in the Gulf
**   Absolute   3 $6**
Everyone wanted to take their shot at destroying the evil that resides in Iraq even today, and for most, this title was as close as they would ever get. While the graphics may seem rudimentary today, they were top notch upon this game's release. The one flaw with this game that was apparent to nearly everyone who played it was the "wrap-around map" that allowed you to go so far south that you would eventually come out on the north side of the map, creating a very unrealistic feel to an otherwise impressive tank simulation.

Super Battletank 2   Absolute   3 $5
Follow up to Super Battletank supports a few new features and better settings in what is otherwise a remake.

Super Black Bass   HOT-B   2 $5
It's like the NES Black Bass by Hot-B, only it's super!

Super Bomberman   Hudson Soft   3 $12
Super Bomberman was the first game in the Bomberman series to really take advanage of multiple player battles. The Super NES multitap was included with Super Bomberman that would allow up to four players to fight in a free for all battle royal. The standard one player mode is a throwback to the NES Bomberman titles, but the fully rendered characters made this eye candy. A must own for the system. It's actually harder to find then it's sequel, Super Bomberman 2.

Super Bomberman 2   Hudson Soft   2 $10
Sequel that reinvented the one player mode into a sort of logic puzzler. As with most post-NES Bomberman games, the lure of Super Bomberman 2 is the multiplayer games, which are considered some of the best every made for any game.

Super Bonk   Hudson Soft   4 $10
This is the sought after SNES adaptation of the popular TurboGrafx series, with bright and colorful graphics and tons of headbutting action.

Super Bowling   Technos   5 $12
Featuring a license from the Young American Bowling Alliance, Super Bowling is like any other ten pin title where you only need to stop a few meters in time to get a strike. To add to the replay value, there was a golf mode added where you would have a limited amount of shots to knock down a variety of pin combinations.

Super Buster Bros.   Capcom   4 $8
This is a remake of the arcade classic where players have to harpoon bubbles in a fixed screen shooter.

Super Caesar's Palace   Virgin   4 $8
Walk around the famous casino placing bets without the added fear of going broke had having to explain the situation to your wife.

Super Castlevania IV   Konami   1 $5
A ground breaking mega hit for the SNES, Castlevania's special effects are still impressive to this day. You guide vampire hunter Simon Belmont on a quest through the infamous castle, dealing with familiar undead enemies with your always present whip. Various mode 7 effects and a fantastic sound track will keep you coming back for more.

Super Conflict: The Mideast
Vic Tokai   4 $8

Super Double Dragon   Tradewest   2 $4
The first Double Dragon game for Super NES features dated gameplay and unresponsive controls.

Super Earth Defense Force
Jaleco   3 $5

Super GameBoy   Nintendo   2 $10
Technically not a game, the Super GameBoy would allow users to play their black and white Game Boy games on television in color. The amount of colors was normally limited to four colors that you could customize. Certain games, like Donkey Kong (later Donkey Kong '94) were specially designed to include more colors and contained custom borders. The Super Game-Boy is an accessory no player should be without. It sure beats squinting your eyes.

Super Ghouls 'N Ghosts   Capcom   2 $4
A new take on the popular Capcom series, you guide often naked knight Sir. Arthur on a quest on a quest to save the women he loves from the clutches of the undead.

Super Goal!   Jaleco   2 $4
Super Nintendo update to the popular NES series.

Super Goal! 2   Jaleco   3 $5
Sequel to the Super Nintendo update of the popular NES series.

Super Godzilla   Toho   3 $5

Super High Impact   Acclaim   2 $4
A simply horrible looking football game released in 1993, this title is not a total wash since it does have solid control.

Super James Pond   American Softworks   4 $8

Super Mario All-Stars   Nintendo   1 $6
Simply put, Mario All-Stars is the greatest collection of games on a single cart ever. Mario All-Stars features all three original Super Mario Brothers game with improved graphics and the ability to save your progress instead of having to play through the entire game in one session. Nintendo could have left it off there, but instead they included the Japanese version of Super Mario Brothers 2, known in All-Stars as the Lost Levels. Lost Levels uses the same game play engine as the original Super Mario Brothers, but with the ability to choose Luigi instead of Mario, giving you increased jumping ability. The Lost Levels is VERY hard, so much in fact that Nintendo Power magazine ran a contest to see if anyone could beat it without using any of the games various warp zones. It's a great way to test how good a gamer you really are. Super Mario All-Stars is a game that any SNES owner should not be without. It's extremely common so finding one should be no problem.

Super Mario Kart   Nintendo   2 $5
Mario Kart practically invented an entire racing genre, and remains one of the most popular game ever. You choose from eight characters in the Mario series, which with unique attributes. You then race for the finish line while picking up coins scattered throughout the twenty courses this game has to offer. Drivers can pick up weapons such as turtle shells that will serve to slow down anyone that gets in your way. The racing modes would have been enough, but Nintendo went all out and included four battle courses that allow two players to try to be the first one to score three hits on your opponent. Beautiful mode 7 graphics add to this timeless classic.

Super Mario RPG: Legend of the Seven Stars
Nintendo   2 $20
A joint effort by Nintendo and Square turned out this incredible adventure will you guide Mario and his allies against the evil Smithy. In the middle of a battle with Bowser, a giant sword slams through the Mushroom Kingdom's palace, causing havoc for both Mario and his mortal enemy. The storyline is great, and although the game is very straight forward, the dialog between Mario and the various characters is often hilarious. Mario RPG offers a wide variety of distractions in the form of mini games and hidden items which keep the game fresh. Fully rendered graphics, a wonderful soundtrack, and responsive play control make this one of the most joyful gaming experiences anyone could ask for. Super Mario RPG was the last big fit for the dying SNES, a fitting swan song to one of the all time great consoles.

Super Mario World   Nintendo   1 $1
When you want to launch a new system, this is the sort of game you need to launch with it. Super Mario World is without doubt one of the best games ever made. You guide Mario through over fifty stages of mountains, moving platforms, lakes, dungeons, and haunted houses. Along the way, you have the ability to ride Yoshi, Mario's loveable dinosaur pal, or take to the skies with a cape if you can grab a feather. Most levels have more then one exit, with each exit altering Mario's path as he tries to make his way to do battle with Bowser. There are 96 exits total, and even the most savvy gamers will have difficulty completing some of the challenging levels that Mario World has to offer. You should have no problem finding a copy of Super Mario World for under five dollars, so what are you waiting for? Go get it now!

Super Mario All-Stars

Super Mario RPG: Legend of the Seven Stars

Who we know as Balrog in Street Fighter II is named M. Bison in Japan. Mike Tyson thought the similarities were a bit too obvious.

Super Mario World 2: Yoshi's Island

Super Metroid

Super Mario World 2: Yoshi's Island
Nintendo   1 $3
As Yoshi, you must save a Baby Mario from Baby Bowser by navigating over forty levels. The child Mario rides on Yoshi's back, and if you are hit by an enemy, Mario will be thrown from off. A timer will begin and you have until the timer reaches zero to recover Mario. At first glance, the graphics look as if they were drawn by a five year old, but it's only part of the genius of this game's Super FX2 chip visuals. The special effects are fantastic, especially that of the bosses, who are simply huge. Yoshi does battle with his enemies by licking up enemies and turning them into eggs. He then shoots his eggs using a cursor. The play control will take a while to get used to, but with the various hidden objects and fun mini-games, Yoshi's Island is a must own for any SNES fan.

Super Metroid   Nintendo   2 $20
A simply brilliant game based on the NES character Samus and her adventure through impressive levels filled with platforms and various enemies. Most gamers consider this game to be the best platform game ever created, and should definitely be played by any SNES owner.

Super Ninja Boy   Culture Brain   5 $15
Action RPG gamers will have a blast with this one - the crisp graphics and amazingly enjoyable game play make Super Ninja Boy a game not to be missed.

Super Noah's Ark 3D   Wisdom Tree   7 $35
Super Noah's Ark 3D is certainly one of the more interesting games on the Super Nintendo, if for no other reason that it is a Christian game that was illegally released, which, besides this, runs on a first-person shooter game engine. This is the only unlicensed SNES game ever released in the U.S.

Super Nova   Taito   3 $5
Super Nova may not be the best shooter to have been released, but it isn't bad. The graphics aren't very interesting, but this game is still worth a try.

Super Off Road   Tradewest   3 $5
As an overhead racer, Super Off Road does not disappoint. The graphics are rather dull, but for a game like this, this can be expected. Still, the game play and upgrade system make this a great game that Super Nintendo collectors should not be without.

Super Off Road: The Baja   Tradewest   2 $4
Though it does have its roots in its predecessor (Super Off Road), Super Off Road: The Baja is a very different game.

Rather than an overhead view of the track, gamers get a third-person driving perspective. It isn't as good as the original, but still captures the feel of off-road racing.

Super Pinball: Behind the Mask
Nintendo   3 $5
Nintendo If you loved games like Pinball and Pinball Fantasies, you'll love Super Pinball: Behind the Mask. There are three stages in this game, and it sure is a great one. However, gamers who don't like pinball games a lot will probably get bored quickly.

Super Play Action Football   Nintendo   3 $4
Though the option to pick between high school, college, and professional modes is nice, Play Action Football just doesn't stand up to some of the other football games on the SNES, and especially on other systems like the Genesis. Stick to Madden.

Super Punch Out!!   Nintendo   3 $10
Fans of the original still debate as to whether Mike Tyson's Punch Out (NES) or the updated Super Punch Out!! is better. Either way, this game is one of the best on the Super Nintendo, and is arguably the best boxing game of all time, rivaling even Ready 2 Rumble on the Dreamcast.

Super Putty   U.S. Gold   3 $5
Humdrum platformers were common in the days of the SNES and Genesis, and Super Putty is a perfect example of this. It isn't horrible, but unfortunately has nothing to offer to make it stand out from other platformers.

Super R-Type   Irem   2 $5
There are better shooters out there, but Super R-Type is still a good one for shooting fans, as its solid gameplay and decent graphics make it a better-than-average game.

Super R.B.I. Baseball
Time Warner Interactive   3 $4
Aside from the detail put into this game, there isn't much of anything about Super R.B.I. Baseball that sets it apart from other baseball sims. Once again, stick to your Genesis for your 16-bit sports game cravings.

Super Scope 6   Nintendo   2 $3
The Super Scope may be one heck of a light gun, but this game for it sure isn't of the same caliber. There are several modes of play, but as with most light gun games, the fun only lasts for so long.

Warping into the Dark World before you are prepared will turn you into a pink bunny in Zelda: A Link to the Past on the SNES.

Super Slam Dunk   Virgin   3 $4

Perhaps there actually are good sports games on the SNES. Unfortunately, this isn't it. The gameplay just isn't very solid, and with all of the great basketball games available for the Genesis, there isn't much of a reason to play this one.

Super Slap Shot   Virgin   3 $5

Another "Super" sports title from Virgin, Super Slap Shot isn't very "super" at all. Stick to NHLPA '93 on your Genesis.

Super Smash T.V.   Acclaim   3 $5

Super Smash T.V. is the remake/update to Smash T.V. on the NES, and is therefore very, very similar. The game is a great one, though, with nice shooting action and a two-player simultaneous mode.

Super Soccer   Nintendo   3 $4

Just as in Super Slap Shot and Super Slam Dunk, Super Soccer isn't very "super." It does have its strong points, and the two-player modes are nice, but with the FIFA series on the market, there are better options available.

Super Soccer Champ   Taito   4 $6

Once again, the FIFA series cannot be matched. This was an early release on the SNES, and because of this, there are just better choices out there, like the aforementioned FIFA games.

Super Solitaire   Beam Software   5 $12

Super Solitaire does have a nice variety of solitaire games, and it amusing for a while. However, it just doesn't last very long, partly due to the obvious lack of a two-player mode.

Super Star Wars   LucasArts   2 $8

With pretty much every element of this game on the level of excellence, there isn't much of a reason to not own this game. It's a great challenge, captures the Star Wars feel, and must be played by all!

Super Star Wars: Return of the Jedi
       JVC   2 $8

Super Star Wars: Return of the Jedi is one of the better games on the Super NES, and is arguably even better than Super Star Wars. It is an action game with multiple kinds of it, and players even have the ability to choose between a variety of characters. Recommended.

Super Star Wars: The Empire Strikes Back
       JVC   2 $8

Again, LucasArts delivered a great game in Super Star Wars: The Emperor Strikes Back. It is very similar in style and presen-

tation to Super Star Wars. The action is still very difficult, yet entertaining, and character selection is still an option.

Super Street Fighter II   Capcom   1 $4

This game is arguably the best fighting game available for the SNES. When Street Fighter II was released, it spawned more clones than the market could handle, and for good reason. This game is simply incredible. It has great graphics, a huge selection of fighters, several modes of play, and a rather deep fighting engine. This game is a MUST-OWN.

Super Strike Eagle   Microprose   2 $3

By today's standards, Super Strike Eagle is laughable. By the standards of 1993 when it was released, it was still laughable. It is a flight sim, and unfortunately not a very good one. Afterburner on the SMS would be a better choice.

Super Tennis   Nintendo   2 $2

Though it isn't perfect, Super Tennis is one of the best tennis games available for the SNES. It is simply a blast to play and has a great two-player mode.

Super Troll Island   American Softworks   6 $18

Super Troll Island is a pretty standard side-scrolling platformer, and not much more. Still, there are worse games out there, so it may be worth a brief look.

Super Turrican   Seika   3 $5

This game is in the same vein as Contra, and although it isn't quite as good, Super Turrican is still a very solid and enjoyable game. It has decent graphics and sound, and the side-scrolling shooting action is a blast.

Super Turrican 2   Ocean   3 $5

From the same developers (Factor 5), Turrican 2 is very similar to its predecessor. Pretty much everything about the game has been improved upon (however slightly) and the action is still just as fun.

Super Valis IV   Atlus   5 $15

Super Valis IV isn't anything special, to be frank. It's a side-scrolling action game, and not anything more than average.

Super Widget   Atlus   5 $12

Super Widget does have nice graphics, and if not for the seemingly millions of other platformers out there, it would be a good game. However, since there are other, better platformers available, Super Widget is nothing more than average.

Suzuka 8 Hours   Namco   3 $5

Sadly, the box art is the prettiest thing about this motorcycle

Super Solitaire

Super Widget

Is your old Playstation action up? Try turning it on its side as this will often stabilize the CD and play the game correctly.

Tecmo Super Bowl

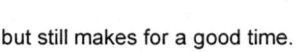

Tetris & Dr. Mario

racing game. It isn't a horrible game by any means, but just barely skids in as "average."

S.W.A.T. Cats   Hudson Soft   4 $8
Another game, another average side-scrolling action game. This game could have been a lot better than it was, but since it really doesn't do anything original, it ends up being yet another humdrum action game.

Syndicate   Ocean   5 $12
On the PC, Syndicate was an awesome action strategy game. On the SNES, though, it is only average. The game is somewhat stripped down, but that can be forgiven to a point. The main problem with the SNES port of Syndicate is the lack of mouse support. Without it, it's just a pain to play.

Taz-Mania   Sunsoft   3 $5
Running racing games aren't a common breed, but this one is actually pretty good. Even if the gameplay stunk (which it doesn't), this game would be worth putting in just to see the graphics.

Tecmo Super Baseball   Tecmo   3 $5
Tecmo Super Baseball completely breaks the rule of Genesis sports games being better than SNES ones, because this is a great game. It has over 700 players included, several fun modes of play, and a battery backup.

Tecmo Super Bowl   Tecmo   2 $8
Besides the rather average graphics, Tecmo Super Bowl excels in all areas. It is simply a lot of fun to play, and for sports fans has tremendous replay value. Recommended.

Tecmo Super Bowl II: Special Edition
      Tecmo   3 $8
Though the graphics have had slight tweaking and there are a few new options, Tecmo Super Bowl II is essentially the same game as its predecessor. Still, it is a lot of fun.

Tecmo Super Bowl III: The Final Edition
      Tecmo   3 $8
In what is probably the best of the Tecmo Super Bowl series, players now have the opportunity to create their own players and customize more. The graphics have been completely changed, and for the better. This is one of the better football games on the SNES.

Tecmo Super NBA Basketball
      Tecmo   2 $4
Once again, Tecmo delivers a great sports title among a sea of mediocre ones. It isn't the best ever, or even very revolutionary,

but still makes for a good time.

Teenage Mutant Ninja Turtles IV: Turtles in Time
      Konami   2 $4
Nice graphics, appropriate music, and a nice arcade feel make this game one of the better side-scrolling beat-'em-ups available. Besides all this, it is a great challenge. Check it out.

Teenage Mutant Ninja Turtles: Tournament Fighters
      Konami   3 $5
TMNT: Tournament Fighters is a decent fighting game, but there are better choices out there. Still, if you can't find Street Fighter II, but strangely found this game, it may be worth purchasing, as it has decent graphics and a solid fighting engine.

Terminator, The   Mindscape   3 $5
Though the game's overall feel and the dark graphics do come out well, The Terminator is as bad of an action video game as it was a movie.

Terminator 2: Judgement Day
      LJN   4 $6
It's amazing that a company could take a poor action side-scroller like The Terminator and actually make it worse. Still, BITS Studios accomplished this, and made T2: Judgment Day a game to stay away from at all costs.

Terminator 2: The Arcade Game
      LJN   2 $4
Thankfully, T2: The Arcade Game is at least a little better than the other Terminator games on the SNES. The graphics are once again effective in creating the right ambiance for the game. Action is decent, but not amazing. This is a very average game.

Tetris & Dr. Mario   Nintendo   3 $8
Two of the best puzzle games on one cartridge certainly isn't a bad thing. Both were classic NES games, for the few who don't remember that, and both come to the SNES in their full glory on a compilation cartridge, in the same way that the Super Mario Bros. games came to the SNES on a single cartridge in what Nintendo called Super Mario All-Stars.

Tetris 2   Nintendo   2 $5
The original was amazingly addictive, and the same can be expected of its sequel. Tetris 2 adds a whole new level of depth to the Tetris formula by making the color of blocks important to eliminating them. Single-player and two-player modes alike make Tetris 2 one of the best puzzle games out there for the system.

There are two variations of the Atari 5200. One version has two control ports, the other has four.

Tetris Attack　　　　　Nintendo　　2　$5

It must be a law that any game with the "Tetris" name on it is a great one, because Tetris Attack is amazing, even though it is very different than most of the Tetris titles out there. Rows of blocks move from the bottom up, rather than the other way around. The game really must be seen to be fully understood, and it is certainly worth figuring out.

Thomas the Tank Engine & Friends
　　　　　　　　THQ　　4　$8

Educational game based on the award winning series of books and television series for preschoolers.

Thunder Spirits　　　Seika　　4　$8

Though there are better side-scrolling shooters out there, Thunder Spirits still offers a decent challenge and some solid blasting fun.

Tick, The　　　Fox Interactive　　5　$12

Quite simply, this title is extremely disappointing and offers little replay value. This game makes standard, average beat-'em-ups look good.

Time Cop　　　JVC　　4　$8

Though it does have nice graphics, the enjoyment level is where Time Cop really falls short of all expectations. Frankly, there isn't any reason to play this game, unless you were a fan of the movie it was based upon.

Time Slip　　　Vic Tokai　　5　$12

Poor graphics, poor sound, and completely uneventful gameplay make Time Slip a Contra clone that isn't worth its weight in tin.

Time Trax　　　Malibu Games　　4　$8

This is a boring action platform game with little replay value.

Tin Star　　　Nintendo　　3　$5

Tin Star may not be the best light gun shooter out there, but it sure is a lot of fun for a little while, anyway. The graphics are very cartoony, and very appropriate.

Tiny Toon Adventures: Buster Busts Loose!
　　　　　　　　Konami　　2　$4

Cartoony graphics, nice music, and solid gameplay make this action platformer a good one. Surprisingly, it is even fun for older gamers, and not just the little ones.

Tiny Toon Adventures: Wacky Sports Challenge
　　　　　　　　Konami　　4　$8

While it is a multi-sports event game, this is an above-average

one. The graphics are very cartoony and very appropriate, and the gameplay is actually fairly enjoyable.

TKO Super Championship Boxing
　　　　　　　　Sofel　　4　$8

With Mike Tyson's Punch Out on the NES and Super Punch Out on the SNES, there is absolutely no reason to own this game, unless you're a collector.

TNN Bass Tounament of Champions
　　　　　American Softworks　　3　$5

Before they were the "National Network," TNN had more fishing shows then you could shake a stick at. Someone must have thought it would be good to license a game based on a low-rated cable network's annual fishing tournament. As it stands, TNN is just as good a fishing game as any of the other ones on the SNES.

Tom & Jerry　　　Hi Tech　　4　$8

This game is probably a lot better of a choice for younger gamers, but still does offer some good fun for older gamers as well. The graphics in Tom & Jerry are great, and though the game itself is pretty average, it is still worth a look.

Tommy Moe's Winter Extreme: Skiing & Snowboarding
　　　　　Electro Brain　　5　$10

For a Super Nintendo game, Tommy Moe's Winter Extreme is a pretty good one. "Extreme" sports games are all too common in today's day and age, but it is refreshing to play a 16-bit game like this one.

Tony Meola's Sidekicks Soccer
　　　　　Electro Brain　　5　$10

The FIFA series is still a better choice, but if for some odd reason you can't find any of them, Tony Meola's Sidekicks Soccer will suffice.

Top Gear　　　Kemco　　1　$3

Aside from the humdrum graphics, Top Gear is one of the best racing games available for the SNES. It has amazing speed, a nice selection of tracks, and is a good challenge. Recommended.

Top Gear 2　　　Kemco　　3　$5

Though it really isn't anything different than the original, Top Gear 2 is still a nice addition to the original. If you only need one Top Gear game, make it this one.

Top Gear 3000　　　Kemco　　4　$8

Four-player racing is nice, but if the game itself isn't very good, there isn't much of a reason to buy the adapter. Top Gear 3000

Tiny Toon Adventures: Wacky Sports Challenge

Top Gear

The Pippin @World has 8 function buttons on top of the console.

SNES

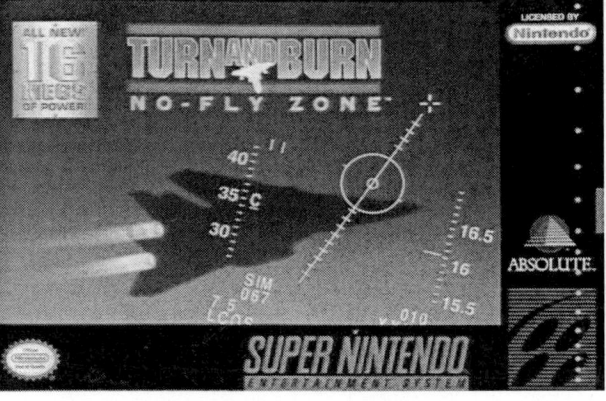

Turn and Burn: No Fly Zone

Ultima: The Black Gate

is a decent futuristic racing game, but is nowhere near the level of quality that the first two in the Top Gear series were at.

Total Carnage　　　**Black Pearl**　　3　　$5
While there isn't anything innovative about this game, it is still a blast from the past. It has great graphics, great sound, and amazingly addictive overhead shooting gameplay. Check this game out as soon as possible.

Toys　　　**Absolute Entertainment**　4　　$10
Based on the movie starring Robin Williams, this is a decent side scrolling platform game.

Troddlers　　　**Seika**　　4　　$8

Troy Aikman NFL Football　**Tradewest**　2　　$4
10 Yard Fight was better than this. Well, maybe not, but Troy Aikman NFL Football is a far cry from what football games were expected to be during the 16-bit days. Stick with the Madden series.

True Lies　　　**LJN**　　4　　$7
In the same vein as, but not up to snuff with Zombies Ate My Neighbors, True Lies happens to be a decent game. It's an overhead shooter, and although it is solid, it just barely makes the "average" mark.

Tuff E Nuff　　　**Jaleco**　　3　　$5
Thank goodness fighting games haven't always been like this one. Quite frankly, Tuff E Nuff just isn't very much fun to play, with a poor fighting engine and boring graphics. Street Fighter II is still a much better choice.

Turn and Burn: No Fly Zone
　　　　　　Absolute　　3　　$5
For a SNES flight simulator, Turn and Burn is a pretty good one. Of course, there are better, more modern flight sims available that put this one to shame, but even considering its age, this game stands up to them quite well.

Twisted Tales of Spike McFang
　　　Bullet-Proof Software　4　　$12
Action RPG's don't get much better than this. The Twisted Tales of Spike McFang combines a good balance of Zelda-esque action and more traditional RPG storytelling through dialogue. Recommended.

Ultima: Runes of Virtue II　**FCI**　　3　　$12
As with Ultima: The Black Gate, Ultima: Runes of Virtue II just isn't as good as it should have been. With other RPGs out for

the SNES and other consoles that are just better, there isn't much of a reason to play all the way through this game.

Ultima VI: The False Prophet
　　　　　　FCI　　4　　$18
Of the Ultima games on the SNES, this one is unquestionably the best of the three. It doesn't match up to the Final Fantasy games by any means, but the game is still very good. The world it takes place in is tremendous, and the story is convincing.

Ultima: The Black Gate　**Pony Canyon/FCI**　5　　$22
Unfortunately, this installment to the Ultima series doesn't quite live up to the quality of some of the other games. For those not familiar with the series, this is a third person RPG.

Ultimate Fighter　　　**Culture Brain**　4　　$8
Street Fighter II rip-offs were common in the days of the SNES, and this is one of them. Unfortunately, it isn't a very good one. Overall, it stands a little bit below average, because of boring graphics, a weak fighting engine, and the lack of anything new.

Ultimate Mortal Kombat 3　**Tradewest**　3　　$5
Besides a few more characters, Ultimate Mortal Kombat 3 is essentially a carbon copy of Mortal Kombat 3. Diehard Mortal Kombat fans will still be happy with this game, but how many MK fans are there anymore? Better fighters are available, but this one is still solid.

Ultraman: Towards the Future
　　　　　　Bandai　　3　　$7

U.N. Squadron　　　**Capcom**　　2　　$4
There are certainly better side-scrolling shooters out there, but U.N. Squadron is a pretty good one. There are three playable characters, and players can buy parts for their planes between levels.

Uncharted Waters　　　**KOEI**　　3　　$10
Uncharted Waters is a very interesting RPG, if nothing else. It combines sailing and action RPG elements to make a rather unique game. Sadly, the game's concept wasn't executed as well as it could have. Still, it is worth a look.

Uncharted Waters: New Horizons
　　　　　　KOEI　　6　　$25

Uniracers　　　**Nintendo**　　3　　$7
Racing fans simply must own this game, as it is one of the most unique games out there for the SNES, or any other console, for

that matter. It's a unicycle racing game, with very nice graphics, decent replay value, a nice multiplayer mode, and an interesting concept. It's speed was unmatched even in the 32 bit era.

Universal Soldier   Accolade   2 $3

Untouchables   Ocean   3 $5
Though The Untouchables does offer an interesting mix of platform gaming and third-person shooting, it is average at best.

Urban Strike   Electronic Arts   2 $3
Continuing along the same lines as the other games in the series (Desert Strike and Jungle Strike), Urban Strike is a very good action shooter. The Genesis version is probably ever-so-slightly better, but the SNES version is still worth a purchase.

Utopia: Creation of a Nation
     Jaleco   4 $10
Construction games are always fun, as long as there is a lot to do. Unfortunately, Utopia (a futuristic construction sim) doesn't live up to the standard set by Sim City. If you do pick this one up, though, make sure you have a mouse handy, because you'll need it to make the game worth your while.

Vegas Stakes   Nintendo   2 $3
Usually, casino games just get old quick. Vegas Stakes, on the other hand, is actually a decent amount of fun, because it has at least a hint of an adventure mode in the game.

Vortex   Electro Brain   3 $5
Ripoffs of great games usually turn out sub-par, and this is a perfect testament to that. Vortex is a complete imitation of Star-Fox, and because it does nothing for the shooting genre or even itself, it ends up being below average. Look elsewhere.

War 2410   Advanced Productions   5 $18

War 3010: Revolution
     Advanced Productions   6 $20

Wario's Woods   Nintendo   3 $5
Though Wario's Woods is an above-average puzzle game, it doesn't match up to Dr. Mario or Tetris. There are several modes of play available, but none of them are as easy to jump into as the aforementioned games.

Warlock   LJN   3 $5
The graphics of this side-scrolling action game do give the right feel for a dark game like this, but most of the rest of the game doesn't match up to what it could have been.

Warp Speed   Accolade   5 $12
No matter how cool the concept, a combat-based game with bad combat usually ends up being a poor game. Warp Speed is exactly this, unfortunately.

Wayne Gretzky and the NHLPA All-Stars
     Time Warner Interactive   2 $3
This game's multiplayer mode is pretty decent, but that's about it. Compared to some of the NHL games on the Genesis, like NHLPA '93, this game looks and plays terribly. Look elsewhere.

Wayne's World   THQ   3 $5
As can be expected, a platformer based on the popular movie *Wayne's World* probably won't be any good. And, it's not. Stick with Super Mario World.

WCW Super Brawl Wrestling
     FCI   3 $3
Hardcore wrestling fans may enjoy this game a lot, but for most, WCW Super Brawl Wrestling gets old fast. For some, it's old before it has even been played.

Weapon Lord   Namco   4 $10
Hardcore fighters will love this game, but casual fighting game fans should probably stick to Mortal Kombat or Street Fighter II. WeaponLord is a weapon fighter with nice graphics, good music, and a fairly deep fighting engine. Recommended.

We're Back - A Dinosaur's Story
     Hi Tech   4 $8

Wheel of Fortune   GameTek   2 $3
Sure, it feels like the gameshow of the same name and fame, but does anybody really want that on their SNES? The game has over 4,000 puzzles, but even so, it just isn't very exciting.

Wheel of Fortune: Deluxe Edition
     GameTek   3 $4

Where In the World is Carmen Sandiego?
     Hi Tech   4 $8
This game was originally a Commodore 64 title, and even then it wasn't very exciting. Still, fans of the show who don't have a version of this for one console or another will probably enjoy this geography edutainment title.

Where in Time is Carmen Sandiego?
     Hi Tech   3 $5
Just as Where in the World is Carmen Sandiego? was a re-hashed SNES game, so too is this game. It has essentially no changes from the NES version, and was originally available for

The Emerson Arcadia features cartridges of different sizes, though there is no apparent reason as to why.

SNES

Wicked 18

Wing Commander: The Secret Missions

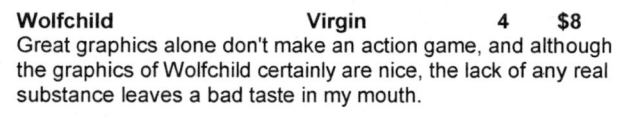

the Commodore 64. It is a little bit of fun, though, especially when two friends who are interested in history are playing together as a team (though there is no two-player mode).

| Whizz | Titus | 3 | $5 |

| Wicked 18 | Bullet-Proof Software | 5 | $15 |

Wicked 18 Golf is a pretty good golf game, with a single fantasy course, and since there are very few on the SNES, it is worth a look. However, there are better games out there in this genre.

| Wild Guns | Natsume | 4 | $8 |

Character selection, multiplayer gameplay, and good graphics all help Wild Guns in becoming a pretty good third-person shooting game.

| Wild Snake | Bullet-Proof Software | 4 | $8 |

It may not be quite as good as some of their other releases, but Bullet-Proof's Wild Snake is still a very good puzzle game. Its graphics are good for a game in the puzzle genre, and the gameplay is rather unique. Worth a look.

| Williams Arcade's Greatest Hits | | | |
| Williams | 3 | $7 |

| Wing Commander | Mindscape | 3 | $5 |

Though Wing Commander is a fairly unique style of game (a space combat simulator), that doesn't mean it is necessarily a good one.

Wing Commander: The Secret Missions

| Mindscape | 4 | $10 |

Wing Commander: The Secret Missions was originally a PC expansion to the PC game. On the SNES, it is essentially the same thing, but works as a standalone title. The game is simply more of the same type of missions found in Wing Commander.

| Wings 2: Aces High | Namco | 5 | $12 |

Winter Olympics Games: Lillehammer '94

| U.S. Gold | 3 | $4 |

Though it does get old rather fast, Winter Olympic Games is one of the best multiple sports events games out there, with nice graphics, average gameplay, and four-player action.

| Wizard of Oz, The | SETA | 3 | $6 |

Wizardry V: Heart of the Maelstrom

| Capcom | 5 | $15 |

| Wolfchild | Virgin | 4 | $8 |

Great graphics alone don't make an action game, and although the graphics of Wolfchild certainly are nice, the lack of any real substance leaves a bad taste in my mouth.

| Wolfenstein 3D | Imagineer | 3 | $5 |

The SNES version may not stand up to the PC original, but Wolfenstein 3D is still a game worth playing. When it was released, it pretty much invented the first-person shooter, and gamers bought it in droves. If you haven't played this game, you need to, if for no other reason than the historical significance it has to the world of video games.

Wolverine: Adamantium Rage

| LJN | 4 | $8 |

| Wordtris | Spectrum Holobyte | 3 | $5 |

It isn't as enjoyable as the original Tetris, but Wordtris was at least built upon a unique concept. It combines elements of the classic Tetris and a board game like Scrabble. It doesn't pull it off perfectly, but there is still fun to be had with it.

| World Cup USA 94 | U.S. Gold | 3 | $4 |

Frankly, this game is bad. The graphics are poor and the control worse. Stay away from this one.

| World Heroes | Sunsoft | 4 | $8 |

Considering the fact that this Street Fighter II clone wasn't even all that good on the Neo Geo AES, it's hard to imagine that the SNES version would be worth playing. Honestly, it isn't. This port of World Heroes is stripped down, and a stripped down version of a poor rip-off in the first place is never a good thing.

| World Heroes 2 | Takara | 4 | $8 |

Thankfully, World Heroes on the Neo Geo AES was a big improvement on the original. On the SNES, the game was still better, but obviously not as good as the Neo Geo version. If you can't afford the Neo Geo one, this will suffice, though.

| World League Soccer | Mindscape | 3 | $5 |

World Soccer '94: Road to Glory

| Atlus | 4 | $6 |
| WWF Raw | LJN | 3 | $4 |

WWF Raw is the sequel to WWF Royal Rumble, and wrestling fans who couldn't get enough of that game will have fun with WWF Raw. However, the game really does nothing new for the genre, so even fans may want to pass this one up.

Fairchild Channel F cartridges closely resemble 8-track tapes.

WWF Royal Rumble   Acclaim   2 $3
Sure, it looks pretty, but WWF Royal Rumble really isn't all that great of a game. Wrestling fans will probably love it, though.

WWF Super Wrestlemania
                Acclaim   2 $3
WWF Super Wrestlemania was the first of Acclaim's wrestling games on the SNES, and it shows. Wrestling fans will probably have fun with it for a while, but it gets old fast.

WWF Wrestlemania: The Arcade Game
                Acclaim   2 $3
Once again, Acclaim releases a wrestling game, and once again, it's not a very good choice for the average gamer. Wrestlemania the Arcade game plays more like Mortal Kombat then a wrestling game. If you absolutely *must* own a WWF game for your Super Nintendo, get WWF Raw or WWF Royal Rumble.

X-Kaliber 2097   Activision   4 $8
In single-player mode, X-Kalibur is a side-scrolling action game, and in two-player mode, it is a fighting game. Unfortunately, neither of these turned out very well, and X-Kalibur ends up being nothing more than average.

X-Men: Mutant Apocalypse
                Capcom   4 $8
Side-scrolling action games seem to come in every form, and this one is in the form and feel of an X-Men comic. The gameplay is average, so only fans of the comics will really have a reason to own this game.

X-Zone   Kemco   3 $5
Owners of the Super Scope 6 get yet another mediocre shooter in X-Zone. Dull, sparse graphics and repetitive gameplay keep this game from being anything worthwhile.

Xardion   Asmik   4 $8
Xardion is yet another side-scrolling shooter, and as many of them are, it is completely average. It's not a bad game, but there isn't anything exciting about it to set it apart from the rest of the pack.

Yoshi's Cookie   Bullet-Proof Software   3 $6
Though it isn't quite on par with Tetris and Dr. Mario, Yoshi's Cookie is still one of the best puzzle games available for any system. This can be expected, of course, because it does come from the same people who brought Tetris to the NES.

Yoshi's Safari   Nintendo   3 $7
As compared to the other Super Scope 6 games on the SNES, Yoshi's Safari is probably one of the better ones, if for no other reason than that it stars everyone's favorite dinosaur, Yoshi. Still, it suffers from the same problem that many games like this do: repetitiveness.

Young Merlin   Virgin   4 $10
There are better RPG's on the SNES, but Young Merlin is still a pretty decent one. The graphics are very nice, the story convincing, and the items to be picked up plentiful. It isn't on par with Final Fantasy, but still deserves a look.

Y's III - Wanderers from Y's
                American Sammy   3 $18
It isn't the best in the Y's series, but Y's III is still a solid RPG. The graphics are good and the gameplay mildly addicting, after the initial hump.

Zero the Kamikaze Squirrel
                Sunsoft   4 $8
While Zero the Kamikaze Squirrel was a little bit above average on the Genesis, the SNES version was a little bit below average. This action platformer is a solid one, with nice graphics, but just doesn't stack up to some of the greats.

Zombies Ate My Neighbors
                Konami   2 $4
For most SNES collectors, Zombies Ate My Neighbors is a must-own. When this game was released, the average top-down view action game was taken to a whole new level. The graphics, sound, and gameplay all come together to produce the feel of a cheap horror flick. Besides this, the game's fifty plus levels and great challenge help it out as well.

Zool: Ninja of the Nth Dimension
                GameTek   4 $8
Zool's cartoony graphics and good challenge make it a pretty decent side-scrolling shooter, but the lack of a high enjoyment level or anything new make it just another game in a sea of better ones.

Zoop   Viacom   3 $5
Zoop is a puzzle gamer's dream quite frankly. It didn't produce a bunch of clones like Tetris did when it was released, but Zoop is one of the most addictive puzzle games ever. The graphics are what can be expected of a puzzle game, but everything else about this game is incredible, especially the replay value. It is also important to note that the controls in the SNES version are much better than the Genesis version. A must-own.

Xardion

Zoop

Those found on the Bally Astrocade resemble cassette tapes.

SNES

Unconfirmed Releases:
While the games listed below are believed to have been released in very limited quantities, we were unable to verify that
they were actually produced. Known prototypes of both the
following games are known to exist.

Bobby's World	**Hi-Tech**
Pinball Fantasies	**GameTek**

HARDWARE

Super Nintendo 1	**Nintendo**	1	$25
Super Nintendo 2	**Nintendo**	3	$35
Standard Controller	**Nintendo**	1	$4
SuperScope	**Nintendo**	2	$15

While comfortable to use as a child, most adults will find that their hands have outgrown the Zapper lightgun for the NES.

Nintendo 64

By: Lucus Barnes

The Nintendo 64 is a definite enigma in the world of video games. What began with a glorious shout in 1996 ended with a tepid whimper at the end of 2001, a victim of burned bridges, unexpected competition, and a restrictive cartridge format. The slow, lingering demise of the N64 elicited little sympathy from an apathetic public, and its final passing into the console abyss went largely unrecognized and unsung. What the N64 did leave behind was an amazingly interesting history and some truly wonderful "must-have" video games.

By the mid 1990's, gamers were looking forward to the next generation of video game hardware. Game developers, in particular, were eager to see an end to the expensive and limiting cartridge format. Market underachievers like the Sega CD, 3DO, and the CD-i had laid the groundwork for mass-acceptance of the gloriously cheap and storage-heavy CD format, and gaming's future looked brighter than ever. Both Sega and newcomer Sony had unveiled their newest CD based consoles, and developers looked to market leader Nintendo to set the gaming world on fire with the announcement of the specifications for their next-generation machine. By early 1994, Nintendo finally started to leak details of a now 64-bit console dubbed "Project Reality" (later renamed "Ultra 64," then finally "Nintendo 64"). Working in cooperation with the high-tech firm Silicon Graphics (widely recognized at the time as being on the forefront of graphics technology), Nintendo assembled a very powerful piece of consumer technology with specifications that were more powerful than those of its rivals. Unfortunately, Nintendo decided to stick with the cartridge format rather than ride the CD wave, a decision that would later come back to haunt them.

The Nintendo 64 was a complete sales smash when it finally debuted in the United States at the end of 1996 and became THE hot toy of the Christmas season. Priced at an extremely reasonable $199, it sold out in most every store across the country (it has been suggested that Nintendo leaked out rumors of console shortages to increase demand when in fact there were plenty of machines on hand.) The critically acclaimed Super Mario 64 sold at a rate of nearly one to one with the console itself, and even lesser games like Cruisin' USA sold millions of copies. The Nintendo 64 took the American market by storm, and game developers started to take notice. Publishers who had been doubtful of the financial prospects of the N64 and its cartridge format suddenly jumped on the bandwagon, eager to develop games of their own. Sales for both the system and its games continued at a hurried rate, with numerous N64 titles topping the sales charts every month. The console hit its stride over the next few years as developers finally came to grips with the complicated hardware and began to produce some truly spectacular games including Goldeneye 007, F-Zero X, Rayman 2, and NFL Blitz. Unfortunately, Nintendo's choice of the cartridge format and its high licensing fees were about to catch up with them.

The Nintendo 64's cartridge format truly is the biggest reason behind the console's relatively under whelming performance in the marketplace (particularly when compared to that of the Playstation.) A game on CD literally costs less than one dollar to manufacture, while a cartridge can cost up to (and over) thirty times as much to make. Furthermore, a CD can hold much more data than the average cartridge, allowing for glorious soundtracks and beautiful game-enhancing video sequences. A cartridge

Shaq's first video game was a fighting game, not a basketball game.

really has no clear advantages over a CD, other than its fast loading times, durability, and classically "solid" feel. Consumer's ended up paying the price for Nintendo's choice since most N64 games were priced anywhere between $10 and $30 more than a comparable CD release on the PSX or Saturn.

Nintendo made sure to loudly trumpet all of the advantages of the cartridge format, particularly the greatly reduced loading times and the sturdiness of the cartridges (the Nintendo 64 console was geared towards a younger audience, and the cartridge format was a better choice for children). In reality, Nintendo stuck with the cartridge format for one simple reason...money! Nintendo had never taken a loss on the sale of its gaming hardware (which is highly unusual) and the addition of a CD drive would have driven up the cost of the console past the monetary limit that Nintendo had set for itself. On a larger scale, Nintendo stood to make a great deal of money off of the production of N64 cartridges for third-party developers. Nintendo had always kept its third-party developers on a tight (and we mean tight) leash, tenaciously fighting off any attempt to break away from its self-serving business model. Nintendo itself manufactured ALL of the actual cartridges that were made for the N64, and Nintendo required that all third-party developers order a minimum number of cartridges. This arrangement might have been just fine for Nintendo, but it was a burden for everyone else. Many game developers simply chose not to support the N64 at all (including Squaresoft, makers of the Final Fantasy series), and those that did often cut down the games to fit on a smaller-sized (and therefore less expensive) cart. Many less-popular games and genres (like RPG's and shooters) never made it onto the Nintendo 64 simply because Nintendo required that the developers order a minimum number of copies. In retrospect, it is amazing that niche titles like Harvest Moon 64, Star Soldier: Vanishing Earth, and Ogre Battle 64 were ever released at all. In several cases, games that were perceived as having "limited appeal" like Stunt Racer 64 and Indiana Jones and the Infernal Machine were never actually available to the public, instead showing up in rental-only form at Blockbuster Video stores.

Regrettably, the Nintendo 64 never really shook off its undeserved reputation as a child's toy, and many of the available games reflect that misconception. The N64 library is heavy on 3-D platformers and wrestling games, yet it is terribly deficient in many other gaming genres, especially fighting games, RPG's, and 2-D shooters. Nintendo never attempted to establish its own Tekken or Virtua Fighter series, and neither Capcom (Street Fighter) nor SNK (King of Fighters) chose to grace the N64 with any of their signature 2-D fighters. The defection of Squaresoft over to Sony's camp was a terrible blow for Nintendo, and many high profile developers chose to shun the console completely. From the beginning, Nintendo had vehemently promised a "quality over quantity" mantra in regard to game development. In truth, many of the N64's initial releases (Cruisin' USA, Mortal Kombat Trilogy) were substandard, refuting Nintendo's claim that they had assembled a "Dream Team" of developers who would only release "Grade A" titles for the new console. To be honest, many N64 titles are merely ports of popular Playstation games. As one would expect, Nintendo or their second-party development house, Rare, developed the best N64 games (all of which are N64 exclusives.)

From a technical standpoint, the Nintendo 64 was (and is) a wonderful piece of hardware. At its core is a custom MIPS 64-bit RISC main CPU running at 93.75 MHz, supported by a 64-bit RISC "Reality Immersion" sound and graphics co-processor running at 62.5 MHz. Capable of CD-quality sound, the N64 console also sports a number of built-in hardware features including support for scaling, rotation, anti-aliasing, texture-mapping, perspective correction, transparency, and much more. In a move that would later prove to be detrimental, Nintendo attempted to provide (and mostly delivered) consumers with a stripped-down Silicon Graphics workstation rather than a simple-to-program, streamlined machine like the Sony Playstation. While the overall Nintendo 64 design is very powerful and versatile, but it is also complicated and presented quite a programming challenge for developers unfamiliar with its complex architecture. The overuse of some of the console's custom hardware resulted in a "blurry" look that would later become a trademark of numerous N64 titles. Some game developers utilized the hardware's built-in ability to produce copious amounts of background fog in an attempt to disguise graphical pop-up (or bad programming, in some cases.) The Nintendo 64 hardware is obviously superior to that of the Playstation in terms of overall processing power (it also supports up to four players right out of the box), but its limited sound storage capabilities and complicated hardware design often resulted in N64 games that looked and sounded inferior to their Playstation counterparts. Furthermore, the innovative (but bizarre-looking) Nintendo 64 controller spawned a great deal of controversy when it was unveiled, and many gamers never really got used to its unusual design (though many others contend that it is one of the best controller designs to date.) One thing is for certain... the Nintendo 64 console itself is very

Metal Gear Solid 2 for the PS2 is reportedly the most expensive video game ever made.

durable, and nearly all of the first-generation N64 machines still function perfectly to this day, long after the fragile and cheaply made first-generation Playstations stopped working.

Nintendo released several interesting peripherals for its console, most notably the Memory Expansion Pak. Very similar in design to the memory cartridges that were available for the Japanese Sega Saturn, the Expansion Pak adds an additional four Megabytes of RAM to that of the base console (it replaces the "Jumper Pak" housed on top of the machine.) It is mostly used to bump particular games into a high-resolution mode, but it can also be used to increase the size of a game's levels (as in Donkey Kong 64) or provide added graphical effects (Quake II.) Quite a few games supported the Expansion Pak, and a couple actually required it (including Legend of Zelda: Majora's Mask). Other notable peripherals include the Rumble Pak (adds vibration and buzzing effects to some games), the Gameboy Transfer Pak (allows the N64 and the Gameboy to exchange data on select Pokemon games) and the microphone that came packaged with Hey You, Pickachu! (for limited voice recognition technology in that game only). Nintendo teased gamers for several years with announcements regarding the 64DD (Disk Drive), an add-on that was to utilize inexpensive readable/writeable disks and greatly increase the size and complexity of the software that was developed for it. Unfortunately, Nintendo ultimately pulled the plug on the 64DD for the American market, and it was only released in Japan in very limited quantities (most of the 64DD's games were moved over to the cartridge format, including the two Zelda games).

The N64 wasn't very successful in Japan (it placed a distant third behind the PSX and the Saturn) and as such is really not much of an importer's machine (especially when compared to something like the Saturn or PC Engine). It is very easy to coax an American N64 into playing Japanese software with the use of a simple, cheap, and widely available converter (really just a pass-through device). The simple fact remains that many of the Japan-only N64 games really aren't suited for American gamers (even those who are import-savvy). If you insist on importing, famed "cult" developer Treasure produced two excellent games for the N64 that were never released in the States. SiN & Punishment is an awesome 3-D shooter with some wild action, incredible graphics, and extremely cool bosses, while Bakuretsu Muteki Bangaio is a very unique and sprite-filled variation on the 2-D scrolling shooter (released for the U.S. Dreamcast as Bangai-O). If you're truly adventurous (and wealthy) you might want to consider acquiring a 64DD. It's a very unique machine with a lot of interesting features including the ability to connect to the internet, though this can be a real chore to do so outside of Japan. While the 64DD software library is meager at best, it does contain a few gems including Mario Artist and the F-Zero Expansion Kit (the latter allows you to design your own tracks and vehicles). The 64DD will set you back a small fortune (around $250) and most of the games contain copious amounts of Japanese text.

Sales began to slow significantly for the Nintendo 64 during the later half of 1999, a mere 3 years after its debut. The Playstation had completely obliterated the Saturn in the gaming wars, and Sega was poised to make an impressive (though short), comeback with its Dreamcast console. Sales of both the N64 hardware and its software dropped dramatically, leading many developers to abandon the platform in droves. In fact, Nintendo had already begun to plan for their next generation of hardware (the Gamecube), and many games that were scheduled to appear on the N64 were either moved over to the GameCube or were cancelled altogether. Nintendo coasted for most of 2000 and 2001, pacing out major releases like Legend of Zelda: Majora's Mask and Conker's Bad Fur Day in an effort to keep the system alive. The abysmal Powerpuff Girls: Chemical X-Traction was the final N64 release, coming out in stores in late 2001. The Nintendo 64 was dead by Christmas 2001, shoved out of the way by the hot new GameCube (many retailers and rental stores had already begun to sell off their extra stock of N64 software long before the holidays.) Nintendo never dropped the price of the console past the $99 mark, and the hardware itself was never "miniaturized" into a smaller, more compact unit (unlike the NES and SNES).

The Nintendo 64, regardless of its checkered past, will always be loved and remembered by those gamers who saw through the hype and misconceptions, gamers who truly appreciated the genius of Nintendo's software development teams. It was the first video game system for a lot of young gamers, and will therefore be remembered fondly as time goes on. The N64 library might not be huge, but it is still full of incredible titles that simply beg to be played again and again. History will probably be kind to the N64, and not just because it was the last cartridge-based home console system. History will remember the Nintendo 64 simply because it was an awesome gaming platform that played host to some truly spectacular games.

Typically, European games will not work on U.S. systems, but Japanese games will.

Aidyn Chronicles: The First Mage

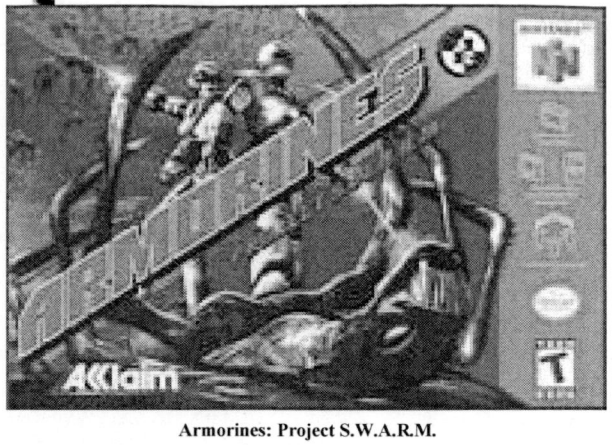

Armorines: Project S.W.A.R.M.

1080° Snowboarding   Nintendo   3 $8
The N64 was home to a respectable number of snowboarding titles, but Nintendo's own effort distinguishes itself from the pack with its beautiful graphics, impressive variety, entertaining tricks, and steep (but ultimately rewarding) leaning curve. Don't pass 1080 up if you're into this sort of game!

A Bug's Life   Activision   4 $12
Unlike most games aimed at children, this 3-D platformer manages to provide enough secret-finding antics to entertain adults as well. The graphics are quite lovely if a bit foggy, but the music is dull and the story unfolds through boring still images and text rather than the video scenes found in the PSX original. This one isn't bad for a movie-based kiddie game.

Aero Gauge   Ascii   2 $5
This poor Wipeout clone suffers from a multitude of sins... terrible graphical pop-up, lousy music, and overly difficult courses. If you're looking for a good futuristic racer for the N64, F-Zero X and Wipeout 64 are far superior to this mess.

AeroFighter's Assault   Video System   3 $7
Choppy graphics, boring gameplay, and frustrating control combine to make this 3-D aircraft shooter a game to avoid if you like your games to be fun. The missions and aerial movement might be realistic, but that doesn't necessarily translate into a good video game.

Aidyn Chronicles: The First Mage
    THQ   5 $25
One of the last third-party games developed for the N64, Aidyn Chronicles was also the first "traditional" RPG released for the system (which says a lot about the N64's dismal RPG situation.) The game is huge, the soundtrack is delightful, and the 3-D graphics aren't bad (especially with the Expansion Pak), but the gameplay is dull and you spend far too much time wandering about for no reason. This one's a bit of a disappointment, to be sure.

All Star Tennis '99   UbiSoft   4 $8
Tennis video games generally qualify as "niche" titles, the excellent Mario Tennis and the Dreamcast's Virtua Striker games being some notable exceptions. AST '99 is a quirky little game with mediocre graphics and average gameplay but just enough bizarre touches to make it rise above the sum of its parts.

All-Star Baseball '99   Acclaim   2 $3
Acclaim has put out more than their fair share of dud games, but their sports titles occasionally earn them some much-needed respectability. ASB'99 is a highly polished baseball simulation featuring the full MLB license, gorgeous graphics, and wonder-

fully intuitive control.

All-Star Baseball 2000   Acclaim   2 $5
Acclaim didn't drop the ball with this update of their popular baseball franchise; an already excellent and beautiful game has been made better with more options and refinements, plus improved A.I. The sound is still weak, though.

All-Star Baseball 2001   Acclaim   4 $7
The best baseball franchise of its era received minor refinements for its yearly update, bringing the series one step closer to perfection. The sound effects and soundtrack are still a bit crappy, but everything else is superlative.

Armorines: Project S.W.A.R.M.
    Acclaim   4 $10
Ever seen the movie Starship Troopers? This first-person shooter (based off an obscure comic and running off the Turok engine) is only missing the movie license to be Starship Troopers: The Video Game. Unfortunately, the game doesn't live up to the action-packed and under-appreciated feature film. The bug-hunting action sucks, the puzzles are stupid, and the control scheme is frustrating and inaccurate.

Army Men: Air Combat   3DO   4 $12
What ranks as the best game in the entire Army Men franchise (which isn't really saying much), Air Combat combines 3DO's signature Tan/Green plastic soldiers with an isometric helicopter shooter highly reminiscent of EA's classic Strike series. It's not a bad game overall, but Nuclear Strike is better.

Army Men: Sarge's Heroes   3DO   3 $8
This shoddy sequel to an equally shoddy PSX game is a poorly designed third-person shooter featuring drab graphics, sparse environments, and schizophrenic camera angles. A shameful waste of plastic (green, tan, or otherwise) if you ask us.

Army Men: Sarge's Heroes 2
    3DO   4 $10
3DO certainly likes to beat their dead horses, don't they? Sarge's Heroes 2 flaunts the same flaws as its predecessor but adds more action to the screen, resulting in even choppier graphics. The levels are a bit better this time around, but the N64 library is loaded with titles better than this one.

Asteroids Hyper 64   Crave   4 $15
Some "updates" of classic games (like Tempest 2000 for the Jaguar) turn out fantastic. Others, like Asteroids Hyper 64, offer little more than the original game with prettier (and sometimes distracting) graphics. What qualified as "fun" back in 1979 doesn't play so well 20 years later, especially when the gameplay is

Modern video game companies lose money on every console they sell, hoping to make it back with software sales.

essentially unchanged and the "new" graphics get in the way of the action.

Automobili Lamborghini   Titus   3 $8
Nearly unpronounceable name aside, this beautiful and fast-moving first-generation racer is great fun and sports a lot of variety. Unfortunately, the game's a bit easy and won't demand much of your attention for more than a day or two.

Banjo-Kazooie   Nintendo   2 $10
The N64 wouldn't have fared nearly so well without Nintendo's second-party development house, Rare. This beautiful and infinitely playable 3-D platform/adventure game may have a few camera problems, but the finely honed gameplay and general sense of fun make it a definite keeper.

Banjo-Tooie   Nintendo   4 $15
Rare's wonderful sequel to Banjo-Kazooie is even deeper and better looking than its predecessor, and that's saying a lot. Crammed full of massive levels, excellent music/sound effects, and memorable characters, this lovingly polished platformer rates as one of the N64's finest titles.

Bassmasters 2000   THQ   4 $10
You're in the minority if you enjoy games based on the "sport" of fishing, but one man's boredom is another man's thrill. Whatever the case, this otherwise average 3-D fishing simulation sports an excellent and very intuitive control scheme that earns it a recommendation for you fishermen out there.

Batman Beyond: Return of the Joker
UbiSoft   5 $20
This side-scrolling 2-D fighting game has almost no redeeming qualities, other than its cool (and completely wasted) license. This kind of game died years ago, and the terrible graphics, boring backgrounds, and frighteningly repetitive "punch and kick" gameplay of this turd isn't going to bring the genre back anytime soon.

BattleTanx   3DO   3 $7
Like the Bomberman series, the Battletanx games are best played with friends. The graphics and gameplay of this mediocre 3-D tank shooter don't offer enough variety for the single player, but there is quite a lot of fun to be had with a group of like-minded friends.

BattleTanx: Global Assault   3DO   4 $10
Unlike many sequels (especially those from 3DO), Global Assault is clearly superior to its predecessor. The levels are much larger and more numerous, the graphics are cleaner, and the tank-blasting action is faster than ever.

Battlezone: Rise of the Black Dogs
Crave   5 $17
This respectable PC port combines elements of many gaming genres, including shooting, racing, and strategy (you're free to choose your level of commitment, ranging from arcade-style action to full-blown simulation.) Unfortunately, the graphics are rather sparse and the multi-player action is mediocre at best.

Beetle Adventure Racing
Electronic Arts   4 $15
Most folks have never heard of this little racing title, and that's a real shame. It's one of the best racers on the 64, packed full of beautiful graphics, precise control, entertaining physics, and loads of racing fun. Neither serious nor whimsical, Beetle Adventure Racing manages to be a jack of all trades and a master of most.

Big Mountain 2000   SouthPeak   6 $20
From a graphical and course design perspective, BM 2000 (no pun intended) is a bit ugly and boring, but the game's long tracks, choice of snowboarding or skiing styles, and good control keep it from slipping off the track into mediocrity.

Bio Freaks   Midway   2 $6
Unfortunately, the N64 is definitely NOT the choice of console among fighting game fans, and with good reason. Midway's bizarre and gory 3-D fighter has nice sound effects, some neat options, and a unique graphical style, but the gameplay pales in comparison to world-class fighters like Tekken and VF.

Blast Corps   Nintendo   2 $5
One of the first N64 games, this oddly entertaining action/puzzle hybrid involves a slow-moving cargo truck bearing a leaky nuclear device on an unstoppable course through a populated city. Your job is to destroy all of the environment hazards in the way of the cargo truck using a series of vehicles (many of which must be earned or discovered.) The graphics are decidedly primitive by later N64 release standards, but the gameplay and considerable challenge are still completely intact.

Blues Brothers 2000   Titus   6 $20
No one quite knows why Titus chose to develop a 3-D platform game around the spectacularly under whelming Blue Brothers license, but here it is nevertheless. With so many similar games available for the N64, it's hard to overlook this one's sloppy controls, average graphics, and repetitive soundtrack.

Body Harvest   Nintendo   2 $5
Like many games that try to combine different gaming genres (driving, shooting, action, exploration), Body Harvest ends up

Banjo-Kazooie

Bio Freaks

Phillips lost more than $1 billion because of the CD-i.

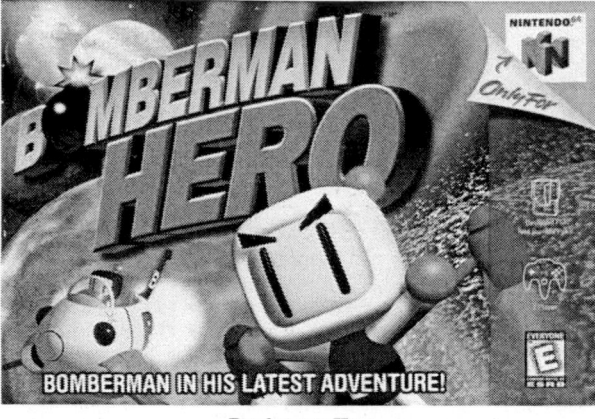

Bomberman Hero

Buck Bumble

being a strange (if interesting) game that masters none of the game styles it tries to incorporate into its varied repartee. Still, the game is mindless fun and quite lengthy, if just a bit frustrating at times.

Bomberman 64 Nintendo 3 $8
This long running series (which hit its zenith on the Super Nintendo and the Saturn) made the jump to 3-D for the N64, but the results are less than impressive. The essential element of "fun" has been generally exorcised, leaving behind little more than a game that looks like Mario 64 but plays like the ghost of the Bomberman many of us once knew and loved.

Bomberman Hero Nintendo 5 $15
The original Bomberman 64 tried to combine the classic multi-player madness of the earlier titles with Mario 64-style gameplay. Bomberman Hero, on the other hand, jettisons the multi-player gameplay entirely in favor of 3-D platform action. The result is a mildly enjoyable game starring one of gaming's most enduring mascots.

Bomberman: Second Attack
　　　　　　　　Vatical 5 $18
While it doesn't return the series to its roots, the sequel to Bomberman 64 represents a definite improvement over the original outing and is great fun when played with friends. The Mario 64-like qualities have been removed for the most part, and the game is more fun to play. The graphics still suck, though.

Bottom of the 9th Konami 3 $4
If you have fuzzy graphics but no MLB license, you'd darn well better have some decent gameplay to tip the scales in your favor. Fortunately, the gameplay engine of this baseball simulation is pretty tight, and the Scenario Mode is a nice touch.

Brunswick Circuit Pro Bowling
　　　　　　　　THQ 4 $12
Aside from the dreadful graphics, this deep, finely-tuned, and surprisingly challenging bowling simulation is one game in an oft-ignored genre that should please even the hardest of hardcore bowling fans (all 10 of them.)

Buck Bumble UbiSoft 3 $8
UbiSoft made several attempts to create a memorable corporate mascot to go along with their awesome Rayman 2. Regrettably, if you can see through the exceedingly foggy graphics of this 3-D action/shooter, you'll find a mediocre game with strictly average level design, frustratingly complex controls, and a tacked-on multiplayer mode.

Bust-A-Move 2: Arcade Edition
　　　　　　　　Acclaim 4 $10
This port of the popular arcade action puzzler seems right at home on the N64 and features better graphics and more frames of animation that its PSX cousin. The N64 controller, in particular, has been well tuned for this title and delivers accurate and precise aiming.

Bust-A-Move '99 Acclaim 5 $15
Like many puzzle game series, most of the titles in the Bust-A-Move franchise are simply variations on the same theme with some minor additions and enhancements added on to each new installment. The second N64 BAM game features the same addictive bubble-popping theatrics the series is known for, along with a cool new edit mode and some enhanced multiplayer action.

California Speed Midway 4 $10
Also known as "How many times can Midway recycle the San Francisco Rush engine," California Speed is a decidedly sub-standard arcade port with shallow gameplay and sub-par graphics. There are a lot of secret tracks and cars to unlock, but the basic racing game is simply too boring to encourage much effort.

Carmageddon 64 Titus 6 $20
Quite possibly one of the worst games released for the Nintendo 64, this combat/racing hybrid rips away all the elements that were entertaining about the PC games and replaces them with laughable graphics and simply awful control. The best part about the original games was the ability to mow down pedestrians. Regrettably, Titus chose to replace the innocent bystanders with slow, green-blooded zombies. How did this mess make it past the testing stages?

Castlevania Konami 3 $12
Many Castlevania purists curse Konami's decision to evolve the classically 2-D series into a 3-D game for Nintendo's console, but the results are impressive nevertheless. The action is fast and furious, the levels are large and interesting, and the feeling of snapping off the head of a running skeleton with your whip is simply luscious.

Castlevania: Legacy of Darkness
　　　　　　　　Konami 6 $25
Not really a sequel at all, this mildly enhanced update to the original N64 Castlevania adds some additional characters, a few extra levels, slightly upgraded graphics, and not much else. Legacy of Darkness was released just a few months after the first game and had a limited production run, making it somewhat collectible.

The JVC X'Eye came with one Genesis style controller, but it carries the logo of JVC, not the Genesis.

good control.

Chameleon Twist SunSoft 2 $6
Yet another "O.K." 3-D platform game, Chameleon Twist features repetitive textures, the standard camera problems inherent of the genre, and not much challenge for experienced gamers. Neither offensive nor innovative, it's just a simple children's action game that was probably produced without a lot of effort.

Chameleon Twist 2 SunSoft 4 $8
Sequels are supposed to offer some improvements over the original game. Unfortunately, SunSoft decided to remove the controllable camera found in the first Chameleon Twist for this second outing, rendering what might have been a decent 3-D platform title virtually unplayable due to cheap deaths.

Charlie Blast's Territory Kemco 5 $12
This obscure and rather bizarre take on the puzzle genre features some pretty respectable puzzle design, but the sparse graphics and sound coupled with the maddeningly sensitive controls earn Charlie a low rung on the puzzle ladder.

Chopper Attack Midway 2 $5
Fuzzy first-generation graphics aside, this 3-D helicopter shooter is actually quite entertaining to play after you get the hang of the complex but well-designed control scheme. Unfortunately, the game is way too short, but the decent mission based combat and copious explosions are great fun while they last.

Clayfighter 63 1/3 Interplay 3 $7
Never a good platform for fighting games, the N64 is home to several duds like this. The original SNES games weren't that great either, but at least the bizarre stop-motion captured "clay" fighters were new and interesting. The third time is definitely NOT the charm in this case...poor graphics, a lousy fighting engine, and obnoxious character chatter don't mix well.

Clayfighter 63 1/3: Sculptor's Cut
Interplay 7 $30
Like the SNES, the N64 was home to a Blockbuster Exclusive game from the Clayfighter fighting series. This mild "upgrade" to a poor fighting game does contain some new characters, moves, and other such nonsense, but the game still sucks. This one is really just for collectors of "rare" games or for someone looking to acquire a "compete" collection.

Command & Conquer Nintendo 4 $15
Real-time strategy games tend to be a fairly rare breed on most consoles, but this very respectable port of the PC smash does the series justice. The sprite-based graphics have been replaced with very nice polygonal models, and the N64 controller, while not as good as a PC mouse, still manages to deliver very

Conker's Bad Fur Day Rare 3 $15
One of the last N64 releases and Rare's final game for the console, CBFD started out as another 3-D platform game in the same vein as Banjo-Kazooie before it was suddenly switched over to an M-rated, potty-mouthed turdfest with moments of real genius (consider a main character who starts the game with a hangover, sings along with a giant mountain of poo, and urinates on others.) The levels are huge, the graphics are gorgeous, and there are tons of awesome multiplayer games to explore.

Cruis'n Exotica Midway 4 $15
Midway's Crusin' arcade series has always been known as the "lite beer" of the racing game world, and this third and final installment is no exception. While better than previous installments, the shallow gameplay and average graphics will have you looking somewhere else for a deeper racing experience.

Cruis'n USA Nintendo 2 $5
One of the very first games for the N64, this really awful racing title deletes the only cool feature (the road kill) from the equally poor (yet wildly popular) arcade original, leaving behind a big mess of shallow gameplay, major graphical pop-up, and a looping soundtrack that will drive you insane.

Cruis'n World Nintendo 3 $12
This sequel to the first racer on the N64 offers several improvements over the original, including better graphics and a less maddening soundtrack. Unfortunately, this is still a below-average racing game on a console loaded with better choices (plus your opponents have a tendency to cheat at the last second of a race.)

Cyber Tiger Electronic Arts 4 $10
Regardless of your feelings for Tiger Woods, you'll end up hating the N64 game that bears his game. The control layout is flawed and hard to manage, the gameplay is boring, and the graphics are simply awful, especially for a game produced in 2000 (when most developers had learned the complexities of the hardware.)

Daikatana Kemco 5 $15
The story behind this game is fascinating. John Romero (one of the fathers of the original DOOM and QUAKE) left the company he co-founded (Id) to start up his own company (Ion Storm) where he was to develop a "revolutionary" first-person shooter for the PC. The resulting mess has become "legendary" in its awfulness. The N64 port is ugly, unpolished, and merely points out the overwhelming flaws of the original PC game. The RPG

Clay Fighter 63 1/3

Cyber Tiger

The Sega CDX has its own logo, completely different than the Sega CD or Genesis.

Donky Kong 64

Doom

and "partner" elements are completely superficial and feel tacked on.

Dark Rift   **Vic Tokai**   **3**   **$8**
The spiritual successor to the wretched PSX/Saturn fighter Criticom, this poorly designed 3-D fighter sports some nice graphics and lighting, but the shallow gameplay is of the button-mashing variety and the overall presentation leaves a lot to be desired.

Deadly Arts   **Konami**   **3**   **$10**
It's kind of funny (in a horrible way) that the PSX and the Saturn received loads of great fighters while the N64 didn't even get ONE truly first-rate fighting game. Deadly Arts has a very interesting "create a fighter" mode, but the rest of the game is mediocre at best.

Destruction Derby 64   **THQ**   **4**   **$12**
One of the better PSX hand-me-downs, Destruction Derby 64 features all of the car-crunching mayhem that made the original games so popular, plus improved graphics, tight control, and great multiplayer action.

Diddy Kong Racing   **Nintendo/Rare**   **3**   **$15**
DKR came out of nowhere during the Christmas of 1997 to become the N64's top cart racer, even surpassing the highly popular (but flawed) Mario Kart 64. Rare was really starting to get the hang of the hardware with this release, and the graphics are still very impressive. If you can stand the excessive cuteness of Diddy and his pals, you'll find a deep and satisfying racer.

Disney's Tarzan   **Activision**   **5**   **$18**
While not quite up to the level of the PSX original, this surprising fun 2-D platform game (with 3-D visuals) has a "classic" feel to it and follows the movie's plot closely (you start out as a young Tarzan and grow from there.) Unfortunately, the control isn't all that it could be, and the cartridge format seems to have hampered some of the storytelling.

Donald Duck: Goin' Quackers
     UbiSoft   **5**   **$18**
A hodgepodge of different scenes from previous games disguised as a 3-D platform game, Goin' Quackers features simple and intuitive control and pretty graphics, but the gameplay is fairly derivative and mainly aimed at children.

Donkey Kong 64   **Nintendo**   **3**   **$25**
The N64 certainly wasn't hurting for 3-D platform games by the time Donkey Kong 64 was released, but it still managed to rise above the masses and stands as one of the system's best games. Rare works their gameplay and graphical magic once

again, coming up with a game that is simply humongous in scope and variety. DK64 requires the Expansion Pak to operate, and it came bundled with the game (hence the higher price for a common release.)

Doom 64   **Midway**   **2**   **$5**
The father of all first-person shooters (Castle Wolfenstein is the grandfather) made an appearance on the N64, complete with some great new levels, pixel-free graphics, and good control. It's a bit dated by today's standards (and is totally fragged by Quake II) but the timeless essence of this classic lives on.

Dr. Mario 64   **Nintendo**   **4**   **$12**
One of the best puzzle game series ever developed for the NES and SNES received a minor 64-bit makeover in this well-received update. The gameplay mechanics are exactly the same as before, but additional features and a wonderful multiplayer mode make this game one to look out for in your hunts.

Dual Heroes   **Electro-Brain**   **3**   **$10**
It's pretty amazing that this turd even made it out the door but it seems that the dearth of N64 fighting games let it slip by quality control. The control is terrible, the graphics are abysmal, and the plot is convoluted, but at least some of the characters look like Power Rangers.

Duck Dodgers Starring Daffy Duck
     Infogrames   **4**   **$15**
How many 3-D platform games can you play without going crazy? The world may never know the answer, but Daffy seems determined to save the world anyway in this licensed game based on one of his most beloved alter egos. Most everything from the graphics to the gameplay are strictly average.

Duke Nukem 64   **GT Interactive**   **3**   **$10**
The 3-D technology of this brash first-person shooter is antiquated when compared to that of Quake II, but this game is more about attitude, great level design, and frenetic shooting action than cutting-edge programming techniques. Nintendo cut out most of the raunchier details (like the strippers and the porno movies) but the fun remains the same.

Duke Nukem: Zero Hour   **GT Interactive**   **3**   **$10**
The Duke went from a first to a third-person perspective for his second outing on the N64, and the results are surprisingly good despite the lack of save points. Much better than its PSX equivalent (Time to Kill), Zero Hour offers great level design, excellent controls, and better than average graphics (which tend to get a bit choppy when using the Expansion Pack, unfortunately.)

186

Earthworm Jim 3D Rockstar 3 $8
Jim's first few outings on the Genesis, SNES, Sega CD, and Saturn were hilarious 2-D platform games with great level design and incredibly bizarre enemies (Professor Monkey-For-A-Head). His first foray into a 3-D world features many of the same good qualities, but the schizophrenic camera ruins what could have been the third great game in the series.

ECW: Hardcore Revolution Acclaim 3 $5
Fans of "real" fighting games generally view the N64 as a substandard console, but it saw more than its fair share of wrestling games (which constitute a completely different gaming genre.) In this case, Hardcore Revolution sports the less-popular ECW license as well as the same old gameplay engine that powered several other wrestling titles from Acclaim.

Excitebike 64 Nintendo 5 $20
The original 8-bit Excitebike was a sensation in the arcades and on the NES way back in the 80's, but the incredible 64-bit update garnered little fanfare and remains one of the N64's best "sleeper" titles. The graphics are simply gorgeous, and the excellent tutorial will lead you through the complex control scheme and have you zipping around the well-designed tracks in no time. You can even unlock the original 8-bit game (plus a special polygonal version of the 8-bit game) if you race well enough.

Extreme-G Acclaim 2 $3
The first installment of Acclaim's futuristic motorcycle racer created quite a stir upon its initial release, mostly due to its wild track design, flashy (if foggy) graphics, and blinding sense of speed. Unfortunately, the game hasn't aged too well and pales in comparison with later releases.

Extreme-G 2 Acclaim 4 $10
Sequels are generally expected to be superior to the original game, but EG2 tries so hard to better its predecessor that it ends up shooting itself in the tire. The handling of the bikes has been greatly improved, but the game is so fast (with a stuttering frame rate) and the lighting effects are so over-used that the game is less fun to play than the first one.

F-1 World Grand Prix Video System 3 $8
This deep (and we mean deep) racing simulation has some frame rate problems and a mediocre soundtrack, but these deficiencies are more than made up for by the huge variety of tracks, drivers, and play modes. The graphics are serviceable, plus the amount of control you have over your car's handling characteristics is incredible.

F-Zero X Nintendo 3 $10
The original SNES F-Zero ranks as one of the best racing

games ever created, and the N64 update certainly does the series justice. The sparse, flat-shaded graphics allow for a zippy frame rate and literally DOZENS of onscreen opponents all around you, plus the track design and rich variety of the courses and vehicles are simply amazing.

F1 Pole Position 64 UbiSoft 3 $5
Unlike the far superior F-1 World Grand Prix, this substandard racer suffers from severe graphical pop-up and plenty of the 64's trademark fog. Some graphical issues are to be expected from a first-generation title, but this game's terrible control makes the first F-1 title for the N64 unusually frustrating.

FIFA '99 Electronic Arts 3 $5
The third and final update of the FIFA franchise on the N64 is nearly perfect, featuring gorgeous visuals and superb A.I. The control is like a finely tuned car, reacting instantly to your every command.

FIFA: Road to the World Cup '98
  Electronic Arts 2 $3
EA gained a better feel for the complicated N64 hardware just in time for the update to their popular FIFA franchise, and the extra programming practice is clearly evident. The graphics are much improved, and the game is much more polished than the first outing.

FIFA Soccer 64 Electronic Arts 2 $3
The first of EA's three FIFA Soccer titles suffered from a myriad of problems including choppy graphics, some problematic camera angles, and an overall rushed feel. It's still a lot of fun, but the sequels are far superior.

Fighter Destiny 2 SouthPeak 4 $10
This respectable sequel to the original Fighters Destiny (don't know what happened to that "s") keeps the innovative point-scoring system of the original, but also retains the exact same graphics and fighting engine. The old adage "if it ain't broke, don't fix it" really shouldn't apply to video games, making FD2 somewhat of a letdown.

Fighters Destiny Ocean 3 $8
One of the better 3-D fighting games for the console (and that's not saying much), Fighters Destiny features a unique point-scoring system coupled with several interesting play modes. The graphics are pretty average and the character design is completely derivative, but the basic gameplay is solid and enjoyable.

Fighting Force 64 Crave 4 $12
This boring port of an equally boring (yet inexplicably popular)

Excitebike 64

FIFA: Road to the World Cup '98

What contribution did the PSX controller give to the world?

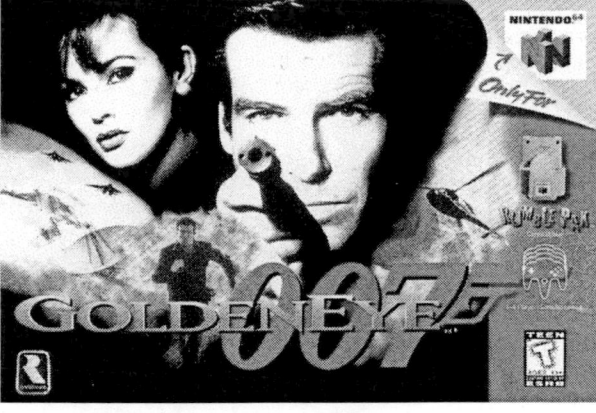

Goldeneye 007

Harvest Moon 64

PSX game really is nothing more than a Final Fight clone set in a 3-D world. You know the drill… punch, kick, repeat. The environments and enemies are drab and repetitive, leading to a game that gets old REAL fast.

Flying Dragon   **Natsume**   **3**   **$7**
Loads of variety doesn't necessarily translate into a good game, a fact aptly demonstrated by this mediocre 3-D fighter. It's packed full of play options including the ability to fight as either normal-sized or "super-deformed" style characters, but the graphics are bland and the gameplay is shallow.

Forsaken 64   **Acclaim**   **2**   **$8**
This souped-up Descent clone tuned out surprising well on the N64, even better than the version for the PSX (a console that was designed to handle fast 3-D games like this.) The control is very responsive once you get the hang of it, and the cool weapons and massive bosses just add to the fun.

Fox Sports College Hoops '99
                    Fox Interactive   **3**   **$4**
The first of the NCAA games for the N64 is a big disappointment, mostly due to the crappy graphics and major slowdown. The gameplay is acceptable, but there are much better choices out there if you want to shoot some hoops.

Gauntlet Legends   **Midway**   **5**   **$20**
Best played with a group of friend, this 90's update to the arcade classic doesn't offer much in the way of a satisfying single player experience. The graphics are pretty close to the arcade original and the sound effects (particularly the booming voice) may bring back some fond memories for some of the older gamers out there, but Gauntlet remains, as always, a party game best played with friends.

Gex 3: Deep Cover Gecko   **Crave**   **3**   **$12**
While not nearly as bad as Gex 64, the second appearance of the smart-talking lizard on the N64 is still not without its problems. The graphics are still sub-par and the voiceover work of comedian Dana Gould is still tired and aggravating, but the gameplay has been upgraded to "average" status.

Gex 64: Enter the Gecko   **Midway**   **2**   **$8**
Crystal Dynamics originally hoped that Gex would become the next Mario, and his only 2-D outing was a highly regarded and good selling platform title on several consoles. Unfortunately, his move to 3-D is plagued with a myriad of problems including shoddy graphics, very bad collision detection, and serious camera issues.

Glover   **Hasbro**   **2**   **$7**
In an effort to launch what they hoped would be a new gaming mascot in the same league as Mario, Hasbro came up with this mixture of several gaming genres including 3-D action, puzzle, and basketball. While certainly not a Mario-killer, Glover is a fairly interesting (if plain-looking) game with a lot of variety and a high degree of challenge.

Goemon's Great Adventure
                    Konami   **4**   **$15**
The second outing of Goemon on American shores revives the addictive 2-D style gameplay of previous Japan-only games, losing the 3-D platform action of Mystical Ninja Staring Goemon. The graphics may be 3-D, but the wonderful gameplay reminds us of the some of the great 16-bit side scrollers of the past.

Golden Nugget 64   **Electronic Arts**   **6**   **$25**
Gambling simulations rarely (if ever) set the video gaming world on fire, but there are a fair number of gamers who enjoy this sort of thing. Golden Nugget is particularly well done, with an excellent interface and pleasant 3-D graphics.

GoldenEye 007   **Nintendo**   **2**   **$7**
One of the best and most popular N64 games of all time, Goldeneye is a superlative corridor shooter featuring incredible graphics, a beautiful soundtrack, excellent control, and superb multiplayer options. Unlike many games of this type, Goldeneye is crammed full of well-designed single-player missions that will keep you busy for weeks.

GT 64: Championship Edition
                    Ocean   **3**   **$5**
Whatever its faults, you have to give this racer credit for being consistent. The graphics are average, the track design is average, the gameplay is average… just about everything reeks of "average."

Harvest Moon 64   **Natsume**   **5**   **$25**
While certainly not an RPG series one would term as "wildly popular", the Harvest Moon games have a very devoted group of fans. For the uninitiated, Harvest Moon's gameplay revolves around… farming and animal husbandry! It's all rather charming and oddly engrossing, even if the graphics and soundtrack are simplistic and the action can best be described as "gentle."

Hercules: The Legendary Journeys
                    Titus   **4**   **$15**
This third person adventure title (based on the strangely influential television series) isn't as bad as it sounds. The graphics are pretty decent for a third-party release, and the game has an effective way of dealing with the collision detection problems

The inclusion of four shoulder buttons instead of just two.

inherent of 3-D games of this type. Like the TV show, Hercules will suck you in and won't let go until it's done.

Hexen GT Interactive 2 $5

A first-person shooter with an RPG slant, this poor conversion of an over-the-hill PC games pales in comparison to similar shooters like Duke Nukem 64, Quake II, and even Doom 64. No improvements seem to have been made to the original, and the march of technology is clearly evident in the blurry graphics and choppy frame rates.

Hey You, Pikachu! Nintendo 3 $15

Nintendo certainly can't be blamed for beating the crap out of the Pikachu cash cow, no matter how child-like some of the games turned out. This rather intriguing experiment is better than most of the Picacrap merchandising efforts and came bundled with a microphone and limited voice recognition capability. Most of the "action" revolves around simple mini-games and puzzle solving, but the concept is interesting (if a bit underdeveloped.)

Hot Wheels Turbo Racing Electronic Arts 4 $15

It may look like a simple racing game aimed strictly at children, but this remarkably imaginative racer is actually quite a bit of fun. The car models (based on actual Hot Wheels toys) are cleanly rendered, and the graphics are fast and colorful. The track design is especially inventive, with loads of jumps, corkscrews, and shortcuts.

Hybrid Heaven Konami 3 $8

Like the name suggests, this game is a combination of several different game styles, but it's hardly a heavenly experience. Part RPG, part bizarre fighter, and part third-person adventure, Hybrid Heaven features a dialog-heavy storyline rifled with poor grammar and boring dialog.

Hydro Thunder Midway 6 $40

Midway certainly graced the N64 with a load of arcade ports, and the conversion of their popular arcade boat racer is surprisingly impressive. The game's visuals, while not as clean as those of the DC version, are quite lovely nevertheless. You'll be sucked in from the moment you place first after getting to the last stretch of a race and hitting a turbo at the base of a ramp, sailing over all your opponents.

Iggy's Reckin' Balls Acclaim 4 $12

Innovation is a rare and appreciated commodity in the video game industry, even if the execution falls a bit flat in the end. This bizarre platform/puzzle/racing hybrid is hard to explain and occasionally harder to play, but it certainly deserves a look from curious gamers looking for something different.

In-Fisherman Bass Hunter 64 Rockstar 5 $15

If you're the type of "sports' gamer who likes to play alone, you might enjoy this lazy fishing game (since there is no multiplayer option.) Unfortunately, this Bass Hunter tries to tow the line between arcade-style action game and full-blown simulation, ending up doing neither genre much justice.

Indiana Jones and the Infernal Machine LucasArts 7 $25

This big-budget Tomb Raider clone was set to explode on the PC, PSX, and N64, but the PC version bombed, the PSX game was cancelled, and the N64 port became a rental-only title at Blockbuster stores. Rarity aside, the game is actually pretty good (excellent graphics, tight control, clever puzzles, and big levels) if a tad unpolished.

Indy Racing 2000 Infogrames 4 $12

It might like a shallow arcade-type racer, but Indy Racing 2000 is actually quite deep and a whole lot of fun. Options abound, and the control, while difficult to master, is very precise once you get the hang of it. Unfortunately, the graphics are dark and lack detail, but it's a small price to play for excellent gameplay.

International Superstar Soccer 64 Konami 2 $4

As the direct competitor to EA's FIFA Soccer 64, most people expected Konami's first soccer effort on the N64 to pale in comparison. The opposite turned out to be true, as the graphics and gameplay are actually better in this game.

International Superstar Soccer '98 Konami 2 $5

Even without the FIFA license, Konami's second soccer effort for the N64 still looks and plays beautifully. The menus could still use some work, but the overall presentation is top-notch.

International Track and Field 2000 Konami 7 $25

The old Track and Filed arcade game was notorious for its tortuous (but still fun) play mechanics, and this 64-bit update is no different. Available only for rental through Blockbuster Stores, this shallow and easy to beat button-mashing fest sports some fine graphics but definitely deserved its rental-only status.

Jeopardy! Take2 Interactive 4 $15

Name the worst N64 game based on a popular syndicated game show. What is Jeopardy? You're correct! This "update" to the popular trivia series features a large repertoire of questions and an easy-to-use interface, but the incredibly flat graphics and

Hybrid Heaven

Indiana Jones and the Infernal Machine

Portable systems see most of their gameplay inside the home of the owner.

The Legend of Zelda: Majora's Mask

The Legend of Zelda: Ocarina of Time

almost non-existent soundtrack practically scream "we expended almost no effort on the making of this game."

Jeremy McGrath Supercross 2000
Acclaim   4 $12
Acclaim is at it again, it seems. Their interpretation on the motocross-racing genre reeks of poor productions values. The graphics are mediocre, the options list is short, and the gameplay is unrealistic and far too easy to master. It's in your best interest to pick up Excitebike 64 instead.

Jet Force Gemini   Rare   2 $10
If you like variety in your 3-D adventures, you're going to love this Rare-produced masterpiece. Like most of the famed developer's releases, this game features wonderful graphics, a great multiplayer mode, huge levels, and imaginative boss characters. Despite a somewhat confusing control scheme, Jet Force Gemini is an incredible title that offers weeks of gameplay.

Ken Griffey Jr.'s Slugfest   Nintendo   2 $5
The second appearance of Ken Griffey Junior on the N64 sports a variety of improvements over its predecessor, most notably in the graphics department. The arcade-style gameplay is much the same, making it the perfect game for younger baseball fans.

Killer Instinct Gold   Nintendo   3 $12
The first two arcade installments of this 2-fighter were wildly popular in the early 90's, but the series appears to have been abandoned. It's certainly no fault of this game, an addictive (if combo-heavy) fighter that combines most everything from KI2 and adds 3-D backgrounds. Some of the animation frames are missing and the FMV sequences are gone because of the cartridge format, but KI Gold remains one of the N64's better fighting titles.

Kirby 64: The Crystal Shards
Nintendo   4 $15
One of the top-selling Nintendo 64 games ever released in Japan, Kirby 64 is somewhat of a letdown. It's a very slow-moving side-scrolling 2-D style game with simple graphics 3-D graphics and a premise involving sucking in your enemies to produce assorted combination attacks. This one is cute, but best left for children.

Knife Edge: Nose Gunner   Vatical/Kemco   2 $5
Essentially a "shooter on rails", Knife Edge can be completed by most gamers in just a few hours. The design of the boss charters is interesting, and the multiplayer mode is a nice touch, but the graphics are far too drab for a rail-based shooter.

Knockout Kings 2000   Electronic Arts   3 $10
It's cool to be able to play as some of the greatest boxers who ever lived (like Ali and Holyfield), but that's about the only thing this lackluster 3-D fighter has going for it. The graphics are pretty (if slow), but all the boxers move exactly the same and your opponent's A.I. is pitiful.

Kobe Byant in NBA Courtside
Nintendo   2 $4
Not a bad effort by developer Left Field Productions, this respectable basketball simulation has good graphics, tight control, and numerous options. Followed by a superior sequel (NBA Courtside 2 Featuring Kobe Bryant.)

Legend of Zelda: Majora's Mask
Nintendo   3 $20
While not as remarkable as its predecessor, Majora's Mask (which originally began life as an N64 DD title) is nevertheless a wonderful addition to the Zelda franchise and a hugely entertaining game in its own right. The graphics (which now REQUIRE the use of the Expansion Pak) are fantastic, but the basic gameplay has changed rather dramatically and isn't quite as enjoyable as that of Ocarina of Time (not surprising, considering how good it is.)

Legend of Zelda: Ocarina of Time
Nintendo   2 $12
Zelda makes the jump to 3-D in a remarkable fashion, resulting is what many believe to be the best game ever produced for the Nintendo 64. Nintendo mastered the inherent problems of navigating in a 3-D world with the innovation Z-button "lock-on" feature, and the gameplay is virtually flawless. The graphics are simply glorious, the soundtrack is beautiful, and the levels are huge and beautifully designed.

Lego Racers   Lego Media   4 $15
It's perfectly acceptable to try and copy Super Mario Kart, but at least copy the GOOD things! This lame racer straight from LegoLand might seem cute at first, but the flawed control, poor track design, and strange battle system with leave you under whelmed. What should have been the game's saving grace (the create-a-racer option) is confusing and convoluted.

Lode Runner 3D   Infogrames   4 $12
When will industry bigwigs ever learn that some classic (and we mean classic) game series just shouldn't make the jump to 3-D? This quirky puzzle game is slow and frustratingly difficult at times, quite the opposite of the original 1980's computer titles.

The Neo-Geo AES is credited with introducing the world's first memory card.

Mace: The Dark Age   Midway   5 $15
This first-generation 3-D fighter (ported form an obscure arcade game) was actually pretty impressive in its day. The fighting engine is rather shallow and the game's speed is a bit on the slow side, but the gorgeous graphics and interesting character design keeps things interesting.

Madden 64   Electronic Arts   2 $2
The Madden Football series began its long and illustrious life way back on the Genesis, and this groundbreaking and wildly popular franchise didn't lose much ground with its first appearance on the N64. The "easy to pick up, hard to put down" quality of the game remains completely intact, and the 3-D visuals are a big improvement over the sprite-based graphics of the 16-bit titles.

Madden NFL '99   Electronic Arts   2 $2
The unstoppable Madden series just got better in 1999, this time featuring the NFL license and some flashy new graphics and player animations. The already tight control is further refined, resulting one of the best-playing football simulations on the 64.

Madden NFL 2000   Electronic Arts   2 $4
Further refinements graced the next installment of this workhorse football series including slightly improved graphics, a cool play editor, and the "Madden Challenge (an engrossing addition that allows you to unlock new teams and stadiums.)

Madden NFL 2001   Electronic Arts   3 $5
You won't discover anything really new in the 2001 update of the long-running franchise… just the same great graphics, features, gameplay, and fun.

Madden NFL 2002   Electronic Arts   5 $15
One of the final releases for the N64, Madden 2002 could have easily been a rehash of Madden 2001 with minor changes. Instead, EA chose to finish out Madden's run on the console with "Madden Classic Mode", one of the neatest additions ever seen in the series. Almost an entirely "new" game in itself, Classic mode looks and plays just like the 16-bit Genesis games of old (and this is a good thing.)

Magical Tetris Challenge   Capcom   4 $15
While it doesn't bring anything new to the Tetris table, this Disney-licensed puzzler offers the same addictive gameplay we've known and loved for years. The graphics are very 16-bit in quality and the soundtrack is almost painful, but the control is very responsive and the Disney characters add a new (if childish) element to the tried-and-true puzzle "action."

Major League Baseball Featuring Ken Griffey Jr.
    Nintendo   2 $3
The first of Ken's two N64 baseball outings, Major League Baseball is a respectable arcade-style game with great control and wonderful camera angles. The graphics aren't much too look at, but the gameplay is solid.

Mario Golf   Nintendo   3 $12
Although a bit too adorable for hard-core golfing fans, Mario Golf toes the line admirably between arcade quickie and real simulation. Looking and playing much the PSX's Hot Shots Golf (not surprising since they were developed by the same company), it features great control and nice, smooth graphics

Mario Kart 64   Nintendo   2 $15
The original SNES Super Mario Kart is widely viewed as one of the best cart racers ever made, which is probably why the 64-bit update received so much criticism. The graphics and soundtrack are lovely, but the A.I. is suspect… your opponents alternate between super-aggressive and borderline moronic. The single player mode borders on boring, but the great multi-player game more than makes up for it.

Mario Party   Nintendo   2 $8
An interesting hybrid of video and board games, the Mario Party series is all about hanging out with your friends in front of the TV and beating the video crap out of each other. Produced by Hudson (the same folks behind the Bomberman games), the first of the trilogy offers a lot of fun multiplayer action, but a boring one-person experience.

Mario Party 2   Nintendo   3 $10
The first Mario Party wasn't bad by any means, but the first sequel is quite a bit better and delivers much more replay value. Some minor refinements have taken place with the graphics, soundtrack, and gameplay, but the new mini-games are far more engrossing than those found in the original. Again, play this cart with a group of friends.

Mario Party 3   Nintendo   4 $20
The last of the Mario Party games and one of the final N64 releases, part 3 offers further enhancements over the original game including more mini-games and an interesting "dual mode" that allows you to have an entertaining gaming experience with just one other person, rather than three or four.

Mario Tennis   Nintendo   3 $15
Developed by Camelot (the same folks behind Mario Golf), Mario Tennis manages to overcome its childish Mario roots and actually challenges the Dreamcast's Virtua Tennis series as the best of the tennis video games. The character selection is large,

Magical Tetris Challenge

Mario Kart 64

Game batteries, such as the one in The Legend of Zelda, are expected to last about five years.

Milo's Astro Lanes

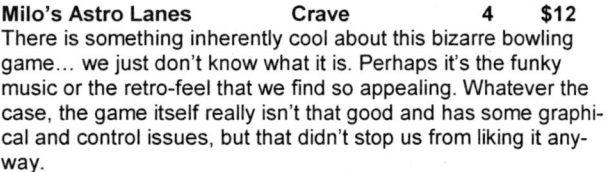

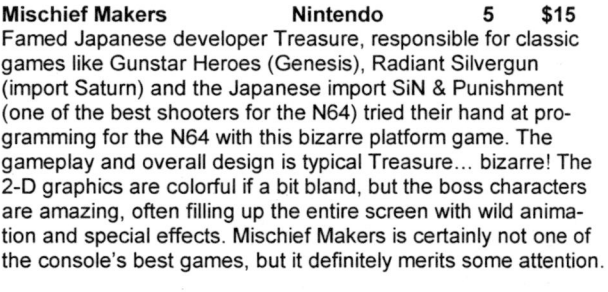

Monopoly

the action is fast, and the game is just so much darn fun to play it's almost sickening.

Mega Man 64   Capcom   4 $15
Why Capcom chose to port over this below average 3-D platform game to the N64 several years after its PSX debut is still a mystery. What's more, the graphics are still fuzzy, the levels are still boring, and nothing new seems to have been added.

Mia Hamm Soccer 64   SouthPeak   5 $10
Just because it's refreshing to see a sports title fronted by a female athlete doesn't mean we're going to go easy on it. This below-average soccer cart doesn't have much to recommend unless you consider ugly graphics, serious slowdown, and an almost completely silent crowd to be positive features.

Mickey's Speedway USA   Nintendo   4 $15
Expectations ran high when Nintendo, Rare, and Disney announced they had joined together to develop a cart racer. Luckily, the results are very impressive and come close to wining the title of "best cart racer for the N64." The graphics (while colorful) really aren't that great, but the voice characterizations and musical score are classic Disnesy. Mickey's Speedway really shines in its large number of options, characters (some hidden), and well-designed tracks. Some of the later tracks require a great deal of skill!

Micro Machines 64 Turbo   Midway   3 $10
A mildly enhanced port of the Playstation's Micro Machines V3, this top-down racing game features tiny cars in big environments. There is some fun to be had here (especially in the new multi-player mode) but the poor camera angles (coupled with the fact that you can't see very far ahead of you) can lead to a very frustrating time. This series has seen better days.

Midway's Greatest Arcade Hits Volume 1
                 Midway   4 $15
OK, now, how many times is Midway planning to put the same group of classic games on one cart (or disk) and charge money for it? Fortunately, these versions of Robotron 2084, Joust, Defender, Sinistar, Spy Hunter, and our personal favorite, Tapper, are all well emulated using the original code. Still, something just doesn't seem right about playing these classics on a regular TV with an N64 controller.

Mike Piazza's StrikeZone   GT Interactive   3 $5
Mike Piazza's StrikeOut is more like it. This dismal baseball simulation sports some of the worst graphics, sound effects, and overall presentation we've seen in some time and should be avoided like a rotten Ballpark Frank.

Milo's Astro Lanes   Crave   4 $12
There is something inherently cool about this bizarre bowling game... we just don't know what it is. Perhaps it's the funky music or the retro-feel that we find so appealing. Whatever the case, the game itself really isn't that good and has some graphical and control issues, but that didn't stop us from liking it anyway.

Mischief Makers   Nintendo   5 $15
Famed Japanese developer Treasure, responsible for classic games like Gunstar Heroes (Genesis), Radiant Silvergun (import Saturn) and the Japanese import SiN & Punishment (one of the best shooters for the N64) tried their hand at programming for the N64 with this bizarre platform game. The gameplay and overall design is typical Treasure... bizarre! The 2-D graphics are colorful if a bit bland, but the boss characters are amazing, often filling up the entire screen with wild animation and special effects. Mischief Makers is certainly not one of the console's best games, but it definitely merits some attention.

Mission: Impossible   Ocean   3 $8
Stuck in development purgatory for over two years, Mission: Impossible was finally released to a less than receptive audience back in 1998. A third-person (rather than first-person) adventure title in the same vein as Goldeneye, M:I suffers from mediocre graphics and very inconsistent mission design. Still, the action is often intense and entertaining.

Monaco Grand Prix   UbiSoft   3 $10
Who says that N64 was a kid's console? They certainly haven't played this deep Formula One simulation. The graphics are more than adequate and the frame rate is high, plus the changes you make to your car actually make a big impact on the way your vehicle handles. There's months of gameplay here if you're willing to invest the time.

Monopoly   Hasbro   4 $15
Why you'd want to hunt down this obscure title when you can just get your own Monopoly board for $10 is beyond us, but otherwise Monopoly 64 does a great job of bringing the family classic into the electronic age. Not much has been added to the experience other than 3-D graphics and the ability to play alone, but fans of the genre will find that to be more than enough.

Monster Truck Madness 64
                 Rockstar   4 $15
There were high-hopes for this "Monster Truck" based rally racer, but the results are less than impressive. Aside from some entertaining options, the game really doesn't have much going for it. The graphics are as muddy are the dirt found in the sprawling environments, and the control mechanics and menu

Not including the directional pad, how many function buttons does the PSX controller have?

interface are completely messed up.

Mortal Kombat 4 Midway 3 $15
One of the best fighting game in the console's entire library, MK4 does an admirable job of emulating the arcade version's beautiful graphics and fast gameplay. It's not arcade-perfect, mind you, but it's close enough, and the soundtrack is a pleasant surprise. The N64 controller gets in the way of the fighting action, though.

Mortal Kombat Mythologies: Sub-Zero
Midway 2 $7
This story-driven take on the Mortal Kombat universe (specifically the character Sub-Zero) is an experiment gone horribly awry. The one-on-one action of the "pure" MK fighting games has been replaced with shoddy platform action and ugly graphics.

Mortal Kombat Trilogy Midway 2 $8
Looking back, it seems that no one was really able to coax a truly stellar fighting game from the N64 hardware (most likely due to the restrictive cartridge format.) MKT combines most of the characters and backgrounds of the previous games into one title, but the graphics are very choppy and the soundtrack borders on abysmal. Occasional pauses, glitches, and other mysterious gremlins don't help much, either. The PSX and Saturn ports are far superior, even with the loading times.

Ms. Pac-Man Maze Madness
Namco 5 $20
Unlike most updates of "classic" games, Maze Madness doesn't embarrass its original subject matter. The pink-bowed mate of the original dot-muncher is back, this time in her own 3-D adventure/puzzle game. The control is simple and precise, the graphics are serviceable, and the music is catchy (even if it does repeat a lot.)

Multi Racing Championship
Ocean 2 $3
If there were a category for "most mediocre N64 racer" MRC would certainly hail as one of the all-time greats. Respectable first-generation graphics and an upbeat soundtrack can't compensate for three meager tracks and poor control.

Mystical Ninja staring Goemon
Konami 4 $12
Up until this release, Goemon games were Japan-only treats. His first appearance on an American console is a bit of a mixed bag, as the wonderful 2-D gameplay of the previous titles has been replaced with Mario-style 3-D action. Mystical Ninja has a very Japanese look and feel that will appeal to some and alien-

ate others.

Nagano Winter Olympics '98
Konami 2 $4
If you're looking for a collection of winter-based sports games, go pick up a Saturn and a copy of Winter Heat instead. This shoddy mishmash of underdeveloped events suffers from very poor control and graphics and appears to have been unfinished when it was shoved out the door to meet a time schedule.

Namco Museum 64 Namco 4 $15
The "other" compilation of classic arcade games crammed onto one cart (Midway's Greatest Arcade Hits Volume 1 came out later), Namco Museum combines the best games out if the five compilation CDs released for the PSX and comes out with a pretty hot little collection. Pac-Man, Ms. Pac-Man, Pole Position, Dig Dug, Galaxian, and Galaga play just like their arcade counterparts, and only the N64 controller prevents this cart from being a classic game fan's dream come true.

NASCAR '99 Electronic Arts 3 $6
Make no mistake about it… this racing simulation is aimed directly at NASCAR fans! The variety of tracks and drivers might intrigue casual gamers, but 50 laps around and around and around the same oval will not appeal to everyone.

NASCAR 2000 Electronic Arts 3 $8
If you liked the EA's previous NASCAR game or are a fan of NASCAR in general, then this is the game for you. This update contains some substantial improvements over the original N64 release, including several new play modes and much nicer graphics.

NBA Courtside 2 Featuring Kobe Bryant
Nintendo 3 $5
This sequel to the original Kobe Bryant is far better than the first game and features much better graphics (especially with the Expansion Pak in place.) The addition of a new arcade style mode is a real treat and is almost like having two games in one.

NBA Hang Time Williams 2 $3
If you were a big fan of the NBA Jam series, you'll feel right at home with the update… otherwise, you'll be bored. It's almost exactly the same game, right down to the 2-D sprite-based graphics and bizarre hidden characters. The new "create a player" mode is kind of cool, but most of you have seen all of this before.

NBA In The Zone '98 Konami 2 $2
Konami's In The Zone series got off to a horrid start with its first release, and there is really no reason to pick it up if you run

Mortal Kombat Mythologies: Sub-Zero

Nagano Winter Olympics '98

Twelve; don't forget to count R3 and L3.

NBA Live '99

The New Tetris

across it (which you will, since it was a strong seller.) The graphics are very blurry, the control is sloppy, and the A.I. will whip your butt on a regular basis (it's practically infallible.)

NBA In The Zone '99   Konami   3 $3
Konami put a little more effort into their second In The Zone game for the N64, but it still isn't that great. The graphics and A.I have been improved, but the jerky camera and silly voice-overs will have you looking around for a better basketball title.

NBA In The Zone 2000   Konami   3 $5
Not much new here for the 64, though most gamers weren't expecting that much anyway for the third and final outing of this mediocre series. The graphics, sound effects, and gameplay offer marginal improvements over previous outings, but there really isn't much to recommend here.

NBA Jam '99   Acclaim   2 $3
Acclaim has released more than their fair share of duds, but the N64 updates of the popular NBA Jam series are some of the bright spots on their otherwise tarnished reputation. The classic "Jam" gameplay is here in full force, plus a very well done simulation mode. It's not perfect, but it sure is fun.

NBA Jam 2000   Acclaim   3 $5
This sequel isn't all that it could have been, but the fun remains the same. The graphics and control show marginal improvement, but Acclaim (and developer Iguana) kind of dropped the ball and missed their chance to really make this a first-class title.

NBA Live '99   Electronic Arts   3 $4
EA's wildly popular basketball simulation makes its first appearance on the N64 in fine style, featuring nice graphics and precise control. You have the ability to customize almost every aspect of the game and make the gameplay as arcade-like or as simulation-like as you desire.

NBA Live 2000   Electronic Arts   3 $5
Sequels to popular sports series have a tendency to add minor enhancements and/or simple changes to the interface, as is the case here. Michael Jordan has been added to the lineup, but most everything else remains the same (the graphics are a bit cleaner, but the frame rate is choppier.) It's still an enjoyable experience overall, but it could have been better.

NBA Showtime: NBA on NBC
**   Midway   3 $5**
Essentially NBA Jam with an NBC affiliation, this port of the arcade original plays well enough, but the graphics and sound didn't survive the programming journey to the N64 hardware very well. It's good fun while it lasts, but it just doesn't last very

long.

New Tetris, The   Nintendo   4 $12
If you've played the "old" Tetris (and we bet that you have), you've essentially played the "new" version as well. The graphics and gameplay have undergone minor enhancements, but Nintendo knew not to mess with the classic formula too much. Multi-player action is where it's at here, and you'll have a blast if you invite a few friends.

NFL Blitz   Midway   2 $6
Football games historically haven't been the most popular genres in arcades, but NFL Blitz created a sensation with its beautiful graphics, fast action, and easy to master gameplay. The N64 port plays just like its arcade parent, even if it doesn't look or sound exactly like it (the frame rate has been slowed down a bit, and the music and voiceovers have been cut to fit the cartridge format.). All in all, one of the best football games available for the N64.

NFL Blitz Special Edition   Midway   7 $25
Midway got a lot of yardage out of the N64 Blitz games, but cart sales had fallen considerably by 2001, leading to this Block-buster rental-only exclusive. Other than seven on seven gameplay and some pretty cool mini-games, it's pretty much the same game as NFL Blitz 2001.

NFL Blitz 2000   Midway   3 $10
The best football series on the 64 received some noticeable improvements over the already excellent original, including faster, smoother graphics and better sound effects and voiceovers. The addition of a four-player mode and more gameplay options only increase the fun.

NFL Blitz 2001   Midway   5 $20
The last of the wide-release Blitz games for the 64 offered further graphical and gameplay enhancements over its predecessors, but nothing really groundbreaking. The Expansion Pak enhanced graphics are as lovely as usual, ranking among the best visuals the N64 ever displayed.

NFL Quarterback Club '98   Acclaim   2 $2
Acclaim's first Quarterback Club game for the N64 sported some amazing graphics (for the time) but the gameplay falls way short of the visuals. The soundtrack and sound effects are very bland, and the A.I. is occasionally so stupid it's hilarious.

NFL Quarterback Club '99   Acclaim   2 $3
The second outing of the Quarterback Club is quite an improvement over the original game, and the graphics look as beautiful as ever. The options and gameplay have been dramatically

Some early video game systems didn't use the TV's speakers, but instead had speakers of their own.

improved, but the single player game (especially the A.I.) is still crappy.

NFL Quarterback Club 2000
Acclaim   2 $4

Graphics aren't everything (or they shouldn't be, at least), and time (and other developers) had caught up with this series by 1999. The single-player game is still weak, and Acclaim's attempt to further enhance the graphics with the Expansion Pak backfired, resulting is some very choppy frame rates.

NFL Quarterback Club 2001
Acclaim   3 $6

Acclaim dropped the graphics down a notch for their final update to the Quarterback Club in an effort to make it more playable, but everything else remains about the same. Madden and Blitz are far better N64 football franchises, and there really is no reason to pick up any of the QC games unless you're after a complete collection.

NHL '99
Electronic Arts   2 $4

Sega owes Electronic Arts a lot of credit for the success of the Genesis console, and the NFL Hockey and Madden sports games were particularly instrumental to the console's success. Essentially a port of the PSX's excellent NHL '98 game, this great-playing hockey simulation sports beautiful graphics, excellent control, and loads of action. Most enthusiasts consider NHL '99 to be the best hockey game on the 64.

NHL Blades of Steel '99
Konami   3 $4

Konami's first attempt at a hockey simulation for the N64 is something of a disaster and soils the once-great Blades of Steel name. The frame rate is slow, the music and sound effects are boring, and the gameplay is dreadfully slow.

NHL Breakaway '98
Acclaim   2 $2

One of the top hockey simulations for the N64, the first of the Breakaway games sports beautiful graphics, naturally cheering sound effects, and flawless analog control. The game's management mode is particularly cool if you appreciate that sort of thing, and the ability to build up points to accomplish all kinds of objectives adds a whole new dimension of interactivity to the gameplay.

NHL Breakaway '99
Acclaim   3 $3

Acclaim did such a fine job with the first NHL Breakaway that they decided to release its sequel virtually unchanged, right down to the same graphics and identical gameplay engine. It's still a lot of fun to play, but you'd think they could have thought of SOMETHING new to add.

Nightmare Creatures
Activision   3 $12

The N64 port of this creepy, gory, and incredibly fun 3-D hack and slash adventure game fixes much of what was wrong with the PSX original and is a blast to play, at least for a while. Set in 19th century London, the game's third-person perspective, darkly atmospheric look, and surprisingly effective use of fog creative a truly scary atmosphere, and the game's control is nearly flawless.

Nuclear Strike 64
THQ   4 $15

The Strike series of helicopter shooters (presented from an isometric perspective) have always captivated players with their frenetic action and high degree of challenge. The "Nuclear" update (which first appeared on the PSX) plays a lot like its 16-bit ancestors (it's not as hard, though) but sports richer, more colorful visuals. The N64's control pad, in particular, works quite well with the game (but the control really isn't analog-supported.)

Off-Road Challenge
Midway   3 $8

One would think that a supposed off-road racer would include the ability to actually go off-road, but the tracks of this poorly designed racing title (itself a port of an equally bad arcade game) are clearly defined and cannot be breached. The graphics are crappy and plagued with pop-up, and the sound effects and soundtrack are plain boring.

Ogre Battle 64: Person of Lordly Caliber
Atlus   6 $40

For such an obscure series with a small (if enthusiastic) fan base, the glorious Ogre Battle strategy/RPG franchise has certainly been seen on a variety of platforms (including the Super Nintendo, PSX, import Saturn, and even the shamefully under appreciated Neo Geo Pocket Color.) Ogre Battle 64 (which is housed in one of the largest N64 carts ever produced) continues the series tradition of sparse (but effective) graphics, a stupendous soundtrack, and engrossing micromanagement driven gameplay. This game certainly requires a definite time commitment (the instruction book is huge) but stands as one of the 64's few must-have releases for adult gamers.

Olympic Hockey: Nagano '98
Midway   4 $5

Midway should be pummeled for using the Wayne Gretzkey game engine for the THIRD time without any enhancements or additions…everything is exactly like the first two games, including the colorful (if simple) 3-D graphics, shallow arcade-style gameplay, and questionable A.I.

Paper Mario
Nintendo   4 $25

The beloved Mario RPG was released at the tail end of the

Nightmare Creatures

Ogre Battle 64: Person of Lordly Caliber

The top of the SNES is rounded to discourage setting drinks on it. Do you know why?

Paper Mario

The Powerpuff Girls: Chemical X-Traction

Super Nintendo's lifespan, and this sequel of sorts arrived late in life for the N64, as well. Ditching the 16-bit game's isometric protective, Paper Mario combines beautifully rendered 3-D environments with paper-thin 2-D characters to come up with a unique visual style all its own. The gameplay and storyline reflect the loving polish of a carefully crafted Nintendo game, and the result is one of the best RPG's for the console, as well as one of its top games overall.

Paperboy   **Midway**   **3**   **$10**
The original arcade version of Paperboy was a cool mission-driven racing/action title with a unique controller styled to look and act like actual bicycle handles. This tepid N64 "update" obviously can't duplicate the arcade's control setup, nor can it duplicate its sense of fun, either. The jump to 3-D doesn't work well with the classic gameplay, and the simple graphics and cheesy soundtrack keep this title mired back in the 1980's.

Penny Racers   **THQ**   **4**   **$12**
This dull and uninspired falls to the back of the pack of the Mario Kart clones, primarily due to its blocky graphics, simplistic soundtrack, and lack of originality (especially in the area of track design.) It's all very derivative and not worth your time.

Perfect Dark   **Nintendo**   **2**   **$10**
Like its unofficial prequel Goldeneye, this glorious first-person shooter is loaded with variety and rewards tenacious players with months of gameplay. Unlike most games of the genre, Perfect Dark offers a well-rounded single-player experience in addition to plenty of multi-player action. You'll need the Expansion Pak to take advantage of all that it has to offer, though.

PGA European Tour   **Infogrames**   **4**   **$8**
There really isn't much to recommend about this dated golf simulator unless you're just bored and want to see the result of lazy programming (as in poor quality graphics, poor controls, and extremely questionable overall design.)

Pilotwings 64   **Nintendo**   **3**   **$12**
Like the SNES before it, the N64 debut lineup (if you can call two games a "lineup") included an odd flight "simulator" of sorts that mainly served as a technological display for the new hardware. As such, this update appears extremely dated when compared to later releases. The sensation of flight is still believable, though, and the game will still hold your interest for awhile.

Pokemon Puzzle League   **Nintendo**   **2**   **$8**
Nintendo didn't miss a chance to slap the Pokemon license onto everything that they could, including this pretty respectable Tetris Attack clone. The graphics certainly don't stress the hardware, but the puzzle action is addicting enough to woo both kids

and adults.

Pokemon Snap   **Nintendo**   **2**   **$6**
You have to give Nintendo credit for trying something different with Pokemon. This bizarre "shooter on rails" has you zipping through various environments, all the while taking pictures of various Pokemon in their natural habitats. It's not as stupid as it sounds. Really!

Pokemon Stadium   **Nintendo**   **2**   **$10**

Best described as a turn-based RPG with no RPG elements, the big draw of Pokemon Stadium is the Transfer Pak that comes with the game. It allows you to upload Pokemon creatures from the Gameboy games and let them fight each other in 3-D on the 64. It's all rather dull, really, unless you're a Pokemon fanatic.

Pokemon Stadium 2   **Nintendo**   **3**   **$15**
While better than the original, PS2 is still for Pokemon fans only. You need to have the Transfer Pak (not included this time) and Gameboy Pokemon Gold and/or Silver to really get your money's worth from this title (and Pokemon fanatics certainly will.)

Polaris SnoCross   **Vatical**   **5**   **$20**
A buggy and unpolished racer based on a "budget" PSX title, Polaris SnoCross sports a multitude of flaws including (but not limited to) lots of graphical pop-up, a really bad soundtrack, collision detection problems, and super-easy (and therefore very limited) gameplay.

Powerpuff Girls: Chemical X-Traction
                    BAM!   **6**   **$25**
Why did this awful-looking, awful-playing, and generally awful Super Smash Brothers clone have to be the LAST Nintendo 64 game? Madden 2002 or Tony Hawk 2 could have easily ended the reign of the console in style, but developer Bam! chose to go ahead and release this pitiful girly game (based on the cartoon series) at the tail end of 2001.

Power Rangers Lightspeed Rescue
                    THQ   **5**   **$15**
Picking on a video game based on the Power Ranger is almost unfair. It's like Don King's hair or Michael Jackson's nose, both of which easily lend themselves to non-stop ridicule. Regrettably, this hilariously awful 3-D "adventure" game (which can be completed in two hours or less) is no different.

Quake   **Midway**   **2**   **$6**
Id's immensely popular first-person shooter made its first appearance on the N64 in great form, albeit without the networked

Spilt drinks was the number one cause of NES repairs in the U.S.

multiplayer options that were an integral part of its immense popularity in the first place (two player deathmatch is available and welcome, but it's not quite the same.) Otherwise, the level design is great, the graphics are near PC-quality, and the N64 control pad proves to be a surprisingly adept ally.

Quake II — Activision — 3 — $10
The Saturn got a port of Quake, and the PSX got a port of Quake II, but only Nintendo's console got ports of both games. It's easily the best of the three, sporting some really nice N64 specific levels plus all of the features that made the original Quake so good. On a technical note, it's nice to see the hardware's features being put to good use… the Expansion Pak adds some neat-o weapons and lighting effects, and it's just plain cool to get right up close to ANY wall or object and see no pixilization whatsoever.

Quest 64 — THQ — 4 — $12
An RPG in the loosest sense with a name as boring as its gameplay, Quest 64 (which was the N64's first role playing game) is incredibly linear and gets old really, really fast. Either of the Zelda games (and even Aidyn Chronicles: The First Mage) offers far better gameplay and a richer storyline.

Rally Challenge 2000 — SouthPeak — 3 — $8
The original Sega Rally '95 (for the Saturn) has YET to be challenged as the king of the rally racers, and this weak effort (five years later) isn't even in the running. Muddy graphics, dreadful voiceovers, and uninspiring track design all combine to form a mediocre game with little to recommend.

Rampage: World Tour — Midway — 3 — $10
The original Rampage arcade game (from 1986) was very cool in a basic "lets just smash everything" kind of way. This sequel is pretty much the exact same game, only with nicer 2-D graphics and bigger levels. Hey Midway… milk has a shelf life, and so did this game.

Rampage 2: The Great Escape — Midway — 4 — $12
Why is this game still here? Did the first boring game actually sell well enough to warrant a barely enhanced sequel? This one is strictly for kids and "classic" fans who haven't played the same exact game on countless other platforms.

Rat Attack — Mindscape — 5 — $20
As far as obscure N64 puzzlers go, this one certainly isn't bad. The graphics are fairly sharp for a console known for blurriness, and the gameplay is addicting enough to sit down with it for a few hours. You'll probably have some mindless fun after you get a hang of the controls and occasionally uncivilized camera an-gles.

Rayman 2: The Great Escape — UbiSoft — 3 — $12
One of the best 3-D platform games ever produced for the N64, this update to the original Rayman was lost in the shuffle and definitely didn't get nearly the attention it deserved. Aside from its brilliant level designed and still-stunning graphics (especially with the Expansion Pak in place), Rayman 2 is full of bizarre characters, wonderful voice work, and loads of offbeat humor.

Razor Freestyle Scooter — Crave — 7 — $25
This Blockbuster exclusive title (based on the budget-priced Dreamcast and PSX games of the same name) is best described as a Tony Hawk game for children. The controls and courses are both simple and easy to master but the challenge level is rather low. Still, the graphics are nice, and the game's low production run and entertaining gameplay assures that it will assume a higher profile as time goes on.

Re-Volt — Acclaim — 3 — $8
A disappointing entry into the kart-racing genre, Re-Volt excels in the areas of graphics and music but fails when it comes to frame rate, control, and playability. Your opponents will dog you mercilessly, and you'll be utterly frustrated by the way your racer seems to stick to the walls of the courses.

Ready 2 Rumble Boxing — Midway — 3 — $5
This port of one of the Dreamcast's higher-profile launch titles is a fun (if shallow) take on the boxer/fighter genre. The graphics are a bit fuzzy and the gameplay isn't deep by any means, but there are certainly worse ways to blow an afternoon.

Ready 2 Rumble Boxing: Round 2 — Midway — 5 — $15
The graphics are a tiny bit cleaner this time around, but no one is fooled. Round 2 is almost the same game as Round 1, just with a few more characters and options. This is the game to get if you don't have the first one, the game to ignore if you do.

Resident Evil 2 — Midway — 4 — $20
Most everyone is familiar with the "survivor horror" concept and execution of the Resident Evil series, and RE2 certainly doesn't disappoint in the gameplay arena. What most people don't know is just how incredible the N64 port of RE2 really is, especially considering the fact that it's all crammed into a cartridge. ALL of the video from the PSX and DC versions has been somehow included here (even if it is grainy) and NOTHING has been cut. The character graphics are all in high-resolution, and the addition of several new gameplay modes not found in the PSX and DC games make this version of RE2 THE one to own.

Quest 64

Rayman 2: The Great Escape

Breaking the "security tabs" at the bottom of the SNES cart slot will allow for Super Famicom games to be played on the U.S. systems.

Ridge Racer 64

Rugrats in Paris: The Movie

Ridge Racer 64   Nintendo   3 $10
It took its sweet time getting here, but the N64 port of the popular PSX series lives up to its reputation as the premiere arcade-style racing franchise. You'll find tracks for several of the PSX games in addition to a new track, smooth graphics, and some of the better racing action available for the console.

Road Rash 64   THQ   4 $15
After several misfires on the PSX, EA's classic motorcycle series finally got back to its combat-intensive roots with this wickedly fun release. The 3-D graphics might be a bit foggy and simplistic, but the control is dead-on and the crash animations are hilarious, making this one of the most entertaining racing games on the 64.

Roadsters   Titus   4 $10
The graphics of this top-down racer might are very impressive, but the gameplay and control leave a lot to be desired, especially when you consider that the physics are completely wrong. The N64 has a library full of competent racers much better than Roadsters.

Robotron 64   Crave   2 $5
This 64-bit update to the frenetic arcade title of old certainly fared better than some other classic games we don't care to name, but they still should have left well enough alone. The gameplay isn't nearly as challenging (or fun) as the timeless original, and the loss of the dual-joystick controls seriously detracts form the overall experience.

Rocket: Robot on Wheels   UbiSoft   4 $15
One of the best of the "unknown" N64 platformers, Rocket sports an amazing amount of gameplay variety, all wrapped in a pretty and fast (if occasionally simple) graphics engine. 3-D adventure games don't get much better than this, and only Rare did it better.

Rugrats in Paris: The Movie
               THQ   4 $15
THQ put a little more effort into their second N64 Rugrats outing (this time set in Paris), and pre-teens all over the country will rejoice at the antics of the blocky children as they wander around. Unfortunately, the mini-games are more entertaining than the main game.

Rugrats: Scavenger Hunt   THQ   3 $10
Slow, slow, slow! We know that this is a game meant for children, but do we have to assume that all children are mindless idiots who enjoy slow and boring games like this? Dull, ugly, droll, and tedious, the first out of the Rugrats on the N64 defi-

nitely deserves to be swept under that rug.

Rush 2: Extreme Racing USA
               Midway   2 $10
The original San Francisco Rush made a surprisingly good appearance on the 64 the first time around, which makes you wonder why this sequel falls a tad short. Truth be known, it's just not as fun the second time around, probably because the ridiculous physics and track design has been toned down in favor of more serious racing action.

S.C.A.R.S.   UbiSoft   4 $12
The original PSX version of S.C.A.R.S. (that stands for Super Computer Animal Racing Simulation if you're curious) wasn't a bad entry in the crowded field of "futuristic combat kart racers", but the N64 port isn't nearly as good. The shoddy graphics and soundtrack, in particular, drag the game down and mire it in a pool of similarly themed N64 racers.

San Francisco Rush   Midway   2 $8
The original Rush game took the arcade world by storm with its over-the-top physics, crazy track design, and loads of shortcuts and secrets. While it lacks the graphical flair of the arcade game, the N64 port of SFR retains all the fun of the arcade and beats the crap out of the wildly inferior PSX version.

San Francisco Rush 2049   Midway   4 $15
This futuristic take on the successful Rush racer series (the third and final installment for the 64) features all of the absurd tracks and cool shortcuts of the arcade original, plus a few new extras including a cart/battle game that's a blast to play, especially in multiplayer mode.

Scooby Doo: Classic Creep Capers
               THQ   4 $15
Like the SNES and Genesis games that preceded it, Classic Creep Capers is a slow-moving adventure/puzzle game based on the groovy ghost-tracking teenagers. The episodic "action" is fairly mundane, consisting of searching for various objects that will lead to the capture of a "creep." The game is mostly aimed at children, but the graphics are nice and the nostalgia factor is high.

Sesame Street: Elmo's Letter Adventure
               NewKidCo   3 $12
As a console ages and is passed on to younger players, developers tend to release more child-oriented fare. This alphabet-based "edutainment" title will most likely appeal to the youngest of players who will be attracted to it's bright colors and impressive voice work and soundtrack.

The Atari 7800 power supply has a proprietary connection to the system, making the task of finding a replacement very difficult.

Sesame Street: Elmo's Number Journey
NewKidCo · 3 · $12

If you've already learned your letters, it might be time to move on to your numbers! This children's game features the same high production values and excellent soundtrack/voice work found in Elmo's Letter Adventure and utilizes the same game engine.

Shadow Man · Acclaim · 3 · $10
Proving once and for all that the N64 wasn't just a children's toy, this 3-D action game contains scenes of sexual bondage, pagan voodoo worship, and sadomasochism. The game itself really isn't that great, but the cut scenes are fabulous and well worth the price of admission.

Shadowgate 64: Trials of the Four Towers
Vatical · 5 · $20

Unlike the beloved NES game that spawned it, Shadowgate 64 is pretty devoid of excitement. A pretty basic dungeon crawler at heart, the game's crappy graphics, average soundtrack, and very slow-paced gameplay will turn off players looking for an enjoyable RPG experience.

Snowboard Kids · Atlus · 2 · $10
Perhaps best described as Mario Kart on top of a snowy mountain, this cute arcade-style racer has some nice track design and a very Japanese feel to it (which isn't a bad thing at all.) The graphics and sound are pretty good, especially when you consider that this was the first N64 game from Atlus.

Snowboard Kids 2 · Atlus · 3 · $15
This well-received sequel to the original Snowboard Kids has been nicely updated and is recommended for both kids and adults. The multiplayer game and graphics have been improved, and several interesting new features (including boss characters) have been added.

South Park · Acclaim · 2 · $5
Released at the peak of South Park mania, this exceptionally foggy first-person shooter is fun until you realize that the A.I. is nonexistent… just wave after wave of repetitive enemies. The game is true to the sprit of the show, though, and some of the weapons (which include urine snowballs and cow rectums) are hilarious.

South Park Rally · Acclaim · 3 · $8
The first game based on the raunchy cartoon series wasn't that good, but it had its moments. Unfortunately, this poor Mario Kart clone is pretty much devoid of good gameplay, instead relying on its license alone. The graphics are respectable by N64 stan-

dards, but the voice characterizations are extremely limited and will drive you crazy after a few races.

South Park: Chef's Luv Shack
Acclaim · 2 · $5

Chef's Luv Shack is about to fall down and he'd better get out where he can! The worst of the N64 trivia titles (like there's a lot of competition) suffers from repetitive voice acting and boring mini-games. The game's biggest flaw is its lack of questions… it won't be long until you see the same questions start to pop up again.

Space Invaders · Activision · 4 · $12
The original arcade version of Space Invaders was the simplest of shooters, so any update would have needed something new to hook more fans. Unfortunately, Activision choose to craft a mediocre and exceptionally easy shooter with boring graphics and an uninspired soundtrack.

Space Station Silicon Valley
Take2 Interactive · 4 · $15

One of the more intriguing and charming N64 games, this cute action/puzzler has a cool plot and a unique hook… you take over the bodies of dead animals, each with specific strengths and abilities (it's not nearly as ghoulish as it sounds.) The graphics aren't that great, but the wide variety of animals, their distinct personalities, and their functions within the game combine to form a truly entertaining (if short) gaming experience.

Spider-Man · Activision · 4 · $20
Spidey's first (and only) starring role on the 64 is nearly identical to the original Playstation release (which utilized the Tony Hawk engine, as does this one.) The developer (Edge of Reality) did a fine job porting over this cool action/adventure title (just as they did with the Tony Hawk games) and truly showcase the 64's 3-D power. The real stars of this game are the gameplay and great control (aside from Spidey, of course.)

Star Fox 64 · Nintendo · 2 · $12
One of the N64's most highly anticipated titles at the time of its release, this sequel to the Super FX-powered SNES 3-D shooter came bundled with the vibrating Rumble Pak. A mixture of rail-based shooting and free-flying action sequences, Star Fox 64 features beautiful (for the time) visuals and flawless control. (Star Fox 64 incorporates some of the level design taken from the unreleased Star Fox 2 for the SNES.)

Star Soldier · Electro-Brain · 6 · $25

Star Soldier: Vanishing Earth
Electro-Brain · 6 · $25

South Park

Space Invaders

There are 48 "invaders" in the original Space Invaders game.

Star Wars: Rogue Squadron

Super Mario 64

As the only overhead scrolling classic-type shooter available for the domestic N64, Star Soldier seems destined to be one of the 64's more collectible games. Unfortunately, the gameplay of this sequel to the NES game is pretty average, and the graphics and soundtrack are decidedly 16-bit in nature.

Star Wars: Episode I, Battle for Naboo
Nintendo/LucasArts   4 $15
The last and rarest of the Star Wars games for the 64, Battle for Naboo replicates the gameplay of Rogue Squadron (and uses the same game engine, as well.) The intense 3-D shooting action remains the same but includes some ground-based missions as well, plus the graphics have been cleaned up a bit and the classic N64 fog has been pushed back.

Star Wars: Episode I Racer
Nintendo/LucasArts   2 $7
One of the fastest racers available for the N64, Episode 1 Racer faithfully duplicates the racing scene from the movie, plus a whole slew of new races on wickedly designed tracks. The graphics are gorgeous, and the feeling of speed is remarkable. Episode 1 Racer also came bundled with a special promotional N64 hardware package, increasing the odds of finding a loose cart.

Star Wars: Rogue Squadron
LucasArts   2 $8
LucasArts took the best part of the first N64 Star Wars game (the snow speeder segment) and based an entire game around it, resulting in one of the console's best 3-D shooters. The use of the RAM Expansion Pak results in some great (if foggy) visuals, and the speech and soundtrack are fantastic.

Star Wars: Shadows of the Empire
Nintendo   2 $5
The first N64 Star Wars game was greeted with loads of press and great enthusiasm, but time has not been kind to it. A combination of different gaming genres, Shadows of the Empire features an impressive opening sequence (the snow speeder level) but is pretty mediocre from then on, a hodgepodge of dungeon crawling, repeating textures, and looping music.

StarCraft 64   Nintendo   5 $40
The N64 was the only home console to receive a port of this groundbreaking PC favorite, and the translation turned out pretty darned well. The graphics aren't as clear as the original and the mission introductions are now text-based, but the engrossing gameplay is fully intact and the 2-player game is a complete blast.

StarShot: Space Circus Fever

Infogrames   3 $10
A 3-D platformer with a puzzle slant, StarShot suffers from the myriad of problems that effect many games of its type; namely, poor control and an untamable camera. The puzzles and storyline are better than average, but the camera issues sink this title down into the abyss of similar titles.

Stunt Racer 64   Midway   8 $35
Yet another N64 title to suffer the ignominy of "rental only" status, Stunt Racer 64 manages to rise above its second-class designation. It's a rather cool game not unlike the San Francisco Rush games featuring beautiful Expansion Pak enhanced visuals and good control. It might be short, but it's sweet nevertheless.

Super Bowling   Tommo   6 $25
It's a bit odd that one of the N64's last games would be a bowling title, but game-staved players were up for most anything by 2001. The alley design is actually quite original and the control, while challenging to learn, is precise. Unfortunately, the graphics are strictly first-generation blurry and the soundtrack is dull.

Super Mario 64   Nintendo   2 $15
Once referred to as "the best game ever made" by a major gaming publication, Super Mario 64 still stands as one of the 64's best titles. As one of the first platform games to finally tame the inherent problems of navigating a completely 3-D world, SM64 captivated gamers with its tight control and appealing level design. The graphics are very plain by later N64 standards, but the appeal of this classic is undisputed.

Super Smash Bros.   Nintendo   3 $15
Nintendo seems determined to slap Mario and his pals into every gaming genre known to man, so why not a fighter? The results are actually pretty fun, but only if you have a group of willing friends (three is best) along for the fight. The graphics are more than adequate, and it's nice to see the N64 appearance of Metroid's Samus Aran, even if she didn't get her own game.

Supercross 2000   Electronic Arts   3 $8
While not up to the level of Excitebike 64, this bike racer combines classic track racing with Tony Hawk-style freestyle action and end of pretty entertaining (if you can look past the occasionally blocky graphics and less than perfect control.)

Superman   Titus   3 $7
Often hailed as "the worst videogame ever made, " this twisted mess of the Superman license was a hot seller nevertheless. Words cannot adequately describe all that things that are just so completely wrong with this 3-D "action" title, so we won't even try. Just avoid it and collect AOL CDs instead.

The Bally Astrocade has a place to store your controllers and cables in the back of the system.

Tetrisphere   Nintendo   4 $15
Originally destined for the Atari Jaguar (of all consoles), this 3-D take on the classic Tetris theme works out better than expected. The two-player mode is a lot of fun, the soundtrack is awesome, and you'll just love it once you get the hang of the 3-D puzzle action.

Tigger's Honey Hunt   NewKidCo   4 $12
A 2-D platform game with 3-D visuals, Tigger's Honey pot is aimed at younger gamers and presents no challenge for adults. The presentation and graphics are very well done, but the complete lack of character voices detracts form the overall experience.

Tom and Jerry: Fists of Furry
    NewKidCo/Mattel   4 $15
A 3-D multi-player brawler similar to Super Smash Brothers, this cutesy fighting game has a popular cartoon character license but it strictly average by most other accounts. The control is simple and easy to learn, but the graphics and soundtrack are plain.

Tom Clancey's Rainbow Six
    Red Storm   4 $15
Unlike most first-person shooters that have you running into the midst of enemies with both guns blasting, this port of the PC hit requires quite a bit of planning and strategy if you hope to get anywhere. Both the single and multi-player games are great, dimmed only by the fact that neither mode is very long. The control and sound are excellent, easily overcoming the game's minor graphical shortcomings.

Tonic Trouble   UbiSoft   3 $10
It's really quite amazing to think that the same company that brought Rayman 2 to the N64 (at around the same time) also came out with this tripe. With boring level design and sluggish character control, it's your basic 3-D platform game gone astray.

Tony Hawk's Pro Skater   Activision   2 $0
If you don't know about the Tony Hawk video game phenomena, you need to get out more. This port of the top-selling Playstation game boasts the same awesome gameplay of the original, plus more fluid animation and a smoother frame rate. The soundtrack has been severely chopped-up, though.

Tony Hawk's Pro Skater 2   Activision   4 $20
The last high-profile N64 release (Madden 2002 was just another evolutionary take on the long-running series, and the Powerpuff Girls just sucked), Pro Skater 2 repeated the first game's replication of the original PSX sequel. The levels are awesome, the gameplay is tight, and Tony Hawk 2 ranks as one of the best games ever made for the N64.

Top Gear Hyperbike   Kemco   4 $10
This me-too dirt bike racer sports a pretty neat level editor mode, but most everything else about it is average. The graphics are about two years too late, and there are several better bike-racing titles to choose from in the N64 library.

Top Gear Overdrive   Kemco   2 $8
It might not be the best racing game on the N64, but this update to the long-running series certainly merits a second look. The graphics are lovely, the control is extremely precise and customizable, and the multiplayer game is a lot of fun.

Top Gear Rally   Kemco/Midway   2 $5
Most video games are attempts to emulate a real-world activity (whether actual or fantasy) that generally make some concessions for the jump from "real world" to "video world." Unfortunately, the makers of Top Gear Rally choose to make the handling and physics of this racer quite life-like, resulting in a heck of a lot of frustration due to constant flipping-over and backing up.

Top Gear Rally 2   Kemco   3 $8
The reigns were loosened up a bit for this sequel to the overly realistic original, and the result is a much better game. The graphics are very colorful (even if the feeling of speed is never readily apparent to any degree) and the control works well. The soundtrack is especially good, featuring lots of good techno and funk.

Toy Story 2   Activision   3 $10
Variety can either be a blessing or a curse, depending on what it is you're talking about. In this case, the Toy Story license is combined with a cornucopia of gaming styles… some good, others not so good. The result in a fairly decent game aimed at youngsters but pleasurable enough for adults to enjoy, too.

Transformers: Beast Wars Transmetals
    BAM!   7 $25
Some of the N64's rental-only titles weren't half bad. Unfortunately, some of them really sucked (like this lame fighter set in the Transformer universe.) It plays a bit like Sega's Virtua On, only without the good graphics and precise control. Seriously, there were reasons why some games were rental-only, and this game is crammed full of them.

Triple Play 2000   Electronic Arts   3 $5
Why does this Nintendo 64 CART have LOADING TIMES? We thought one of the benefits of the cartridge format (the only

Tigger's Honey Hunt

Top Gear Rally

There are three versions of the Mattel Intellivision (four if you count the Sears model).

Turok 2: Seeds of Evil

Vigilante 8

benefit, really, other than the solid feel and tough nature of the carts themselves) was the lack of loading times. The game itself is not worth the wait, as it's a slow-moving baseball "simulation" with poor graphics and no depth.

Turok 2: Seeds of Evil   Acclaim   2 $5
The dinosaur hunter's second gory outing on the N64 sports some of the most impressive visuals the console ever saw, but Acclaims over-dependence on the Expansion Pak results in moments of exceptionally choppy graphics and slow frame rates. Additionally, the ingenious level design and devious enemy A.I. is nearly ruined by levels that are just too large and save points that are few and far between.

Turok 3: Shadow of Oblivion
Acclaim   5 $15
Acclaim ditched the Expansion Pak in order to smooth out the frame rate when they designed Turok's fourth and final N64 game (it can still be used to bump the game into high-resolution mode), plus they added the much-appreciated ability to save at will. The result is the best game in the series, and a fine foundation on which to continue the saga on more powerful hardware.

Turok: Dinosaur Hunter   Acclaim   2 $5
One of the first third-part games to really demonstrate the power of the N64 hardware, this bloody first-person shooter features impressive graphics (though the fog is extra thick), cool biomechanical enemies, and a high degree of challenge. It might not look like much now, but this game was SO cool back in 1997.

Turok: Rage Wars   Acclaim   3 $8
Networked first-person PC games like Quake 2 were all the rage during the late 90's, encouraging Acclaim to develop a multiplayer arena-style fragfest using the Turok license. Unfortunately, the N64 is not a PC, and Rage Wars is not Quake II. The poorly designed levels and crappy single-player experience don't help matters, either.

Twisted Edge Extreme Snowboarding
Kemco/Midway   2 $10
This game went head to head with 1080 Snowboarding and ended up getting a big wet snowball right in its face. It's not a bad snowboarding simulation, but the N64 library is full of better looking and better playing games just like it, making Twisted Edge a game just for collectors.

V-Rally Edition '99   Infogrames   2 $5
Quite possibly one of the worst looking and worst sounding racing games on the 64, V-Rally doesn't play so great, either. When you're done gawking at the pop-up laden visuals and laughing at the sound effects, you'll be rushing to find a better

racing game to plug in.

Vigilante 8   Activision   3 $8
What was so good about the PSX version of this thinly disguised Twisted Metal clone is even better on the N64, with sharper graphics, additional levels, and intense multiplayer action. The frame rates take a hit when the action is intense and the Expansion Pak is in place, but this title is hard to beat as a party game.

Vigilante 8: Second Offensive
Activision   4 $12
Sequels are generally better than the originals, but Vigilante 8 seems to be the exception that bucks the trend. There's nothing really WRONG with it, really, but it just isn't as fun. Several new features have been added to the mix and the graphics are oh so sharp with the Expansion Pak, but the levels just don't seem as good as those in the first game and the control is too twitchy.

Virtual Chess 64   Titus   6 $15
A true "niche" title if there ever was one, Virtual Chess 64 does a surprisingly good job of bringing the classic thinking man's game to virtual life. The game's A.I. is advanced enough for even "good" chess players, and the tutorial section is so well designed that it could easily serve as a teaching tool for beginning chess players.

Virtual Pool 64   Crave   3 $12
The graphics, control, and overall presentation of this pool simulation is game is all very well done and professional, but who really cares? Only die-hard hustlers will get anything out of this one, good control or not. It's all a bit boring, really, but aspiring pool sharks might have fun playing with its balls for a while.

Waialae Country Club: True Golf Classics
Nintendo   3 $5
With only one available course (Hawaii's Waialae in Honalulu), Nintendo's first golf simulation for the N64 comes off as lacking in overall variety. If you disregard the dated graphics and fluctuating frame rate, the rest of the game is actually pretty good, especially the finely honed gameplay.

War Gods   Williams   2 $5
War Gods was intended to serve as Midway's test bed towards bringing the Mortal Komat games into 3-D. It's even been rumored that War Gods actually started out as Mortal Kombat 3-D. Whatever the case, it's a good thing this crap wasn't released with the MK name attached to it because fans would have been pissed. The graphics suck, the gameplay is slow, and is character design is among the worst ever seen in a fighting game

202

(Kabuki Jo?) The N64 port is actually better than the arcade original!

Wave Race 64 — Nintendo — 2 — $8
It might not seem that impressive today, but this jet ski racer caused some major waves upon its initial release way back in the early days of the 64. The control and track design are simply divine, and the realistic tidal movement of the water and the corresponding waves have yet to be topped by any game like it, before or since.

Wayne Gretzkey's 3D Hockey — Nintendo — 2 — $2
One of the very first N64 sports games, this entertaining arcade-style title features colorful cartoon-style graphics and fast gameplay. It might not look like that much today, but this game was a heck of a lot of fun back in '96 and hasn't lost much of its entertainment value.

Wayne Gretzkey's 3D Hockey '98 — Midway — 3 — $3
Sloth (as in laziness) is one of the original seven deadly sins, and Midway definitely committed a sin when it released this update to the original Wayne Gretzkey's 3D Hockey with almost no improvements whatsoever except for much more skilled (and irritating) goalies.

WCW Backstage Assault — Electronic Arts — 3 — $12
Perhaps realizing that wrestling fans were looking for something a bit new, EA took a radical approach with their second N64 wrestling title (last such game for the console) and got rid of the ring completely. All of the fighting action takes place in staging areas, lockers rooms, packing lots, and the like. It's an interesting idea, but WCW Backstage Assault uses the same game engine as WCW Mayhem, making the fighting action feel strangely out of place. It doesn't help that the graphics and framerates seem to have suffered a hit

WCW Mayhem — Electronic Arts — 2 — $8
Wrestling fans were expecting a lot when EA grabbed the WCW license, and the resulting game garnered mostly positive reviews upon its release. Unlike previous N64 wrestling games, EA went with a much more arcade-like feel to the fighting engine, resulting is some wild action. Unfortunately, the characters look a bit odd and the graphics aren't as good as they could have been.

WCW Nitro — THQ — 3 — $5
The last (and worst) of THQ's wrestling games for the N64 utilizes an entirely new game engine based on the older Playstation game of the same name. There are loads of hidden characters to unlock, but the ugly graphics, crappy control, and too-fast frame rate are major distractions.

WCW vs. NWO: World Tour — THQ — 2 — $4
The first of THQ's best-selling wrestling titles for the 64, this fully licensed brawler sports a huge variety of characters and options but is plagued by graphical glitches and sluggish control. Fortunately, it's completely redeemed by the multiplayer mode (which allows up to four players to sling each other around the ring, and it's incredibly fun to play or watch.)

WCW/NWO Revenge — THQ — 3 — $6
Why spend development dollars on a new game when you can just re-use the one from last year? Recycling the same basic game engine is nothing new, but it's much more apparent in titles like this. Sure, the graphics and options have been improved and expanded, but everything else is much the same. The multiplayer mode is still fun as hell, though.

Wetrix — Ocean — 4 — $15
It's hard not to like a good puzzle game, no matter what "kind" of gamer you consider yourself to be. This thinking-man's puzzler is definitely a "good" game and should keep even the most action-oriented gamer entertained with its addictive gameplay involving water and your ability to keep it contained in 3-D receptacles. There are all sorts of options, play modes, and other niceties, making Wetrix one of the best of the N64 puzzle games.

Wheel of Fortune — Take2 Interactive — 4 — $15
Most gamers knows what they are getting themselves into when (and if) they buy a video game based on the popular and long-running game show. The 64-bit interpretation is actually a lot of fun to play (for gamers and non-gamers alike) and does a great job of capturing the "feel" of the show itself. The graphics aren't particularly flashy, but the camera work is nice and you'll hardly ever see the same puzzle twice in a row. Invite a few friends over (or even your Mom) and have some fun.

WinBack: Covert Operations — Koei — 4 — $15
You can't blame the developers of WinBack for setting their aspirations high. Unfortunately, their benchmarks were Goldeneye and Metal Gear Solid, and this problematic and often boring "covert ops" shooter falls pretty short of the games that inspired it. The graphics aren't bad, but the silly A.I and problematic camera detract from what could have been a memorable experience.

Waverace 64   Wetrix

DayStar, a "distribution" company similar in style to Amway, sold more Bandai Pippins in the U.S. than Bandai did.

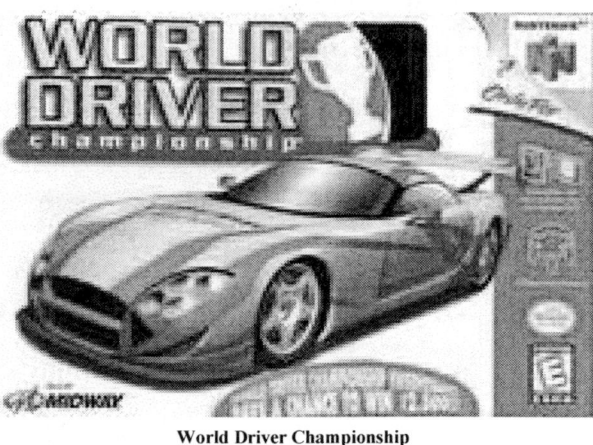

World Driver Championship

The World is Not Enough

Wipeout 64 Midway 2 $6

The original Playstation version of Wipeout caused quite a stir, and its sequel (Wipeout XL) is widely considered to be among the very best of the "futuristic hover pod racers." The N64 variation features all-new track design similar to that of the first PSX title coupled with the better handling and less-frustrating control of the second. The graphics are a bit fuzzy and the soundtrack is a complete (and much worse) departure from the original's techno feast, but the very fast frame rate and multiplayer option (the first for the series) make Wipeout 64 a keeper.

World Cup '98 Electronic Arts 3 $5

Ever had the urge to play as one of the World Cup teams? If so, here's your chance. The team roster of World Cup '98 is quite a bit smaller than that of FIFA '99, but the tight control, smooth graphics, and brilliant A.I. remain, plus it contains several appreciated new features including more strategic gameplay and a cool in-game management mode.

World Driver Championship

Midway 3 $6

If you have what it takes to "finish" this deep, difficult, and gloriously beautiful racer, then you have good reason to be proud of yourself. Midway pulled out all the stops for this one, and you'd better get in the slow lane if you're looking for a cheap arcade experience. The control (while excellent) takes a bit of time to get used to, but you won't mind when your gazing at the wonderful visuals.

World Is Not Enough, The Electronic Arts 4 $15

Since it wasn't developed by Rare, this first-person shooter really can't be called the sequel to the superlative Goldeneye. Whatever the case, the influence of the earlier game is readily apparent, from the skulking around to the carefully crafted storyline. Regardless of its pedigree (or lack thereof), it's still a great game overall, featuring great graphics and level design… it's just not nearly as good as Goldeneye.

Worms Armageddon Infogrames 5 $20

If you haven't played any of the Worms games, then you and your friends are in for a real old-school treat. The hilariously animated bomb-lobbing worms have returned in this extremely cool turn-based strategy game, complete with wonderful 2-D graphics and ferocious A.I that will whip your wormy butt if you try to play it alone. Worms Armageddon is the best of the series to be released thus far.

WWF Attitude Acclaim 2 $4

The first of Acclaim's wrestling games based on the WWF license (Warzone) was a sales and critical smash, so why mess around too much with success? Aside from an updated wrestler

roster, marginally improved graphics, and a few new features, this is pretty much the same game as before. The new introductions and create-a-wrestler mode are a lot of fun, though.

WWF No Mercy THQ 3 $8

It appears that THQ didn't have to rush so much for their second N64 game bearing the coveted WWF license, and the extra development time shows. The multiplayer game is just as much of a riot as it ever was, and the new "SmackDown Mall" is a welcome and refreshing feature that allows a great deal of customization.

WWF Warzone Acclaim 2 $3

Acclaim isn't known for being a "quality over quantity" kind of company, but they did OK with their immensely popular wrestling titles. The first of their efforts for the N64, WWF Warzone moves away from the button-mashing theatrics of the 16-bit wrestling games and adds some real gameplay (plus sweet graphics and tons of different play modes.)

WWF Wrestlemania 2000 THQ 3 $5

This was the first of THQ's N64 wrestling game to bear the highly desirable WWF license, but it seems that they didn't have a whole lot of time to get this one to market. It's pretty much the exact same game as WCW/NWO Revenge with the same sound and graphical flaws, but the multiplayer game is still tough to beat.

Xena: Warrior Princess, The Talisman of Fate

Titus 4 $15

One of the better-looking fighters on the N64, The Talisman of Fate is in no way related to the Xena hack and slash adventure game released for the PSX. It might be pretty, but the gameplay is extremely shallow and two-dimensional, especially for such a lovely 3-D game. The music is pretty bad, too, but some of the voice work is bizarre enough to be entertaining.

Yoshi's Story Nintendo 3 $15

This disappointing and poorly-received sequel to the SNES's Yoshi's Island (itself a sequel to the original Super Mario World) has some nice 2-D graphics augmented with some cool 3-D effects, but the classic Mario-style gameplay has been way over-simplified, making Yoshi's Story a game best suited for youngsters.

Grand Theft Auto III for the PS2 is forbidden in Australia.

HARDWARE

Nintendo 64   Nintendo   1 $30

Standard Controller   Nintendo   1 $5
This innovative design was questioned by many at first, but after a little practice, this controller can fit most hands without any trouble. This controller is even preferred by many over that of the PSX.

Controller Pak   Nintendo   1 $2
Used to store save information for games that don't have battery backups.

Expansion Pak   Nintendo   3 $10
Necessary for some later games, this replaces the standard jumper pack housed in the front of the N64 system, and features more RAM.

Rumble Pak   Nintendo   1 $3
Force feedback is utilized through the attachment of these packs into the controller port.

Yoshi's Story

Controller Pak

205

By law, all video game light guns must be made in one of several colors, day glow orange among them.

Nintendo Virtual Boy

By: Andy Slaven

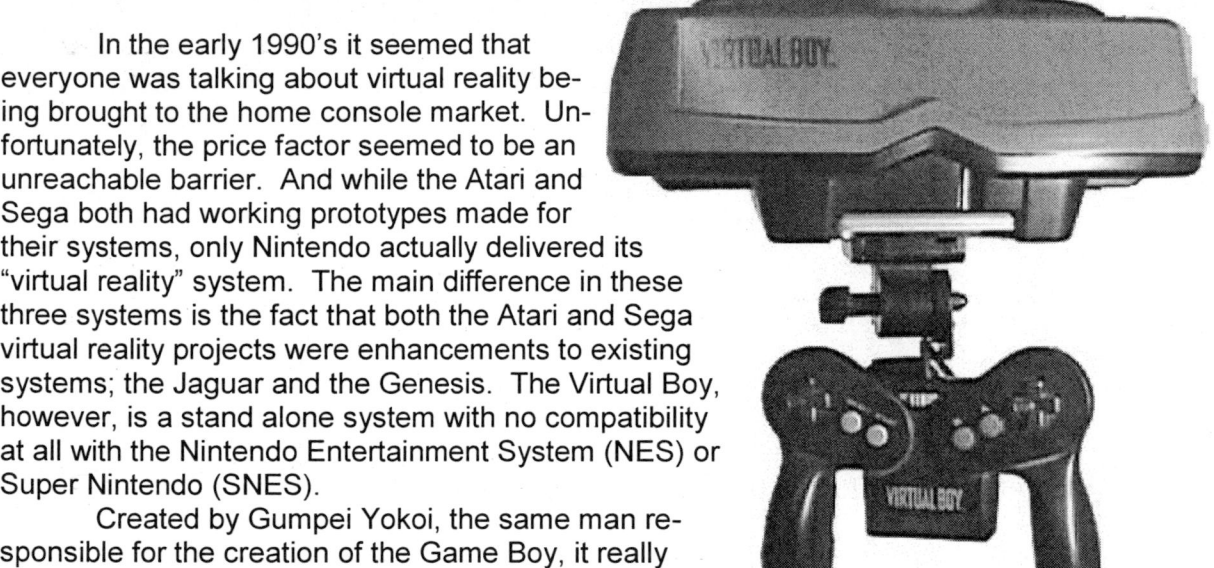

In the early 1990's it seemed that everyone was talking about virtual reality being brought to the home console market. Unfortunately, the price factor seemed to be an unreachable barrier. And while the Atari and Sega both had working prototypes made for their systems, only Nintendo actually delivered its "virtual reality" system. The main difference in these three systems is the fact that both the Atari and Sega virtual reality projects were enhancements to existing systems; the Jaguar and the Genesis. The Virtual Boy, however, is a stand alone system with no compatibility at all with the Nintendo Entertainment System (NES) or Super Nintendo (SNES).

Created by Gumpei Yokoi, the same man responsible for the creation of the Game Boy, it really comes as a surprise how badly this project came out. The system itself stands on two spindly legs and allows the user to hold a controller while looking into the immerse viewer. The screen only displays one color; red. This color is projected with a background of black, giving a slight 3-D appearance. By 3-D, I simply mean that 2-D images appear to be at different depths on the screen.

Released unsuccessfully in Japan in 1995, it was quickly brought to the U.S. using a unique marketing scheme. The system and two games could be rented as a package from Blockbuster Video. This was done in an attempt to build interest in the system before it was officially released for sale. Even with this strategy, the price was quickly reduced due to lagging sales.

One issue that concerned many consumers was the fact that headaches often occurred while playing these games for more than a few minutes. Due to this, the games automatically pause after 15 minutes of continuous play. This feature seems a little strange, but as horrible as the games on this system may seem to be, it is true that time passes easily while playing.

This system doesn't offer much in the way of "must have" games. It is not easily portable and is a bit awkward to keep set up for play at home. It hurts the player's eyes and face, and can often be difficult to hear. But with all of its problems, it is still often believed that the Virtual Boy has one of the best controllers of any system. It can be used by left and right handed players with ease and is very comfortable to hold. Oddly enough, the power supply is actually plugged in through a port on the controller.

While the system is fun to play on occasion, it is a far cry from a great system. At the very best, it might be considered "amusing". It still amazes me that this system actually made it past the drawing board.

What did Lucus say after playing Rad Racer with the Power Glove in the movie The Wizard?

Mario Clash

Red Alarm

Teleroboxer

Virtual League Baseball

3D Tetris Nintendo 5 $12
A nice twist on the classic game. This version gives the player a 3-D perspective to the original.

Galactic Pinball Nintendo 2 $3
Seen from the front of the pinball machine, this pinball game gives a good sense of depth and perspective. This is perhaps one of the most entertaining Virtual Boy games since it can be played for just a few minutes at a time and still be fun. The short game length greatly reduces the amount of headaches caused by this system.

Golf T&E Soft 3 $4
Even the greens are red in this game. And it is this unfortunate lack of color that makes this game very difficult to master. A game built around precision, golf doesn't translate well into a system that only has one color and limited graphical capabilities.

Jack Brothers Atlus 7 $25
With six main levels and many areas within each, this game can take quite a while to finish. With an increasing difficulty level and the amount of time necessary to finish it, eye strain may have you screaming for mercy long before you're screaming victory.

Mario Clash Nintendo 4 $0

Mario's Tennis Nintendo 1 $2
This is the pack-in game for the Virtual Boy system. It is very fun and very addictive, but unfortunately, due to the Virtual Boy's design, it is only playable by one person at a time.

Nester's Funky Bowling Nintendo 6 $15
It seems that every system requires at least one bowling game, and this is the Virtual Boy's entry. It can be overly difficult at times, and the attempt at depth in this game actually makes it more difficult.

Panic Bomber Hudson Soft 4 $8

Red Alarm T&E Soft 4 $10
A real attempt at a 3-D game, the immersive quality of the Virtual Boy's visor makes the effect impressive for such a relatively slow system. But, everything being considered, the game play and graphics are mediocre, and the novelty wears off quickly.

Teleroboxer Nintendo 4 $10
Similar to the Punch Out!! Series, this game features robots as your opponents. With nice 3-D effects and easy controls, this game can be a lot of fun to play.

Vertical Force Hudson Soft 3 $4
Every system needs a "shooter" and this is it. Great for a quick game fix.

Virtual Boy Wario Land Nintendo 5 $10
A little monotonous at times, this game plays very similarly to the original Super Mario Brothers, with the exception that you play Wario. There are different levels upon which your character can move, and it is a fun game when played in moderation.

Virtual League Baseball Kemco 4 $8
Very difficult to become good at, this game suffers from the lack of graphical capabilities of the system. The single color and odd view make this game frustrating at best.

Waterworld Ocean 6 $20
A very repetitive game, Waterworld is only desired for its rarity. Being the scarcest of the U.S. Virtual Boy games can't save this Ocean title from being bad.

HARDWARE

Virtual Boy System Nintendo 4 $30

Virtual Boy Hard Case Nintendo 7 $45

Virtual Boy Wario Land   Water World

"I love the Power Glove. It's so bad."

CD-i

Philips CD-i
By: Andy Slaven

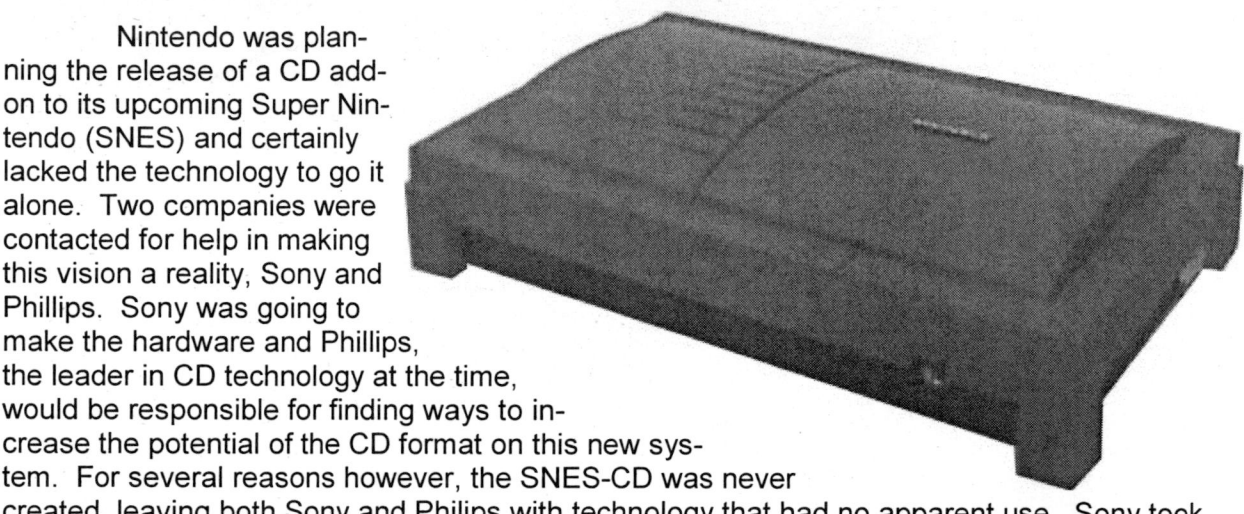

Nintendo was planning the release of a CD add-on to its upcoming Super Nintendo (SNES) and certainly lacked the technology to go it alone. Two companies were contacted for help in making this vision a reality, Sony and Phillips. Sony was going to make the hardware and Phillips, the leader in CD technology at the time, would be responsible for finding ways to increase the potential of the CD format on this new system. For several reasons however, the SNES-CD was never created, leaving both Sony and Philips with technology that had no apparent use. Sony took this technology and eventually turned it into the Sony Playstation. Philips took their experiences with Nintendo and created the CD-i.

CD-i, or Compact Disc Interactive, is a 16-bit system that was released in 1991 and takes on many forms. Originally marketed as a multimedia device toward both consumers and the professional market, the system met with an unreceptive audience and seemed sure to be removed completely from the marketplace. It was during this time that consumers could walk into any Sears department store and see a CD-i kiosk with various types of software playing on it, most of which were either family oriented software or children's learning media (edutainment). In addition to playing this type of media, the CD-i was also capable of playing both regular CD's and Video CD's, making the viewing of movies in MPEG-1 format a possibility. An abundance of movies were made available in this format, and can still be found very cheaply via the internet.

In 1994, as failure seemed eminent, Phillips decided to make a radical change of marketing scheme and began to promote the CD-i as a gaming machine instead. Not only was there a shift in software production from multimedia titles to that of games, but a new CD-i console was also released in the form of the CD-i 450. The CD-i 450 looked like a game console, with a flip-top lid and a controller that was wired to the system, instead of using IR wireless remotes. For the price of $300, you could now own a CD-i game system and one game (Burn Cycle was included in the package). The 450 also included a concealed expansion port that would accept the digital video cartridge that was necessary to play FMV intensive games. However, this cartridge added $150 to the total price tag, and many consumers were drawn to the 3DO, which was now sporting a price between $400 and $500, depending on location. In answer to this dilemma, the CD-i 550 was released. The 550 is basically a CD-i 450 with a built in digital video cartridge, and sold for around $400. This strategy worked to a point, but by this time most consumers had already sided with either the 3DO or had committed to the less expensive CD-i 450 console. This made the 550 a relative failure, though it is still the preferable CD-i system of gamers.

At the time of this book's printing, the most expensive PSX game ever released in the U.S. is a Best Buy compilation CD. Cost: $100

As part of the move toward a more game oriented software lineup, Philips began to commission the construction of various game controllers. The best controllers, made by Logitec, are similar to those seen on other consoles of the time, and are actually very easy to get used to. These gamepad controllers are an essential item when playing some of the more action oriented games such as Hotel Mario and the Zelda titles. Which brings us to our next point...the inclusion of Nintendo owned characters on the Philips system.

As part of the arrangement between Philips and Nintendo when working together on the SNES-CD, Philips retained the rights to make 4 games containing Nintendo owned characters. From this agreement sprung three Zelda titles and one Mario title, of which only Hotel Mario and Zelda's Adventure are worth owning. The other two Zelda games, Link: The Faces of Evil and Zelda: The Wand of Gamelon are among the most common games for the system as they were promoted proudly by Philips in an effort to raise interest for the system. Unfortunately for those who bought into this hype, these titles are abysmal and certainly don't do justice to the Zelda franchise.

With early blunders in marketing and a very high price tag, the CD-i was simply in the wrong place at the wrong time. Had a gaming stance been taken upon the launch of the system, things might have turned out differently for Phillips. As fate would have It, the CD-i caused Philips to lose over $1,000,000,000.00 (Yes, that's one BILLION dollars.) An interesting system with several quality titles to offer, the CD-i is not only a fun piece of gaming history to own, but can typically be found at relatively good prices. The software, for the most part, can also be found very cheaply on the internet, though it is a bit difficult to come across in video game resale shops. The fan base for this system is worldwide and can sometimes seem fanatical, as is often the case with the more obscure systems. Development by individuals for this console continues even today. While certainly not to be considered a success by anyone's definition, this is a game system that should not be overlooked as an innovator, and would make a nice addition to anyone's video game collection.

***Note: Due to the fact that the overwhelming majority of games for the CD-i were published by Philips Media, the developer has been listed after the game review when it is different than the Publisher. The CD-i has thousands of titles available for it, the large majority of which are either application software or home-brew programs. We have selected only those titles that are considered to be gaming software. This selection was made with several criteria in mind, the most important of which was the type of interaction. A few edutainment titles were included, but these were marketed toward older children and serve as true entertainment more than most other edutainment titles. Also, due to the widespread use of the CD-i worldwide, some of the titles listed may have never seen a true U.S. release, but are readily available within the U.S. and play in English on U.S. systems with no trouble. Typically this type of software would not be listed in a section, but due to the international availability of the system and the advent of internet sales, it has become nearly impossible to determine with any amount of accuracy which titles were and were not released specifically for the U.S. market. Still, even with the inclusion of several of what are sure to be European releases, the games listed within this guide should retain their printed rarities and values due to the ease of acquisition of these titles.

CD-i

The 7th Guest

Atlantis: The Last Resort

The Apprentice

Battleship

3rd Degree   **Philips Media**   5 $8
A party style game, this title is a game show of sorts in which contestants must answer various questions and perform on-screen tasks. Obviously intended for adults, this game supports from three to six players. Similar in style and quality to Zand-host and Station Invasion for the 3DO.

7th Guest, The   **Philips Media**   4 $15
One of the best known titles for the CD-i, this point and click adventure places you squarely inside of a haunted mansion with a multitude of puzzles that must be solved in order to escape. Some very difficult challenges are included in this game, all accompanied by some of the best graphics of the time. This is a must have for the CD-i. **Developed by:** Philips Freeland Studios

ABC Sports Presents: Power Hitter
                        Philips Media   4 $8
In this title you must face off against Dennis Eckersley and Dave Stewart, winners of the Cy Young and MVP awards respec-tively. But instead of just swinging away, there are also mana-gerial aspects to this game such as managing the team and assigning batting orders. While this title did have potential, it does fall short in several areas, most notably the lack of control over an entire team, but instead just the batter. **Developed by:** Fathom Pictures

ABC Sports Presents: The Palm Springs Open
                        Philips Media   5 $15
This is an average golf simulation that offers some very nice graphics. Control seems very limited with no choice of direction or stance, and is a real setback for this game. Sound effects are done relatively well, but background music is sparse, re-placed instead with natural sounds. What makes this game stand out from other golf games of the time is the fact that all the graphics are digitized, offering real views of real courses, and the use of real players. **Developed by:** Fathom Pictures

Accellerator   **SPC Vision**   4 $8
A fun driving game featuring six opponents, this title offers vari-ous hazards and weapons such as jumps and bombs. The CPU's AI seems a bit simplistic, and often cheats to get the advantage.

Alice in Wonderland   **Philips Media**   5 $12
An adventure game played in the third person, this title offers the creative feature found within the novel and some interesting game play, though unlike more recent renditions of this story in computer games, this title seems to be suitable for younger players instead of mainstream gamers. The goal of this game is to crowned Queen, and it features claymation characters. **De-veloped by:** Spinnaker Software

Alien Gate   **Philips Media**   4 $8
This vertically scrolling shooter offers game play similar in style to Galga, but without the classic feel and creativity. Still a fun game, though without a loyal following and a history as interest-ing as that of Galga's, this title is simply one of many in a crowded genre. But with a shortage of arcade style games for the CD-I, this is a nice option for those wanting a more classic feel with solid shooting action. **Developed by:** SPC Vision

Apprentice, The   **Philips Media**   4 $8
The digital video cartridge is actually an option for this game, and its inclusion opens different animations and expands the overall quality of the graphics within the game. An action plat-form game, take the role of Marvin as you traverse unique levels throughout the kingdom. This is a surprisingly enjoyable title featuring nice graphics, sound and control. **Developed by:** Vision Factory

Arcade Classics   **Philips Media**   5 $12
This title features the following classic games: Ms. Pacman, Galaxian, and Galga. You will definitely need the game pad controller for this game. **Developed by:** Namco Ltd.

Asterix Caesar's Challenge
                        Philips Media   4 $8
An interactive board game, this title offers a story line to help explain what is going on and to add depth. The village name is Asterix, not yours, and you have been issued a challenge by Caesar that must be carried out through using the board inter-face. **Developed by:** Infogrames

Atlantis: The Last Resort   **Philips Media**   4 $8
A FMV tunnel shooter at heart, this game is played under the premise that you must fly through caverns to find and destroy a virus that has mutated all marine life. This title requires the digital video cartridge. **Developed by:** Philips ADS

Axis and Allies   **Philips Media**   4 $12
A classic strategy game set in 1942, you must choose a side of the war to participate in and make strategic moves to secure victory. Up to five people can play, either against each other, or as a unit opposing the CD-i. Either way this is an enjoyable translation of the board game by Milton Bradley. **Developed by:** CapDisc

Backgammon   **Philips Media**   4 $5
Well, it's backgammon on your TV. If you like the game, then this title will be enjoyable. But, if you're like the rest of the world, it is just another game that is best played by others, pref-erably not in CD-i format. **Developed by:** CapDisc

Battleship   **Philips Media**   5 $10
Taking a game like Battleship and turning it into a video game

In the movie War Games, what game taught the computer that Global Thermonuclear War could have no winner?

was just a matter of time. And this time around, your brother won't be moving his ships around when you leave the room for two seconds, nor will it look at the placement of your ships. And very rarely will it beat you up if you happen to win, though it does happen on occasion. A simple concept made digital, this version does the original justice and offers simple game play that is easy for all levels. **Developed by:** CapDisc

Body Slam
See Mutant Rampage.

Brain Dead 13   **Philips Media**   **4**   **$7**
With the aid of the digital video cartridge, this title is played much in the same style as Space Ace and Dragon's Lair, with the proper button press at the proper time. There is no way around it, you will need to practice and use much trial and error to complete this game. Still, it has some very nice graphics and is very enjoyable for fans of interactive cartoons/movies. **Developed by:** ICDI

Burn: Cycle   **Philips Media**   **3**   **$5**
You are on a quest to find out who has implanted a computer virus in your brain while you were sleeping. Perhaps it's just me, but it would be more of a mystery as to who implanted a COMPUTER in my head. This is a shooting game that uses full screen FMV that has definitely aged poorly. Control seems to be very accurate, though it will take some getting used to. This title was advertised copiously when the CD-i was in stores and is one of the most common titles available. **Developed by:** Trip Media

Caesar's World of Boxing   **Philips Media**   **3**   **$10**
When the CD-i was still on Best Buy store shelves, this title was usually the one playing. For the time, this boxing game had impressive 3-D effects and great sound, though even with the game pad controller it was difficult to maneuver your boxer efficiently. Surprisingly, this title requires the digital video cartridge, though it is not apparent where it is actually used within the game. Perhaps if you had considered buying a CD-i when it was first released, this title may bring back some good memories. Or, if you spent $500 on a CD-i, perhaps it will cause nightmares. **Developed by:** CD-i Systems

Caesar's World of Gambling
           Philips Media   **4**   **$8**
Most gambling games appear to be the same, as does this one. With various games to be played in Caesar's Palace, this casino simulation should be enjoyable for chronic gamblers, but can easily be replaced with the plethora of gambling games available on nearly every console ever made. **Developed by:** CD-i Systems

CD Shoot   **Philips Media**   **4**   **$10**
A skeet shooting game, this title offers various styles including

trap, ball trap, English skeet and Olympic style competition. **Developed by:** Eaglevision Interactive

Chaos Control   **Philips Media**   **4**   **$8**
This is a rail shooter in which you have no control over the movement of you space craft. You simply shoot anything that comes into your sites and enjoy the occasional anime style FMV sequences when they appear. This is a very short game that requires the use of the digital video cartridge, and can be fun for the first few times it is played. Unfortunately, as is the case with most rail games, this title quickly becomes predictable and looses the initial challenge. **Developed by:** Infogrames

Clue   **Philips Media**   **4**   **$7**
Of important historical note, Clue is the first CD-i title that necessitated the content advisory label, although it is unclear as to why. FMV sequences are used to tell the tale in this translation of the popular board game. Unfortunately a limited number of possible endings (12) greatly reduces the replay value of this game. Still, it is very enjoyable, and just like the board game, once you have abstained for a while, it will regain its original appeal and challenge. The digital video cartridge is required for this title. **Developed by:** 3T Productions

Clue: The Mystery Continues
           Philips Media   **4**   **$8**
The second installment in this series is every bit as good as the first. Adding new scenarios and FMV sequences, this will help solve the problem of knowing what the outcome will be. The digital video cartridge is necessary to play this title as well. **Developed by:** 3T Productions

Connect Four   **Philips Media**   **4**   **$5**
A popular game in the 1980's, this game makes an appearance on the CD-i as well. It would seem refreshing that such a simple game could be made for a video game system, but also frustrating that it was released by itself instead of a compilation of some sort. For the price of this game new, one could have bought 3 of the original version, and still had enough to buy a checker board. **Developed by:** CapDisc

Creature Shock   **Philips Media**   **4**   **$10**
This is a rail shooter in which control is minimal, but from the first person perspective you must control the aiming and firing of your weapon. Available on several platforms, including the Saturn and PSX (though in "Special Edition" format), this title requires the digital video cartridge. **Developed by:** Virgin Interactive

Crime Patrol   **Philips Media**   **4**   **$7**
This shooting game requires both the game gun and the digital video cartridge. While not considered to be of the same caliber as today's arcade FPS games, this title was ahead of its time and is still enjoyable. Available for the Sega CD and 3DO as

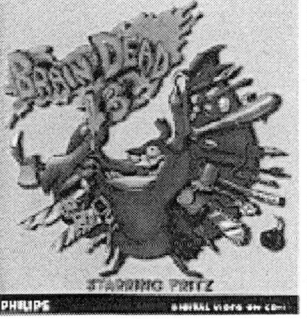
Brain Dead 13

CD Shoot

Clue

Connect Four

CD-i

Earth Command

Dark Castle

Dimo's Quest

Dragon's Lair II: Timewarp

well, this title also spawned an improved sequel. **Developed by:** CapDisc

Crimp Patrol 2: Drug Wars   Philips Media   4 $7
With improvements to both the accuracy of the game gun recognition and graphics alike, this shooting game is better than the first, although obviously of reduced quality when compared to the arcade version. This title requires both the game gun and the digital video cartridge. **Developed by:** CapDisc

Dame Was Loaded, The   Philips Media   5 $12
A period game interfaced via point and click control, this title wasn't a big seller, but is a quality game. Also available for PC, this version is actually preferable considering the trouble often associated with running old software on new PC's. There are slight variations between this version and the PC version, but most are minor and the result of hardware limitations.

Dark Castle   Philips Media   4 $8
Available for several systems, platform games are not the CD-i's strong suit. In this game you will face three main levels while trying to prove yourself worthy of facing the Black Knight. Control can be difficult to get used to and sound and graphics both seem to be unrefined. While not a complete disappointment, this title could have used a bit more work before it was released on the CD-i. **Developed by:** PIMA

Defender of the Crown   Philips Media   4 $7
This extremely popular PC game is best known to console gamers by its appearance on the NES. Classic strategy intertwined with action scenes make your quest to unite England a very entertaining one. Just make sure not to impale your jousting opponent's horse as this will cause you to be despised by the people (or, if you're jousting with a friend's character, it could easily find you with a black eye.) **Developed by:** Philips Interactive Media

Déjà Vu   Philips Media   4 $12
This graphic adventure places you in the role of...well, that's part of what you're trying to figure out. On a quest to find your identity, among other things, you will utilize varied items and clues to make your way. Very challenging for gamers new to the genre, this title is a favorite of many. Also available for the NES, this version has improved graphics and sound. **Developed by:** ICOM Simulations

Déjà Vu 2: Lost in Las Vegas
**   Philips Media   5 $15**
Played in the same style as the first installment, this title places you, obviously, in Las Vegas. This time around, the graphics have notably improved, though the sound seems to have gotten worse. While it lacks the originality of the first game, this title should still be enjoyable for anyone who enjoys graphic adven-

tures. **Developed by:** ICOM Simulations

Dimo's Quest   Philips Media   4 $7
Viewed from overhead, this puzzle game requires you to avoid certain obstacles and various enemies in order to collect all the objects from each room. Once a room is clear, you can progress to the next. Though this idea is hardly original, it is a very enjoyable game based on a simple concept that is good for not only adults, but for improving the problem solving skills of children. **Developed by:** SPC Vision

Dragon's Lair   Philips Media   3 $5
The digital video cartridge is necessary to play this classic arcade game. This version of Dragon's Lair is surprisingly of very high quality with very clear video and audio. The control could be improved, but many controller problems are solved when the game pad is used. **Developed by:** Super Club Home Entertainment

Dragon's Lair II: Timewarp Philips Media   4 $7
Of equal quality of the first installment, this title also requires the digital video cartridge. This time around, you're not going after a dragon, but instead an evil wizard that you must chase through time. **Developed by:** Super Club Home Entertainment

Earth Command   Philips Media   4 $8
In this title you are in control of a U.N. command post in outer space and contend with detrimental situations that face the earth. A world sim at heart, the main goal of this title is to properly balance the economic status of the Earth by controlling other factors including development speed of humans and construction rates.

Effacer: Hangman of the 25th Century
**   Philips Media   5 $10**
Unlike most puzzle games of this type, the 40,000 puzzles should not become repetitious too quickly. This is a game of hangman in a futuristic style that places you in the land of Urgrik, and often times will find you facing aliens that actually use misspelled words to throw you off course. While this is a simple game by design, the new factors make it enjoyable. **Developed by:** CapDisc

Escape from CyberCity   Philips Media   4 $8
A very difficult shooting game for the CD-i, this title uses what would be called cell shading by today's standards. Very Japanese in feel, this is an odd game to have been released on the decidedly American CD-i system. While it may seem impossible at first, this title can become enjoyable after much practice. Unlike other shooting games, this one almost guarantees to never become easy. **Developed by:** Fathom Pictures

Flashback Philips Media 5 $15
In a quest to regain your memory you must overcome unique level designs and the occasional villain. Sporting some very nice graphics for the system and sparse, yet good sound effects, this is a very enjoyable game all around. **Developed by:** Tiertex

Girl's Club Philips Media 4 $3
This is a girl's interactive dating game that utilizes FMV. While obviously designed for young girls, its recommended age (10-13) places it outside of children's learning media, so it makes the list regardless of the intended audience's gender. **Developed by:** Philips POV

Go Older Games/Good Deal Games 9 $10
Only recently made available, this game's origin is much older than that of the classic game Othello. With a relatively strong fan base around the world and requiring a strategic mind, Go should be an entertaining game to play on your CD-i.

Golden Oldies I Philips Media 4 $10
Replaying classic games on new systems is something that has become very popular recently. This compilation contains Guardian (a Defender clone with improved graphics) and Invaders (a less than subtle rip-off of Space Invaders). While it is doubtful that rights were secured for either one of these games, it is hard to go wrong with a classic. These two games both play very well, and Invaders is especially nice with the updated graphics and very solid control. If you like classic gaming, this title might interest you. However, be warned, if you either don't like classics, or have an aversion to the classics being altered, you might want to steer clear of this title.

Golden Oldies II Philips Media 4 $10
Another compilation of classic games featuring improved graphics and altered names. This title features Blockbuster, a Breakout clone, and Bughunt, a Centipede clone. Classic game fans rejoice.

Great American Golf 1 Philips Media 4 $7
Take a historical trip through golf's past in this first volume that covers golf before 1960. You will also be able to play a round at Far Hills in this title as well as take a quiz covering golf history. **Developed by:** NDRA

Great American Golf 2 Philips Media 4 $7
Covering the history of golf from 1960 through 1990, this title picks up where the first volume left off. Featuring new courses, this game allows for play at a different course and with the aid of several golf greats. **Developed by:** NDRA

Great Day at the Races, A
 Philips Media 4 $8
A teaching tool of sorts, this title features video of actual horse races and teaches the basics of learning how to choose a winner, from picking the right horse for the right condition to picking the right jockey. **Developed by:** Philips Interactive

Haunted House Philips Media 4 $5
Designed for younger players, this might hold some interest for fans of the Jan Pienkowski book on which it is based. The object is to find various keys hidden throughout the mansion and find a way out.

Hotel Mario Philips Media 4 $12
Believe it or not, this title is perhaps one of the most addicting Mario installments to date! While often overlooked by the average gamer as what appears to be a sub par game, the puzzle based levels are of increasing difficulty and offer a variety of challenges. The simple objective is to close all the doors on each level, but with various enemies reopening them, variable floors (such as ice), and even the occasional power outage that makes you play in the dark, this title is sure to make fans of the original Mario Brothers very happy. **Developed by:** Philips Fantasy Factory

Inca Philips Media 5 $12
An outer space adventure, the story serves as a nice backdrop and describes how the Huayna Capac has taken time, matter and energy and cast them into space for safe keeping. Using nine magical jewels to help you on your quest, you must locate and defeat these three forces. **Developed by:** Coktel Vision

International Tennis Open (one player)
 Philips Media 4 $8
An average tennis game with below average graphics, this more common version of the game only supports one player at a time. **Developed by:** Infogrames

International Tennis Open (two player)
 Philips Media 5 $10
With the exception of the ability to play with a second human player, this title is identical to the one above. As with most games, the game pad style controller is almost essential to do well with this title. **Developed by:** Infogrames

Jack Sprite Vs. Crimson Ghost
 Older Games 9 N/A*
*Just recently announced as a title to be released at the Classic Gaming Expo in 2002, the release price, and subsequent value are unknown at this time.

Jeopardy! Philips Media 4 $8
Based on the TV show by the same name, this answer/question game is a mind teaser that tests general knowledge. Unfortunately, the inclusion of a finite number of problems reduces replay value after it has been played more than a few times.

Flashback

Hotel Mario

International Tennis Open
(2 Player)

Jeopardy!

...on the antenna and in the antenna access room. When Alec reaches the area, he'll be blown to bits without a fight.

CD-i

The Last Bounty Hunter

Lemmings

Link: The Faces of Evil

Litil Divil

Jigsaw: The Ultimate Electronic Challenge
Philips Media   4 $5
This is a nice puzzle game that allows you to choose the picture you would like to put together, and then have it cut into pieces. Over 3000 pictures are included in this game waiting to be turned into puzzles. **Developed by:** Nova Logic

Joker's Wild!, The   Philips Media   4 $5
Based on the TV show of limited popularity, this seems an odd choice of inspiration. This title offers very little true challenge, though it is interesting for fans of the original show.

Joker's Wild Jr., The   Philips Media   4 $5
This appears to be the same as the original installment in this series with the exception of the challenge being reduced.

Joy of Sex, The   Philips Media   5 $12
An adult oriented interactive movie, this offers very little interactivity and is really very boring. But with enough hard work and dedication, you might just get to see a semi-nude woman portrayed in 32-bit graphics. Woohoo!

Kether   Philips Media   4 $8
It seems odd that the creators of this game chose the combinations of elements they did to create what became a smorgasbord of simplicity. Your missions will begin with a short flight to one of five castles. The flying sequence is on par with others for the CD-I, but don't offer too much entertainment. Once at the castle, an extremely simple puzzle must be solved in order to continue along. And finally, once past the gate puzzle, there is a pathetic first person shooter mode through various mazes to find various runes. Tossed together in what can only be described as a "fruit salad of disappointment", Kether will probably only entertain young children (though its obvious audience was players in their late teens.) **Developed by:** Infogrames

Kingdom: The Far Reaches
Philips Media   4 $7
Requiring the digital video cartridge to play properly, this title is done in the same stile as Dragon's Lair, with the need to press the appropriate button at the right time. An over world map allows for travel to different areas and doesn't lock you into a very strict order of events. Once mastered, this title can be enjoyable, but is frustrating on the onset. **Developed by:** Cap-Disc

Kingdom II: Shadoan   Philips Media   5 $10
Similar to the first installment, a new story line accompanies identical game play. With the inclusion of completely new areas and a new challenge, this should be popular with fans of the original. **Developed by:** CapDisc

L'Affaire Morloy   Philips Media   5 $12
Take the role of Paul Keirn, a reporter for the Liberation newspaper, in an effort to rescue your kidnapped girlfriend Virginie. Taking place in real time, you have 48 hours to solve the mystery with the aid of FMV sequences to interview suspects and informants, as well as evaluating evidence.

Labyrinth of Crete   Philips Media   4 $10

Laser Lords   Philips Media   4 $8
Let's face it, some games just aren't any good. While the story of being abducted by an alien while hitchhiking may set up what should be an interesting story, boring game play, awful sound and very shoddy graphics make this a title to avoid. With the occasional RPG element, this platform/adventure game takes a similar form to that of Link: The Faces of Evil. Unfortunately, this game doesn't share the same popular franchise name that Link does, and as such is an absolute disaster. **Developed by:** Spinnaker Software

Last Bounty Hunter, The   Philips Media   4 $8
This is the little known third installment to the Mad Dog McCree trilogy. You're going to need both the light gun and the digital video cartridge to play this game. **Developed by:** CapDisc

Lemmings   Philips Media   4 $7
Seemingly available on every system ever made, this game seems to cause people to flock to it...to follow it blindly...they just must follow, regardless of the consequences. Must follow... **Developed by:** Psygnosis

Link: The Faces of Evil   Philips Media   3 $12
Zelda on the CD-i? Actually, this is only one of three Zelda titles available for the system. Due to contractual agreements with Nintendo, Phillips retained the rights to produce several games using Nintendo characters. Unfortunately this platform based action game is extremely difficult to play and is a complete diversion from the love story line of Zelda. Still, it is a must have title for fans of the Zelda series. **Developed by:** Animation Magic

Litil Divil   Philips Media   4 $10
A nice adventure game of varying difficulty, and utilizing the digital video cartridge (required), this title offers some very entertaining game play. With intermittent video clips to keep the story moving and engaging puzzle/action sequences, this game should be enjoyable for most ages. On a mission to deliver dinner to the devil himself, you play a lesser devil...a.k.a. "Litil Divil". This title was heavily advertised for the CD-I after its release and was one of the better sellers for the system. **Developed by:** Gremlin

Lords of the Rising Sun   Philips Media   4 $10
Available for PC and several console systems, this strategy

214

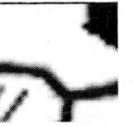

game takes place in feudal Japan. Take the role of one of three different characters in a quest to rule all of Japan. Interlaced action sequences break up the monotony of standard strategy screens, much in the way Defender of the Crown was played. **Developed by:** Philips POV

Lost Eden   Philips Media   5 $12
Due to the graphic intensity of this title, the digital video card is required. Also available on the 3DO, this title is a firs person adventure using a point and click interface similar in style to Myst. You must first learn how to operate the citadel, and then must learn how to construct new ones to continue the defense of this land from the reptilian scourge. Your great-grandfather built the original towers to protect the land, but his son (your grandfather) stole the secret of their construction and destroyed them so that they could never be operated. Beautiful graphics and a nice soundtrack make this adventure both entertaining and relaxing. **Developed by:** Cryo Interactive Entertainment

Lost Ride   Philips Media   5 $15
Don't write this game off as just another rail game until you play it! Requiring the digital video cartridge for a game that seemed so simple at first was a bit odd, but after playing it, you will realize why it is needed. Basically played as a passenger that shoots various enemies, the basic premise is similar to most other rail shooters, but that's where the similarities end. With extremely detailed levels and great sound effects come together to offer a world similar in overall feel to that found in the game Myst. And while the game can freeze from time to time, this is mainly due to the amount of information being processed for each level. In addition to the amazing graphics and sound, it is most notable that this game uses randomly generated levels. While this type of technique is hated by the entire gaming community (though it remains in use by lazy game developers even today), it really ads replay value to this type of game. While the typical rail shooter would allow you to quickly learn the patterns of your enemies as they appear onscreen, the randomized levels offer a changed game each time you play through. This game is a definite must-have for CD-I owners.

Lucky Luke: The Videogame
     Philips Media   4 $10
Utilizing the digital video cartridge, this game offers 24 levels of chasing down the Daltons as Luke himself. Playable by children as young as 11 (or so the box says), this title should offer the occasional challenge for anyone who plays it. **Developed by:** SPC Vision

Mad Dog McCree   Philips Media   3 $8
Digital video is used for this title, and as such requires the use of the digital video cartridge. Go head to head with outlaws in the old west in a quick draw contest. Very popular in arcades for is use of FMV, this title requires the game gun controller.

Developed by: CapDisc

Mad Dog II: The Lost Gold   Philips Media   4 $10
More of the same from the first installment, this title also requires both the game gun and the digital video cartridge. While at the time this was cutting edge technology, it is a shame that both games weren't combined onto one CD. Once the patterns of your opponents are learned, this title looses all of its original challenge. **Developed by:** CapDisc

Marco Polo   Philips Media   5 $12
Much like the Columbus title for the VIS, this title offers a chance to follow Marco Polo on his voyage through China to the Gobi Desert. Full of information about this historic traveler, interaction keeps it entertaining. **Developed by:** Infogrames

Mega Maze   Philips Media   4 $8
This game offers 164 mazes containing various obstacles to make your passage more difficult. The "character" within is actually a ball that must be rolled from start to finish, offering very addictive game play. **Developed by:** CapDisc/Axis Interactive

Merlin's Apprentice   Philips Media   4 $10
Three customizable levels and 30 puzzles will test your logic in this game, designed to find who will become the next apprentice of Merlin. **Developed by:** Philips

Micro Machines   Philips Media   4 $12
While it is certainly more fun to play on the NES or the Genesis, this title still entertains on the CD-I as it is one of the few multiplayer titles available. While the graphics and sound do not meet the standard set by earlier versions, this installment was nice for owners of a system that saw so many edutainment titles released for it. **Developed by:** Codemasters

Monty Python's Invasion from Planet Skyron
     Philips Media   5 $15
Holding true to Monty Python's legacy, this is a very odd game featuring invading aliens with the intent of destroying the Earth. This game requires the digital video cartridge. **Developed by:** Daedalus CD-I Productions

Mutant Rampage (a.k.a. Body Slam)
     Philips Media   4 $7
Take the roles of three separate characters in this futuristic fighting game. You will face 10 different cybernetic teams of varying difficulty and must utilize the different attributes of each character in order to survive this challenge. This game requires the digital video cartridge. **Developed by:** Animation Magic

Myst   Philips Media   4 $12
A favorite among millions of gamers, Myst makes a good showing on the CD-i. With rendered still images that you must trav-

Marco Polo   Mega Maze   Monty Python's Invasion from Planet Skyron   Myst

Lunar for the PSX is a remake of the Sega CD version, but key elements and portions of the story line have both been changed to add variety.

CD-i

Name That Tune

Pin Ball

Secret Mission

Shaolin's Road

erse using a point and click interface, these strange worlds will keep puzzle solvers busy for quite a while. However, after it is beaten the game fails to be challenging at all. **Developed by:** Cyan/Sunsoft

Mystic Midway: Phantom Express
      Philips Media 5 $12
A rail shooter and sequel to Rest in Pieces below, this title takes place on a roller coaster where various ghosts and ghouls will pop up briefly, creating only a short window for you to take aim and fire. **Developed by:** Philips POV

Mystic Midway: Rest in Pieces
      Philips Media 4 $10
A shooting game with ghosts as your targets, this title offers several FMV sequences and entertaining graphics and game play. **Developed by:** Philips POV

Name That Tune Philips Media 4 $5
How many notes will it take you to guess the song being played? A seemingly boring title on first inspection, this game can actually become entertaining when you realize that what were once popular songs have now been reduced to obscurities on this title. **Developed by:** Philips Fantasy Factory

NFL Hall of Fame Football Philips Media 4 $10
Recruit players and form an all-star team to face 40 other teams in this arcade style football game. Also included is a tour of the Football Hall of Fame in this title that requires the use of the digital video cartridge. **Developed by:** CapDisc

NFL Instant Replay Philips Media 5 $10
Take the role of a referee in this game. Instead of making the plays, you are making calls on them. Making the right decision will add points to your score, raising you within the ranks of the best referees around. Since this title utilizes FMV sequences for the majority of the game, it does require the digital video cartridge. **Developed by:** CapDisc

NFL Trivia Challenge Philips Media 4 $10
Simply a trivia game based on NFL teams and players, this title will only be interesting to those with a good understanding of football's past. Some of the questions can actually be challenging for even the most thorough football aficionado, though the challenge is depleted once the questions have been cycled through. **Developed by:** CapDisc

Othello   Philips Media 4 $8
The ancient board game brought into the digital world, this title is a collector's-only game since better versions can easily be played on almost any PC. With black and white stones, the objective is to monopolize the board with your color by strategically placing your stones in relation to your opponent's. **Devel-**

oped by: Codim Interactive Media

Pac Panic   Philips Media 6 $12
This block-aligning puzzle game stars Pac-Man in one of his most obscure appearances on a home console. Addictive game play makes this title enjoyable, though it seems to have little to do with the actual Pac-Man character. **Developed by:** Philips Media Games

Pin Ball   Philips Media 4 $8
While this isn't the greatest pinball simulation available, it is a nice diversion to play from time to time. The "machines" lack the originality that makes other pinball video games enjoyable however, and it can quickly become boring or frustrating without the use of a game pad controller. **Developed by:** CapDisc

Plunderball   Older Games 9 N/A*
*Just recently announced as a title to be released at the Classic Gaming Expo in 2002, the release price, and subsequent value are unknown at this time.

Rise of the Robots Philips Media 4 $5
This title could have been much better, though regardless of platform this game fails to perform to its full potential. Take on the various working robots of an industrial factory that have malfunctioned in one-on-one 2-D fighting. The occasional animation makes this title stand out from cartridge versions of the game however, though by today's standards it isn't much to brag about. This title requires the digital video cartridge. **Developed by:** CapDisc

Sargon Chess Philips Media 3 $5
Classic chess is brought to the CD-I with this game featuring 16 difficulty levels and an advanced chess program designed to keep things challenging. **Developed by:** Spinnaker Software

Scotland Yard Interactive Philips Media 5 $12
This game places you in the well known gumshoe's...shoes, where you can play against the computer, nicknamed Robi, in mysteries designed to challenge your mind instead of your thumbs. **Developed by:** Audio Visuellen Medien

Secret Mission Philips Media 5 $10
Similar in graphical style to Sherlock Holmes for the 3DO, this title is a slow paced game that sees you enter Indochina as a secret agent. The story line begins with your identity unknown even to you, this title is reminiscent of Déjà Vu, though it is more of a slow adventure game than a graphic adventure. This title is definitely intended for an older audience, though more because of its speed and less because of its content. This game should be very enjoyable for gamers who are tired of the common brainless games so often ported from the arcade to the home. **Developed by:** Microids

In order to use a Game Genie on the NES 2, a special adaptor is needed, though these are very uncommon.

Shaolin's Road   Philips Media   5 $12
This action game places you in a role where you must avenge your father's death by learning new techniques of kung-fu and using them against those responsible. **Developed by:** Infogrames

Solar Crusade   Infrogames   4 $10
Actually released after Phillips had stopped support for the CD-I, this game features some amazing graphics, blending both animation and FMV for a unique experience. In addition to some of the nicer graphics for the CD-I, this title also features some very odd, though high quality sound and music. Solid control rounds out the package to make this a very nice game for the system. This title requires the digital video cartridge.

Space Ace   Philips Media   3 $5
In the same style as Dragon's Lair, this title requires the pushing of a specific button at a specific time and requires much practice. With some very impressive animation and very enjoyable sound, this version of Space Ace is one of the better home console titles. It also requires the digital video cartridge to play properly. **Developed by:** International Creative Digital Image

Space Ranger   Older Games   9   N/A*
*Just recently announced as a title to be released at the Classic Gaming Expo in 2002, the release price, and subsequent value are unknown at this time.

Spin Ball   Philips Media
See Zenith

Steel Machine   Philips Media   4 $8
Pilot the Steel Machine against six battle cruisers heading toward earth in an attempt to knock out each ship's main reactor. **Developed by:** SPC Vision

Striker Pro   Philips Media   4 $8
An average soccer game with lackluster graphics and sound, the control can be impossible without a game pad style controller, and is even difficult when using one. While it isn't a horribly bad title, there are many other soccer games of higher quality readily available on many other consoles. **Developed by:** Rage Software International

Tetris   Philips Media   3 $5
Widely considered to be the worst rendition of Tetris on a home console, what should be a very basic control scheme becomes a nightmare with apparent lags in responsiveness to your inputs. The graphics are sharp, though this is no bragging feat considering the context of the classic falling-blocks game. **Developed by:** Philips POV

Tetsuo Gaiden   New Frontier   6 $15

This is a very entertaining shooter that features FMV backgrounds and very precise control. While most shooters of this sort are dismissed as clones of the classics, this title does a nice job of blending new elements into the mix to keep it both true to the originals and also keep it entertaining. **Developed by:** Creative Media

Text Tiles   Philips Media   4 $5
Similar in style to Scrabble, this puzzle game relies on your vocabulary to form the most intricate words possible with the letters you are given. The one feature that sets this game apart from the classic board game is the fact that all of your moves are timed. **Developed by:** CapDisc

Thunder in Paradise   Philips Media   3 $5
The digital video cartridge is necessary if you want to see Terry "Hulk" Hogan star in this interactive movie. With shooting segments and a story based on the amusing TV show by the same name, this title is mildly entertaining, though certainly lacking in both sound and control quality. The graphics, while grainy, were still ahead of their time when this game was released. **Developed by:** Berk/Schwartz Bonnan Productions

Ultra CD-i Soccer   Philips Media   5 $10
While the graphics seem simple by today's standards, the various play modes, including two on two and league play, make this title featuring 72 European soccer teams enjoyable and long lasting. The digital video cartridge is required for this game. **Developed by:** Krisalis Software Ltd.

Video Speedway   Philips Media   5 $10
A Formula 1 simulation, this title features several different classes of kart races and one of the earliest replay modes seen on a home console. **Developed by:** Interactive Support Group

Voyeur   Philips Media   3 $8
The topic of much controversy when it was released, Voyeur places you behind a telephoto lens aimed at the open windows of a nearby mansion. Trying to unravel a mystery, this is actually an interactive movie that requires that you look into the right room at the right time in order to find clues. Once solved however, this title is easily beaten again. **Developed by:** Philips POV

Wacky World of Miniature Golf, The
Philips Media   5 $10
Featuring 18 holes, this title could have offered much more, but those available are of interesting design and feature some nice surprises. Eugene Levy narrates this enjoyable miniature golf game.

Whack-A-Bubble   Philips Media   4 $5
A mentally challenging puzzle game with over 100 levels, every stage is timed making some of the more difficult levels ex-

Steel Machine

Striker Pro

Thunder in Paradise

The Wacky World of Miniature Golf

The most effective weapon against the tank in Bloody Wolf for the TG-16 is the knife.

CD-i

Zelda's Adventure

Zelda: The Wand of Gamelon

tremely challenging.

Who Shot Johnny Rock?   Philips Media   3 $5
While the digital video cartridge and game gun are both required for this title, it is still an entertaining game. Very challenging at first, once enough time has been invested, this shooting game becomes predictable, though never truly easy. Enemies will pop up from every possible location for only a brief moment before they will shoot you. Quick reflexes are a must for this title. Using a VCR to record your progress, this title is entertaining to watch on VHS after you have completed it. This way, you will actually have time to listen to the dialog and watch the often amusing actors. **Developed by:** CapDisc

Wordplay   Philips Media   4 $5
Featuring a four player mode, this puzzle game challenges you to collect letters and then form words with them. Similar in goal to Text Tiles, the game play is completely different. **Developed by:** Backs Electronic Publishing Ltd.

World Cup Golf   Philips Media   4 $8
Requiring the digital video cartridge, this title reproduces the Hyatt Beach Golf Course as you play through the World Cup Golf tournament. This title even features a driving range. **Developed by:** US Gold

Zelda's Adventure   Philips Media   7 $75
Definitely the most expensive game for the CD-i, Zelda's Adventure is the only Zelda title on the CD-i that even comes close to doing the series justice. Seen from an overhead perspective like the original game, you control Zelda instead of link. Everything is digitized, so the graphics don't appear to move smoothly, nor are they very creative. Fortunately a very high skill level is attached to this game and assures that it won't be beaten in a day. With an extensive over world and quite a few dungeons that must be explored, this title is entertaining for fans of the series, though is next to impossible to find. **Developed by:** Viridis

Zelda: The Wand of Gamelon
                    Philips Media   3 $12
Nearly identical in game play to Link: The Faces of Evil, this title is a disappointment all around. Difficult control and unoriginal level design made this Zelda game a complete failure. Fans of the series will lower their heads in shame as they see what Phillips did with an otherwise unblemished franchise. Although, once the new Zelda for the Game Cube is released, this title may or may not look so bad. Only time will tell. **Developed by:** Animation Magic

Zenith (a.k.a. Spin Ball)   Philips Media   4 $8
This pinball simulation features some very nice additions to the

board including a flying mode, teleportation and death beams. Due to the graphic intensity of this title, this game does require the digital video cartridge. **Developed by:** Radarsoft

Zombi Dinos   Philips Media   5 $10
This adventure game sends you back in time 200 million years in order to stop "Brain Blobs" from turning dinosaurs into walking zombies. This title features FMV sequences for interaction with characters and stop motion techniques to animate the 14 various types of dinosaurs. **Developed by:** Philips POV

HARDWARE

CD-i 200/220   Philips/Magnavox   4 $40
This model was standard early in the lifecycle of this system and was designed to fit into a home entertainment center.

CD-i 450   Philips/Magnavox   4 $45
Constructed from more inexpensive parts and using a corded controller, this was the first attempt at making the CD-i into a real game machine.

CD-i 550   Philips/Magnavox   6 $85
Basically the same as the 450 model, this version includes a built in digital video cartridge, making it much more versatile. While basically just a 450 with the cartridge installed, this system is the most desirable for gamers, and as such is worth more than the sum of its parts.

Digital Video Cartridge   Philips/Magnavox   3 $20
Several versions were made for both consumer models of the system and for professional models. It is important to make sure that the cartridge will fit into the system you are buying it for.

Gamepad   Philips/Magnavox   4 $15
By far the best controller available for the CD-i and certainly the most ergonomic, this controller is very comfortable and offers the familiar directional pad and three button configuration.

Peacekeeper   Philips/Magnavox   4 $12
An accurate light gun, this is the only option available for this system. It can be used with quite a few games, and is identical in shape and feel to many other revolver style light guns.

Roller Controller   Philips/Magnavox   4 $12
Often called the "track ball", this most certainly is not a true trackball. Instead, this controller is actually designed for kids and children's software, though it can be used as an oversized one-handed controller if the need arises.

Thumbstick   Philips/Magnavox   3 $10
Packaged with early versions of the 200 and 220, and several other non-consumer models, this stick is awkward to use and is certainly not the preferable controller to be used for games.

Touchpad   Philips/Magnavox   5 $12
Built by Logitec, and the first game controller of its type for use with any CD-i system, this controller can be used ambidextrously since it can be held upside down.

Trackerball   Philips/Magnavox   6 $15
A very nice trackball, this device is normally used for professional applications, though several games (such as Myst) would accept this type of interface quite easily.

Zelda and Super Mario Bros. were both part of a breakfast cereal licensed by Nintendo.

Pioneer LaserActive
By: Vincent Yang and Andy Slaven

Of all the rare systems that died off quickly, most of them have very small game selections, or weren't innovative in any way. Certain systems were developed not only for software of their own systems, but they also incorporated technologies and features that allowed you to use them for something else (they can run other types of software). The company that really put this idea through its paces was Pioneer, in 1993, with the LaserActive.

Contrary to popular belief, Sony's Playstation 2 is not the first system that embraces the idea of a console as an home entertainment center, specifically the ability to watch movies in addition to playing video games. It was Pioneer. What is a LaserActive? It is composed of the main player, the CLD-A100 which allows you to play laserdisc (LD) movies, music LDs and music CDs. In addition to the player, one needs to purchase various modules to add additional features to the LaserActive player. With the Sega Genesis module PAC-S10, you can play MegaLD, Sega Genesis and Sega CD games. With the NEC Turbografix (TG-16) module PAC-N10, you can play LD-Rom2, TG-16 hucards, Turbo CD, Turbo Super CD, as well as PC-Engine CD and Super CD games, without any territorial locks. You must have at least one of the game modules to play any of the LD games offered, and both the Sega and NEC modules to play all of the LaserActive games available.

In addition to the game modules, there are two additional types of modules you can use on the LaserActive system. The first is the karaoke module PAC-K1. This module has a number of volume and sound controls plus a microphone jack. One can play karaoke LDs with the PAC-K1 and sing along using the included microphone. The other module is a computer interface, PAC-PC1, although the actual release of this module has not been confirmed. This piece of hardware connects the Laseractive to a PC with a 386 processor. Another accessory worth noting is the 3D goggle and adapter that enhances the gaming visuals of certain LaserActive titles that support this piece of hardware. If you have all the modules and combine all the features of this system, there are thousands of movies and games you can play on the Laseractive. When considering both domestic and Japanese titles, the PC-Engine has more than 700 games, while the Sega Genesis/CD has well over 1000 games.

In the U.S., due to the astronomical price tag, the system failed almost immediately. Right after the launch of the system, the player itself was $1000, each of the game modules cost $600 each and the karaoke module cost $300. The games were $120 each with the exception of "3D Museum", which came with paper 3D glasses and cost $180.

In Japan, during the early 90s, it was an economic boom, and the LaserActive system lasted for a while as a high-end interactive gaming and entertainment system. The system was supported for about 2 years until 1995, at which point all development for this system was ceased. What really ended support for the LaserActive was the fact that in order to play any LaserActive title, you needed either a Sega or NEC module, which was just too much money for the majority of consumers.

There are 31 unique titles worldwide, each title requiring that the specified module be inserted in order to play. Seven games were published that would work on either MegaLD or LD-Rom2 formats. The MegaLD format is compatible with 24 of the 31 games, and is by far the most common choice for those interested in starting a Laseractive collection. In the U.S. however, only 18 games were published. Fifteen of those 18 titles were for the MegaLD module, leaving only 3 games specifically designed to work with the TurboGrafx module. This is most likely due to the lack of popularity of the TG-16 in U.S., and NEC's subsequent view of the market.

All of the LaserActive games are universally compatible. This means that there are no territorial lockouts, which allows for the play of Japanese LD games on U.S. systems and visa versa. Almost all games that were published in both Japan and the U.S. have both languages available, thought Don Quixote and Goku are notable exceptions, being produced in both Japanese-only and English-only versions. Also, some Japanese-only titles have English as an available option, making one wonder if they were eventually intended for an American release as well. An interesting side note is the fact that Goku, 3D Museum, Blue Chicago Blues, and Melon Brains were made available for both MegaLD and LD-Rom2 in Japan, but were only released in the more common MegaLD format in the US due to limited number of TG-16 modules sold.

Most of the LD games' graphics consist of a background and a foreground where the background graphics are mostly video and pre-rendered images and the foreground graphics are like traditional 16-bit 2D animations that you control. One major limitation of the LD games however, is the fact that the background graphics have a time limit of sorts. Since it is playing from a LD track that is only recorded for a certain period of time, the level on which this background is used must be completed before the track is completed. This becomes very evident in shooting games that typically would have no time limit.

While the LaserActive was certainly an attempt at innovation, and will always have a loyal following in the U.S., it stands as a failed attempt at bringing several types of entertainment together. And while other companies tried similar projects that were intended to unite more than one form of entertainment, no other company offered to combine three proven technologies (LD, Genesis and TG-16) into one unit. Ultimately, consumers just were not willing to pay $2,000 for a LD player and a video game system that could be purchased separately for less than $1,000.

Stormlord for the Genesis was originally designed by Color Dreams for the NES. It is unknown how RazorSoft came into its possession.

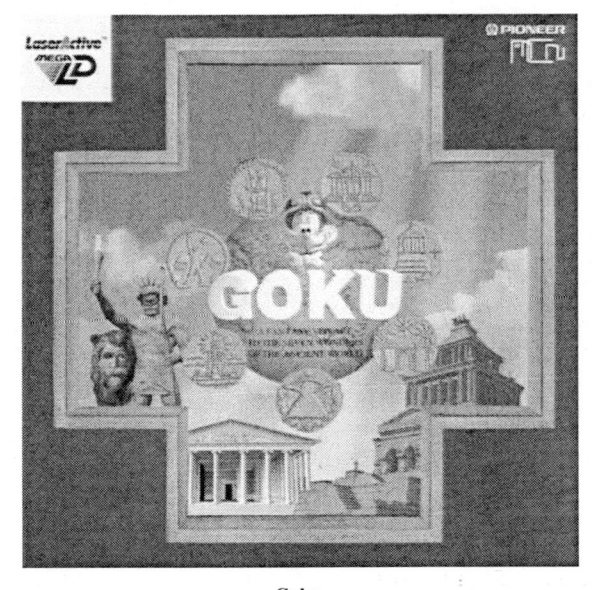

Goku

Manhattan Requiem

3D Museum   Multimedia Creators Network 8 $125
Not really a game but simply an illustration of LaserActive
graphics and what the system is capable of, it comes with a
sheet of goggles (6 pair in total total), but of 3 different types
(LCD, Red and Blue, and Parallax). (MegaLD required)

Blue Chicago Blues   Riverhill Soft   8 $130
The sequel to Manhattan Requiem, this game takes place in
Chicago, rather than New York. You are JB Harold, you need to
solve a case and make choices on what to do. Each choice you
make may end the game if it's a mistake, with the endings displayed in FMV sequences. This is one of the most sought after
LaserActive titles. (MegaLD required)

Don Quixote   Premier International   5 $30
This is a first person RPG with cartoon style graphics. The
graphics are done very well, but control can be very difficult,
especially when moving through the streets. (MegaLD required)

Ghost Rush   Pioneer   5 $30
A house is haunted and your mission is to capture the ghost
inside. A very unique idea, however the controls are not easy to
get master. (MegaLD required)

Goku   Pioneer/Multimedia Creators Network
                                              5 $25
The best edutainment title on the LaserActive, you are Goku,
the ancient Chinese character. This game takes you through
the Seven Wonders of the World. When you go through each
wonder, you'll be given 2 paths, which can sometimes return
you to the same location. U.S. and Japanese versions are available, but only in their respective languages. (MegaLD required)

Great Pyramid, The   Pioneer   4 $25
An edutainment title about the pyramids, this title starts out with
a 10 minute tour of the Pyramids. You will be able to navigate
throughout the structure any way you want, in addition to exploring some of the unsolved mysteries of the pyramids. (MegaLD
required)

Hi-Roller Battle   Pioneer   5 $30
You take control of the gunship in this mediocre helicopter title.
The backgrounds are all recorded, so just like other LD games,

you'll memorize the location and pattern of enemies after you've
played through a few times. But the later stages still remain very
difficult. (MegaLD required)

Hyperion   Taito   4 $25
A space shooter considered by many to be among Taito's best
for the system, six stages just aren't enough to satisfy hardcore
gamers. And while it may be lacking in certain areas, namely
graphics, this title is relatively easy to find for the system.
(MegaLD required)

I Will: The Story of London   Pioneer   4 $30
In this full motion video RPG about an time generator that has
been stolen, you play the part of Catherine Holmes. You will
help investigate the theft of the generator, on the first side of the
LD, while side 2 of the disc will take you to Britain's most popular sightseeing spots. (MegaLD required)

Manhattan Requiem   Riverhill Soft   4 $40
This is the first in the "JB Harold series". (LD-ROM2 required)

Melon Brains   Pioneer/Multimedia Creators Network
                                              5 $25
A study of dolphins, side A will take you through an archive of
dolphin images while side B, Dolphin Odyssey, provides footage
of where dolphins live and their environments. Both U.S. and
Japanese versions were released, but only in their respective
languages. (MegaLD required)

Pyramid Patrol   Taito   4 $30
Considered the best shooter for LaserActive by many (maybe
because everyone has it), you take command of a space craft
and shoot the incoming missiles. It is simply a matter of memo-
rizing where the shots come from and going through the pyramid inside. The levels are moderately hard, but the last boss is
decidedly very difficult. (MegaLD required)

Quiz Econosaurus   Hudson Soft   4 $25
An environmental quiz game by Hudson Soft, it is divided into 6
sections (Earth, Land, See, Air, etc.) Since this was originally a
Japanese version, some "correct answers" are questionable by
Western standards. Proceeds from the sales of this game were
go the World Wildlife Fund. (LD-ROM2 required)

Road Prosecutor   Taito   5 $45

One of the most sought after titles, this is basically a racing game using Dragon's Lair type control. Once you follow all of the commands properly, you advance to the next stage. This title becomes very difficult toward the end however. (MegaLD required)

Rocket Coaster   Taito   5 $30

This racing game is one in which the pre-recorded tracks will actually end the game if a level is not finished in time. Also, control seems very jumpy on this game, as over-steering is often a problem. (MegaLD required)

Space Berserker   Pioneer   6 $40

Similar to Hyperion, in each mission you are to clear a specified area full of battle ships. The main complaint about this game is its short length, only 3 stages long. But the game play is solid and the graphics are among the best for the system. (MegaLD required)

Triadstone   Sega   4 $35

Sega's only title, but also one of the best, this is basically a Dragon's Lair clone, but one that is very well done. There are 8 levels in total, but the last 3 levels are extremely difficult. You will have to memorize the commands and time them perfectly in order to finish this game. (MegaLD required)

Vajra   Pioneer   4 $30

The first game for the LD-ROM2 at launch, a 3D shooter that no one else attempted, you will fly through the city with the goal of destroying any robots along your way. There are five stages in total, with the last 2 being very difficult to master. But with enough practice, it simply becomes a matter of knowing the upcoming enemy positions. (LD-ROM2 required)

3-D Goggles   Pioneer   8 $325

These goggles are installed into the Laseractive system via the adapter built for this purpose. It is extremely difficult to find this piece of hardware in working condition and complete however. And while this enormous price is often demanded in the U.S., Japanese versions of these goggles can often be purchased, unopened, for less than $100.

Karaoke Module   Pioneer   4 $40

This module was packaged with a microphone and enables the use of thousands of existing karaoke LD's, most of which are manufactured in China and Japan.

LD-ROM2 Module   Pioneer   7 $130

This module is used to add the capability of playing TG-16, TG-CD and Super CD games. Of important note is the fact that this module will accept the Arcade Card Pro by NEC, but it is EXTREMELY difficult to remove, and may require disassembly of the unit in order to extract it.

MegaLD Module   Pioneer   4 $70

This module is used to add the capability of playing Genesis, Megadrive, Sega CD and MegaLD games.

HARDWARE

LaserActive System   Pioneer   4 $200

It is important to note that this system only plays Laserdiscs and CD's without the addition of additional modules.

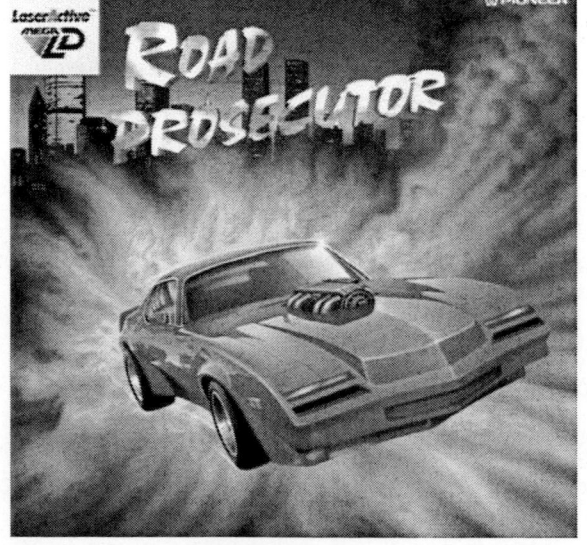

Road Prosecutor

Triad Stone

Can you name the first console to have "online capabilities?"

RDI Halcyon

By: Michael Collins

One meaning of the word "halcyon" is "golden." Unfortunately for the creators of the RDI Halcyon, there was nothing golden about the short life of this system. It was way ahead of its time, and this is probably what killed it off so quickly. Released to small markets as early as 1984, and later to larger markets in 1985, the Halcyon was priced at over $2,000. Obviously, a price tag like this for a LaserDisc player/interactive machine was not attractive to most consumers at the time. Because of this, the system didn't even last to the end of 1985, and sadly, only two games were actually released for it.

The system itself is, as stated previously, a LaserDisc player. A keyboard was available for the unit, and a microphone headset was used for voice recognition. Unfortunately, neither of these peripherals saw much use due to the fact that the Halcyon's library was, and would remain, almost non-existent.

Packaged with the Halcyon was a game that did use the voice recognition capabilities of the system: Thayer's Quest. Players made decisions in this action game via the keyboard, and watched animated sequences play onscreen. The only other game that was actually released for the system was a football game: Raiders vs. Chargers. Though it does use real game footage in interesting ways, the price tag of just under $100 didn't drive consumers to purchase the game, after having spent several thousand on the system itself.

Several other games other than the two released were in the works or even finished. There was a planned sequel to Raiders vs. Chargers, called Dallas vs. Washington. Several titles were little more than interactive software, as opposed to true "games." A good example of this would be The Spirit of Whittier Mansion.

The Halcyon could have actually been a great console. The power under its hood could easily bring the arcade experience home, but the lack of third-party support, the financial troubles of RDI and the ridiculously high price of the machine doomed it before it was even released.

The Atari 2600, with the modem available from GameLine.

HAL

RELEASED GAMES

of North America.

Raiders vs. Chargers   RDI   9 $250
This title was actually more of an interactive football title than a game, because it used actual footage from a Raiders vs. Chargers NFL game. Because of this, it was very limited in what could be done -- most of the "game" is simply watching video of plays that were chosen. In the arcades, this game was simply titled "NFL Football." The planned sequel to this game (Dallas vs. Washington) was never released.

Thayer's Quest   RDI   9 $200
This game was a "pack-in" game for the Halcyon. In it, players must return five relics to essentially save the world from a crazed wizard. The graphics are much different than that of Raiders vs. Chargers -- it looks like a cartoon rather than real video footage. Also of note: this game uses the Halcyon's voice synthesis.

HARDWARE

RDI Halcyon   RDI   9 $1800

PLANNED RELEASES

The notes on these unreleased games are from research, not actual gameplay.

Dallas vs. Washington   RDI
The Planned sequel to Raiders vs. Chargers which was never released.

Orpheus   RDI
Orpheus is set in a classic Greek mythological world. In it, players must guide Orpheus to bring his friend Eurydice back to life.

Shadow of the Stars   RDI
Shadow of the Stars is set far in the future, and somewhere among nine planets is destiny. The graphics look very much like a cartoon, as several Halcyon titles do.

Spirit of Whittier Mansion, The
           RDI
This is an interactive horror title, in which a newlywed couple spends the night in a haunted mansion.

Voyage to the New World   RDI
Voyage to the New World is basically a quest to find the lost explorer John Cabot, who is somewhere in the uncharted land

Raiders vs. Chargers (Screenshot)

Thayer's Quest (Screenshot)

Sunday Funday was the last cartridge ever released for the NES.

Sega Master System
By: Michael Collins

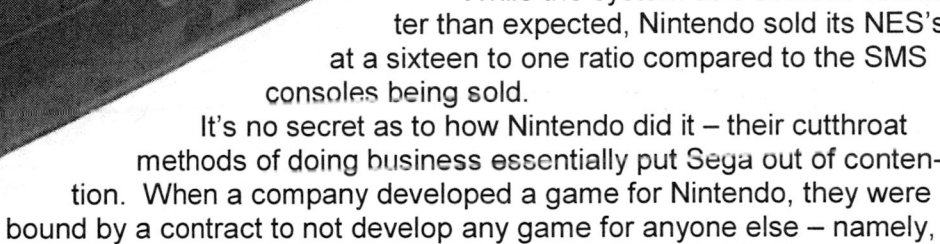

Soon after the ground-shaking release of Nintendo's NES in the States, Sega released what they dubbed the "Master System." At launch (June of 1986), the Master System was priced at $200.

While the system sold somewhat better than expected, Nintendo sold its NES's at a sixteen to one ratio compared to the SMS consoles being sold.

It's no secret as to how Nintendo did it – their cutthroat methods of doing business essentially put Sega out of contention. When a company developed a game for Nintendo, they were bound by a contract to not develop any game for anyone else – namely, Sega. After a few short years, Nintendo had near complete domination of the video game market, and in 1987, Sega's CEO, Hayao Nakayama, arranged for the marketing rights for the Master System to be sold to Tonka. However, this really did nothing for Sega, Tonka, or the Master System. Tonka didn't do much to help the console, and Sega lacked the funds to do anything either.

Several variations of the Master System consoles do exist. First, there is the most common version which was released at launch, and usually included a light gun and Hang-On/Safari Hunt. This version of the hardware had the standard cartridge slot on top, coupled by the slot for card games near the controller ports. These "card" games resemble TurboGrafx-16 HuCards, and while they have less storage capacity for game code than the SMS cartridges, they are extremely convenient.

Later, in 1990, Sega reacquired the full rights to their Master System, and everything that went along with it. They then released a stripped down, sleeker-looking version of the Master System, which they creatively dubbed the "Master System II." Alex Kidd in Miracle World was built into the console, but this version SMS did have its flaws. There was no expansion port, no reset button, and most importantly, there was no game card slot.

Outside of America, the SMS had more success. In Europe, Sega continued production of the Master System until 1996. In Brazil, several other variations of the SMS hardware were released under the Tec Toy license, including the Master System III, which was essentially Master System II in a new case. A pink Master System, dubbed the "Sega Master System Girl," was targeted at female gamers, and is extremely hard to come across. Several new games were released well into the 90's as well, including Virtua Fighter Animation and Super Street Fighter II.

The Master System's controller was pretty standard. While it was essentially the same two-button design as the NES's revolutionary design, it was no longer anything new. The original control pads did have small joysticks that screwed into the control pads, but these were quickly discontinued because of complaints from parents that they were hazardous to small children.

Very few peripherals were released for the Master System, and only one that saw mass

Of those polled, 78% said they were disappointed with the storyline in Metal Gear Solid 2.

SMS

production was really very unique. The Light Phaser was comparable to the NES's light gun, and in fact was released because of the popularity of Duck Hunt on the NES. The Light Phaser really wasn't anything special, but the 3D glasses that were released for the Master System were. Games like Zaxxon 3D and Space Harrier 3D brought gamers experiences that were, for the time, unreal.

While the SMS is a very entertaining system to own and collect for, its ultimate demise was due to not only the marketing strategy of Sega and Tonka, but also due to the restrictions on developers by Nintendo. It really is sad to see how poorly the Master System did in America, especially when one looks at what games were released in other countries of the world. The release list here in America may be small, but it's a good one. Quality titles litter it, and if you're an import collector, the SMS has even more to offer you.

***Note: Due to the durability of the snap cases included with Sega Master System games, the prices and rarities should be used with the assumption that the games are complete, including at the very least the box, but should also include the manual.

A pink (and portable) version of the SMS was made available in Brazil, and titled SMS-Girl.

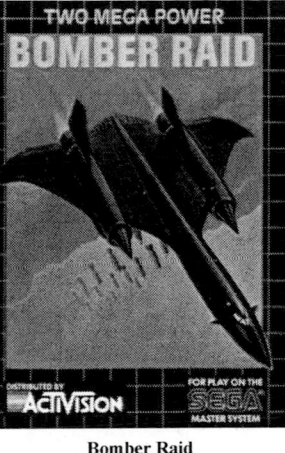

After Burner   Alex Kidd in Shinobi World   Aztec Adventure   Bomber Raid

Action Fighter   Sega   3 $5
Action Fighter is one of the harder games on the Master System. However, its arcade-style gameplay and colorful graphics keep it interesting. If you haven't played this game yet, it is worth looking into.

Aerial Assault   Sega   4 $15
Aerial Assault is another of the extremely impressive graphical masterpieces on the Master System. It is a side-scrolling shooter, and although it was somewhat of a late release, it is certainly a very solid game all-around.

Afterburner   Sega   3 $7
At the time of its release, Afterburner was revolutionary because of its 3D graphics and blazing speed. Although it is nothing amazing compared to the games of today, Afterburner is still an amazingly addictive shooter, with great arcade-style gameplay. Try this one out if you haven't already.

Alex Kidd: Lost Stars   Sega   3 $10
Bright graphics and strangely addictive gameplay make this Alex Kidd game a decent one, but not necessarily the best in the series. Also of note: the music in this game is incredible.

Alex Kidd: High Tech World
                         Sega   4 $15
As a video game, this one is fairly good. As an Alex Kidd game, however, it doesn't quite stand up as high as it could (and probably should) have. The graphics are nice, the sound is decent, and although they won't be wowed, fans of the Alex Kidd series will be satisfied.

Alex Kidd: Miracle World   Sega   2 $8
Alex Kidd in Miracle World is yet another incredibly addictive and engrossing platformer for the Sega Master System. Great graphics, cool puzzles, and solid gamelpay make this a game that no Master System fanatic should miss out on.

Alex Kidd: Shinobi World   Sega   7 $45
Although it did not see the widespread distribution that some of the other Alex Kidd games did, Alex Kidd in Shinobi World was and is a blast. It makes several obvious references to another SMS game (Shinobi, of course), and does so in a somewhat comical way. This game is easy, but addictive and all kinds of fun.

Alf   Sega   6 $20
Do not play this game. It is just horribly boring. Although the graphics and sound are close to average for the Master System,

the gameplay is simply horrid. Even the coolness of Alf himself cannot save this poor excuse for a platformer.

Alien Syndrome   Sega   4 $15
Although saving hostages and killing the aliens that are endangering them can be amusing for a while, it doesn't last forever. The graphics in this game are decent and the gameplay simple.

Altered Beast   Sega   4 $15
Side-scrolling beat-'em-ups can be a blast, and this is one of the decent ones on the Master System, but Altered Beast was much better on the Genesis, plain and simple. Player and enemy sprites are fairly large, and the graphics are solid.

Astro Warrior   Sega   3 $7
While it does lack the depth and longevity of a game like Phantasy Star, Astro Warrior does have its strong points. Graphics and sound are decent, and the gameplay is great. This game is easy to get into, easy to put back down, and perfect for the short gaming sessions we all have.

Aztec Adventure   Sega   3 $7
Even the bright, cartoony graphics and catchy (yet repetitive) music of this game don't really make it a game that is worthwhile. However, it can be mildly amusing at parties, if someone dresses up as the main character, Niño.

Black Belt   Sega   1 $5
Black Belt is very, very similar to Kung Fu on the NES. It is fun for a while, but simply punching and kicking the same enemies over and over again is only enjoyable for so long. The graphics and sound are decent.

Blade Eagle 3D   Sega   2 $5
Blade Eagle 3D is one of the cooler games that use the SMS's 3D glasses. It is a space shooter, and is a lot of fun. The 3D graphics are great, and work well with the game. Unlike some of the 3D SMS games, Blade Eagle 3D requires them, rather than just supporting them.

Bomber Raid   Activision   4 $15
Bomber Raid is a bottom-to-top scrolling shooter. It has nice, tight control, great graphics, and decent music. Different types of weapons and enemies keep things interesting. Recommended.

Buster Douglas Boxing   Sega   8 $50
For boxing fans, Buster Douglas Boxing is the only choice on the Master System aside from Rocky. Buster Douglas Boxing is

nothing more than average -- graphically and otherwise. The controls are decent, and the ability to customize the fighters is nice, but it just isn't all that amazing overall.

California Games   Sega   3 $10
With only a few events to participate in, and none of them being very exciting or even remotely interesting, this game should be avoided by all means necessary. For fans of multiple-event games, the NES's World Events is a much better choice.

Captain Silver   Sega   3 $8
Nice graphics, great music, and solid gameplay make Captain Silver a game that shouldn't be missed. Players can even purchase items in stores to help their character. Captain Silver is certainly one of the deeper side-scrollers on the Master System.

Casino Games   Sega   3 $7
Although the pinball mode is enjoyable for a little while, even that couldn't keep Casino Games from being what the average casino-based video game is: boring. Still, it is more fun than many in the genre, like the infamous (and ridiculously expensive) Panesian games.

Castle of Illusion   Sega   7 $35
Side-scrolling platformers don't get much better than this. Bright, cartoony graphics and solid gameplay make Castle of Illusion (which stars Disney's own mouse duo: Mickey and Minnie) a game that is certainly worth looking for.

Choplifter   Sega   2 $5
While the graphics and sounds aren't up to par with the arcade original, Choplifter is still a good port. The main draw to this game is the arcade feel and arcade gameplay.

Cloud Master   Sega   3 $8
Although Cloud Master does have a very small number of good qualities, this game should probably be avoided by most. The graphics could have been good had there been more variation in them, and the same goes for the gameplay. Stick with Fantasy Zone for your side-scrolling shooting needs.

Columns   Sega   4 $15
What is there to say, really? If you haven't played this game yet and have even thought about liking puzzle games, you need to own this one. Bright, colorful graphics, very appropriate music, and a great balance of simplicity and complexity make Columns a puzzle game that no gamer should be without.

Cyborg Hunter   Activision   5 $20

Cyborg Hunter is a typical alien-killing game. The graphics, sound, and most everything else are all very average. However, the main thing that brings this game down are the controls - they feel very clumsy and awkward at times.

Dead Angle   Sega   3 $8
Dead Angle is one of the more unique games for the Master System. It is a shooter, and although difficult, it can be a lot of fun. The graphics are nice, and different than most games of the time. Good luck finding a copy, though.

Dick Tracy   Sega   5 $20
"Uninspiring," "uneventful," and "unoriginal" are all words that can be used to describe this game. Although the graphics and colors are appropriate for a Dick Tracy game, this beat-'em-up (with guns) side-scroller was and is too boring to be worth purchasing for anything more than a collector's showcase.

Double Dragon   Sega   1 $5
Double Dragon is, as always, a blast. Although the storyline is completely unoriginal, the other elements of the game make up for it and more. Unlike many other beat-'em-ups of the time, players can pick up weapons to use against the baddies. Also of note is the interesting plot twist at the end of the two-player game. Definitely recommended.

E-SWAT   Sega   3 $10
Side-scrolling games were common in the days of the SMS and NES, and E-SWAT is another of them. It isn't anything amazing, but this game is a good challenge at the very least.

Enduro Racer   Sega   3 $10
Enduro racer is one of those games that is is easy to find yourself saying, "One more time!" over and over again. The 3/4 view (much like that of Paperboy) is perfect for this game. Enduro Racer is similar to Excitebike on the NES, but it has better and more varied graphics, deeper gameplay (bikes can be upgrades), and overall better single player mode.

F-16 Falcon (Card)   Sega   2 $5
A simple graphical style lets this game focus on the in-cockpit flying action of this game. And though limited in both scope and performance, the HUD really gives a realistic feel to an otherwise simple game.

Fantasy Zone   Sega   3 $8
Bright, colorful graphics, very catchy tunes, and surprisingly addictive gameplay make Fantasy Zone one of the best side-scrolling shooters on the SMS. Don't be fooled by the cutesy

Captain Silver   Double Dragon   Enduro Racer   F-16 Fighting Falcon

Major League Baseball for the Mattel Intellivision was the first game to ever depict dust.

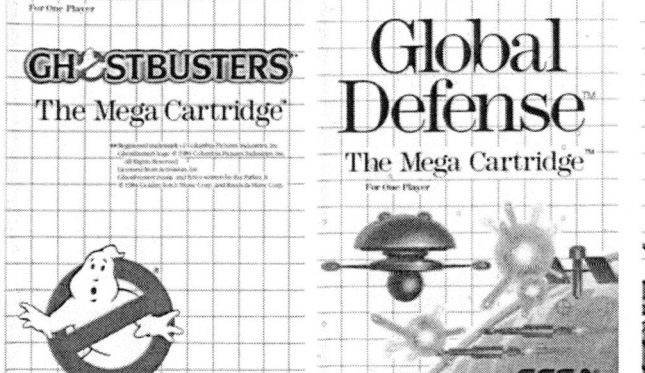

Ghostbusters   Global Defense

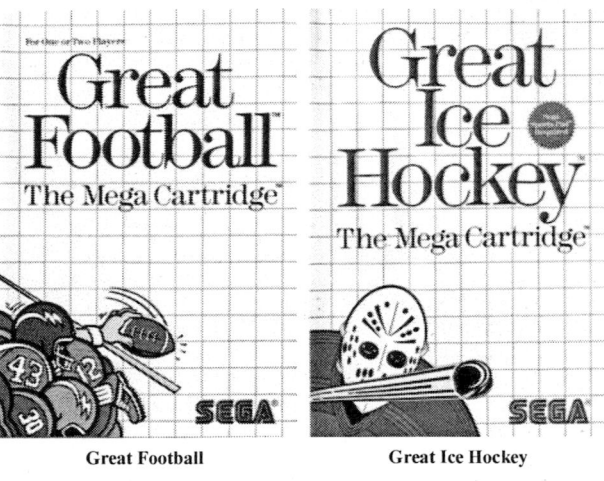

Great Football   Great Ice Hockey

graphics, though: this game is a real challenge. Players also have the ability to upgrade their ships, adding a lot of depth and longevity to the game.

Fantasy Zone 2   Sega   3 $12
Fantasy Zone 2 is extremely similar to its predecessor. The graphics are still so ridiculously bright that it feels as if the game is on LSD, but the fun (and challenging) gameplay remains intact. Shooting fans will not be disappointed.

Fantasy Zone 3: The Maze   Sega   4 $15
If you enjoyed Pac-Man, enjoyed Fantasy Zone, and the prospect of playing a hybrid of the two sounds promising to you, you just might enjoy the third installment to the Fantasy Zone series. Although it is essentially Pac-Man with weapons and brighter colors, Fantasy Zone: The Maze is certainly a nice departure from the standard Fantasy Zone style game.

Galaxy Force   Activision   4 $10

Gangster Town   Sega   3 $7
Gangster Town is pretty much another typical light phaser game. There is however a nice two-player cooperative mode. As for the graphics and sound: they are a little bit above average, and not much more.

Ghost House (Card)   Sega   2 $5
Although the story is fairly unoriginal, Ghost House is still an above average game. The (somewhat repetitive) gameplay is enjoyable, and although they aren't incredible, the graphics are nice.

Ghostbusters   Sega   2 $5
Ghostbusters has to be one of the most boring and uneventful games on the Master System. Other than the great music, there really is no reason to play this game. The graphics and confusing gameplay are both too boring to bear.

Ghouls and Ghosts   Sega   4 $15
This is a port of the arcade title, and although it was released late in the SMS's lifecycle, it is still relatively common due to a large number having been produced.

Global Defense   Sega   3 $7

Golden Axe   Sega   4 $10
The Genesis port of this arcade smash-hit is a better one, but for a Master System game, Golden Axe is amazing. The character sprites are huge, sounds are perfect, and although the

game does feel a little choppy, it is still a blast.

Golden Axe Warrior   Sega   6 $35
As far as RPG's go on the SMS, gamers were treated. Not only did they get the amazing and revolutionary Phantasy Star, but Golden Axe Warrior (a blatant rip off of Nintendo's Legend of Zelda) was released as well. Solid gameplay and a convincing storyline make this a game not to be missed.

Golvellius: Valley of Doom   Sega   4 $15

Great Baseball   Sega   2 $4
Ironically, Great Baseball really isn't very great at all. The pitching and batting systems are actually pretty good, as are the graphics. However, the fielding and base-running elements of play are horrible. Fielding is slow, and base-running is fast. It just seems like the opposite of what it should be. Oh, and the sound effects for the crowd are horrendous.

Great Basketball   Sega   2 $4
Since this is really the only choice for basketball gaming on the SMS, it is probably the best. Sadly, the "best" isn't all that great. While it is solid for an 8-bit basketball game, is hasn't stood against the test of time.

Great Football   Sega   2 $4

Great Golf   Sega   2 $4
Great Golf is a fairly decent game. It's no Hot Shots Golf, but for the SMS, it is pretty good. There was close attention paid to detail of the actual golfing elements of the game when Great Golf was made. Overall, it's pretty fun, but can be frustrating.

Great Ice Hockey   Sega   2 $4
This game is really bad. For one thing, the graphics are very weak. However, the main problem with this game is that the controls are seriously messed up. About the only good thing about Great Ice Hockey is the music.

Great Soccer   Sega   2 $4

Great Volleyball   Sega   3 $5
Great Volleyball is one of the better games in Sega's series of "great" sports titles on the SMS. It does take a lot of practice to be good at this game, and thankfully, there is a practice mode. Bright graphics and music add to this game as well.

Hang On / Astro Warrior   Sega   1 $3
As with Hang On / Safari Hunt, both games on the Hang On /

Where was the hammer hidden in the NES game The Adventures of Link?

Astro Warrior cart are great ones, but neither will take up the kind of time a good RPG does. Hang On is a repetitive, but fun, motorcycle racer, and Astro Warrior is a space shooter which is also repetitive, but lots of fun can be had with it.

Hang On / Safari Hunt   Sega   1 $3
Both of the games included on this cart are good ones, but neither is anything that will take up twenty hours or more of your time. Hang On is a repetitive, but fun, motorcycle racer, and Safari Hunt is an average light phaser shooting game.

Joe Montana Football   Sega   5 $15
For the time, this game was amazing. The only thing really lacking about it was decent sounds. Otherwise, this is a great football game, and certainly better than Great Football. There are lots of teams to play as and many, many plays to run. Excellent.

Kenseiden   Sega   3 $12
Kenseiden is another great side-scrolling action game on the SMS. It is somewhat similar to Shinobi, but instead of a ninja, players take control of a samurai warrior. As opposed to a game like My Hero, where players are limited to only a few moves, Hayato (the game's main character) has many attacks at his disposal.

King's Quest: Quest for the Crown
**   Parker Brothers   4 $15**
King's Quest isn't for everyone. The game is a sort of puzzle RPG, with a pretty good storyline. However, it is extremely challenging, and can be very, very frustrating to play.

Kung Fu Kid   Sega   2 $5
Kung Fu Kid is actually a very good game, despite the fact that it has absolutely no storyline whatsoever. In each level, players must make their way through a maze, and at the end of the maze, fight a final boss. This is actually very challenging, especially after the first few levels of the game. Graphics and music are above average.

Lord of the Sword   Sega   2 $8
This game is really bad. For one thing, is is an (action) RPG with no save function, which really takes away from the game. Secondly, the most important part of the game - the action - is slow, boring, and feels like more of a chore than anything even remotely enjoyable.

Marksman Shooting / Trap Shooting
**   Sega   2 $7**

Maze Hunter 3D   Sega   3 $10
For the puzzle gamer, Maze Hunter 3D is a must-own. The game takes a while to get into, but can be a lot of fun once you get the hang of it. As is obvious by this game's title, it supports the 3D glasses.

Michael Jackson's Moonwalker
**   Sega   6 $30**
It's surprising that Michael Jackson still has any fans at all today, but even more surprising is that a video game with his name on it was actually released. Michael Jackson's Moonwalker has some comic (and for some, nostalgic,) value, but that's about it.

Miracle Warriors: Seal of the Dark Lord
**   Sega   3 $18**
Although it isn't on the same level of greatness that Phantasy Star is, Miracle Warriors is still an above average RPG. It does take a while to get into, but after the initial hump, Miracle Warriors can be fairly engrossing.

Missile Defense 3D   Sega   2 $7
Where most of the light phaser games available for the Master System are completely unoriginal, Missile Defense 3D surprisingly is not. Using the 3D glasses, shooting games on the SMS were brought to a whole new level of ingenuity with the release of this game.

Monopoly   Sega   3 $12
If you liked the board game, stick to the board game (unless, of course, if you want to play against the computer). Essentially, this game is an exact port of the board game original, but unfortunately doesn't feel quite the same.

Montezuma's Revenge   Parker Brothers   4 $20

My Hero (Card)   Sega   2 $7
Even though the enemies in My Hero repeat themselves often (as common as in most beat-'em-ups), this is still a very solid game. The speed is just right, the graphics crisp, and the presentation good. Check this game out if you haven't done so yet.

Ninja, The   Sega   2 $4
       The Ninja is probably one of the worst games available for the SMS. It is an action game, and could have been many times better than it is if it weren't so ridiculously difficult. Still, it does have decent graphics and great music.

King's Quest: Quest for the Crown   Lord of the Sword   Michael Jackson's Moonwalker   Miracle Warriors: Seal of the Dark Lord

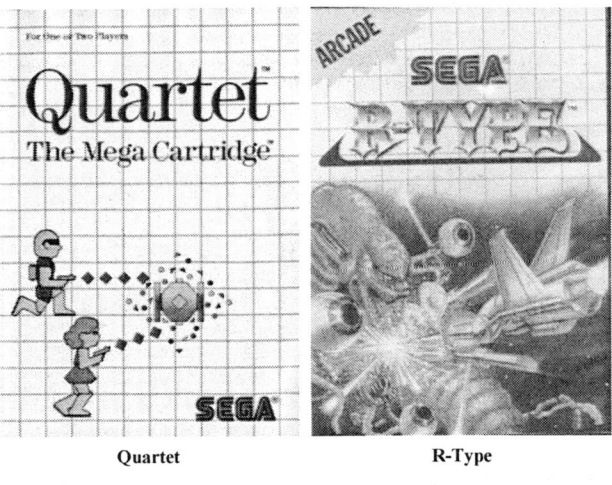

| Out Run 3-D | Phantasy Star | Quartet | R-Type |

Out Run   Sega   2 $7

For racing game fans, Out Run is a must-own. It isn't quite arcade-perfect, but the SMS version is still an excellent port of the original. Gameplay, graphics, and music combine to make one of the better games available for Sega's classic system.

Paperboy   Sega   3 $10

This game is a true classic. It takes what is usually a chore (delivering the daily newspaper to the neighbors) and makes it all kinds of fun. Paperboy uses the rather uncommon 3/4 view, which is very appropriate for a game like this. Always fun to pull out once in a while.

Parlour Games   Sega   4 $15

Actually a collection of games, this title includes both darts and pool.

Penguin Land   Sega   3 $10

Hardcore puzzle fans who have mastered Columns will be pleased with this title as it is extremely challenging and puts gameplay over graphics. Penguin and puzzle game fans alike will be pleased.

Phantasy Star   Sega   6 $45

Phantasy Star is considered by many to be the best SMS game of all time, and it is certainly one of the best RPG's of all time. The game was simply amazing as compared to many games of its day, with revolutionary 3D dungeons, more than fifty hours of playtime, and much, much more.

Poseiden Wars 3D   Sega   3 $8

Power Strike (Black & White Label)
     Sega   7 $45

Power Strike is another great shooter for the SMS. Addictive gameplay is the main reason to play this game, and the nice graphics, sound, and bonus weapons are just a few of the extras included on the cart. The B&W label version was a Sega Club exclusive and is very difficult to find.

Power Strike (Blue Label)   Sega   5 $20

This version was made available to the general public and is much more common, yet the game itself is identical to the one above.

Pro Wrestling   Sega   2 $5

With a surprisingly large number of moves available and some cool Mexican wrestlers to play as, Pro Wrestling is worth trying out. Nice music and the ability to tag team are added in bo-

nuses. However, after playing wrestling and fighting games of today, this game does feel very repetetive, very fast. Still, it is good fun for a few rounds.

Psycho Fox   Sega   4 $20

Psycho Fox is a pretty typical platformer, and for being completely unoriginal, it loses points for that. Besides this, the controls are just a pain in the wazoo to master. The cutesy graphics and music just can't save this one.

Quartet   Sega   4 $15

Quartet is a fairly decent side-scrolling shooter/platformer. The graphics and sound are great, and very fitting for the game. However, the controls don't feel quite right. In particular, jumping feels very "floaty."

R-Type   Sega   2 $0

Along with RPG's, the SMS does shooters best, and R-Type is a perfect example of this. The game is challenging, has cool bosses and weapons, and is an overall great translation of the arcade original.

Rambo III   Sega   2 $5

Rambo III is yet another light phaser game. As for the gameplay: you already know exactly what it's like in reading that. Thankfully, this game is challenging, and is one of the best-looking SMS light phaser games available.

Rambo Blood Part II   Sega   2 $5

Rambo II has oftentimes been compared to Ikari Warriors on the NES, and for good reasons. The object of the game is simple: kill everything in sight. Although this is a blast for a while, it does eventually get too repetitive to bear.

Rampage   Activision   4 $18

This is the game that started it all: an entire series of games based solely on the mindless, yet incredibly satisfying, destruction of everything in sight. While racking up high scores in single player mode is a blast, it is even more fun with a friend.

Rastan   Sega   3 $10

Rastan could have been many times better if not for the horrible controls. It has a very arcade-like feel, nice graphics, and incredible music. The game is a hack-'n'-slash platformer that had a lot of potential, but as stated above suffers too much from poor controls.

R.C. Grand Prix   Seismic   3 $10

Even though it is a blatant and complete rip-off of RC Pro Am,

A hack of the early NES game Duck Hunt is available on the internet, in which you can shoot your dog when he laughs at you for missing.

RC Grand Prix is a decent game. It has nice graphics and fairly interesting gameplay, since vehicles can be upgraded. However, this type of game only lasts for so long before it gets old.

Reggie Jackson Baseball   Sega   1 $5
This is quite possibly the best baseball game on the SMS (of only two that were released domestically). It has crisp graphics, is fun to play, and has a nice extra mode: a home run contest.

Rescue Mission   Sega   3 $8
Missile Defense 3D aside, Rescue Mission is the most unique light phaser game available for SMS gamers. Rather than simply blasting objects or enemies, players must protect on-screen characters. Very interesting and refreshing, as compared to many light phaser games.

Rocky   Sega   2 $5
Since the only other choice for a boxing game on the SMS is Buster Douglas Boxing, Rocky at least deserves a round or two. If nothing else, it does have detailed graphics and very fitting music.

Shanghai   Sega   2 $7
While it isn't as good as Shanghai Triple Threat on the 3DO, that can't be expected of a SMS game, either. For puzzle gamers, Shanghai is still an excellent choice. For those unfamiliar with the game, it is a sort of solitaire game with tiles. It must be played to be understood.

Shinobi   Sega   3 $10
Although the graphics of Shinobi aren't as good as those of Strider, the game as a whole is much better. It is an arcade port of the popular ninja action game, and the arcade feel is intact. While it is simple, it is still all kinds of fun.

Shooting Gallery   Sega   1 $5
As far as light phaser games go, Shooting Gallery is a great one. It has a wide variety of things to shoot, from ducks to balloons. For fans of this type of game, Shooting Gallery is a must-own.

Slap Shot   Sega   4 $10
Oftentimes, sports games just do not age very well. Slap Shot is one of those games. Although the prospect of playing hockey on your SMS may sound as cool as ice, this game is just too slow and easy to be worth much playtime.

Sonic the Hedgehog   Sega   6 $30
It's too bad that this game saw such a late release on the Master System. Sonic the Hedgehog could have done for the SMS what Super Mario Bros. did for the NES, but just came out too late. As for the game itself: it's a high-speed action platformer, starring Sonic, everyone's favorite blue hedgehog.

Space Harrier   Sega   3 $10
Even though some consider the 3D version to be better, Space Harrier is still one of the best shooters available for the SMS. It has nice, clean graphics, a pseudo-3D perspective (much like that of Afterburner), and some of the best music on the SMS.

Space Harrier 3-D   Sega   5 $20
Space Harrier 3D features support for the Master System's 3D glasses, and some nice, new background graphics. The game can also be played in 2D mode, for those without the glasses. But containing more than just the 3-D upgrades, many consider this title to be a true sequel to the first installment. As with the original, Space Harrier 3D is fun, but gets repetitive.

SpellCaster   Sega   4 $15
While many side-scrolling action games of the day had ridiculously simple (if existent) storylines, the story in Spellcaster is actually very interesting. While there are some control issues, practice can make perfect. Decent graphics and very fitting music are icing on the cake.

Spiderman   Sega   6 $25
Suffering from many of the same problems other Spiderman-based games have, this platformer is something to stay away from, unless you're a huge fan of the spider dude himself. Although the graphics are gorgeous, the control problems are too glaring to be overlooked.

Sports Pad Football   Sega   2 $5

Spy vs. Spy (Card)   Sega   2 $7
Quite obviously based on the Mad comic strip, the object of this game is to simply blow up your opponent. Spy vs. Spy is average as a single-player game, and a little bit above average as a two-player game.

Strider   Sega   5 $25
For an arcade conversion, Strider is pretty good (although the Genesis version is better). It is a ninja action game with nice, vibrant graphics and decent sound.

Super Monaco Grand Prix   Sega   3 $10
If you like games like Out Run, you might enjoy this one. However, it is very similar to many racing games of the day: it is

Shanghai   Space Harrier 3-D

SpellCaster   Spy vs. Spy

To date, most still believe the SMS 3D glasses to be the best available for any console.

| Thunder Blade | Walter Payton Football |

| Where in the World is Carmen Sandiego? | Y's: The Vanished Omens |

extremely repetitive.

Super Tennis (Card)   Sega   2 $7
Since it is rather old, it is excusable that this game has very few ways of increasing replay value. There is only one opponent, and this takes a significant chunk away from Super Tennis. This is a very average tennis game, and there isn't much else to say about it.

Teddy Boy (Card)   Sega   2 $7
Although Teddy Boy is a pretty unique platformer in the way that enemies are dealt with (they are turned into small balls and collected), the game just isn't all that great. Teddy Boy is sort of like a cake with too much icing -- too sweet to handle. There just isn't enough substance in the gameplay, and all the pretty graphics in the world don't make up for that.

Thunder Blade   Sega   4 $10
The SMS is host to a slew of arcade port, and this is one of the better ones. Thunder Blade is a shooter, and just as others on this system, it has awesome gameplay, incredible graphics, and is a good challenge.

Time Soldiers   Sega   4 $15
As a single-player game, Time Soldiers is decent. As a two-player cooperative game though, is is incredibly fun. Time Soldiers is a challenging, somewhat repetitive, game in which players will destroy almost anything and everything they encounter. Try it out, especially with a friend.

TransBot (Card)   Sega   3 $8
Although it isn't quite on the level of R-Type, TransBot is still a great side-scrolling shooter. The sounds, graphics, and gameplay all work well together, and although the game is obviously repetetive, it is still a lot of fun to pull out once in a while.

Vigilante   Sega   2 $7
Vigilante is a pretty typical beat-'em-up. It even has the typical (and very unoriginal) storyline of having to save the girl, who in this case, is named Maria. The graphics and music in this game are great, but the game itself could have been better. The major flaw of Vigilante is the difficulty level -- it's just too hard, and action isn't all that much fun.

Walter Payton Football   Sega   3 $8
As long as you don't need the latest and greatest in 3D graphics or the most recent rosters and franchises, Walter Payton Football deserves some of your football gaming time. It is leagues ahead of games like 10 Yard Fight, and better than Great Foot-

ball as well.

Wanted   Sega   3 $8
Wanted is yet another standard light phaser game. Shooting the baddies and collecting power-ups are pretty much the only things to do in this western-style game, but it is still enjoyable.

Where in the World is Carmen Sandiego?
Parker Brothers   4 $15
If you were a fan of the TV series, you'll probably be a fan of this game. Based upon the same research and search out style of detective work, Where in the World is Carmen Sandiego? is a solid game for a somewhat select audience. It isn't for everybody, but some are sure to be pleased.

WonderBoy   Sega   1 $4
WonderBoy is a great game, plain and simple. If you've never played the game, think about Adventure Island on the NES and you'll have a great idea about what this action platformer is all about. While this (the first) WonderBoy game is a great one, the second and third games in the series are generally considered to be better ones.

WonderBoy III: The Dragon's Trap
Sega   5 $25
WonderBoy III starts off right where the second game in the series left off. The game feels almost identical to its predecessor, but is a little more action oriented. This installment in the series is considered by many to be the best.

WonderBoy: Monster Land
Sega   4 $15
Although it isn't the best action side-scroller of all time, this installment (the second) in the WonderBoy series is one of the best. It is good all-around: solid controls, detailed graphics, and decent sound make it a great game.

World Grand Prix   Sega   4 $15

Y's - Vanished Omens   Sega   5 $25
Similar in style to the Legend of Zelda on the NES, but probably not quite as epic, Y's was one of the many excellent SMS RPG's. It is more action-oriented than some, and although the character sprites are relatively small, the graphics were pretty good considering when it was released.

Zaxxon 3D   Sega   2 $8
Zaxxon 3D captures the arcade feel of the original and does it in 3D, using the Master System's 3D glasses. For those who don't

Many games now carry seizure warnings due to the fact that certain games have caused numerous seizures in Japan.

have the glasses, Zaxxon 3D can be played in a 2D mode.

Zillion   **Sega**   **3**   **$8**
Zillion is yet another shooting game, but rather than being a strict blaster, there are some elements of an action RPG in this game. There are more objectives to complete, areas to explore, and Zillion stays challenging throughout the game.

Zillion 2: Tri Formation   **Sega**   **3**   **$8**
This is more of the same, but many feel that the first title is the better of the two.

HARDWARE

Sega Master System   **Sega**   **2**   **$15**
The original SMS system with cartridge and card slots.

Sega Master System 2   **Sega**   **5**   **$40**
The smaller of the two systems, this later release lacks a card slot.

3-D Glasses   **Sega**   **7**   **$70**
Some of the best console 3-D effects on any system can be utilized with these glasses, though they are becoming very difficult to find.

Controller   **Sega**   **2**   **$5**
Several varieties exist including a very difficult-to-find version with a small joystick on the pad, but this is the basic model without anything in the center of the directional pad.

Control Stick   **Sega**   **4**   **$10**
Gamers found the layout of this stick difficult to use since the stick itself is on the right side of the controller.

Light Phaser   **Sega**   **2**   **$10**
All black and very cool looking, the only fault with this controller is the rigid angle at which the handle makes to the barrel, but otherwise a very good light gun.

Sports Pad   **Sega**   **4**   **$10**
This is a roller ball for the SMS, though it was never really supported very well by any games.

To continue with the medical warnings, some games even contain a, "Consult your doctor before use" warning.

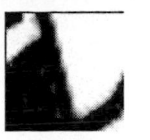

Sega Genesis

By: Lucus Barnes, Michael Collins, & Andy Slaven

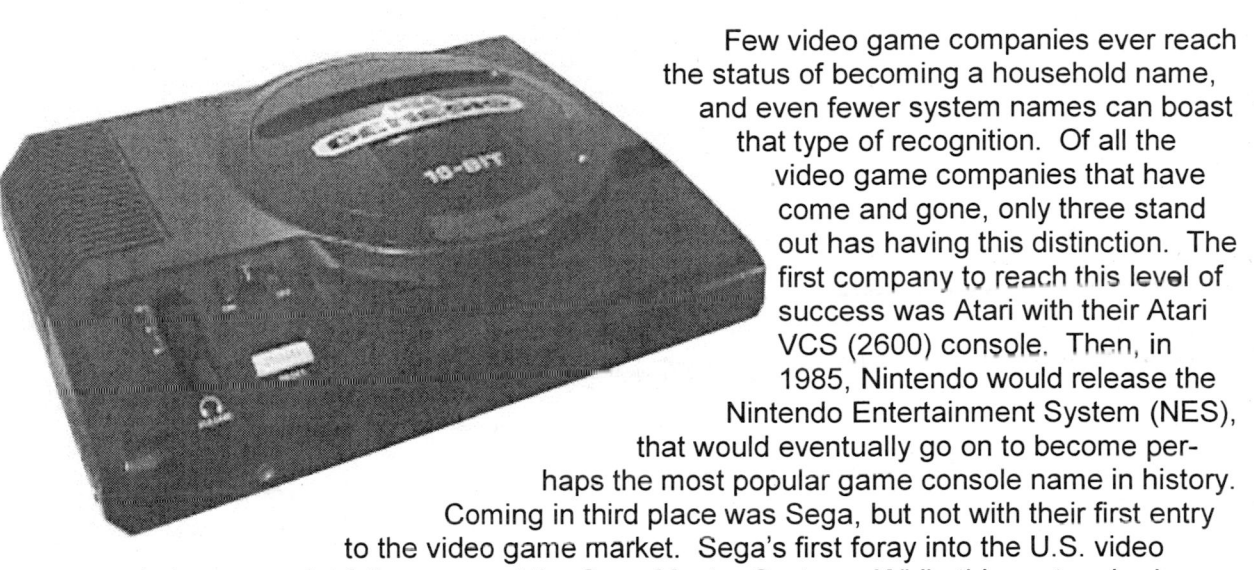

Few video game companies ever reach the status of becoming a household name, and even fewer system names can boast that type of recognition. Of all the video game companies that have come and gone, only three stand out has having this distinction. The first company to reach this level of success was Atari with their Atari VCS (2600) console. Then, in 1985, Nintendo would release the Nintendo Entertainment System (NES), that would eventually go on to become perhaps the most popular game console name in history. Coming in third place was Sega, but not with their first entry to the video game market. Sega's first foray into the U.S. video game market was a quiet failure named the Sega Master System. While this system had many high quality games produced for it, Sega was simply unable to combat Nintendo and their ingenious marketing techniques (read; strong-arm marketing techniques). It wasn't until August of 1989 that Sega would step into the spotlight of video games with the release of the Sega Genesis.

Using the Motorola 68000 processor, the Genesis was as powerful as some computers on the market, and was capable of playing games unlike anything seen on a home console before. The first advertisements that demonstrated this power proudly featured footage of the pack-in game Altered Beast. An arcade title of reasonable success, it would make the transition to the Genesis in fine form, and would amaze gamers who had become used to the graphics on the NES. Convincing these gamers to actually buy the console was a different story however, as most had spent a lot of money on NES games and controllers. In addition to competition from Nintendo, NEC had recently released the TurboGrafx-16 (TG-16), and was also boasting 16-bit technology. At the time, the TG-16's potential for success was still unknown, and Sega was facing an uphill battle.

One thing that Sega had in its favor was the quantity of arcade games that it owned the rights to. Sega was a respected arcade company and had many loyal fans. This would be their primary market for the first year after launch. To keep the owners of the Sega Master System happy, Sega released the Power Base adapter that allowed for SMS games to be played on the Genesis as well.

By 1991, the Genesis was already considered a success, but one game was about to skyrocket the system to the number one position among video game consoles. When Sonic the Hedgehog was released, Sega realized that they had an overnight success on their hands. This game alone was responsible for moving millions of systems, and would strike a nerve among the general video game community that would eventually cause late conformers to upgrade to Sega's newest console. However, 1991 was also the year that Nintendo released

In 1993, 1/3 of all U.S. households owned at least one video game system.

their Super Nintendo Entertainment System (SNES), and Sega had a brand new system to worry about competing with.

As the SNES became more popular, Sega was looking for a way to differentiate itself from Nintendo. The SNES had a large number of high quality games being produced for it, and among them were some of the best RPG's ever made. Sega decided to stick to their strong points and began to develop heavily for various lines of sports titles. History will probably record the Genesis as being a "sports console" for this very reason, and it is certainly true that some of the best sports games ever made for any home console were created for the Genesis.

In October of 1992, Sega released the Sega CD, an add-on console that allowed for the use of CD format games on the system. Nintendo quickly countered with the promise of a CD system of their own, and began working with both Sony and Philips to create a CD-based add-on for the SNES, though it would never materialize.

As the system was growing old, and gamers were beginning to tire of updates to popular sports titles, Sega decided to release a system to hold them over until the release of the Saturn. The Sega 32x was released in November of 1994, but was quickly deemed a complete failure and pulled from store shelves within a year of its release.

The Genesis had lasted for nearly six years by the time the Sega Saturn was released in May of 1995, but this wasn't quite the end of the Genesis' story. In September of 1995, Sony released the Playstation (PSX), a system that would dominate the market for the next five years. The PSX was actually a result of the project started by Nintendo to create a CD-based add on. When Nintendo declared that they no longer had any interest in creating the system, Sony took their hardware design and created this monster of a system. At this point it was a head to head battle between the Sega Saturn and the Sony Playstation, and the Sega Genesis would quietly phase its way into becoming an obsolete system. Though the Genesis would later be re-released in 1997 by Majesco in the form of the Genesis 3, it would never again be considered a mainstream console.

The Sega Genesis is one of many systems that would come and go between 1990 and 1995, one of the most active periods in video game history. With an enormous library of quality games, an amazing array of sports titles, and some of the best RPG's to ever be released in the U.S., the Genesis remains a favorite of many gamers (not just retro-gamers.) It is not uncommon to see a Genesis still hooked to the TV of sports fans, sitting next to their XBox or PS2. It is doubtful that any future system will ever last as an effective game platform for six years, making the Genesis one of the most successful video game consoles in history.

***Note: This section has been compiled and created over a period of years, and is one of the most complex chapters in the VGB guide. Due to the extremely large number of games, and the fact that no Genesis list has ever been constructed without error, it is probable that some mistakes were made in this first printing. If an omission of any game has been made, please contact the VGB staff so that the correction can be made. To date, this is the most complete and most accurate Genesis list of its kind, and the only available rarity/price guide ever created in print for the Genesis.

Can you name the four original Game Informer reviewing staff? (Answers over the next four pages)

| Aerobiz Supersonic | After Burner II | Air Buster | Aladdin |

3 Ninjas Kick Back Sony Imagesoft 3 $5
This is a mediocre platform game based on the equally mediocre feature film of the same name.

6 Pack Sega 3 $5
This handy compilation pack of six classic Genesis games includes Sonic the Hedgehog, Golden Axe, Streets of Rage, Revenge of Shinobi, Columns, and Super Hang-On.

688 Attack Sub Electronic Arts 3 $8
Not a member of your most popular gaming genres, this submarine simulation is nevertheless impressive and is still a great deal of fun to play even today.

Aaahh!!! Real Monsters Viacom 2 $4
The original cartoon series was actually kind of cool in a gross way, but this dull platform game fails to live up to its source material.

Abrams Battletank Electronic Arts 3 $5
This tank game won't appeal to players looking for a quick arcade-style fix, but hard-core simulation fans will probably enjoy it.

Action 52 Active Enterprises 6 $35
This compilation cart might claim to contain 52 separate arcade-style games, but ALL of the pitifully simplistic games on Action 52 play about as well as a bunch of bad Atari 2600 games. Action 52 was also produced in a rare NES version with nearly identical graphics.

Addams Family, The Ocean/Acclaim 2 $2
Based on the movie of the same name, this poor and frustrating platform game will disappoint gamers and movie fans alike.

Addams Family Values Ocean/Acclaim 3 $3
The bad platform "action" of the first Addams Family game was jettisoned in favor of an enjoyable RPG-style game presented from a top-down perspective.

Adventures of Rocky and Bullwinkle, The
 Absolute 4 $10
The original cartoon series is great, but the platform game based on its namesake is a waste of plastic and a perfectly good ROM chip. It seems that some classic cartoon series were made into cool video games... others missed the boat entirely. Rocky and Bullwinkle are still on the dock, waiting for a competent developer to make a good game bearing their likenesses.

Aero The Acrobat Sunsoft 2 $2
Another "better than it has a right to be" Sonic clone, Aero hits the bulls eye in most every category (graphics, control, level design, game play) except for soundtrack (which will drive you crazy.)

Aero The Acrobat 2 Sunsoft 3 $3
This sequel features more of the same great platform action from the original game plus better music. It was followed by a another sequel (of sorts) called Zero the Kamikaze Squirrel

Aerobiz KOEI 6 $25
Have you grown tired of managing cities and theme parks? Well, here is a chance to run an airport. This excellent and complex simulation (it's Koei, you know) has a broader appeal than many of the company's other games and is worth hunting down.

Aerobiz Supersonic KOEI 7 $35
Why mess with success? This "update" to the original airport operations simulator features more options and airplanes. This is the game to get if you have neither, but it's hard to find.

After Burner 2 Sega 3 $6
Ported from the classic "behind the plane" pseudo 3-D shooter, Afterburner 2 is nearly arcade-perfect save for some frame rate and scaling issues.

Air Buster Hudson Soft 4 $8
While not terribly difficult, this awesome horizontal shooter sports impressive graphics, excellent control, and near-perfect gameplay.

Air Diver Asmik/Sega 2 $5
One of the first titles released on the Genesis, this game features a view from inside the cockpit and features graphics very similar in style to those seen in After Burner. The music, while certainly not of high quality sound, is still entertaining if for no other reason than the tracks sampled when a boss is encountered. Land on a flying aircraft carrier between each level in order to refuel and to reload your weapons. Unlike most games of the time though, this title would allow you to try to conquer any section of the world, regardless of the difficulty, in any order you choose. It shouldn't take more than an hour or two to complete this game.

Aladdin Disney/Virgin 2 $4
One of the best-looking platform games ever made for the Genesis, this game is based on the Disney film of the same name and features gorgeous animation (Aladdin was the test

bed for some new graphics techniques) and copious amounts of color. The gameplay isn't bad, either.

Alex Kidd In the Enchanted Castle
Sega   6 $20
This old Master System favorite made an appearance on the Genesis in fine form, featuring all the great platform action the series is known for.

Alien 3   Acclaim   2 $3
The dark and generally boring movie was a BIG disappointment after the stellar Aliens (part 2) flick, but this action/platform game is actually pretty good and features some nice graphics and game play.

Alien Storm   Sega   3 $2
This is a decent (but not great) futuristic Streets of Rage clone ported from an old arcade game.

Alisia Dragoon   Game Arts   4 $10
As action games starring sexy female characters go, this one is entertaining and will hold your interest once you invest some time and effort.

Altered Beast   Sega   1 $1
The Genesis and Turbo Grafx-16 were the among the first home consoles to truly offer an arcade experience at home (some earlier consoles came close, but they hosted far simpler games.) Altered Beast was an inexplicably popular arcade game that was ported over to the Genesis almost perfectly and remains one of its most common "early" titles. Unfortunately, the game itself is pretty weak, a standard side-scrolling action title.

Amazing Tennis   Absolute Entertainment   2 $4
This is your standard run-of-the-mill tennis simulation with average graphics and gameplay.

American Gladiators   Gametek   3 $5
Pretty bad as far as multi-games go, this cart is based on the once-popular television series featuring well- muscled (and digitally oiled) male and female "gladiators" facing off against "normal" contestants.

Andre Agassi Tennis   TecMagik   3 $5
A nice looking tennis game, the actual game play is lacking and creates a substandard experience overall.

Animaniacs   Konami   3 $4
Quite a bit different from its SNES cousin, this platform game

based on the wacky cartoon series adds humor, good graphics, and some puzzles to the otherwise standard mix

Aquatic Games   Electronic Arts   4 $10
It's like a water-based Track and Field game with decent graphics and gameplay.

Arcade Classics   Sega   5 $15
This compilation pack of Centipede, Missile Command, and Ultra Pong is pretty darned archaic by even mid 1990's standards and suffers due to the absence of the original controllers (trackball or paddle.)

Arch Rivals   Midway/Acclaim   2 $2
The gameplay isn't that remarkable, but this popular arcade port laid the foundation for the popular NBA Jam series.

Arcus Odyssey   Sega/Wolf Team   4 $8
This is a well-designed and entertaining isometric shooter with lots of fun action and good graphics (for the period.)

Ariel: The Little Mermaid   Blue Sky/Disney   3 $5
An early Genesis release based on the cartoon feature, Ariel has lovely graphics and solid gameplay (but many of the later Disney games are better.)

Arnold Palmer Tournament Golf
Sega   3 $7
This is an early (and it shows) golfing sim featuring the grandfather of tournament golf.

Arrow Flash   Renovation/Sega   4 $6
We hate to put down a space shooter as we happen to be great fans of the genre, but Arrow Flash doesn't look like much effort was put into the graphics and the gameplay.

Art Alive   Sega   5 $15
Basically Mario Paint for the Genesis, this edutainment title is one of the few releases to utilize the Sega Mouse.

Art Of Fighting   Takara   2 $2
Akin to a melding of Streets of Rage and Street Fighter 2, this action-packed brawler is great fun while it lasts.

Asterix & The Great Rescue
Infogrames   6 $22
Americans aren't very familiar with the cartoon antics of Asterix and Obelix, but this well-designed action/platform game introduces them in fine form.

Aladdin   Altered Beast

Arrow Flash   Art Alive

B.O.B.

Ballz

Barney's Hide & Seek Game

Bass Masters Classic Pro Edition

Atomic Robo Kid   Treco   4 $8
This bland horizontal shooter has some decent graphics but the soundtrack is annoying and the gameplay is questionable.

Atomic Runner   Data East   4 $8
This is a bad port of an arcade action game that wasn't that good to begin with.

ATP Tour Championship Tennis
Sega   3 $3
If you like your tennis games visually pleasing and full of great gameplay, then you've found your match with this excellent simulation.

Awesome Possum   Tengen   4 $10
"Awesome Possum" really isn't the title we would have picked for this environmentally conscious platform game. "Mediocre Marsupial" would have been more accurate.

B.O.B.   Electronic Arts   4 $8
Humor can be a good thing in a video game, and B.O.B. is just silly enough to lift this otherwise standard platform game a bit above the level of its competitors.

Baby's Day Out   Hi-Tech Enterprises   5 $12
Come on... the title alone suggests that this movie-based platform game is going to suck. It does.

Back To The Future 3   Probe/Arena   5 $15
The first movie in the series was great, the second was mediocre, and the third movie blew chunks. This "action" game is just like the third movie.

Ballz   Accolade   3 $5
It's technically impressive that the developers were able to pull off a 3-D style fighting game on the Genesis (the characters are composed of shaded balls rather than polygons) but the fighting engine is weak.

Barbie - Super Model   Hi-Tech   4 $12
If you're a straight male and you bought this game looking for some solid gameplay, then you may want to consider therapy. If you bought it for your daughter or niece, then you can be forgiven, as she will probably enjoy the terrible sound, graphics, and gameplay of this... thing.

Barbie - Vacation Adventure
Hi-Tech   5 $15

It's got better graphics than its predecessor, but most everything else is about the same in this dull licensed product aimed strictly at pre-teen girls.

Barkley Shut Up And Jam   Accolade   1 $1
It's not Shaq Fu, and we can be thankful for that. Otherwise, this NBA Jam-style two-on-two basketball game is entertaining if not exceptional.

Barkley Shut Up And Jam 2
Accolade   2 $2
This sequel to the moderately popular basketball game features slightly better graphics and gameplay than the original.

Barney's Hide & Seek Game
Lyon Group   5 $10
Don't even bother with this wildly irritating edutainment title (starring that awful purple dinosaur) unless you have a pre-schooler, in which case you should buy this game. They will play it for hours and leave you alone.

Bass Masters Classic   THQ   4 $10
Certainly not the best fishing simulator for the Genesis, this product-driven game is rather boring.

Bass Masters Classic - Pro Edition
THQ   4 $12
This is an enhanced version of the original Bass Masters Classics game featuring better graphics and more refined gameplay.

Batman   Sunsoft   5 $16
All of Sunsoft's Batman titles are bad platformers in most every area. This is the first of the three and appears be nothing more than a slightly enhanced port of the NES game (itself based on the first movie.)

Batman & Robin, The Adventures of
Acclaim   4 $6
Widely acknowledged as the best of the Genesis Batman titles, this game (based on the television series) is an awesome action/platformer with fantastic graphics and great level design.

Batman Forever   Acclaim   2 $4
Acclaim chose to jettison the standard platform elements of previous Batman games in favor of some one-one-one fighting action, and the results aren't bad. The levels and player selection get old fast, but the fighting engine is solid.

Batman Returns   Sunsoft   4 $8
Hardly anyone liked the movie, and hardly anyone liked the game, either. The third title in Sunsoft's Batman games uses the same tired game engine as the first two entries (though it does look and play a bit better than before.)

Batman Revenge of Joker
   Sunsoft   4 $8
Based on the comic book rather than a movie, this lame continuation of Sunsoft's Batman games continues the series' tradition of stale graphics and gameplay.

Battle Frenzy   Domark   5 $12
The Genesis hardware really wasn't designed to do first-person shooters, and this mediocre Wolfenstein 3-D clone shows it.

Battle Master   Arena/Mirrorsoft   3 $5
This is a rather simple (even shallow) RPG best suited for more action-loving gamers or those new to the genre.

Battle Squadron   Electronic Arts   6 $15
This colorful and well-designed shooter will please fans of the genre and might even produce a few converts as well.

Battletech   FASA/Activision   3 $5
Mech (giant robot tanks) games are a popular sub-genre, and this isometric shooter has more going for it than just a great license. Most gamers are sucked right into the action, making this one of the true "must-have" games for the Genesis.

Battletoads   Rare/Tradewest   4 $6
This appears to be a nicely upgraded port of the popular (and difficult) NES action/fighting game.

Battletoads & Double Dragon
   Rare/Tradewest   4 $8
More of a straightforward fighting game that its predecessor, this title joins two popular licenses and actually makes it work.

Beast Wrestler   Sega   3 $5
One of the more bizarre games available for the Genesis, Beast Wrestler combines the play mechanics of a fighting game with an isometric visual presentation. The result is odd but strangely entertaining.

Beauty & The Beast - Belle's Quest
   Sunsoft   3 $5
This is a mediocre platform game sporting a Disney license and surprisingly average visuals.

Beauty & The Beast - Roar of the Beast
   Sunsoft   3 $5
It might look better that Belle's Quest, but the second game in the series (which concentrates on the Beast) plays poorly and isn't worth the effort.

Beavis and Butthead   Viacom   3 $4
How many of you remember the ridiculous antic of these two MTV fools? Regardless of your memory, most gamers can't help but be entertained by this cool "interactive cartoon." Don't confuse this with the lame and very different platform game that was released for the SNES.

Beethoven   THQ   5 $12
The feature film starring the lovable dog was a surprise hit… to bad the lame platform action of this disappointment isn't so lovable.

Bernstein Bears Camping Adventure
   Real Time Associates   3 $4
You'd expect a game centered on the Bernstein Bears to be stupid and easy, but this well-designed platform game will charm both young and old (or at least older) gamers alike.

Best of The Best   Loricel/Sega   1 $2
As Genesis kickboxing games go, it very well may be the best of the best. Of course, there's not much competition (the game itself is average on most accounts.)

Beyond Oasis   Sega   4 $8
This wonderfully entertaining action/RPG is viewed from a top-down perspective and features gorgeous graphics and a good story. It was followed by an excellent sequel (The Legend of Oasis) for the Sega Saturn.

Bible Adventures   Wisdom Tree   7 $35
Try as they might, Wisdom Tree never could popularize their odd mix of arcade-style mini-games and biblical quotes. Like most Wisdom Tree "games," Bible Adventures was sold mostly through Christian bookstores and had low production runs.

Bill Walsh Football   Electronic Arts   2 $5
It utilizes the fantastic Madden Football game engine, so you'd expect this college football simulation to be great. You would be correct.

Bill Walsh Football '95   Electronic Arts   2 $4
More of the same, and that's a good thing. Followed by two

Battle Master

Battletoads

Beavis and Butt-Head

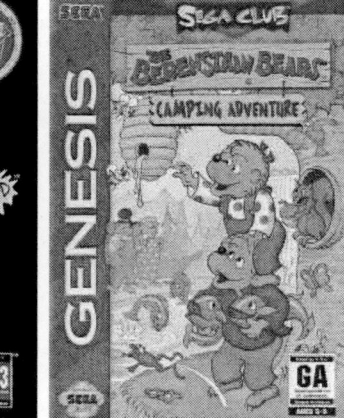

Bernstein Bears Camping Adventure

| Blaster Master 2 | Bonanza Brothers | Bubble and Squeek | Buck Rogers: Countdown to Doomsday |

more sequels (College Football '96 and '97.)

Bimini Run Sega 3 $4
This early (and dull) arcade port features a convoluted plot involving powerboat racing and some criminal shenanigans.

Bio-Hazard Battle Sega 2 $4
One of your better Genesis 2-D space shooters, this R-Type clone features some great boss design and a difficulty level that ramps up quickly.

Blades of Vengeance Electronic Arts 2 $4
D & D style fantasy meets hack and slash action in this cool title featuring great visuals and sound effects.

Blaster Master 2 Sunsoft 4 $10
The original NES game is considered a classic among many gamers, and this sequel faithfully continues the action-packed 2-D tank action.

Block Out Electronic Arts 2 $4
Most everybody likes Tetris, and this 3-D clone will suck puzzle fans right in and keep them entertained for days.

Blockbuster World Video Game Championship II Acclaim 8 $90
This title was used by Blockbuster Video and contained two games: Judge Dread and NBA Jam Tournament Edition. While it is believed that two other carts exist in this series, we were unable to confirm their existence. If you have either volume 1 or volume 3, please contact the Video Game Bible staff.

Body Count Sega 4 $10
No, this has nothing to do with the controversial rap album from back in the day. It's actually a very difficult gun shooter that shouldn't be played if all you have is a standard Genesis control pad.

Bonanza Brothers Sega 3 $5
This is an interesting, unique, and often difficult platform game ported from the arcade original.

Bonkers Disney 3 $5
Yet another Disney television cartoon game, Bonkers isn't as visually pleasing as some other Disney releases and the gameplay is strictly for kids.

Boogerman: A Pick and Flick Adventure Interplay 3 $6

Juvenile and often very average in its platform action, Boogerman nevertheless remains one of the console's more distinctive and entertaining games. The fact that the title character farts, burps, and flicks boogers throughout the whole thing may have something to do with it.

Boxing Legends of the Ring Electrobrain 3 $3
This is a fairly respectable boxing game populated by middleweight boxers, most of whom you won't recognize (we suppose you have to bite off an ear to get noticed these days.)

Bram Stoker's Dracula Sony Imagesoft 3 $5
The movie pretty much sucked, but this awesome action/platform game will mesmerize you with its tight game engine and lovely graphics.

Brett Hull Hockey '95 Accolade 1 $2
The developers chose to use an Isometric perspective for this otherwise average hockey sim, and it's the only reason to pick it up over the cornucopia of better playing Genesis hockey games that are available for a song.

Brutal: Paws of Fury GameTek 3 $5
This very fast-playing and often overly challenging Street Fighter II clone features a zany cast of animal characters and a solid fighting engine.

Bubba & Stix Core 2 $3
Pretty to look at, this irritatingly difficult platform game won't stay plugged in your Genesis for long.

Bubble and Squeek Sunsoft 2 $3
This is an overly sugary Sonic clone that misses its intended target by a wide margin.

Bubsy in Fractured Fairy Tales Accolade 2 $3
This Sonic wannabe sports nice control and very colorful graphics, but the one-hit kills will get on your nerves, as will some of Bubsy's one-liners.

Bubsy 2 Accolade 3 $5
Accolade ditched the one hit kills and introduced some sharp new graphical effects for this far superior sequel to the original Sonic clone.

Buck Rogers: Countdown to Doomsday Electronic Arts 4 $5

Boxes for both The Legend of Zelda and Firehawk for the NES contained cutout sections on their boxes to show the metallic cartridge inside.

Completely different from the classic Colecovision and Atari 5200 shooter, this overly complex strategy game requires a very thorough reading of the thick manual before it begins to make any sense.

Budokan: The Martial Spirit

Electronic Arts   2 $5

This early fighting game is very shallow and dated compared to later offerings in the genre.

Bugs Bunny Double Trouble

Warner Interactive 4 $6

It's Bugs! Thankfully, the developers choose to devote some time and attention to our favorite wascally wabbit, resulting in a beautiful (but occasionally frustrating) game that does justice to the cartoons.

Bulls vs. Blazers   Electronic Arts   1 $1

This is the fourth entry in EA's well-designed NBA Playoffs basketball series.

Bulls vs. Lakers   Electronic Arts   1 $1

This is the second entry in EA's well-designed NBA Playoffs basketball series

Burning Force   Namco   2 $3

It's not bad as pseudo 3-D shooters go, but the Genesis isn't quite powerful enough to deliver the scaling effects that this sort of game requires (Panorama Cotton notwithstanding.)

Buster Douglas Knock-Out Boxing

Taito   1 $2

This is yet another crappy 2-D fighting game with a celebrity on the box cover.

Cadash   Taito   2 $4

This game can't decide if it's a straight action game or an RPG and ends up doing neither genre very well.

Caesar's Palace   Virgin/Majesto   3 $4

Like to gamble but don't want to lose your money? You're sure to enjoy this well designed gambling simulation.

Cal Ripken Jr. Baseball   Mindscape   1 $2

It would be easy to dismiss the baseball game as just another mindless contender in a sea of similar titles, but Cal actually has a game to be proud of.

Caliber .50   Seta   3 $4

Iraki Warriors clones came and went with monotonous regularity during the 16-bit era, but this shooter sticks out in our minds as one of the best.

California Games   Epyx   1 $1

Talk about your oldies but goodies… this collection of beach-based mini-games appeared in one form or another on countless computers and consoles, and the Genesis port is the best of the best.

Cannon Fodder   Virgin   5 $12

Based on a series of computer games, Cannon Fodder is a great action/simulation/mission-based affair with cartoonish graphics, a good soundtrack, entertaining sound effects, and excellent control.

Captain America and the Avengers

Data East   2 $5

Comics-based games have an iffy track record. Regrettably, this dull fighting/platform game is saddled with poor graphics and sound effects.

Castle of Illusion Starring Mickey Mouse

Disney   4 $8

Mickey had a very successful run of games on the Genesis, and this fine action/platformer is among the best of the lot, featuring fine graphics and gameplay.

Castlevania Bloodlines   Konami   3 $10

As the only game in the vaulted Castlevania series to appear on the console, Bloodlines is often subjected to undue criticism due to its later timeline and rather dull soundtrack (the curse of the Z-80 sound chip.) In reality, it's a completely awesome, fast-playing addition to the series that ranks as one of the best action/adventure games on the Genesis.

Centurion: Defender of Rome

Electronic Arts   1 $4

Better make sure you have the manual before you decide to tackle this complex simulation game based on Roman history.

Chakan: The Forever Man   Sega   1 $2

We remember a lot of hoopla and excitement surrounding this action game when it was first released, but we fail to see its appeal now. It just seems really dated.

Champion's World Class Soccer

Acclaim   2 $2

Don't bother paying much for this mediocre soccer simulation,

Buster Douglas Knock-Out Boxing

Caesar's Palace

Castle of Illusion Starring Mickey Mouse

Chakan

The Game Handler, a one handed controller, was officially endorsed by the "One Handed Popcorn Eaters of America."

Chavez II

Chester Cheetah 2: Wild Wild Quest

Clay Fighter

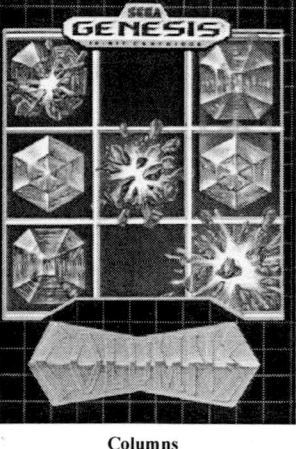

Columns

especially when you have so many better choices to pick from.

Championship Bowling   Mentrix   5 $12
Bowling games are an acquired taste, and that taste is hard to acquire when the graphics are ugly and the music is irritating. The actual gameplay isn't hard to get into, though.

Championship Pool   Mindscape   2 $4
Options abound in this plain-looking but fantastic-playing video ode to the sport of billiards.

Championship Pro-Am   Tradewest   3 $4
Remote controlled cars are great toys, and they can make the transition into great videogames, too. This seemingly simple racing title will hook you from the get-go.

Chase HQ 2   Taito   4 $6
Try as it might, the Genesis can't quite match the visuals of the arcade original of this popular racer. Fortunately, the smooth racing action made the programming odyssey intact.

Chavez 2   American Software   4 $6

Chester Cheetah: Too Cool To Fool
**   Kaneko   2 $4**
The 7-Up soda mascot (Cool Spot) got two games, so why not the feline from Cheetos? Fortunately, the tasty cheese snacks are WAY better than this dreadfully derivative platformer.

Chester Cheetah 2: Wild Wild Quest
**   Kaneko   2 $4**
It seems that the first cheesy game sold well enough to warrant a sequel, so here we are, stuck in crappy platform game purgatory yet again.

Chi Chi's Pro Challenge Golf
**   Virgin   3 $4**
This is a respectable golfing sim sporting legend Chi Chi Rodriguez

Chiki Chiki Boys   Capcom   4 $7
Colorful title and graphics aside, this very Japanese platformer is average in most respects.

Chuck Rock   Virgin   4 $8
Uproariously funny and original, this Sonic wannabe attracted hoards of fans with its gorgeous graphics and tight, tight gameplay.

Chuck Rock 2: Son of Chuck
**   Virgin   2 $4**
Even funnier than the original, this sequel to the popular platformer is just as good (if not better) than the original.

Clay Fighter   Interplay   3 $5
This Street Fighter 2 clone ditches a "normal" graphical style in favor of fighters derived from motion-captured clay models in various fighting positions. Their one-liners are kind of funny, but the fighting engine is weak.

Cliffhanger   Sony   3 $4
Contrary to popular belief, not all Sylvester Stallone's more recent movies are bad. Regrettably, this dull platform game fails to capture any of the excitement of the feature film.

Clue   Parker Brothers   3 $4
Want to play a round of the classic mystery board game? Then go buy the board game. This dull video game version might be cheaper and smaller than the original but you'll still have to haul out your Genesis to play it or take it on trips.

Coach K Basketball   Electronic Arts   2 $4
This is one of the best basketball games available for the Genesis (it should be… it utilizes the superlative NBA Live game engine.) Go buy it now.

College Football USA '96   Electronic Arts   1 $1
This continuation of the Bill Walsh football series (he left to go to the NFL) retains the same fantastic gameplay engine of the Madden game engine.

College Football USA '97: The Road to New Orleans
**   Electronic Arts   1 $2**
This is the final installment of the excellent college football series (still using the finely-tuned Madden engine.)

College Football's National Championship
**   Sega   1 $1**
Sega's wonderful NFL game engine was used for this equally good simulation featuring college teams. The graphics and gameplay are as deep and rich their big-team daddies.

College Football's National Championship 2
**   Sega   1 $2**
You'll get more of the same great gameplay that's expected from one of Sega's flagship sporting simulations.

S.C.A.T. stands for Special Cybernetic Attack Team.

GEN

College Slam   Acclaim   1 $1
This offshoot of the NBA Jam series utilizes the same game engine but features college players instead of NBA players. It's also considered by some to be the best 2-on-2 basketball game for the Genesis.

Columns   Sega   1 $2
This is Sega's direct competitor to the Tetris puzzle game, and the action is just as addictive as the venerable classic.

Columns 3: Revenge of Columns
    Sega   4 $8
Superficial improvements and an attempt at a storyline are about all this update adds to the original foundation of the superb original.

Combat Cars   Accolade   2 $4
This Micro Machine clone (viewed from a top-top perspective) features very fast and colorful graphics, cool weapons, and an entertaining split-screen 2-player mode.

Comix Zone   Sega   3 $8
Sega's exceptionally cool melding of the action/platform genre with a comic book-style graphical presentation didn't get the recognition it deserved. To make up for that, you should find the game right now to see what everyone missed.

Contra Hard Corps   Konami   2 $8
The only game in the beloved Contra series to make it to the Genesis is also one of the most difficult, but that's no surprise. The faster (than the SNES) Genesis CPU is utilized to the max, and the speed and intensity of this side-scrolling shooter just doesn't let up.

Cool Spot   Virgin   3 $7
Not bad as games based on corporate mascots go (in this case 7-Up), this side-scrolling platform title sports just enough variety and good gameplay to earn it a recommendation. It was followed by a sequel that used a different (isometric) graphical style.

Cosmic Spacehead   Codemasters   3 $6
This is a silly and unremarkable platform game that few remember and fewer will want to play.

Crack Down   Sage's Creation   1 $3
This port of an old Contra-style arcade game is really showing its age, but it's worth a quick look if you have nothing better to do.

Crue Ball   Electronic Arts   2 $4
Remember the metal/make-up/big hair band Motley Crue? Their album "Dr. Feelgood" (newly released at the time) served as the basis for a pretty respectable pinball simulation, believe it or not. Unfortunately, the Genesis isn't capable of duplicating the album's tracks, but that probably for the best.

Crusaders of the Century   Atlus   6 $18
Nintendo's Zelda series inspired a rash of mostly lame clones, but a few are good enough to be mentioned in the same sentence... like Crusaders of the Century.

Crystal's Pony Tales   Sega   4 $6
You knew this was going to be a lame platform game aimed at little girls, didn't you? You're so smart. The graphics aren't bad, but the gameplay is strictly child's play.

Cutthroat Island   Acclaim   3 $2
Geena Davis' pirate movie remains one of the biggest cinematic flops of all time when viewed from a development cost versus total profits basis, but Acclaim didn't know that when this game was in development. Appropriately, the game mirrors the laughably bad movie perfectly, and platform games with movie licenses rarely get any worse than this.

Cyber Cop   Virgin   2 $3
Another attempt at a Wolfenstein 3-D clone for the Genesis gone awry... did anyone ever fully realize that the hardware just wasn't up to the task?

Cyberball   Tengen   2 $3
A futuristic take on the game of football sounds like a fine idea, but the game engine underneath just isn't up to the task of delivering a satisfying gaming experience.

Cyborg Justice   Sega   3 $6
This dull and repetitive fighting game is unusual only in the fact that it allows you to build your robotic fighters from a series of parts, all of which supposedly have different characteristic but don't seem to effect the fighting action very much.

Dark Castle   Electronic Arts   2 $5
Who let this bad platform game slip by quality control? Wretched sound and really bad graphics do not a good game make.

Dashin' Desperados   Data East   2 $4

Contra Hard Corps   Cool SPot   Cosmic Spacehead   Crystal's Pony Tale

244

There is no boomerang in The Adventures of Link.

Deadly Moves

Death Duel

Decap Attack

Dick Tracy

Not bad as far as Sonic clones go, this silly but entertaining title also features an unusual split screen mode.

David Crane's Amazing Tennis

Absolute	2	$3

There is no reason whatsoever to purchase this simply wretched tennis "simulation", even if you do have an extra twenty-five cents in your pocket.

David Robinson's Supreme Court

ACME Entertainment	2	$3

This is a mediocre arcade-style basketball game featuring David Robinson (and has nothing whatsoever to do with our nation's highest court.)

Davis Cup World Tour Tennis

Tengen	2	$2

One of your better tennis games for the Genesis, Davis Cup features excellent control and gameplay, plus a bunch of options.

Deadly Moves

Kaneco	2	$3

Street Fighter II clones came and went with monotonous regularity during the 16-bit era, and we weren't sad to see this underdeveloped effort disappear without much fanfare.

Death and Return of Superman, The

Sunsoft	5	$14

The second and best of the two Superman titles for the Genesis, this interesting action/fighting game is based on the famous comic storyline that featured the Man of Steel's supposed demise.

Death Duel

Sega	2	$3

Need another light gun shooter to add to your Genesis library? You'd do well to skip this dull and poorly playing title and look elsewhere.

Decap Attack

Sega	2	$4

This is a decent (if not great) Mario World clone featuring a decapitated mummy as the main character.

Demolition Man

Acclaim	3	$5

Cliffhanger and Demolition Man are two surprisingly good feature films that marked a brief comeback for Sylvester Stallone. This enjoyable action game is far and away the better of the two games based on the movies.

Desert Demolition

Blue Sky	2	$3

Wile E. Coyote and the Road Runner are at it again in the strikingly beautiful platform game based on the twisted cartoon shorts.

Desert Strike: Return to the Gulf

Electronic Arts	2	$3

The first of the three isometric helicopter shooters released for the Genesis under the Strike banner, Desert Strike is the least impressive of the series from a graphical standpoint. Thankfully, the gameplay is as addictive (and difficult) as ever.

Devilish

Sega	5	$14

Great idea aside, this new twist on Breakout isn't done well and fails to offer an entertaining gaming experience.

Dick Tracy

Sega	3	$3

Bad movie, bad soundtrack (other than Vogue), bad feelings about this terrible platform game... it's just a whole lot of bad.

Dick Vitale's "Awesome Baby" College Hoops

Time/Warner Interactive	1	$2

One of few Genesis games to utilize a first-person perspective, this basketball simulation doesn't play as well as more conventional efforts but still manages to entertain.

Dino Land

Wolf Team	6	$18

This is a respectable pinball simulation that's nearly derailed by its overly cute dinosaur-laden visual style.

Dinosaurs For Hire

Sega	4	$8

Guys love dinosaurs and guys love videogames, hence the relatively common appearance of the creatures on the Genesis. This above-average action game is especially humorous and worth hunting down.

DJ Boy

Kaneko	5	$12

This is a Double Dragon clone aimed at younger gamers, and they are probably the only ones who will be able to stomach the game's irritating soundtrack.

Donald Duck Starring Maui Mallard

Disney	5	$12

This is yet another pretty-looking but average-playing licensed title from Disney.

Doom Troopers: The Mutant Chronicles

Playmates Interactive	4	$6

How did we miss this one? An action/shooter in the same tradition as Gunstar Heroes, this dark, gory, and exceptionality vio-

In order to successfully complete Adventure for the Atari 2600, you must return the Chalice to the Golden Castle.

lent platform game backs up its creepy themes with some darn fine gameplay.

Double Dragon   Accolade   3 $8
Also known as the game that spawned a thousand clones, this side-scrolling brawler set the genre standard for years to come but appears rather dated now.

Double Dragon 3   Accolade   2 $7
The trend-setting series started to show its age rather early in this sequel (part 2 never made it to the Genesis) and the lack of innovation proves to be detrimental from a gameplay standpoint.

Double Dragon V: The Shadow Falls
    Legend/Tradewest   6 $25
Acclaim ditched the side-scrolling antics of the original games in favor of a poor Street Fighter II clone, ending the series with a whimper.

Double Dribble: The Playoff Edition
    Konami   2 $3
This is an enjoyable sequel to an early (yet entertaining) arcade basketball game that set the stage for the later NBA Jam series.

Dr. Robotnik's Mean Bean Machine
    Sega   3 $5
This excellent Tetris clone replaced the visuals of the highly popular Japanese game (originally called Puyo Puyo) with characters from the Sonic games.

Dragon: The Bruce Lee Story
    Virgin   4 $4
There really wasn't a need to tarnish the legend of martial arts master Bruce Lee with this simply wretched fighter, but they did it anyway. Shameful!

Dragon's Fury   Techno Soft   3 $5
Gothic fantasy and hot pinball action meet in this super simulation. You'll love the graphic, sound effects, and overall theme.

Dune: The Battle For Arakis
    Westwood Studios   5 $20
Based on the beloved novels, this excellent strategy game comes with its own built-in tutorial (you'll need it) and some of the best gameplay of its type available for the Genesis.

Dynamite Duke   Sega   2 $4
Get your light gun out 'cause you're going to need it if you actually expect to enjoy all that this well-designed shooter has to offer.

Dynamite Headdy   Treasure   4 $12
One of the true Genesis "sleepers", this wonderful platform game (from famed developer Treasure, makers of Gunstar Heroes and the Japanese Saturn's Radiant Silvergun) is jam-packed full of gloriously colorful levels, incredibly imaginative enemies and bosses, smooth gameplay, and precise control.

E-Swat: Cyber Police   Sega   1 $2
The rather elderly arcade original that inspired this action game still has a certain old-school appeal about it, but the game just didn't port over to the Genesis very well.

Earnest Evans   Wolfteam   1 $3
You should know that when a game developer names their newest release "Earnest Evans" that you're in for a dull, repetitive, and completely derivative platform game. You're right again.

Earth Defense   Realtec   5 $14
This is a fairly standard middle-of-the-road 2-D shooter with scattered power-ups and large boss characters.

Earthworm Jim   Shiny/Playmates   2 $7
You haven't heard of the gun-toting, head-snapping earthworm? How about Professor Monkey-For-A-Head? If not, you're going to love the hilarious antics and fast action of this popular platform/shooting game.

Earthworm Jim 2   Shiny/Playmates   3 $10
Most everyone who played the first game loved it, and those warm, wormy feelings continue for this excellent sequel to the action classic. Part 2 features some neat mini-games plus some cool shooting levels.

Ecco Jr.   Sega   5 $15
It's Ecco the Dolphin for youngsters, and the puzzles aren't quite so devious. The excellent graphics, musical score, and level design remain the same.

Ecco The Dolphin   Sega   2 $4
Sega's environmentally friendly action game features lush graphics and sound, but some of the puzzles will have you tearing your hair out. It was followed by two sequels on the Genesis, two games on the Sega CD that are nearly identical to the Genesis games, and one absolutely gorgeous but massively irritating 3-D update that has appeared on several next-generation platforms.

Double Dragon V: The Shadow
Falls   Double Dribble: The Playoff
Edition

Dragon: The Bruce Lee Story   Dragon's Revenge

GD-ROM, in reference to the Dreamcast, means GigaDisc ROM.

Ecco: The Tides of Time   Elemental Master   Eternal Champions   Ex-Mutants

Ecco: The Tides Of Time   Sega   1 $4
The second of Sega's beautiful action games starring Ecco is very much like the first game (in a good way), plus you have the ability to transform into other marine life.

El Viento   Renovation   2 $3
This is a very dated-looking action/platform game with a silly plot and bad characterizations.

Elemental Master   TechnoSoft   6 $18
This is an excellent top-down shooter featuring some cool levels and fiendishly hard bosses.

ESPN Baseball   Sony Imagesoft   1 $1
The ESPN games run the gamut between excellent and terrible. This baseball sim features very good graphics and game play and will appeal to most sports games fans.

ESPN Hockey   Sony Imagesoft   1 $1
Not far off the mark set by the EA's NHL games, ESPN Hockey came as something of a shock to the critics who were expecting something much less competent from Sony Imagesoft.

ESPN Speed World   Sony Imagesoft   2 $3
The worst of the ESPN games is a terrible stock car racing game with truly remarkable graphics and sound... remarkably bad!

ESPN Sunday Night NFL   Sony Imagesoft   1 $1
Poor visuals and soundtrack aside, this otherwise competent football simulation plays well enough to give it a try.

Eternal Champions   Sega   1 $3
This poor Street Fighter II clone attracted a lot of attention upon its initial release, but there's really nothing special to be found here. The Sega CD sequel, on the other hand, is an incredibly cool and GORY fighter full of depth and variety.

Evander Holyfield's "Real Deal" Boxing
Acme Interactive   1 $2
This respectable boxing simulation is unusual in that it focuses more on Evander Holyfield rather than a variety of different fighters.

Ex-Mutants   Malibu Interactive   1 $3
If you can't guess the comic book inspiration for this lame platform game, you may have been dropped on your head as a child. (Hint: X-men.)

Exodus: Journey to the Promised Land
Wisdom Tree   7 $35
If you have an urge to take control of Moses and get up to speed on the book of Exodus, then this is the game for you. Otherwise, it's a standard action game with a biblical twist.

Exosquad   Playmates   3 $8
The different styles of various gaming genres range from superb to merely decent in the rather impressive game based on the animated TV series. The first-person segments of the game are particularly well done.

F1 World Championship Edition (1994)
Acclaim   4 $8
This is actually the sequel to Formula One, and offers both graphical improvements and a feeling of more speed.

F1 World Championship Edition (1995)
Acclaim   4 $10
A continuation in the series, this title is the best of the three released.

F-117 Night Storm   Electronic Arts   2 $4
Not all of the flight simulators on the Genesis were bad... EA actually did a mighty fine job with this one by working within the confines of the hardware.

F-15 Strike Eagle 2   MicroProse   2 $5
The Genesis saw more than its share of PC ports, and their quality differed wildly. Regrettably, this translation of the formerly impressive flight simulator is a big old mess and is best avoided.

F-22 Interceptor   Electronic Arts   1 $2
Polygonal graphics and the Genesis hardware don't seem to mix well, and this poor excuse for a flight simulator certainly supports that assessment.

FIFA International Soccer   Electronic Arts   1 $2
The first game in what is widely considered to be THE definitive soccer game on the Genesis, International Soccer introduced most of the traits that the series became known for: sharp isometric graphics, a huge variety of options, and exceptional control.

FIFA Soccer '95   Electronic Arts   1 $2
This is a mild upgrade of the first FIFA Soccer game.

Sonic Adventure was the first U.S. Dreamcast game to feature online play.

FIFA Soccer '96   Electronic Arts 1 $2
The FIFA series received its first real boost with the addition of smarter AI and better graphics.

FIFA Soccer '97 Gold   Electronic Arts 2 $4
Indoor arenas and an excellent "create a team" option were the big draws for this update of the popular series.

FIFA Soccer '98 - Road To The World Cup
        Electronic Arts 3 $5
The last of the FIFA games for the Genesis, '98 isn't different enough from previous entries in the series to warrant a purchase unless you're a collector.

Faery Tale Adventure, The
        Electronic Arts 3 $4
Dated graphics and irritating soundtrack aside, this influential and now-classic RPG is good, solid entertainment.

Family Feud   Gametek 4 $8
The video games based on the Family Feud game show are always good for a laugh, but console ports suffer from the lack of a keyboard and the fact that spelling is very important. Little details that make you miss a question (like typing "Dr." instead of "Doctor") suggest that the developers might have napped on the job.

Fantasia   Disney 3 $6
This is one of Disney's many Mickey Mouse games (now taking inspiration from the animated movie of the same name.)

Fantastic Dizzy   Codemasters 2 $4
Yet another platformer for the Genesis, this unusual little game manages to set itself apart form the crowd with its above-average graphics, sound, and play mechanics.

Fatal Fury   Takara 2 $3
You can see where the Neo-Geo's legendary King of Fighters series began in this otherwise unimpressive Street Fighter II clone

Fatal Fury 2   Takara 3 $5
This is a respectably improved sequel to the popular fighting series sporting more characters and better graphics.

Fatal Labyrinth   Sega 2 $3
Rather dated and old looking, this top-down action/RPG still manages to play well enough to warrant a second look.

Fatal Rewind   Psygnosis 3 $5
This port of a classic computer action/platform title has its fans, but most casual gamers will be put off by the game's frustratingly high difficulty level.

Ferrari Grand Prix Challenge
        Flying Edge 2 $4
This is an entertaining but ultimately forgettable racing time featuring the Ferrari license.

Fido Dido   Kaneko 5 $10
No one really remembers this little lost gem, and that's a real shame. There was some real imagination present in this cool platform game featuring great graphics and gameplay.

Fighting Masters   Treco 6 $18
Street Fighter II spawned a myriad of clones... some good, some bad. This is one of the bad ones.

Final Zone   Renovation 2 $4
Do you enjoy mech games? If so, you'll likely have some fun with this cool little isometric shooter.

Fire Shark   Dreamworks 5 $12
If you're a collector of old-style vertical shooters, be sure not to miss this one. Otherwise, you'll probably get bored quickly as the overall game design is fairly weak.

Flashback : The Quest for Identity
        U.S. Gold 2 $8
Surprising in its complexity, this engrossing action/strategy title features a great plot and wonderful graphics. It can be a bit difficult, though.

Flicky   Sega 5 $12
The Genesis library has games for kids, adults, and everyone in between. This overly cute platform game is strictly for the children.

Flintstones , The   Taito 4 $8
Unlike the different SNES game of the same name, this above-average platform game features some nice graphics and good gameplay.

Foreman For Real   Acclaim 3 $6
If you liked Punch-Out! for the NES or the SNES, you'll probably enjoy this similarly-playing boxing simulation.

Fighting Masters   Fire Shark   Flashback: The Quest for Identity   Flicky

The arcade classic Tempest was released in 1981.

Fun 'N' Games

Funny World/Balloon Boy

Gaiares

General Chaos

Forgotten Worlds   Capcom   3 $7
One of your better "old school" space shooters for the console, Forgotten Worlds is a very good conversion of an even older arcade game.

Formula One   Domark   3 $6
This is a very good Formula One simulation presented from a fast-moving first person view. The control is excellent as well.

Frank Thomas 'Big Hurt' Baseball
   Acclaim   1 $2
This is a mediocre baseball sim fronted by MLB star Frank Thomas.

Frogger   Majesco   4 $8
This perfect port of the arcade classic is unusual in that it doesn't offer anything new over the original, but perhaps that's the point. Regardless, Frogger was the LAST Genesis game released in the United States and is way better than the surprisingly poor SNES game.

Fun 'N' Games   Tradewest   4 $8
Edutainment and entertainment don't go together where adults are involved, so save this one for the kids.

Funny World/Balloon Boy   Realtec   5 $15

G-Loc: Air Battle   Sega   2 $3
It might look like a true-blue flight simulation at first, but this 3-D shooter retains the "jump in and play" feel of the original arcade game.

Gadget Twins   Gametek   2 $2
This is a very pretty and colorful Sonic clone that shot itself in the foot in the area of control..

Gaiares   Renovation   6 $25
As one of the rarer and more enjoyable shooters for the Genesis, this innovative game features some unique play mechanics, cool graphics, and a great sense of speed.

Gain Ground   Sega   3 $4
The original version of this safari-themed arcade shooter wasn't that good to start with, and this slow-playing port suffers from overly difficult gameplay and an average visual presentation.

Galaxy Force 2   Sega   2 $2
The arcade version of Galaxy Force 2 was simply amazing

when it first appeared in the early 1990's, especially in its deluxe cabinet guise. Unfortunately, the Genesis simply can't handle the complex graphics and intense scaling effects of its arcade parent, though the gameplay is mostly intact (the Japanese Saturn is host to a perfect version of Galaxy Force II in case you're interested.)

Garfield: Caught In The Act
   Sega   4 $8
Like the smartass cartoon? You'll probably enjoy this colorful platform game that's not as easy to finish as its childish license would have you believe.

Gargoyles   Buena Vista Interactive   2 $4
The dark and gothic atmosphere of the original animated series would seem to be a natural for a video game, and this equally dark and gothic platform game features great graphics and respectable gameplay

Gauntlet 4   Tengen   4 $10
If you haven't played some version of the original overhead dungeon crawler, you need to get out more! Part 4 adds a fairly interesting plot plus some RPG elements to the mix.

Gemfire   KOEI   3 $7
Not that great as far Koei games go, this shallow and rather undeveloped strategy game features gameplay similar to the classic board game Risk.

General Chaos   Electronic Arts   4 $8
Fans of the action/strategy genre will be completely addicted to this clever and well-written title... others may find themselves bored.

Generations Lost   Time Warner   3 $7
This rather cool action game is similar to Flashback and features entertaining gameplay and good graphics.

Genghis Khan 2: Clan of the Grey Wolf
   Koei   7 $30
One of the best of the "deep" strategy games for the Genesis, this title (from the masters of the genre) mixes the gameplay of the Romance of the 3 Kingdoms series with the exploits of Genghis Khan.

George Foreman's Knock-Out Boxing
   Acclaim   2 $4
The aging heavyweight has hawked more than just grills and mufflers... he also has his own mediocre boxing sim to sell to

the unsuspecting masses.

Ghostbusters   Sega   4 $8
Many Genesis platform games feature great graphics but stuttering, underdeveloped gameplay. This release (based on the popular feature film) is the opposite as it looks shoddy but plays well.

Ghouls 'N Ghosts   Capcom   4 $8
Capcom's legendary arcade action/platformer made an appearance on the Genesis in fine style, featuring all the excellent graphics (particularly for such an early release) and truly superb gameplay that made the original game (Ghost's & Goblins) so fantastic. The SNES game of the same name features better graphics, enhanced gameplay, and a far superior soundtrack, but it's riddled with atrocious slowdown.

Gods   Mindscape   3 $5
Not at all what you'd think, Gods is an excellent action/platform title featuring great graphics, sound, and gameplay.

Golden Axe   Sega   2 $6
The original arcade scrolling fighter was wildly popular in its day but has fallen on hard times as of late (the last entry in the series was for the Sega Saturn in the mid 1990's.) This early Genesis release was impressive in 1989 but fails to impress nowadays.

Golden Axe 2   Sega   4 $8
This mildly enhanced update to the arcade favorite features some new fighters and moves, plus slightly better graphics and sound.

Goofy's Hysterical History Tour
    Absolute Entertainment   5 $15
Best left to the youngsters, this licensed ode to childish antics has an interesting concept but simplistic execution.

Granada   Renovation   4 $6
You'd be wise to seek out this frenetic top-down sprite fest if you like your shooters wild and furious.

Great Waldo Search   THQ   3 $5
Remember those inexplicably popular picture books where you had to hunt down the tiny nerdish Waldo in a sea of similarly dressed people? For the uninitiated, that crap was horrible, and this game is just the same old stuff in digital form.

Greatest Heavyweights of the Ring
    Sega   2 $4
This is a very good boxing simulation featuring most of history's finest heavyweight stars.

Greendog : The Beached Surfer Dude
    Sega   3 $5
Sega tried on numerous occasions (and with varying degrees of success) to debut a corporate mascot that would match the popularity of Sonic (Ecco, Ristar, Vectorman) but this lame platform is substandard on all accounts.

Grindstormer   Tengen   3 $4
This is an excellent, fast-moving, and very challenging vertical shooter that will certainly please fans of the genre.

Growl   Taito   6 $18
Amusing name aside, this pitiful platform/fighting game sports an environmentally friendly storyline but a very gamer-unfriendly design.

Gunship   U.S. Gold   4 $8
This port of the classic computer flight simulator is eclipsed by better entries and is really meant only for real sim fans and those who remember the original and want to play it again.

Gunstar Heroes   Treasure   4 $20
It's simply not possible to assign any one game the title of "The best game on the Sega Genesis," but if you could, Gunstar Heroes would be among the finalists. Famed developer Treasure pulled out all the stops on this insanely intense platform shooter packed full of hardware-defying effects and some of the coolest bosses and level design you're ever seen. Long live 2-D gaming!

Hard Drivin'   Tengen   2 $4
Some arcade games just shouldn't have been shoehorned onto Genesis hardware, and Atari's early polygonal racer is definitely one of those games. The frame rate, in particular, is so slow and stutters so badly that the game is borderline unplayable.

Hardball!   Accolade   1 $1
This early baseball sim laid the groundwork for later releases from Sega and EA (though its historical significance seems to have been forgotten.) Many of the features we take for granted in baseball games were introduced, including the first-person home plate view and the deeper, less arcade-style gameplay.

Hardball 3   Accolade   2 $2
The graphics received a substantial overhaul for this update to

Ghostbusters

                  Ghouls 'N Ghosts

Golden Axe

                  Hardball!

Known as Rockman in Japan, Megaman has a sister named Roll...Rock and Roll.

| The Haunting Starring Polterguy | Heavy Nova | Herzog Zwei | The Immortal |

the popular baseball simulation, and the gameplay is more re-fined.

Hardball '94   Accolade   2 $2
Following in the footsteps of other sports game, the Hardball series didn't see much in the way of substantial enhancements for its yearly updates

Hardball '95   Accolade   2 $3
This is more of the same from the venerable Hardball series, but that's not a bad thing.

Haunting Starring Polterguy, The
     Electronic Arts   3 $5
Like many games presented from an isometric perspective, this title suffers from some control issues. Luckily, the graphics are nice and the "ghostly" concept is original.

Head-On Soccer   U.S. Gold   2 $3
Not quite arcade-style action, not quite full-on simulation, Heads-On Soccer toes the line between the two and mostly succeeds with its simple yet gameplay-oriented approach to the soccer genre.

Heavy Nova   Micronet   6 $20
It might sound like a cool 2-D shooter, but in reality Heavy Nova is a poorly designed fighting game featuring robot combatants and a tacked-on platform mode.

Hellfire   NCS/Toaplan   3 $4
Not bad as 2-D shooters go, Hellfire features some cool level design and decent gameplay.

Herzog Zwei   Technosoft   7 $35
Generally recognized as one of the first real-time strategy games available on a home console, Herzog Zwei disappeared without a trace not long after its original release but has since been recognized and celebrated for its ground-breaking status. It's now one of then more sought-after (and entertaining) Genesis collectibles.

High Seas Havoc   Data East   2 $4
This is a well-designed platform game with good graphics and entertaining gameplay.

Hit The Ice   Taito   5 $12
If you're the type of gamer who shuns the deeper NFL games from Sega or EA, you might want to give this fast-moving arcade-style release a try.

Home Alone   THQ   1 $1
What exactly were you expecting? This crap platform game based on the popular movie series is loaded full of bad humor and irritatingly cheap gameplay.

Home Alone 2   THQ   1 $2
The first Home Alone movie was pretty good (admit it) and the first sequel wasn't bad either. Unfortunately, the sequel to the first game is just as bad as the original. Let's be glad they never made a Home Alone 3 (or maybe it would have been better since the movie sucked?)

Hook   Sony Imagesoft   2 $3
Like the ultimately dreadful movie that spawned it, this licensed game has some cute bits but the whole package is less than the sum of its parts

Humans, The   Gametek   2 $4
This is a cute Lemmings clone done in by sloppy control.

Hurricanes   U.S. Gold   2 $2
Is this supposed to be a soccer game? It sure doesn't play like one. It's more like a football game, and a poorly done one at that.

IMG International Tour Tennis
     Electronic Arts   2 $3
This is another excellent sporting simulation from the masters of the sporting simulations, Electronic Arts.

Immortal, The   Electronic Arts   2 $6
Certainly one of the Genesis all-time greats, this darkly atmospheric RPG plays host to some truly great 16-bit graphics and a very cool storyline.

Incredible Crash Test Dummies, The
     Leisure Concepts   3 $5
Anyone remember the auto safety commercials starring Vince and Larry, the talking Crash Test Dummies? They were popular enough to inspire this lame side-scrolling platform game. Funny how we haven't seen them in a while…

Incredible Hulk, The   U.S. Gold   2 $4
Aside from his appearances in Capcom's 2-D fighters, the big green man's gaming excursions have been mediocre at best. This is a pitiful side-scroller with ugly graphics and bad level design.

When you lose all your men in Ikari Warriors for the NES, quickly press A B B A in order to continue.

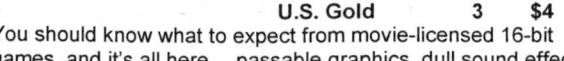

Indiana Jones and the Last Crusade
U.S. Gold   3 $4
You should know what to expect from movie-licensed 16-bit games, and it's all here... passable graphics, dull sound effects, boring gameplay.

Insector X   Taito   3 $5
This is your fairly standard side-scrolling shooter with average graphics and gameplay. You might want to pick it up if it's cheap.

Ishido: The Way of the Stones
Accolade   4 $8
You don't see many "Asian tile" games here in the states, but the genre is widely popular in the Far East. Its simple yet addictive gameplay won't appeal to hard-core action fans, but many others will be intrigued.

It Came From The Desert   Electronic Arts   4 $8
The original game of the same name is an old computer favorite, but its translation to the Genesis was cruel, leaving in its wake an overly difficult action/shooter with RPG elements.

Izzy's Quest for the Olympic Rings
U.S. Gold   3 $4
If you didn't live in Atlanta, Georgia, you probably didn't know that Dizzy was the mascot of the 1996 summer games. You probably wouldn't remember this middle of the road platform game either, as it is neither offensive nor memorable.

Jack Nikalus Power Challenge Golf   Accolade 2 $4
Thankfully, Jack Niklaus's golf game on the Genesis is a good one. It isn't in the same league as Niklaus himself, but it's still a good golf sim for fans and newbies alike.

James Bond: The Duel   Sony Imagesoft   5 $12
Action games don't get much worse than this tripe. The gameplay of James Bond: The Duel is inexcusable... gamers should stay away from this one, and game collectors should just leave it on their shelves.

James Pond: Underwater Agent
Electronic Arts   2 $3
Back in the 16-bit days, James Pond came around when characters like Mario, Sonic, and Ecco were in their heyday. Although he didn't exactly take the world by storm, he certainly reached his prime during the same time period. Combining craziness with great action-packed gameplay, graphics, and

sound, James Pond became a household...er...well-known name. Try this one out if you haven't done so yet.

James Pond 2: Codename Robocod
Electronic Arts   2 $4
Awesome control, great graphics and sound, and all kinds of wackiness made James Pond 2: Robocod as cool as its title.

James Pond 3: Operation Starfish
Electronic Arts   3 $4
This sequel continues with the typical wackiness that the series has become known for, and does it in an innovative action/adventure style that makes the game hard to put down. This one is widely considered to be the best in the series.

Jammit   Virgin Games   1 $1
Rather than centering on professional or college basketball, Jammit is a street basketball game. It's nice to see something a little different among many, many very similar basketball games on the Genesis, but Jammit is unfortunately only an average game.

Jennifer Capriatti Tennis   Telnet   1 $2
There are lots of players to choose from, but the overly easy gameplay and overall poor design keeps this mediocre tennis sim off the court.

Jeopardy!   Gametek   3 $5
Looking to show off your trivia skills? The graphics and sound of this gaming version of the long-running TV game show are quite antiquated, but the wide variety of question categories will please fans of the genre. Too bad games of this type don't play well with console controllers.

Jeopardy! Deluxe   Gametek   3 $6
Jeopardy Deluxe is really nothing more than a rehashed version of the original, with new questions (or answers, depending on how you look at it).

Jeopardy!: Sports Edition   Gametek   2 $4
As the title suggests, this is a specialized version of Jeopardy aimed at sports fanatics.

Jewel Master   Sega   3 $5
This game could have been a great platformer, but it feels very unfinished. The spell system (which had the potential to be interesting) is merely frustrating.

James Bond: The Duel   Jeopardy!   Jeopardy!: Sports Edition   Jewel Master

The Flame Whip is the most powerful weapon in Castlevania II: Simon's Quest.

John Madden Football '93

John Madden Football '93

Jordan vs. Bird

Judge Dredd

Joe & Mac   **Takara** 3 $6
Platformers come in all varieties imaginable, and this is one falls directly in the center of them all. The level design is interesting, but the sound and animation are poor.

Joe Montana Football **Sega** 1 $1
This was a good game on the Master System, but the Genesis "update" is inexcusably dated.

Joe Montana Football 2 **Sega** 1 $1
This was the first game to feature Sega's "Sports Talk" feature, giving gamers some in-game commentary to go along with their shoddy football action.

Joe Montana Sportstalk Football '94
    Sega 1 $1
The game engine for the formerly mediocre football franchise has been given a good overhaul, and it shows.

Joe Montana Sportstalk Football '95
    Sega 1 $2
This is pretty much a rehash of Joe Montana Sportstalk Football '94 with minor changes.

John Madden Football **Electronic Arts** 1 $1
When John Madden Football was released in 1991, a whole new type of football game was available for gamers everywhere. There were more plays to choose from than ever before, statistics upon statistics, and a great game engine. Many, many others imitated the series, but none could match Madden in terms of gameplay, graphics, and all-around quality.

John Madden Football '92 **Electronic Arts** 1 $1
This is basically the first Madden game with some mostly minor enhancements and some rather creepy digital animations of John Madden.

John Madden Football '93 **Electronic Arts** 1 $1
The third of the Genesis Madden games improved upon the first two titles in the series considerably. The graphics are upgraded quite a bit, a no-huddle offense option is included, and the digital animation that was added in the '92 version of the game is improved.

John Madden '93: Championship Edition
    Electronic Arts 7 $20
Aside from the extra all-time greatest NFL teams, there was nothing different about this "Championship Edition" of the '93 Madden game other than the fact it was available only through rental outlets.

John Madden NFL '94 **Electronic Arts** 1 $1
John Madden '94 is generally thought to be the most significant games in the series, and not just because it was the first game to feature the NFL license. The graphics are enhanced, more players are available, and the game engine is smoother.

John Madden NFL '95 **Electronic Arts** 1 $1
If you only buy one Madden game (and how many does one need, really?), make it this one or '97. The gameplay is probably the best in this version of the series.

John Madden NFL '96 **Electronic Arts** 1 $1
This version of the game does include a four-player simultaneous play option (which is nice) but the rest of John Madden '96 doesn't quite live up to Madden '95.

John Madden NFL '97 **Electronic Arts** 2 $2
The gameplay engine was returned to fantastic shape for the '97 update. This game is arguably the best in the series, right next to Madden '95.

John Madden NFL '98 **THQ/EA** 3 $5
The last in the series on the Genesis, Madden '98 is a decent football game, but the series was played out by this time (eclipsed by next-generation console versions.)

Jordan vs. Bird **Electronic Arts** 1 $2
Some sports games just can't pass the test of time. This one does, however, since it's still a solid game.

Joshua   **Wisdom Tree** 7 $35
Wisdom Tree is infamous for illegally releasing... Christian games, ironically. This is one of them, and although it isn't terrible, there isn't anything exciting about this platformer.

Judge Dredd   **Acclaim** 2 $3
Thankfully, the video game translation of the popular comic book character was better than the movie rendition. Judge Dredd is a fairly good sci-fi platformer, and although it doesn't push the envelope, it's worth picking up.

Junction   **Konami** 4 $8
Hardcore puzzle gamers may find some enjoyment in this puzzler, but most should probably stick to Columns as it is a better game on all levels.

Pauline is the name of the girl being held by Donky Kong in the original DK games.

Jungle Book, The   Disney/Virgin Interactive   4 $8
This platformer is obviously based on the Disney cartoon movie of the same name, and is just as good, sporting great graphics, control, and sound effects.

Jungle Strike   Electronic Arts   1 $2
This is the second entry in the Strike series of helicopter shooters and features the same cool graphics, sound, and tough gameplay found in all the games.

Jurassic Park   Ocean   2 $4
Based on the extremely popular movie of the same name, Jurassic Park is one of the better platformers available on the Genesis. It has great action, nice graphics, and the ability to choose between two characters - a Raptor and Alan Grant (the paleontologist from the movie).

Jurassic Park: Rampage Edition
    Blue Sky   3 $5
Rampage Edition is very similar to the first Jurassic Park game on the Genesis. Basically, the programmers decided to give Grant a *huge* arsenal of weapons to use against the dinosaurs, making his character a lot more interesting.

Jurassic Park 2: The Lost World
    Appaloosa Interactive   4 $8
This is a pretty average action/shooting game, and not much more. The graphics are bright and detailed, but the gameplay is nothing all that exciting and pales in comparison to the first two Lost World games. This was one of the last Genesis releases.

Justice League Task Force
    Acclaim   2 $3
This is disappointingly average fighting game featuring a select group of superhero characters. We remember looking forward to this title with great anticipation, but Acclaim dropped the ball and delivered a mediocre and shallow fighter unworthy of its license.

Ka Ge Ki: Fists of Steel   Kaneko   5 $12
A somewhat strange (yet still uninspiring) side-scrolling beat-em-up, Ka Ge Ki should probably be avoided except for the sake of owning it as part of a collection.

Kid Chameleon   Sega   4 $8
Kid Chameleon is one of the cooler (and most often overlooked) platformers out there for the Genesis. It uses some interesting game mechanics, including several different character transformations.

King of the Monsters   Takara   3 $5
Hardcore fighting fans will be pleased with this Neo Geo arcade port, regardless of the fact that it is essentially a mindless button-masher and there are only four fighters to choose from.

King of the Monsters 2   Takara   4 $8
You'll get more of the same mass destruction of the first game plus a few additional enhancements and characters.

King Salmon: The Big Catch
    Sage's Creation   3 $5
It might not be the "king" of fishing games, but it certainly isn't the court jester, either. Try it out if you don't have any other fishing games for the Genesis.

King's Bounty: The Conquerors Quest
    Electronic Arts   6 $25
The graphics are nothing to gawk at, but strategy/RPG fans will enjoy King's Bounty great strategy gameplay.

Klax   Tengen   3 $6
Klax's appearance on the Genesis is a welcome one as puzzle games don't get much better than this. Unfortunately, the developers chose not to push the Genesis hardware to any degree, resulting in a game that looks and sounds worse that its TG-16 counterpart.

Lakers vs. Celtics   Electronic Arts   2 $3
This is the first entry in EA's well-designed NBA Playoffs basketball series.

Landstalker   Climax/Sega   4 $12
Landstalker is one of the best of the "undiscovered" action/RPG's on the Genesis. Great isometric graphics and engrossing gameplay combine to make this one a really enjoyable experience.

Last Action Hero, The   Sony Imagesoft   2 $3
While the graphics and presentation of this game are nice and pretty, the gameplay is nearly as bad as the movie (and that's awfully bad, folks.)

Last Battle   Sega   2 $4
Known as Fist of the North Star in Japan, this side-scrolling fighter has limited action but decent graphics and sound. The extreme gore of the Japanese game has been exorcised.

Lawnmower Man   Time/Warner   2 $4
Based on the movie of the same name, The Lawnmower Man is

Jungle Strike   Klax   Landstalker   Last Battle

Pac-Man was first released in 1980.

| The Lion King | The Little Mermaid | The Lost Vikings | Lotus II: RECS |

a cool and innovative but entirely too difficult platform game.

Legend of Galahad, The Electronic Arts 3 $5
This decent action of this platform game is somewhat thwarted by exceedingly ugly graphics and design work.

Legend of Toki - Going Ape Spit, The
TAD/Sega 3 $4
You'll find some pretty neat graphical tricks in this otherwise standard platform game, but not much else.

Lemmings Psygnosis 2 $4
This is about as cool as it gets for puzzle/strategy gaming on the Genesis. Gamers take control of cute little lemmings and dole out specific tasks in order to help the group to safety. The game is pretty simple, but the strategy involved in getting everything to work out can be very challenging.

Lemmings 2: The Tribes Psygnosis 3 $4
Based on the same style of gameplay as the original, this sequel requires players to utilize different tribes of Lemmings to reach their goal.

Lethal Enforcers Konami 1 $2
Although it isn't quite up to par with the arcade game of the same name, the Genesis port of Lethal Enforcers is still a solid light gun game that deserves a second look.

Lethal Enforcers 2 Konami 1 $3
Set in a western environment, Lethal Enforcers 2 is an excellent sequel with a whole arsenal of cool weapons, great graphics, and solid gameplay.

LHX Attack Chopper Electronic Arts 1 $2
As a flight simulator, LHX Attack Chopper is one of the better games available for the Genesis. It allows gamers to pilot their choice of two different copters in a slew of missions across Europe, Asia, and the Middle East.

Liberty or Death Koei 7 $35
Historical simulations aren't common for any console, but the Genesis had a few (and this is one of the best ones.) Liberty or Death allows gamers to choose which side they want to represent during the American Revolution.

Light Crusader Treasure/Sega 2 $4
As a challenging and occasionally frustrating RPG, Light Crusader succeeds. Unfortunately, it falls short of being one of the

all-time greats (even if famed developer Treasure did have a hand in it.)

Lion King, The Disney 1 $4
Although the story behind The Lion King is completely ridiculous, this game is refreshingly enjoyable due to the bright graphics and nice action-based gameplay.

Little Mermaid, The Disney/Virgin 2 $3
Again, Disney delivers a great platformer based upon one of their animated films. The graphics are bright and colorful, and the gameplay is actually quite enjoyable, even for older gamers.

Lobo Ocean 4 $8
For the uninitiated, Lobo is a comic book character that slaughtered everyone on his planet because he felt like it, has heavy metal music constantly streaming into is brain, and works as a bounty hunter... for the pleasure of killing rather than the money he earns in doing so. Regrettably, this platform game based on his namesake isn't nearly as entertaining as the license.

Lost Vikings, The Interplay 3 $5
An addictive puzzle/strategy game in the tradition of Lemmings, The Lost Vikings has some nice graphics, challenging levels, and unique humor. Players must switch between three Viking characters (each with different abilities) in order to progress.

Lotus II: RECS Electronic Arts 3 $7
RECS (Race Environment Construction System) is a cool racer with good graphics and a great track creation interface.

Lotus Turbo Challenge Electronic Arts 4 $8
This game is a competent but ultimately repetitive racer that could have used some more work to make it stick out from the crowd of similar titles.

Magic School Bus, The Sega 5 $12
As the name suggests, this excellent edutainment title is aimed squarely at children, preferably YOUNG children.

M.U.S.H.A. Seismic 7 $40
This hyper-fast top-down shooter is considered my many hardcore fans of the genre to be one of the best 16-bit shooters ever made. M.U.S.H.A. (Metallic Uniframe Super Hybrid Armor) features an awesome storyline, great graphics, and a superb soundtrack.

Man Overboard Codemasters 5 $12
The Titanic-style concept of saving passengers from a sinking

The American release of Final Fantasy II is the same game as the Japanese release of Final Fantasy IV.

ocean liner is original, but the execution of this innovative platform game fails to live up to its lofty aspirations.

Marble Madness   Electronic Arts   4 $8
This neat action/puzzle hybrid created quite in stir in arcades when it was released back in the 1980's, and the Genesis port is nearly arcade-perfect. The isometric perspective and funky soundtrack have been retained, but the loss of the trackball controller proves to be detrimental to the gameplay.

Mario Andretti Racing   Electronic Arts   2 $3
This is a is a good-looking first-person F1 racing game featuring dull sound effects but excellent control.

Mario Lemieux Hockey   Sega   1 $2
You'd be wise to stick with one of EA's NFL offerings if you need a hockey fix… this is a below-average hockey game on all levels.

Marko's Magic Soccer Ball
    Domark   4 $8
This is a unique action/platformer in that the title character uses a soccer ball to defeat his enemies. The graphics, sound, and overall design are all top-notch.

Marsupilami   Sega   4 $8
Although the controls can be somewhat difficult to handle, Marsupilami (based on a Saturday morning cartoon of the same name) is a solid action/platformer.

Marvel Land   Namco   5 $12
This cool platform game was overlooked upon its initial release, and that's a real shame. Although it doesn't have a lot of eye-candy, this is a very enjoyable and challenging game worthy of your attention.

Mary Shelley's Frankenstein
    Sony Imagesoft   3 $6
Yes, indeed… Sony created yet another patchwork monster with this banal platform game based on the bad movie.

Master of Monsters   Systemsoft   6 $30
Although it does take some getting used to the odd control scheme, Master of Monsters is still an excellent turn-based strategy game.

Math Blasters: Episode I
    Davidson Software   5 $12
As you might have ascertained from the title, Math Blasters is

an "edutainment" game. Surprisingly, it does a decent job of making math fun.

Maximum Carnage   Acclaim   2 $5
Even though it does star the popular Spiderman and his nemesis Carnage, this beat-em-up gets way too old way too fast. There's not much reason to play through the whole thing unless you're a comic book junkie.

Mazin Saga: Mutant Fighter
    Sega   2 $4
Mazin Saga is a rather humdrum, uneventful action game. The graphics and game play are average at best.

McDonald's Treasure Land Adventure
    Treasure   5 $12
You wouldn't expect a game based on the world's most popular fast food franchise to be any good, but famed developer Treasure does a fine job of bringing some proper entertainment to this fun platform title.

Mega Bomberman   Hudson Soft   5 $15
It's Bomberman on the Genesis, for Pete's sake! This game is one of the original multiplayer classics, and if you don't have a home version of Bomberman yet, this is one of the (many) great ones.

Mega Turrican   Data East   2 $4
Intense action, very crisp graphics, and fitting music make this one of the better action games on the Genesis. Recommended.

Menacer 6-Pack   Sega   3 $8
The Menacer 6-Pak has six games that support Sega's Menacer light gun including Pest Control, Whackball, Rockman's Zone, Frontline, Space Station Defender, and Ready! Aim! Tomatoes! Unfortunately, none of them are that good (there's a reason why the peripheral didn't last long.)

Mercs   Capcom   3 $4
Mercs is somewhat of a rip-off of SNK's Guerilla War, but at least it's a well-done rip-off of a great game.

Michael Jackson's Moonwalker
    Sega   3 $5
Unfortunately, the enjoyable platform gameplay of Moonwalker is overshadowed by events that have taken place since the game's release. The plot centers on Michael's music (duplicated poorly, but about as well as can be expected) and his efforts to save a group of young children from a group of thugs.

Marble Madness   Math Blaster: Episode 1   McDonald's Treasure Land Adventure   Michael Jackson's Moonwalker

The American release of Final Fantasy III is the same game as the Japanese release of Final Fantasy VI.

| Mickey's Ultimate Challenge | Mig-29 Fighter Pilot | Might and Magic: Gates to Another World | Monopoly |

Mick & Mack: As the Global Gladiators
Virgin   3 $4
This licensed platform game (featuring fast food giant McDonald's) is actually very good. The visuals, game play, and overall design reflect some real thought and effort.

Mickey & Minney: The Great Circus Mystery
Capcom   4 $8
Disney recycled the wonderful Castle of Illusion game engine for this excellent addition to the platform game series starring Disney's classic cartoon characters.

Mickey Mania   Sega   4 $8
This game is a MUST-own for fans of Mickey Mouse! It looks, plays, and feels exactly like a cartoon, and the first level is even completely in black and white, just like a classic short.

Mickey's Ultimate Challenge
Sony   4 $8
This is a pretty cool action/puzzle game with great cartoony graphics, but it's really not much of a challenge, especially for experienced puzzle fans.

Micro Machines   Codemasters   4 $8
This entertaining and sought-after game is a unique racer in which competitors race in cars that are dwarfed by the environments (kind of like racing a Hot Wheels car in a full-sized home.)

Midnight Resistance   Data East   3 $4
This is a very competent port of the original arcade game (itself a very good Contra clone.)

MiG-29 Fighter Pilot   Domark   4 $8
This upgrade to the NES game corrects many of the original's deficiencies, adding better sound, smoother scaling effects, and more mission variety.

Might & Magic: Gates To Another World
Electronic Arts   5 $15
The original PC RPG was a great game in its day, but it didn't translate well to the Genesis hardware (more a fault of the interface/controller than anything else.)

Mighty Max, The Adventures Of
Ocean   3 $3
This colorful platform game has a very cartoon-like feel to it, along with decent gameplay and good level design.

Mighty Morphin Power Rangers
Bandai   1 $2
No one could escape the clutches of the popular children's show (a mixture of costumed American actors mixed and an old Japanese live-action show), not even the Genesis. This is a simple side-scrolling fighter with a very low challenge (and tolerance) factor.

Mighty Morphin Power Rangers: The Movie
Bandai   2 $2
Once again we are subjected to the Power Rangers and their side-scrolling universe... at least there is a nice variety of moves and the graphics are detailed and colorful.

Mike Ditka Football   Accolade   1 $1
This is an early and inexcusably poor Madden clone that is bettered by dozens of similar titles.

Minnesota Fats: Pool Legend
Data East   4 $10
Pool games don't get much better than this. Minnesota Fats: Pool Legend sports a nice versus mode, a great tournament mode, and even allows players to complete a series of trick shots.

Miracle Piano Teaching System, The
Software Toolworks   6 $22

MLBPA Baseball   Electronic Arts   1 $2
This baseball simulation is one of the better games of its type available for the Genesis. The gameplay is all kinds of fun, and the great graphics and options only add to the experience.

Monopoly   Parker Brothers   4 $10
Like many board games converted over to a digital format, Monopoly suffers from the complete lack of interaction with actual human players. The thrill of landing on Boardwalk is gone, as is the total greed factor. Of course, this changes completely when you get some friends to play with you!

Mortal Kombat   Acclaim   1 $2
Back in the day, Mortal Kombat made all kinds of news for being one of the most violent and controversial fighting games ever. The popular "fatality" moves at the end of fights were half the reason to play, and the Genesis version received special press because it had blood and the original fatalities of the arcade game (as opposed to the censored SNES port, which sold about half as well.)

What game does this quote come from?: "Oh no, the truck have started to move!"

Mortal Kombat 2   Acclaim   1 $2
Most Mortal Kombat fans consider MKII to be the best game in the series due to its better graphics and smoother gameplay. The Genesis port is better than the first game in every way, but Nintendo wised up the second time around and allowed the SNES port (which has more colors and a much better sound-track) to include all the blood and gore, making it the version to get. A superior version of Mortal Kombat 2 is also available for the 32x, but it's still not quite as good as the SNES port.

Mr. Nutz   Ocean   5 $12
Colorful graphics aside, the silly title of this otherwise respect-able (if easy) platform game assured that it would be the butt of many jokes.

Ms. Pac-Man   Namco/Tengen   4 $12
Few gamers deny that Ms. Pac Man is the most beloved install-ment in the hyper-popular series of dot-eaters, and the sales figures for this arcade-perfect port reflect her continued popular-ity. Too bad the Genesis control pad doesn't work well with this sort of game.

Muhammad Ali Heavyweight Boxing
                   Virgin   2 $4
Boxing games are a rare breed for most every home console, and the Genesis was no exception. This innovative and deep fighter rates as one of its best boxing simulations.

Mutant League Football   Electronic Arts   2 $6
This is certainly one of the most brutal football games ever made. Rather than engage in a "normal" football game where the object of the game is to score the most points, Mutant League Football requires you to completely destroy, maim, and punish one's opponents. Hardcore sports junkies may not like this as much as some of the Madden games, but Mutant League Football wasn't meant to appeal to Madden fans any-way.

Mutant League Hockey   Electronic Arts   3 $6
As in Mutant League Football, you must maim, crush, and even kill your opponents in addition to scoring points. Chainsaws, hammers, and demons are only some of the weapons you can use to aid you in your goal(s).

Mystic Defender   Sega   6 $22
This is an early Genesis release, and it shows. Pretty much everything about this action/shooting game screams of medioc-rity, aside from the interesting control scheme (later revived for

one of the rarest Saturn games of all, the Japanese import Psy-chic Killer Assassin Taromaru.)

NBA Action '94   Sega   1 $1
The first of Sega's in-house basketball series features cool 3-D graphics and a fairly tight gameplay engine.

NBA Action '95   Sega   1 $1
Rather than merely update the first game in the series, Sega chose to overhaul it completely, and the results are less than impressive. The graphics are poor and the gameplay is stilted.

NBA All-Star Challenge   Acclaim   1 $1
As with all too many of the Genesis sports title, this game is merely a half-hearted clone... of Super One-on-One, in this case.

NBA Hang Time   Midway   1 $1
Fast and furious gameplay makes this NBA Jam clone worth a shot (if you haven't already played a hundred other Genesis sports games.)

NBA Jam   Acclaim   1 $2
Midway's now-classic 2-on-2-basketball arcade sensation made an appearance on most every console of the period and sold millions of copies. It's easy to see why... the over-the-top ar-cade-style action is great fun, as is discovering all the secret characters. Unfortunately, the Genesis port loses the big heads and scaling effects of its arcade parent, but the gameplay is as sensational as ever.

NBA Jam: Tournament Edition
                   Acclaim   1 $2
Even though NBA Jam: T.E. was basically just an attempt to make more money of the license with a mild upgrade, it's still moderately better than the original. The graphics and sound haven't changed, but new features include updated rosters and secret characters, court "hotspots," and more. A nearly arcade-perfect version of NBA Jam TE is available for the 32x.

NBA Live '95   Electronic Arts   1 $1
The first game in the series brought a whole new kind of basket-ball game to the Genesis. Its graphics, sound, gameplay, and control were way beyond anything else sports gamers had seen up to that point.

NBA Live '96   Electronic Arts   1 $1
The first update in the popular basketball series takes an al-ready amazing basketball sim and makes it better with updated

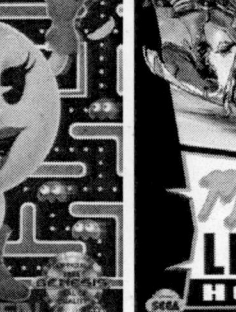

Ms. Pac-Man   Mutant League Hockey   NBA Action '94   NBA All-Star Challenge

| NBA Live '97 | NCAA Football | NFL Quarterback Club | NHL '96 |

rosters and a great create-a-player interface.

NBA Live '97 Electronic Arts 1 $1
The gameplay is the same, but the cheesy new presentation is distracting.

NBA Live '98 T*HQ 2 $4
This was the last game in the superlative basketball series and one of the final Genesis releases.

NBA Showdown '94 Electronic Arts 1 $1
This very competent but rather dated basketball release uses the same game engine as the NBA Playoffs series games (Bulls vs. Blazers, Lakers vs. Celtics, etc.) and it shows.

NCAA Final Four Basketball
Electronic Arts 1 $1
It's not the best playing basketball game on the Genesis, but it provides enough sporting entertainment to warrant a look.

NCAA Football Mindscape 1 $1
Too.... many.... football games.... This one is just another of them. Although it is refreshing to at least see the teams of the NCAA instead of those of the NFL, this game just isn't anything special.

NFL Quarterback Club Acclaim 1 $2
Back in the 16-bit days, the NFL Quarterback Club series was actually quite good. The game is a complete Madden clone, but it's still a great deal of fun to play and miles ahead of the 32 bit travesties. An excellent version of NFL Quarterback Club is available for the 32x.

NFL Quarterback Club '96
Acclaim 1 $3
This is a mildly updated revision to the popular and well-received football sim.

NHL '95 Electronic Arts 1 $1
The series was back on track for 1995, sporting smoother graphics and gameplay.

NHL '96 Electronic Arts 1 $1
Considered by many to be the best game in the franchise, NHL '96 is the smoothest and most refined entry in the series.

NHL '97 Electronic Arts 1 $1
Aside from the updated rosters, NHL '97 is pretty much the same game as NHL '96.

NHL '98 Electronic Arts 3 $5
EA played it safe and stuck with a mildly updated version of the '96 game for the last Genesis NHL release (which was also one of the final games for the console.)

NHL All-Star Hockey '95 Sega 1 $2
Sega's sports division didn't disappoint when they released this bombshell of a hockey game... the graphics, gameplay, and control are all top-notch.

NHL Hockey Electronic Arts 1 $1
The first game in what would become one of the best-selling franchises on the Genesis, EA's first attempt at a hockey simulation pales in comparison to later releases but was a stunning omen of what was to come later.

NHL Hockey '93 Electronic Arts 1 $1
The '92 update is very similar to the first game.

NHL Hockey '94 Electronic Arts 1 $1
EA took a step backward with their '94 update, leaving gamers to wonder why they hadn't left well enough alone.

NHLPA '93 Electronic Arts 1 $2
This stellar update to the popular hockey series features awesome graphics, great sound, and an incredibly smooth gameplay engine.

Nigel Mansell's World Championship Racing
Acclaim 2 $3
This is one of the smoothest and best-playing F1 racers on the Genesis.

No Escape Sony Imagesoft 2 $4
Few people claim to be real fans of the original feature film, and even fewer gamers admit to liking this lame platform adventure.

Nobunga's Ambition Koei 6 $25
This is a historical strategy game centering on the infamous Japanese warlord (as well as one of the best games of its type available for the Genesis.) Strategy fans will love it.

Normy's Beach Babe-o-Rama
Electronic Arts 3 $4
Although the storyline is completely ridiculous, this action platformer is a good time if for no other reason than the rampant humor.

What are the three parts of the Triforce in the Zelda series?

Olympic Gold - Barcelona '92

       U.S. Gold 2 $4

As can be expected, Olympic Gold isn't much more than a mindless button-masher. Some of the events are enjoyable, but the replay value is limited.

Olympic Summer Games - Atlanta '96

       U.S. Gold 2 $4

Considered by its fan to be the best game in the series (but that's not really saying a lot), Summer Games features a variety of summer Olympic events.

Olympic Winter Games - Lillehammer '94

       U.S. Gold 3 $5

This is the winter update to the semi-popular Olympic trilogy.

Onslaught   Accolade 3 $5

This is a "medieval" action game with a cool theme but ancient gameplay and dated graphics.

Ooze, The   Sega 4 $8

This unique, original, and often overlooked action title is great fun to play.

Operation Europe: Path To Victory

       Koei 7 $30

Quite possibly our personal vote for the best historic simulation on the Genesis, this excellent World War II game (from Koei, of course) allows you to pick sides and determine your own outcome of the war.

Out of This World Interplay 2 $7

This 2-D adventure game defies description… part platformer, part puzzler, part cinematic fantasy trip, Out of this World is a methodical, frustratingly difficult, and thoroughly mesmerizing game that needs to be played to be appreciated.

Outlander   Mindscape 6 $20

A successful melding of two different gaming genres with a post-apocalyptic world reminiscent of Mel Gibson's Road Warrior feature film, this excellent cart features first-person combat racing as well as side-scrolling shooting action.

OutRun   Sega 3 $5

Sega's classic racing title (quite possibly the most influential racing game ever made) debuted on the Genesis in fine style, losing only a small portion of its speed and visual splendor. Everything is here… the cross-country courses, your blonde

(and occasionally bitchy) girlfriend, the whizzing scaling effects, plus all the cool cars…. the Corvettes, the Bugs, the Porches, and the Ferrari, of course!

OutRun 2019   Sega 4 $8

This futuristic update on the classic Outrun theme adds some new features including upgraded graphics, more speed, more challenging courses, and road hazards.

OutRunners   Sega 4 $10

The big draws of this well-received sequel to the original racer are the addition of a 2-player split screen mode and some new car choices.

Pac-Attack   Namco 4 $10

Although Pac-Attack is at least partially a Tetris rip-off, it's still different enough to be a great puzzler.

Pac-Man 2: The New Adventures

       Namco 4 $12

The point-and-click controls of this Pac spin-off would have probably worked better on a PC, but the humorous attitude and colorful graphics of this interesting platform game make it all worth the effort.

Pac-Mania   Tengen 5 $12

Hardcore Pac-Man fans will probably have a good time with this one, but that's about it. Pac-Mania is basically just a souped up version of the original game with some isometric 3-D graphics and some new play mechanics. There's a reason why this one never made it big in arcades…

Pacific Theatre of Operations

       KOEI 5 $14

P.T.O. is yet another Koei simulation game with a decidedly historical theme. There's a nice two-player mode, a whole boatload of maps, and lots more. Followed by a sequel on the Sega Saturn.

Pagemaster   Probe 3 $3

The original feature film (starring Home Alone's Macaulay Culkin) was an unexpected flop, leaving the video game to flounder on its own. It's really not bad as far as licensed platform games go, but the terrible marketing campaign and the movie's bad press conspired to leave this one in the discount bin.

Paperboy   Tengen 3 $4

If you already have another version of this classic arcade favorite on the NES or SMS, there's really not any reason to get an-

Onslaught

Out of this World

Outlander

Outrun

| Pele II: World Tournament Soccer | Phantasy Star II | Phantasy Star III | Phantasy Star IV |

other one. Everything remains the same, including the isometric visuals, dull soundtrack, and frustrating control.

Paperboy 2   Tengen   4 $10
This sequel to the original racing/action game has somewhat updated graphics, faster game play, and the option of playing as a Papergirl (hold us back.)

Pat Riley Basketball   Sega   1 $1
This early basketball effort from Sega shows its age badly with its archaic graphics and unrefined gameplay.

Pebble Beach Golf Links   T&E Soft/Sega   2 $3
This is arguably the best Genesis golf sim ever released, even better than EA's excellent PGA Golf series. It features great courses, super gameplay, and captures the feel of golf quite well.

Pele Soccer   Accolade   3 $4
This is an obvious rip-off of EA's soccer games, only without the smooth gameplay and precise control. It plays well enough, but there are far better choices available.

Pele 2: World Tournament Soccer
**   Accolade   3 $4**
This is a graphically enhanced update to the original FIFA clone.

Pete Sampras Tennis   Codemasters   2 $4
Haven't played all the Genesis tennis titles? The pride of total completion is the only reason to pick up and play this mediocre release.

Pete Sampras Tennis '96 Codemasters   3 $5
What happened?!? The substandard graphics and gameplay of the original release have been completely overhauled for this excellent sequel.

PGA European Tour   Electronic Arts 2 $4
European Tour is very similar to al the other PGA games, but with one obvious change - the courses and players are European.

PGA Tour Golf   Electronic Arts 2 $5
The first of the awesome PGA golfing games only has four courses, but the great gameplay hints of what was to come from later releases.

PGA Tour Golf 2   Electronic Arts 3 $5
The second game in the otherwise excellent golfing games was

the first installment to showcase the series glaring flaw... slow loading times (which were offset by excellent graphics.)

PGA Tour Golf 3   Electronic Arts 3 $5
Like many EA sports games, the third installment in the popular golfing franchise features mildly enhanced graphics and a few updates here and there.

PGA Tour Golf '96   Electronic Arts 3 $5
EA finished off their popular golf franchise in style with some of the best graphics and gameplay the console ever saw (in a golfing simulation, that is.)

Phantasy Star 2   Sega   4 $22
Many RPG fans consider the original Phantasy Star (for the Sega Master System) to be one of the finest role-playing games ever created. Sega took special care not to tarnish the sacred name of their beloved franchise, and PS2 retains the look and feel of the original while expanding and enhancing the graphics, soundtrack and storyline in several key areas. The end result is a rich and satisfying RPG that ranks as one of the best games for the Genesis.

Phantasy Star 3   Sega   3 $15
More of a side-story than a true continuation of the influential series of role playing games, PS3 features more characters and several separate endings which manifest themselves depending on how well the game is played. Considered by many to be the weakest entry in the series, PS3 nevertheless is a stellar RPG.

Phantasy Star 4   Sega   5 $30
Sega came full circle with their third and final Phantasy Star game for the Genesis (one of the most expensive 16-bit games ever released in the States.) The gloriously deep and complex storyline is augmented by some of the best graphics the console ever saw, and the soundtrack is truly rousing (by Genesis standards, at least.) All in all, a remarkable effort in a remarkable series of games, and one that should be in every collector's library.

Phantom 2040   Viacom   4 $8
Action and animation fans will certainly be pleased with this game, set in a futuristic environment and featuring great graphics and solid gameplay.

Phelios   Apollo/Namco   6 $18
While it isn't the best space shooter to ever grace the Genesis, the respectable graphics and admirable attempt at some sort of storyline allow Phelios to rise above the crowd of similar shoot-

Atari was originally going to be called Syzygy, but the name had already been taken.

ers.

Pigskin Footbrawl　　　　**Razorsoft**　　**4**　　**$10**
If nothing else, Pigskin Football is a unique and interesting game. Rather than just being another Madden or Joe Montana clone, this game is set in the Middle Ages. Two battling kingdoms must settle their disputes on the gridiron with weapons and armor.

Pink Goes To Hollywood　　**TekMagic**　　**4**　　**$8**
The gameplay fails to rise above the level of average, but the graphics and soundtrack of this otherwise forgettable platform adventure will make you wonder if the Genesis had a few more tricks up its graphical and audio sleeves.

Pinocchio　　　　　　**Disney/Virgin**　　**5**　　**$12**
Like many other Disney-themed platformers of the time (The Lion King, Jungle Book, etc.), Pinocchio is one of the best-looking games on the Genesis (and has solid gameplay to back up its pleasing visuals.)

Pirates! Gold　　　　**Micropose**　　**6**　　**$22**
You wouldn't expect any Genesis game with the word "Pirate" in the title to be anything more than a crappy platform game, but both of the console's Pirate-named releases are excellent. Pirates! Gold is a simply wonderful RPG with great graphics and deep gameplay.

Pirates Of Dark Water　　**Sunsoft**　　**2**　　**$4**
This obscure little release is near the top of the list of Genesis action/adventure games. It features some interesting gameplay elements including the ability to switch between characters during gameplay and three quests to be completed. Based on the unsuccessful cartoon series of the same name.

Pitfall: The Mayan Adventure
　　　　　　　　　　Activision　　**3**　　**$4**
Activision's lush update to their classic Atari 2600 game (which is hidden within) features all the elements you expect from a good platform game… tons of different environments (including the obligatory mine cart level), great graphics, and flawless control… too bad it's so darn hard. A mildly enhanced version of Pitfall is also available for the 32x.

Pit-Fighter: The Ultimate Competition
　　　　　　　　　　Tengen　　**2**　　**$5**
It may have been the inspiration for Mortal Kombat, but the dated graphics and gameplay of this tired fighter will inspire you

to play something else.

Pocahontas　　　　**Disney/Virgin**　　**4**　　**$8**
One of the best and most difficult of the Disney platformers, this puzzle-intensive entry features lush graphics and a wide range of play mechanics.

Populous　　　　　**Electronic Arts**　　**2**　　**$4**
Revolutionary at the time of its release, Populous was the originator of the "God Game" genre (the premise of the game is to build, populate, edit, and basically play God in the world you create.) Unfortunately, the standard Genesis game pad often proves to be a hindrance.

Power Instinct　　　　**Atlus**　　**3**　　**$5**
The fighting engine is better than we expected, but the grainy graphics and tinny soundtrack conspire to ruin an otherwise respectable Street Fighter II clone.

Powerball　　　　　**Namco**　　**3**　　**$5**
This silly Speedball clone is too slow-paced to warrant more than a few minutes playtime.

Power Monger　　　　**Electronic Arts**　　**2**　　**$4**
This glorious strategy game (from the makers of Populous) pays homage to its inspiration in many ways but adds deeper, more intense gameplay involving futuristic battles, alliances, and more.

Predator 2　　　　　**Acclaim**　　**3**　　**$7**
This movie-based shooter is better than most games of its type, but the action gets old way too fast.

Primal Rage　　　　**Time Warner**　　**3**　　**$8**
The inexplicably popular fighting game featuring motion-captured dinosaur models made its way to nearly ever console of the era. It's really nothing more than a poor Mortal Kombat clone. Compared to the arcade game, the Genesis port has washed-out graphics, smaller characters, and poor sound. A mildly enhanced version of Primal Rage is also available for the 32x.

Prime Time NFL Football With Dion Sanders
　　　　　　　　　　Sega　　**2**　　**$4**
This is a very solid football game in Sega's NFL Football series featuring the endorsement of Dion Sanders.

Prince Of Persia　　　　**Domark**　　**3**　　**$5**
Quite a bit different from your standard platform game, Prince of

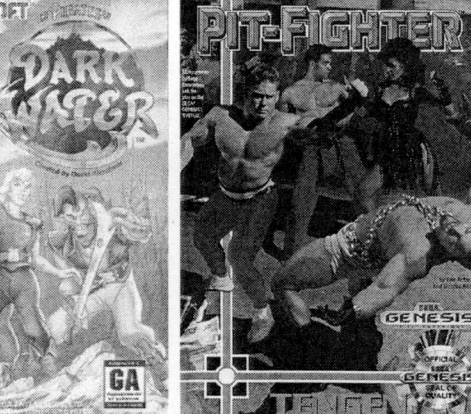

Pink Goes To Hollywood　　　　**Pirates! Gold**　　　　**Pirates of Dark Water**　　　　**Pit-Fighter**

The Atari 2600 game E.T. is actually mapped around a cube, making it difficult to know where you will wind up next.

Quad Challenge Race Drivin' R.B.I. Baseball 3 Red Zone

Persia stresses timing and patience over button-pressing antics. The graphics and animation are beautiful.

Pro Quarterback   Tradewest   2 $4
You've got to give the developer some credit for trying to push the Genesis hardware, but the first-person perspective of the choppy and poor playing football sim just pushes the console a bit too hard.

Puggsy   Psygnosis   5 $15
One of the better platform games available for the Genesis (and that's saying a lot), Puggsy features charming graphics and well-designed puzzle gameplay.

Punisher , The   Marvel Games   4 $8
There really isn't anything exciting about this beat-em-up. Punching, kicking, and repeating are about all there is to it.

QuackShot Starring Donald Duck
                              Disney   5 $12
This is an average Disney platformer with some great graphics and sound but mediocre gameplay.

Quad Challenge   Namco   4 $8
Although somewhat dated, Quad Challenge is still a decent racing game for those who want something different than Out-Run or Super Monaco GP.

Race Drivin'   Tengen   4 $8
This sequel to the popular arcade racer Hard Drivin' features a new track editor and even more slowdown and frame rate issues. Some games just should have never been ported to the Genesis.

Radical Rex   Activision   2 $4
This is a platformer with cutesy graphics, a dinosaur that rides a skateboard, and quirky humor around every corner. It isn't the best, but it's certainly above average.

Raiden Trad   Micronet   6 $18
Cool power-ups, big weapons, and amazing graphics make Raiden Trad a very enjoyable and worthwhile top-down shooter, especially for fans of the genre.

Rambo 3   Carloco   2 $4
It might be a rip-off of Ikari Warriors, but Rambo 3 is still a very solid and enjoyable shooter. It's based on the worst of the Rambo movies (starring our favorite moron, Sylvester Stallone.)

Rampart   Tengen   3 $5
Let's see what we have here… you're in control of a tiny little castle lobbing tiny little cannonballs at tiny little sailing ships. Every few minutes you get to rebuild your tiny little castle with tiny little Tetris-style bricks. If the time runs out before your tiny little walls are complete, you lose. The graphics are lame and the soundtrack is weak. Funny how this tiny little release (ported from an arcade game) didn't leave our Genesis for weeks and weeks on end…

Ranger X   Gau Enetrtainment   4 $8
Shooting games this good don't come along very often… the graphics are simply amazing, the gameplay is very addictive, and the level design is ingenious. Check it out!

Rastan Saga 2   Taito   6 $22
Gamers who like hack and slash action games will be pleased with Rastan Saga 2, but this sort of thing gets old awful quick!

RBI Baseball 3   Tengen   1 $2
Emphasizing arcade-style gameplay over a more true-to-life simulation style, the RBI Baseball series is a nice break from some of the other baseball games on the Genesis.

RBI Baseball 4   Tengen   1 $2
This is a mildly enhanced update of the popular arcade-style baseball game.

RBI Baseball '93   Tengen   2 $4
This is a mildly enhanced update of the popular arcade-style baseball game.

RBI Baseball '94   Tengen   2 $4
This is the last of the of the popular arcade-style baseball games for the Genesis.

Red Zone   Scavenger   2 $4
This is among the best shooters available for the Genesis. Players take control of an Apache helicopter in what is one of the most graphically advanced games for this system, plus the gameplay is great, too. This is a must-own for hardcore shooting game fans.

Ren & Stimpy: Stimpy's Invention
                              Viacom   3 $4
Based on the cartoon of the same name, this Ren & Stimpy platformer features great graphics, good gameplay, and some great humor.

Star Fox 64 was the first N64 title to support the Rumble Pak feature.

Revenge of Shinobi   Sega   2 $4
This entertaining action game is similar to the beloved arcade originals and is a lot of fun to play.

Revolution X   Acclaim   2 $4
What a graphically ugly, tragically sounding, pitifully playing mess! This wretched port of the oddly popular gun shooter (featuring the rock band Aerosmith) is just so bad on so many levels that it's best to just forget that it ever existed.

Richard Scarry's Busytown
                    Novatrade   4 $10
This edutainment game is based on the popular series of children's books and manages to both educate and entertain with its blend of puzzles and mini-games.

Rings of Power   Electronic Arts   3 $8
Infamous for its nudity "Easter Egg," this lackluster RPG is eclipsed by far better games of its type. The graphics aren't attractive, the animation isn't smooth, and the game isn't based on The Lord of the Rings (fooled again.)

Rise of the Robots   Acclaim   2 $4
This awful Street Fighter II clone got a lot of press for its beautiful rendered graphics, but things go downhill FAST once the 'action' starts and the flaws of the wretched fighting engine become apparent.

Risk   Parker Brothers   4 $12
Even if you weren't a big fan of the board game, this strategy game deserves a look. Although it's fairly simplistic as far as graphics go, the original game of conquest makes a good transition to the Genesis.

Risky Woods   Electronic Arts   3 $5
This game has nothing whatsoever to do with golf or Tiger Woods… it's actually an above-average action game with an interesting plot and solid gameplay.

Ristar   Sega   3 $5
Beautiful graphics and a lovely soundtrack alone aren't enough to save even the best intentioned of games (even Sega's own Sonic clones), and Ristar is a perfect example of visual splendor and catchy music over game design. This platformer's gameplay is decent enough, but the levels aren't very inspiring.

Road Blasters   Tengen   2 $4
Repetitive gameplay aside, this is a solid port of the archaic arcade combat racer.

Road Rash   Electronic Arts   2 $5
Electronic Arts combined the thrill of cross-country motorcycle racing with brutal combat and came up with one doozy of a franchise. Beat, pummel, and wreck your opponents with a variety of nasty weapons, all while trying to make it to the finish line first.

Road Rash 2   Electronic Arts   3 $6
Part 2 is arguably the best game in the popular racing/combat series. It feels much smoother than the original, and allows two players to go up against one another.

Road Rash 3   Electronic Arts   4 $8
The last of the Rash series for the Genesis sports of the best gameplay of the trio, but the visuals have taken a hit in the smoothness department.

Robocop 3   Acclaim   4 $8
This game is pretty much what you expected… a very average side-scrolling release saddled with a crappy movie license.

Robocop vs. Terminator   Virgin   4 $8
No one expected much from this movie series combo game, but the developers managed to get most everything right. The graphics, music, gameplay, and dark theme are just right… too bad the game is just so darn hard!

Rocket Knight Adventures   Konami   3 $5
While very derivative of Contra, this colorful action title is well designed and full of fast gameplay and solid (if garish) visuals.

Rock 'n' Roll Racing   Interplay   4 $12
It's not quite as good as the better-sounding SNES port, but this isometric combat racer is still one of the most addictive and entertaining games on the Genesis console. Best played with a group of like-minded friends, Rock 'n' Roll racing will bring out the jerk in all of us (and that's a good thing in some circumstances.) It's too bad that the similarly themed Biker Mice From Mars (check the SNES section) didn't get a Genesis version.

Roger Clemens MVP Baseball
                    Acclaim   1 $2
This is a generic and ultimately forgettable baseball sim bearing the likeness of Roger Clemens.

Rolling Thunder 2   Namco   2 $4
The original Rolling Thunder was an early arcade platform/ action shooter that stressed precise control and quick reflexes

      Revenge of Shinobi   Risk   Road Rash 3   Rocket Knight Adventures

The GameBoy Light was never released in the U.S., only Japan received this version.

| Shadow Blasters | Shadow Dancer | Shadow of the Beast | Shadowrun |

over flashy graphics and sound. The sequels are much the same, offering great gameplay and solid level design.

Rolling Thunder 3   Namco   3 $5
A bit more puzzle-intensive and frustrating than the first sequel, Rolling Thunder 3 still manages to provide hours of fun for gamers with fast reflexes and a tolerance for memorization.

Rolo to the Rescue   Electronic Arts   6 $18
This is a Mario clone starring a variety of animal characters... cute but highly derivative.

Romance of Three Kingdoms 2   Koei   3 $10
Most historical simulation enthusiasts rate Koei's Romance series to be the top games in the genre, and with good reason. The graphics aren't much, but the storyline (involving Japan's bloody evolution to a unified country) is simply fascinating, and the strategy-based gameplay is rich and satisfying

Romance of Three Kingdoms 3   Koei   4 $15
If you played the first game, you know what to expect from this deep and long-lasting historical simulation from the masters of the genre.

Rugby World Cup '95   Electronic Arts   2 $4
This is a very solid simulation centered around the British sport of Rugby (aka American football with different rules.)

Sagaia   Taito   4 $8
Known in Japan as Darius 2, this port of the arcade shooter features washed-out graphics but fast and furious gameplay.

Saint Sword   Taito   5 $12
This generic side-scrolling title was ported from an obscure arcade game.

Samurai Shodown   Takara   2 $4
This port of the popular Neo-Geo fighter retains the basic gameplay of the original but looses the scaling graphics, big characters, and much of the soundtrack.

Saturday Night Slam Masters   Capcom   5 $15
This wildly entertaining fighter is widely considered to be the best of the Genesis wrestling games.

Scooby Doo Mystery   Sunsoft   6 $40

Completely different from the lame SNES Scooby Doo game, this late-release single-player RPG is a great deal of fun to play and features a very cool graphical style.

Seaquest DSV   THQ   3 $5
This mediocre isometric shooter based on the mediocre (and short-lived) television series is nothing but a cheap rip-off of EA's Strike series.

Sesame Street: Counting Cafe   Infogrames   5 $10
Not bad as edutainment titles go, this counting teacher is well designed and professionally done.

Shadow Blasters   Sage's Creation/Sigma Enterprises   6 $18
Don't waste too much time looking for this boring side-scrolling fighter.

Shadow Dancer   Sega   3 $5
An offshoot of the classic Shinobi series, this 2-D scrolling fighter features decent level design and good graphics.

Shadow of The Beast   Electronic Arts   3 $5
While not up to the level of the original computer release, the Genesis port of this beloved platform game retains the lush graphics and solid gameplay that made the first one so great.

Shadow of The Beast 2   Electronic Arts   3 $5
It was hard to improve on the original, but EA managed to make the second edition of their superlative platform game even better.

Shadowrun   FASA Corporation   4 $10
This futuristic and action-packed classic features an awesome storyline and engrossing gameplay.

Shanghai 2: Dragon's Eye   Koei   4 $10
If you like Asian tile-dropping games, you'll be more than satisfied. If not, go elsewhere.

Shaq Fu   Electronic Arts   2 $1
Legendary in its awfulness, this dreadful fighting game has almost no redeeming characteristics.

Shining Force   Sega   3 $15
Viewed by many as one of the best games ever released on the Genesis and second only to the Phantasy Star series for pure role-playing fun, this revolutionary title set the stage for count-

Where does Majora's Mask take place?

less imitators with its seamless blend of strategy and role-playing elements.

Shining Force 2 Sega 4 $25
Just when we though things couldn't get any better, this superior sequel arrived featuring more of everything that made the first game so great. The third game in the series wouldn't appear until 1998 as one of the last Sega Saturn releases (with a print run of only 5000 copies.)

Shining in the Darkness Sega 4 $8
This simpler yet equally engaging offshoot of the Shining series captivated gamers with its own distinct brand of gameplay, spawning its own sequel on the Saturn.

Shinobi 3: Return of the Ninja Master
Sega 4 $8
Some series go way past their shelf date, but this sequel to the sequel to the arcade hit is surprisingly entertaining, as well as more that a bit challenging.

Shove It ! The Warehouse Game
Dreamworks 5 $15
Very similar in execution to those maddening little square slide puzzles, Shove It! has a cool design and a high degree of challenge.

Side Pocket Data East 4 $10
This is an above-average pool simulation with great gameplay and precise control.

Simpsons: Bart vs. The Space Mutants, The
Acclaim 4 $8
The first of the games based on the popular cartoon sitcom falls flat, mostly because it relies too much on its license and not enough on solid platform action.

Simpsons: Bart's Nightmare, The
Acclaim 3 $5
One of the better games to use the Simpsons license, Bart's Nightmare is a fairly solid action/platform title.

Simpsons: Krusty's Super Funhouse, The
Acclaim 3 $4
This Lemmings clone plays well enough but doesn't do much with its great Simpsons source material.

Simpsons: The Itchy & Scratchy Game, The
Acclaim 3 $5

Not much of a game to be honest, but this wacky title (based on the violent cartoons of the sick cat and mouse duo) is just bizarre enough to be fun.

Simpsons: Virtual Bart, The
Acclaim 4 $8
A compilation of several different gaming genres, this uneven game careens wildly from fun to boring.

Skeleton Krew Core 8 $45
The Genesis was home to several difficult yet excellent isometric shooters, and this is one of the best ones available.

Skitchin' Electronic Arts 3 $4
How strange… the same graphics as Road Rash, the same developers as Road Rash… it looks like E.A took the Road Rash game engine and substituted roller blades (that doesn't mean it's not fun.)

Slaughter Sport Razorsoft 3 $5
One of the worst fighters ever made for the Genesis, this awful Street Fighter 2 clone looks and plays like a bad Nintendo or Master System game.

Smoke & Mirrors Interactive Magic 4 $8
This is a fairly well designed puzzle game.

Socket: Time Dominator Vic Tokai 3 $5
This is a surprisingly decent Sonic clone on a platform simply loaded with Sonic clones.

Sol-Deace Wolfteam 3 $5
Known as Sol-Feace on the Sega CD (it's basically the same game), this well-balanced side-scrolling space shooter is full of great power-ups and bosses.

Soldier of Fortune Bitmap Brothers 3 $5
This futuristic (and much-loved) shooter is packed full of action and variety and should not be missed.

Sonic & Knuckles Sega 4 $10
Considered by some to be the best game in the Sonic series, this innovative release contains a "lock-on" cart pass-through feature that allows you to play Sonic 2 or 3 with the Knuckles character (you actually plug Sonic 2,3, or even Sonic 1 into the slot at the top of the cart.) Unfortunately, gamers were tired of the formulaic gameplay and the cart sold below expectations.

Shining Force

Shining Force II

Shinobi III: Return of the Ninja Master

Shove It! The Warehouse Game

Sonic Spinball

Sorcerer's Kingdom

Space Harrier II

Space Invaders '91

Sonic 3D Blast   Sega   4 $8
It's visually beautiful and very playable, but this isometric plat-form game moves much slower than we expect from Sonic and it probably should have been called something else. A nearly identical version is available for the Sega Saturn.

Sonic Classics 3 in 1   Sega   4 $8
This combo cart featured Sonic 1, Sonic 2, and the puzzler Dr. Robotnik's Mean Bean Machine.

Sonic Spinball   Sega   3 $4
Sega tried to parlay the success of the Sonic character into a pinball game, but the results are disappointing.

Sonic The Hedgehog   Sega   1 $1
Certainly one of THE milestones in gaming history, this colorful and fast moving side-scroller not only spawned numerous se-quels but also most probably saved the Genesis from extinction. Sega even used Sonic to coin a new marketing phrase to de-scribe the "speed" of the Genesis…"blast processing."

Sonic The Hedgehog 2   Sega   1 $1
One of the most popular (and most common) games ever re-leased for the Genesis, Sonic 2 improved on the original formula in many ways and featured Tails, another playable character.

Sonic The Hedgehog 3   Sega   2 $2
Sega gave Sonic a more aggressive look for his second Gene-sis sequel and added a boss character at the end of each level (which are larger than in previous games.)

Sorcerer's Kingdom   Treco   6 $22
An RPG in the tradition of Phantasy Star, this title's excellent gameplay triumphs over its wretched graphics and soundtrack.

Space Harrier 2   Sega   5 $15
A sequel to one of the all-time great arcade games, this bizarre shooter is presented from a pseudo 3-D perspective and fea-tures cool enemies and a realistic sense of speed (too bad the scaling is choppy.)

Space Invaders 91   Taito   6 $20
A mostly cosmetic update of the original arcade shooting clas-sic, Space Invaders 91 offers enhanced graphics but the old-school action tends to get old fast.

Sparkster   Konami   3 $4
Sometimes referred to as Rocket Knight 2, this fun Contra clone features garish graphics and awesome gameplay.

Speedball 2   Arena   3 $5
A violent and fast paced ode to the sport of rollerball, this futur-istic sporting game features fantastic graphics and gameplay.

Spiderman vs. The Kingpin
    Sega   2 $5
Spiderman popped up in several Genesis games, but none of them are truly great. This generic side-scroller is a mediocre (if passably playable) early release.

Spiderman: Maximum Carnage
    LJN   3 $5
The last of the Spiderman games released for the console, Maximum Carnage is yet another action/platformer that really doesn't do anything to redeem the injustices of the previous offerings.

Spiderman: Separation Anxiety
    Acclaim   3 $5
One of the better Spiderman titles, Separation Anxiety has an interesting plot line, decent graphics, and good gameplay.

Spiderman: The Animated Series
    Acclaim   4 $8
You'd think that a game based on an animated series would have a chance to rise above the mediocrity of other games, but the opposite is true in this case. The graphics and gameplay are substandard at best, and the soundtrack is abysmal.

Spiderman: and the X-Men: Arcade's Revenge
    Flying Edge   4 $10
Spiderman and the X-Men might have seemed like a great mix of two licenses, but the resulting game is stupid and often frus-trating.

Spiritual Warfare   Wisdom Tree   7 $35
Wisdom Tree was (fairly) well known for its video games steeped with biblical themes. Unfortunately, this poor (and diffi-cult to locate) Zelda clone doesn't do justice to either its inspira-tion or its source material.

Splatterhouse 2   Namco   6 $25
The original Splatterhouse only appeared in arcades and on the TG-16, but this sequel does the gory side-scrolling series jus-tice. It's kind of like a video game version of Friday the 13th meets The Texas Chainsaw Massacre.

Zelda wasn't even in the game Link's Awakening!

Splatterhouse 3   Namco   5 $18
Improvements abound in the second sequel to the gory side scroller, including better graphics, pseudo 3-D visuals, improved gameplay, and cool cinemas.

Spot Goes To Hollywood   Interplay   3 $5
An isometric platform game fronted by the corporate mascot for 7-Up, Spot sports some really nice graphics but the odd perspective gets in the way.

Star Control   Electronic Arts   4 $12
A port of an old PC title, this action/strategy game is loaded with fine tactical gameplay and lots of variety.

Star Trek DS9   Playmates   3 $6
More of a puzzle-strategy game that the platform title that many expected, DS9 is slow-moving and best suited for fans of the series (all eight of them.)

Star Trek: The Next Generation
                    Spectrum Holobyte   4 $8
Games based in the Star Trek universe tend to be pretty mediocre, and TNG is no exception. There is some fun to be had, but you'll lose interest FAST once you start wandering the endless underground tunnels looking for miners (take Troi with you!)

Starflight   Electronic Arts   4 $8
The graphics and soundtrack might be primitive, but the fun of this space exploration title is a fresh as ever.

Stargate   Tantalus/Probe/Acclaim   4 $8
This is NOT the game commonly known as Defender 2. It's an action/platformer (based on the sci-fi movie of the same name) that looks, sounds, and plays very well, but it's just a wee bit too hard for its own good.

Steel Empire   Flying Edge   4 $8
The Genesis was home to many overhead space shooters, but Steel Empire distinguishes itself from the pack with its cool graphics and overall design.

Steel Talons   Tengen   3 $5
This helicopter flight simulator has more of an arcade-type feel than others in the genre and plays very well.

Stormlord   Razorsoft   4 $10
This is a poor side-scrolling affair with not much to offer even the most casual of gamer.

Street Fighter 2: Champion Edition
                    Capcom   2 $4
The original Street Fighter II arcade game spawned countless imitators and is universally viewed as the game that brought people back to arcades. The SNES may have gotten an exclusive on the original SF2, but the Genesis scored this superior sequel (viewed by many purists as the best in the series.)

Street Racer   Vivid Image   3 $5
While certainly not up to the technical level of the gorgeous "mode-7" Super Nintendo version, this well-done Mario Kart clone is still mighty impressive from a speed and visual standpoint (plus it sports better gameplay and control that its SNES cousin.)

Street Smart   SNK   5 $12
Stunning in its mediocrity, this poor Double Dragon/Street Fighter clone is boring and easily forgettable.

Streets Of Rage   Sega   4 $8
A favorite of many Genesis fans, the first of the Streets of Rage brawlers features loads of fighting moving and a very good soundtrack.

Streets Of Rage 2   Sega   4 $8
This highly regarded sequel has even more characters and moves than the first game, plus an equally great soundtrack.

Streets Of Rage 3   Sega   4 $10
Bad things are said to come in threes, and that might hold true for GOOD things as well. This final outing in the Street of Rage series adds even more characters and gameplay variety (but the soundtrack is weak, unfortunately.)

Strider   Sega   4 $8
One of the first games to really demonstrate that the Genesis was capable of accurate arcade ports, Strider is a classic side-scrolling action title. It might look dated now, but gamers went wild over this one when it first came out.

Strider Returns: Journey From Darkness
                    Sega   3 $6
This sequel to the side-scrolling classic isn't nearly as good as the original and has been pretty much forgotten over the years.

Subterrania   Zyrinx   3 $5
This overly complicated and often frustrating underground shooter has its fans, but it won't appeal to everyone.

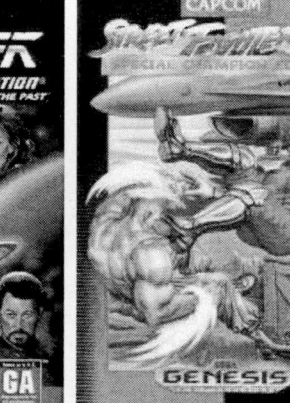
Star Trek: The Next Generation

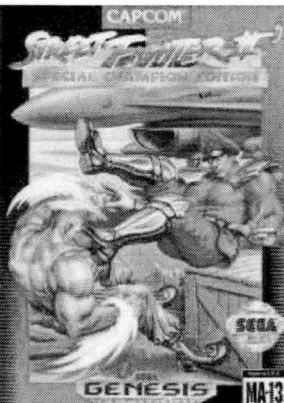
Street Fighter II: Special Champion Edition

Strider

Sub Terrania

Total Eclipse Turbo, an update to the 3DO title, was the first U.S. Playstation release.

Super Hang-On

Super Hydlide

Super Thunder Blade

Sword of Sodan

Summer Challenge   Accolade   3 $5
Like its cousin Winter Challenge, this hodge-podge of summer Olympics events is a lackluster mix of bad graphics and dull sound effects.

Sunset Riders   Konami   4 $10
One of the relatively few Genesis games to use a gun-style controller, this surprisingly faithful port of the 2-D Western-themed arcade game is an entertaining (if short) diversion with a fair amount of humor.

Super Airwolf   Kyugo Trading   3 $5
The Genesis library is replete with many excellent shooters, so you'd be better off skipping this lousy game based on the 1980's television series.

Super Baseball 2020   SNK/Electronic Arts   3 $5
This port of the arcade game features most of the entertaining "futuristic baseball" gameplay and numerous options that made the original so appealing.

Super Battleship   Synergistic/Mindscape   4 $8
Great board games have a tendency to make poor video games, and this take on the classic "You sank my battleship!" action of the original is simply too complicated for fans of the low-tech version.

Super Battletank: War In The Gulf
    Absolute   2 $4
Ouch! This dull and horrible looking tank-based shooter might have turned out better on a 32-bit console, but it's just too much for the Genesis to handle (plus the gameplay stinks.)

Super Hang-On   Sega   4 $8
Sega's classic motorcycle racing game made a stellar appearance on the Genesis and is nearly arcade-perfect (aside from the arcade's revolutionary cycle set-up) and is way better than the Master System port.

Super High Impact   Midway/Arena   3 $5
One of the better football games available for the Genesis (and that's saying a lot), this port of the arcade game features nice graphics, solid gameplay, and a bunch of neat additions that you won't find in other football releases.

Super Hydlide   Seismic   4 $6
This mediocre action/RPG isn't much fun and is best forgotten. Sadly, a dreadful update called Virtual Hydlide was the first RPG to appear on the ill-fated Sega Saturn and is even worse

than this one.

Super Monaco GP   Sega   4 $8
This was the first (and still one of the better) F-1 racing simulations released for the Genesis.

Super Off Road   Tradewest   3 $6
This port of the four-player arcade favorite has not aged well, and the tiny cars don't handle well with home controllers.

Super Ping-Pong   Pure Byte   4 $10
Yes, it's just what you expected… Pong with a slight graphical makeover. Not much of a start, and the Genesis control pad just wasn't designed for this type of game.

Super Smash TV   Acclaim   3 $5
This arena-based shooter isn't up to the level of the superlative SNES cart, but the incredible gameplay of this arcade port is still as fun as ever, especially when playing with a friend (just don't use the standard 3-button control pad!)

Super Street Fighter 2   Capcom   2 $4
The largest game (in terms of memory) to ever grace the Genesis, this upgrade of the classic SF2 fighting series features 16 playable characters and an enhanced version of the flawless fighting engine the franchise is known for.

Super Thunder Blade   Sega   2 $4
The stuttering frame rate and choppy scaling of this helicopter shooter suggest that the Genesis really can't handle the visuals of the arcade parent (or the developers weren't trying hard enough.)

Super Volleyball   System Video   3 $5
This arcade-style volleyball game is strictly mediocre by most accounts.

Superman   Sunsoft   4 $8
This boring side-scrolling is reminiscent of dozens of other mediocre games and is a waste of the Superman license (though not nearly as bad as Superman for the N64.)

Sword of Sodan   Electronic Arts   3 $7
Another mild upgrade to an 8-bit cart, Sword of Sodan sports better graphics but terrible gameplay.

Sword of Vermilion   Sega   3 $12
This early but enjoyable Genesis RPG shows some real attention to detail and is worth hunting down.

The Magnavox Odyssey was the first home video game console ever released.

Syd of Valis   Telenet   6 $18
Also know as "superdeformed Valis", this re-interpretation of the classic platform series is a silly and fun-free mess.

Sylvester & Tweety Cagey Capers
      TecMagik   4 $8
Many of the Loony Tunes titles are surprisingly good, and this addictive and challenging platform game is among the best of the lot.

Syndicate   Electronic Arts   2 $4
This port of the popular PC game didn't translate too well to the Genesis, though the base game is still a wonderfully complex, bloody, and entertaining action/strategy title that will keep you busy for a while.

Talespin   Disney/Magical   4 $8
Not one of Disney's better offerings, this standard platform game has banal graphics and paint-by-numbers gameplay.

Target Earth   Real Tec   4 $8
One of the most difficult shooters on the Genesis, this wildly underrated 2-D mech game features wonderful cinemas and a great storyline. (A glorious yet still hugely difficult sequel appeared for the Japanese Sega Saturn under the name Assault Suits Leynos 2.)

Task Force Harrier EX   Treco   3 $5
This port of the obscure 2-D arcade shooter is average in most respects and is really best suited for hard-core shooter fans only.

Taz Mania   Headgames/Sega   2 $4
Taz was done a MAJOR disservice by this poorly designed and overly difficult platformer (based on the classic cartoon shorts.)

Taz Mania 2: Escape From Mars
      Headgames/Sega   3 $5
The first Taz game evidently sold well enough to warrant a sequel, but the deficiencies of the first game have just been repeated here.

Team USA Basketball   Electronic Arts   3 $5
This is a great-playing basketball sim (utilizing the NBA Playoffs engine) featuring a "dream team" of Olympic players.

Technoclash   Zono/Electronic Arts   2 $5
Las Vega might not seem the best setting for an RPG, but it works in this interesting and entertaining release.

Technocop   Razorsoft   3 $5
A favorite among shooter fans, Technocop puts you in control of a lawman who gets to hunt down criminals in his flashy car. It might sound silly, but the gameplay and humor are just right.

Tecmo Super Baseball   Tecmo   2 $5
This conversion of the popular arcade baseball quickie runs straight down the middle as far as Genesis baseball games go.

Tecmo Super Bowl   Tecmo   3 $6
Unlike many of EA's sporting offerings, Tecmo's sports titles stress arcade-style action over simulation-style gameplay. This first game in the popular football series isn't much different from the NES game, simplistic graphics and all.

Tecmo Super Bowl 2   Tecmo   4 $8
This much-improved update to the original game features a new visual style and an all-new gameplay engine.

Tecmo Super Bowl 3   Tecmo   4 $10
As is generally the case with sports games, this final update of the popular arcade-style football franchise is the one to get as it is the most refined and has the most features.

Tecmo Super Hockey   Tecmo   3 $5
This is a popular arcade-style hockey game that you can jump right in and play.

Tecmo Super NBA Basketball
      Tecmo   3 $5
Like most of Tecmo's games, NBA Basketball shuns serious simulation in favor of easy and fun arcade-style action.

Tecmo World Cup '92   Tecmo   2 $4
If you like your hockey games easy to learn and quick to play, you'll enjoy this fast-paced arcade-style title.

Teenage Mutant Ninja Turtles: Tournament Fighters
      Konami   4 $8
The character designs are kind of silly, but many hard-core fighting fans consider this game to be one of the best Street Fighter 2 clones ever devised.

Teenage Mutant Ninja Turtles: Hyperstone Heist
      Konami   3 $5
This is a fairly standard platform/fighting game featuring the once wildly popular pizza-eating mutants.

Sword of Vermillion

Task Force Harrier EX

Taz Mania

Technoclash

If you follow the storyline, The Adventures of Link is the last Zelda game to take place.

Theme Park   Thunder Force II   Thunder Force III   Time Killers

Terminator   Virgin   3 $5
Actually the last of the Genesis Terminator games, this fairly decent side-scroller is the best game in the series.

Terminator 2: Judgement Day
       Acclaim   2 $4
The first of the two platform games based on the Terminator movies is below average, especially compared with its sequel (Terminator.)

Terminator 2: The Arcade Game
       Acclaim   2 $4
Like Revolution X, this bad port of an already mediocre arcade gun shooter shouldn't have been ported to the Genesis and is nearly unplayable with the standard control pad.

Test Drive 2: The Duel   Accolade   3 $4
Some gamers say that racing games didn't really come "alive" until the 32-bit consoles, but this rather primitive racing title still manages to provide enough entertainment value to warrant a purchase.

Theme Park   Electronic Arts   5 $18
This gentle simulation puts you in control of the day-to-day operations of an amusement park (including employee relations, fast-food selection, and ride design.) It might sound dull, but give it a chance and you'll be completely and utterly hooked.

Thomas The Tank   Britt Alcott LTD   5 $12
This cute and well-designed little edutainment title is based on the popular TV series.

Thunder Force 2   Technosoft   2 $4
Some of the most popular shooters ever released for the Genesis, the Thunder Force series is packed full of fast action and good graphics. Part 2 features both vertical and horizontal shooting stages.

Thunder Force 3   Technosoft   2 $5
The vertical shooting sequences of part 2 were ditched for this sequel, but the graphics and weapons have been improved.

Thunder Force 4: Lightning Force
       Technosoft   4 $8
As expected, the final appearance of the Thunder Force series on the Genesis is the best of the three. The series would continue on the PSX and import Saturn.

Thunder Fox   Taito   4 $6
This dull platform game is poorly designed and badly dated.

Tick, The   Fox   3 $5
Unlike many games based on animated TV shows, this fighting/platform release is every bit as funny, imaginative, and original as its source material.

Time Killers   THQ   7 $40
This rare and excessively gory fighter (based on a bad arcade game) is best known for it notoriety and not much else. The graphics and soundtrack are laughable, easily surpassed by some 8-bit NES games. At least you can dismember your opponents with a chainsaw and watch the blood fly.

Tinhead   Microprose   4 $8
The gameplay is slower than you'd expect, but everything else about this Sonic clone is top-notch, including the graphics, sound effects, and level design

Tiny Toons: Acme All Stars
       Konami   3 $5
Konami took a different approach to their second Tiny Tunes offering on the Genesis, and this compilation of sports-based minigames is just as appealing and fun to play as the platform game.

Tiny Toons: Buster's Hidden Treasure
       Konami   3 $5
The solid platform action and cute graphics found in the underrated NES games were enhanced and perfected in this quality release.

TNN Outdoors '96   Electronic Arts   4 $8
The first of EA's two fishing simulations for the Genesis isn't bad, but the soundtrack is laughable.

TNN Outdoors Bass Tournament
       Electronic Arts   5 $15
Not much different from the first game, but the one to get if you're into this sort of thing.

Todd's Adventures in Slime World
       Epyx   3 $5
This dull and ugly platform/action title sports 8-bit graphics and awkward control and is best avoided.

Toe Jam & Earl   Sega   6 $30
Widely seen as one of the best and funniest action/platform

Pac-Man Fever was written by Buckner and Garcia.

titles on the Genesis, the first game starring the prehistoric duo is beautiful, action-packed, and just a wee bit too short.

Toe Jam & Earl 2: Panic on Funkotron
Sega 3 $6
You'll get more of the same from this sequel, and that's definitely not a bad thing. The graphics are even better than those in the first game.

Tom & Jerry: Frantic Antics
High-Tech Expressions 4 $10
They might call the antics frantic, but we call it "standard fill in the blanks platform game." Still, they used a good template, and the action is mostly entertaining.

Tommy Lasorda Baseball Sega 1 $1
This is an early but fairly competent baseball sim featuring the endorsement of Tommy Lasorda.

Tony LaRussa Baseball
Strategic Simulations 1 $2
It might not look or sound pretty, but the gameplay engine is this very good baseball sim is tight.

Tony LaRussa Baseball 95
Strategic Simulations 1 $2
This is a mildly enhanced version of the first Tony LaRussa Baseball.

Top Gear 2 Kemco 4 $8
The long-running series of arcade racing games made one appearance on the Genesis and ranks as one of the console's best racers. The graphics are rather plain, but the smooth scaling and tight gameplay make for a very enjoyable racing experience.

Toughman Contest Electronic Arts 2 $4
This tepid fighting game is presented from a third-person perspective (kind of like Punch Out!) and has very few redeeming characteristics. A mildly "enhanced" port of Toughman Contest is also available for the 32x.

Toxic Crusaders Playmates Interactive 3 $6
This wretched arcade port (itself based on a couple of low-budget cult films) is a bad action game by all accounts.

Toy Story Disney 3 $5
One of the best-looking games ever produced for the Genesis, this excellent platform game is surprisingly faithful to the original

movie. The movie's rendered graphics have been recreated to a surprising degree.

Toys Absolute 5 $12
This action game is just as terrible as the stupid Robin William's game that spawned it.

Trampoline Terror Dreamworks 4 $8
You'd figure a game that used Q-Bert as its inspiration would have to be good, but this bizarre top-down action game fails to live up to its potential.

Traysia Telnet Japan 6 $20
This is a simple yet entertaining RPG best suited for gamers new to the genre.

Triple Play '96 Electronic Arts 2 $4
EA does it again with this excellent baseball sim.

Triple Play Gold Edition Electronic Arts 2 $4
This update to the excellent Triple Play '96 is considered to be one of the top baseball sims on the Genesis.

Triple Score Sega 2 $4
This compilation pack includes the games Columns, Super Hang-On, and World Championship Soccer.

Trouble Shooter Vic Tokai 3 $5
This is a below-average action shooter starring a couple of Japanese girls.

Troy Aikman Football Williams 1 $2
If you're going to copy Madden, you'd better try to it right. Unfortunately, poor graphics and animations sideline this one.

True Lies Acclaim 4 $6
Not bad as far as movie games go, this shooter doesn't contain any close-ups of Jamie Lee taking her clothes off (she's so hot) and we are so disappointed.

Truxton Toaplan 2 $4
Originally an arcade game, this vertical shooter is mediocre and is strictly for shooter fans.

Turrican Accolade/Ballistix 4 $8
Followed by a far superior sequel (Mega Turrican), this very difficult Contra clone features some great graphics but the gameplay could be better.

Toe Jam & Earl

Toe Jam & Earl 2: Panic on Funkotron

Tommy Lasorda Baseball

Trampoline Terror!

Sony has no official mascot.

Uncharted Waters	Unnecessary Roughness '95	Valis: The Phantasm Soldier	Valis III

Twin Cobra Treco 2 $4
This tedious and mostly unoriginal shooter has substandard graphics and slow gameplay.

Two Crude Dudes Data East 3 $5
If you liked Double Dragon, you'll probably enjoy this side scrolling fighting game, too.

Tyrants: Fight Through Time Virgin 4 $10
Populous is a great strategy game, and this respectable semi-clone incorporates many of the same resource management elements that made it so good.

Ultimate Mortal Kombat 3 Williams 2 $4
All of the Mortal Kombat carts were big sellers, even the late-release 16-bit carts that were pale imitations of their 32-bit cousins. Williams tried its best to cram the visuals and audio of the arcade fighter into this cart, but the results demonstrate that the Genesis just wasn't up to the task.

Ultimate Qix Taito 7 $30
This update to the classic puzzle/strategy game isn't quite as good as the simpler original (the graphics tend to be somewhat of a distraction) but it's still incredibly addictive nonetheless.

Ultimate Soccer Sega 2 $2
This is a very good arcade-style alternative to the more serious FIFA Soccer titles.

Uncharted Waters Koei 4 $8
Koei is known for their deep simulations, but this ocean-based title is far surpassed by its sequel.

Uncharted Waters: New Horizons Koei 5 $12
Better than its predecessor in every respect, this deep and engrossing simulation will keep you busy for months (if this is your sort of thing.)

Universal Soldier Ballistic 2 $4
Side-scrolling shooters attached to movie licenses come and go, and this mediocre title pretty much came and went.

Unnecessary Roughness '95 Accolade 2 $4
This is a slow moving and fairly dull interpretation of a standard Genesis football game.

Urban Strike Electronic Arts 3 $6
This was the last game in EA's excellent series of isometric shooters to appear on the Genesis. It retains the cool graphics and high difficulty level of its forbearers.

VR Troopers Sega 3 $5
Not bad as far as SF2 clones go, but the graphics are weak and the whole license is very tired.

Valis: The Phantasm Soldier Renovation 2 $5
The first of the three Valis games for the Genesis is a decent platform game starring a group of aggressive teenage girls.

Valis 3 Renovation 2 $6
More difficult than the first game, Valis 3 has better enemies and more gameplay options.

Vapor Trail Renovation 8 $20
Gameplay and level design are king in Vapor Trail, certainly one of the best vertical shooters available for the Genesis.

Vector Man Sega 1 $2
Considered by many to be one of the best games ever made for the console, this hardware-defying action/platform title features flawless gameplay and some of the smoothest and most fluid graphics the Genesis ever produced. Vectorman is certainly one of the all-time greats!

Vector Man 2 Sega 2 $2
This late-release sequel contains more of the same great action and superb graphics that are found in the first game, and that's definitely a good thing.

Viewpoint American Sammy 3 $5
Not bad as far as ports of Neo Geo arcade games go, but the gameplay of the isometric shooter is difficult (so say the least) and the graphics are plagued with slowdown.

Virtua Fighter 2 Sega 2 $4
Sega's groundbreaking fighter was ported over to the Genesis with much of the gameplay and fighting moves intact (though the 3-D polygonal graphics are now presented in 2-D, like Street Fighter 2.) The fully polygonal and far superior 32x version is nearly as good as the arcade original (but the graphics are a little rough around the edges.)

Virtua Racing Sega 1 $4
One of the most expensive games ever released for the Gene-

Steve Jobs, of Apple fame, created the game Breakout.

sis, Virtua Racing is the only game to feature the SVP processing chip (similar to the FX chip found in some SNES cartridges like Doom and StarFox.) The chip allowed the console to display more complex graphics than it could do on its own, but it was prohibitively expensive to produce. While certainly not up to the visual caliber of the arcade, Saturn, or even 32x versions, the Genesis port is still quite impressive and very playable.

Virtual Pinball   Electronic Arts   4 $8
This is a very well designed and great-playing pinball sim full of cool options.

Wacky Worlds Creativity Studio
                             Sega   5 $12
Strictly a kid's game (though it does feature some popular Sega characters like Sonic and Echo), this paint/activity edutainment title was one of the few games to utilize the Sega Mouse.

Wardner   Visco   7 $32
Ported perfectly from the arcade original, this platform game has good gameplay and graphics.

Warlock   Real Time Associates   3 $5
This visually stunning release is based on the silly (especially part 2) movie franchise of the same name (starring Julian Sands as the warlock.) Sadly, the gameplay sucks, completely destroying what promise the lush visuals might have offered.

Warp Speed   Accolade   3 $5
This game can't decide if it's an arcade shooter or a flight simulator, but we know that we don't like it.

Warrior Of Rome   Micronet   5 $15
Quite enjoyable as non-Koei historical simulations go, this game is set in Rome, obviously, and features a high level of challenge.

Warrior Of Rome II   Micronet   7 $35

Warriors of the Eternal Sun
                             Capcom/TSR   5 $20
Popular license aside, this Ultima clone is good enough to attract players that aren't familiar with the classic D&D franchise. Those of us who are in the know will enjoy it even more.

Warsong   Treco   6 $25
This early Genesis release is a fairly basic strategy/RPG with rather unremarkable graphics and gameplay. The storyline, on the other hand, is very engrossing and should keep you playing until the end.

Waterworld   Ocean   3 $5
It might be lovely to look at, but this isometric shooter based on the bloated whale of a movie (one of the most expensive feature films ever made) is almost impossible to play (and therefore enjoy.)

Wayne Gretzky Hockey and the NHLPA All-Stars
                             Time Warner   1 $2
This seemingly half-finished hockey sim has poor control but the fights are really entertaining.

Wayne's World   THQ   1 $2
Stay far away from this dumb-looking and poor-playing mess of a platform game based on the feature films.

We're Back: A Dinosaurs Tale
                             Funcom   4 $8
This is a surprisingly well-executed game featuring lots of arcade-style minigames and some really sweet graphics.

Weaponlord   Namco   3 $6
Namco tried their hand at a 2-D fighter, and the result is surprisingly complex and deep, sporting several additions not found in the SNES port. The character design, play mechanics, and overall variety are very impressive (but easy to overlook if you're looking for a fast fight.)

Whac A Critter   Realtec   7 $40*
Have you ever played the Whac-A-Critter carnival game? This is it's video equivalent, and it even came packaged with a special controller (which is required to play.) *This price includes the special controller included with the game.

Wheel Of Fortune   Gametek   4 $8
You know what to expect from the gameplay, but you might be a bit surprised by the shoddy presentation.

Wheel Of Fortune: Deluxe Edition
                             Gametek   4 $8
The graphics and digitized graphics are much improved over the original game, but the gameplay remains the same.

Where In The World Is Carmen Sandiego?
                             Electronic Arts   4 $10
This is the "geography" based game in the highly regarded edutainment series.

Where In Time Is Carmen Sandiego?

Wardner   Warsong   Warrior of Rome II   Whack-A-Critter

The Nights controller for the Saturn was the basis for the Dreamcast controller.

Wiz 'N' Liz

Wolfchild

Wonderboy in Monster World

World Heroes

[Wiz 'N' Liz] Electonic Arts 3 $5
This is the "history" based game in the highly regarded edutainment series.

Whip Rush 2222 AD Renovation 2 $4
This is an early R-Type shooter that will most likely appeal to fans new to the genre

Williams: Arcade's Greatest Hits
Williams 3 $5
This compilation pack of the classic arcade games Defender, Stargate, Joust, Robotron 2084, and Sinistar are well-emulated and great fun to play.

Wimbeldon Championship Tennis
Sega 2 $4
This late-release game is thought by many to be the best tennis game available for the Genesis due to its superlative gameplay and thoughtful design.

Wings Of War Masiya 4 $8
Pretty good as Genesis shooters go, this obscure release has some nice gameplay and a good overall design.

Winter Challenge Accolade 3 $5
Like its cousin Summer Challenge, this hodge-podge of winter Olympics events is a lackluster mix of bad graphics and dull sound effects.

Wiz 'N' Liz Sega 5 $10
A serious contender for the title of "the best Sonic clone on the Genesis," Wiz & Liz features lush graphics and very solid gameplay.

Wolfchild Virgin 5 $15
This is a popular (and very common) action game with dated graphics but solid gameplay.

Wolverine: Adamantium Rage
Acclaim 3 $5
This is one of the better titles in the X-Men series of action/platform games for the Genesis.

Wonder Boy In Monster World
Sega 3 $5
Sega's series of popular action/platform games was upgraded to 16-bit in great form.

Wonder Boy 3: Monster Lair

Sega 4 $8
This is another fine addition in the Wonder Boy series of action/platform games featuring more of the same colorful graphics, great level design, and tight control.

World Championship Soccer
Sega 2 $2
Sega is known for their sports titles, but they really dropped the ball with this wretched soccer simulation that's riddled with flaws.

World Championship Soccer 2
Sega 2 $3
This sequel might be bigger, but it's not much better that the first game and it pales in comparison to EA's soccer games.

World Class Soccer Sega 2 $2
This is yet another mediocre soccer sim from Sega

World Class Leaderboard Access/Hertex 2 $2
The best golfing simulator on the Genesis hands-down, this faithful port of the computer classic has something to offer for everyone.

World Heroes SNK 2 $4
It obviously can't compare to the original arcade version, but this decent port is more than just your average Street Fighter 2 clone with different fighters.

World of Illusion Starring Mickey Mouse and Donald Duck
Disney 4 $8
This game is the sequel to Castle of Illusion (and every bit as wonderful as its predecessor.) It's an action/platformer featuring cartoony graphics, great music, and addictive gameplay.

World Series Baseball Sega 1 $2
Sega's superlative baseball franchise is the only real competition to EA's Triple Play series, ranking among the top sports games ever produced for the Genesis. A mildly enhanced version of World Series Baseball (featuring Deion Sanders) is also available for the 32x.

World Series Baseball '95 Sega 1 $2
This is essentially the same game as the first World Series Baseball with some minor upgrades and additions.

World Series Baseball '96 Sega 2 $2
This is essentially the same game as the first World Series Baseball with some minor upgrades and additions.

In which game do you play a plumber who is trying to "get the girl" by making all the right choices?

World Series Baseball '98   Sega   3 $5
One of the last games released for the Genesis, this is essentially the same game as the first World Series Baseball with some minor upgrades and additions.

WWF Raw   Flying Edge/Acclaim   2 $4
This is a fairly respectable wrestling game with a lot of moves and variety but rather washed-out graphics. An enhanced port of WWF Raw is also available for the 32x.

WWF Royal Rumble
           Flying Edge   3 $5
This mildly improved sequel to Super Wrestlemania has some new characters and some better graphics, but it's still terrible.

WWF Super Wrestlemania
           Flying Edge   3 $5
The first and worst of this generally crappy fighting series has almost no redeeming characteristics whatsoever.

WWF Wrestlmania: The Arcade Game
           Midway   2 $4
As the name suggests, this is a port of the popular arcade brawler. It's best described as a wrestling version of Mortal Kombat with similar digitalized graphics but no fatalities. An enhanced port of Wrestlemania: The Arcade Game is also available for the 32x.

X-Men   Marvel/Sega   2 $3
Aside from its cool license, the first of the Genesis X-Men games is a mediocre platform game with bland graphics and gameplay.

X-Men 2: Clone Wars   Marvel/Headgames   2 $3
The graphics and gameplay of this sequel to the first best seller have been considerably improved, resulting in a fine game for fans of the comic books (and even non-fans.)

X-Perts   Sega   3 $5
One of the last Genesis releases, X-Perts attempts to replicate the rendered graphics of the SNES Donkey Kong Country games. It mostly succeeds from a visual standpoint, but the gameplay is convoluted and excessively frustrating.

Y's 3: Wanderers From Y's   Sega   5 $22
This is one the top RPG's to appear on the Genesis, period. Y's 3 has it all... a great storyline, precise control, thoughtful design, lush graphics, excellent soundtrack... it's all there!

Yogi Bear's Cartoon Capers
           Empire   5 $12
It might look like a cartoon, but the gameplay of the shoddy platform game falls flat on its face.

Young Indiana Jones   Lucusfilm Games   3 $5
In the mood for another mediocre game saddled with a mildly popular license? Here you go!

Zany Golf   Electronic Arts   4 $8
Not bad for an early release based on an old PC game, this golf simulation takes place on a miniature golf course and is well designed and very playable.

Zero The Kamikaze Squirrel
           Sunsoft   4 $8
The third game in the excellent Aero the Acrobat platform series is the considered to be the best of the lot due to its refined gameplay and better soundtrack.

Zero Tolerance   Accolade   4 $8
As one of the very few first-person shooters available for the Genesis, Zero Tolerance really tests the limits of the hardware. The viewing window in tiny and the frame rate stutters like nobody's business, but this was so cool back in the day.

Zombies Ate My Neighbors
           Konami   4 $8
Don't let the silly title fool you... this is one serious (if hilarious) game! The shooting action is very reminiscent of Robotron 2084, and the levels and enemies are just too cool. Be sure to hunt this one down!

Zool the Ninja   Gremlin/Electronic Arts   3 $5
This is a fairly respectable Sonic clone with good graphics and control.

Zoom   Discovery Software   5 $15
This 3-D style maze game features some really cool graphics, but the control has some issues that should have been worked out.

Zoop   Viacom New Media   2 $4
This difficult puzzle game is intriguing but perhaps best suited for gamers with extra keen hand/eye coordination.

X-Men   Y's 3: Wanderers From Y's

Young Indiana Jones   Zombies Ate My Neighbors

Plumbers Don't Wear Ties for the 3DO.

HARDWARE

Sega Genesis 1   Sega   1 $12
The largest of the three units, this version even had a volume control on the console.

Sega Genesis 2   Sega   1 $12
Smaller than the first model, this system was less expensive to make and is best for using with the 32x.

Sega Genesis 3   Majesco   3 $20
Made by Majesco at extremely low cost, this system is extremely small and sparse. With no power light and only the bare essentials for connections, this was sold for $49.99 new. This model will not work with the Sega CD or 32x however.

3 Button Controller   Sega   1 $3
Three buttons actually seemed like a lot in a world dominated by the NES, but it added a lot of new options that the NES could never offer with only 2 buttons.

6 Button Controller   Sega   1 $5
Released after fighting games became more popular (notably Street Fighter 2), this controller is often considered to be more comfortable and easier to use, though it is a bit small for larger hands.

Activator   Sega   4 $15
Made specifically for Eternal Champions, it will work with other fighting games as well. Laid on the floor in an octagon around the standing player, body movements were (supposed) to be translated into onscreen movements. It really was a lot of fun to watch other people jumping around, but wasn't very effective as a controller.

Menacer Light Gun   Sega   3 $8
Rumors about that Nintendo and Sega had a bet to see who could make the most laughable light gun for their new consoles. The SNES got the SuperScope, and the Genesis got this monstrosity. With a huge lens, awkwardly placed butt stock, binocular-scope-thingy and a very uncomfortable arrangement of buttons for fingers other than your trigger finger, this is definitely one of the worst light guns ever created.

Power Base Converter   Sega   4 $20
This allows for the use of Sega Master System Games on your Sega Genesis model 1.

The Pippin @World was the first console to come packaged with a modem, while the Dreamcast had the first built-in modem.

Sega CD

By: Andy Slaven and Michael Thomasson

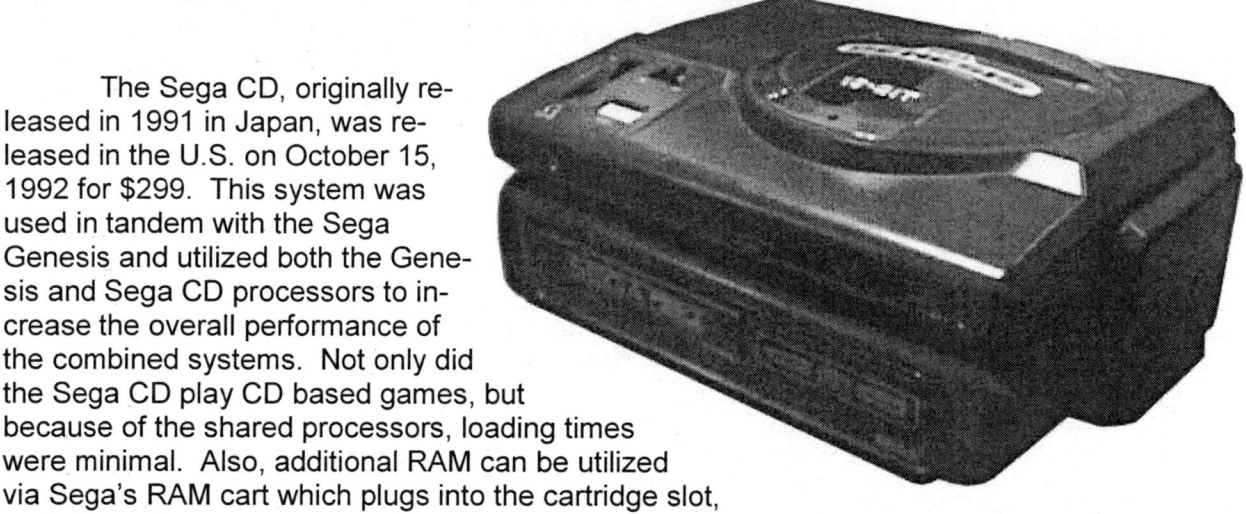

The Sega CD, originally released in 1991 in Japan, was released in the U.S. on October 15, 1992 for $299. This system was used in tandem with the Sega Genesis and utilized both the Genesis and Sega CD processors to increase the overall performance of the combined systems. Not only did the Sega CD play CD based games, but because of the shared processors, loading times were minimal. Also, additional RAM can be utilized via Sega's RAM cart which plugs into the cartridge slot, and allows for more game save information to be stored. While the Sega sold over 200,000 units in the first 2 ½ months, a second version (Sega CD2) was released in 1993 in order to reduce the cost. The first design featured a front loading CD tray that used a motor to accept and eject disks, and was much bulkier since it sat under the Genesis system. The less expensive second version, however, featured a top loading design that replaced the expansive front loading feature with a simple flip top lid.

The intent of the Sega CD was to allow gamers to add CD capabilities to their existing game system, much like NEC did with the TG-16 CD add-on. At the time, a stand-alone CD based system would be too expensive to produce for the average consumer, so Sega decided that in order to reach the best market available, they would simply expand the capabilities of the Genesis. Unfortunately there were some compatibility issues with the different versions of the Sega CD and the different models of the Sega Genesis. While it is true that occasionally certain Genesis models won't work with the original Sega CD, the Sega CD2 offers compatibility for both the first and second version of the Genesis, but will not work with the Genesis 3 (by Majesco).

Games for the Sega CD can best be described as a mixed bag. Sega seemed intent on bringing full motion video (FMV) games to the mainstream consumer. Night Trap is a notorious FMV game that is known for its controversy and horrible video sequences. Interactive video didn't offer the versatility necessary to make a game enjoyable for consumers, and while quite a few were made during this time, the genre never caught on. The Sega CD is a showcase of sorts for this type of game, though most of them are nearly unplayable.

As the Sega CD's consumer base grew, so interest in the development community grew as well. Aside from the two variations of Sega CD systems made by Sega, there is also JVC's X'Eye, the Sega CDX, and the Sega module for the Pioneer LaserActive. All of these systems were capable of playing Sega CD's and represent all of the Sega CD compatible systems released in the U.S. Other Sega CD systems were released overseas, such as the Aiwa Mega CD system that resembled a small   boom-box type radio, but would accept

Some Pong systems can run on batteries as well as a wall socket.

Megadrive and Sega CD titles as well.

The JVC X'Eye, originally released in Japan as the Wondermega, is a combination of both the Sega Genesis and the Sega CD into one console about the size of the first Genesis model. It originally sold for $499 and came packaged with three titles, including Compton's Multimedia Encyclopedia. Made by JVC in combination with Sega, the X'Eye was designed to be a high end version of the Sega CD that would offer increased audio quality and more convenience than hooking up both a Genesis and Sega CD. When compared to CD players of the time, the X'Eye was actually as good, if not better, than the best consumer CD players on the market. Still, audiophiles didn't buy the system due to the fact that it wasn't properly marketed as a viable music platform. Instead, the unit was sold as a game/music system that didn't catch the attention of either gamers or music aficionados. It also included one Genesis style controller that was imprinted with the JVC name in the center. While the X'Eye didn't sell very well in the U.S., it seemed to be a hit in Japan where use of the karaoke function was a major bonus for most consumers. Also, the X'Eye did not support the Sega 32x system, though it is unlikely that this had anything to do with poor sales.

The CDX, originally known as the Multi Mega X in Japan, was released in the U.S. in 1994 for a staggering price of $400. This system is capable of playing both Genesis and Sega CD games, but is no larger than a portable CD player of the time. The ability to play both Genesis and Sega CD games on such a compact machine is still amazing to collectors today, and the Sega CDX is still the Sega CD system of choice for gamers. And while the CDX will not play certain games properly, such as Jurassic Park and My Paint, it is the best system to play games such as Bug Blasters and Star Strike on. Also, the CDX will accept the 32x, BUT it is prone to overheat and can cause electrocution to the user. This prompted Sega to cancel any further announcements that the two systems were compatible. Aside from the possibility of killing yourself in the attempt to combine the two systems, it could also destroy the CDX in the process, making it a true tragedy. So don't try it!

The Sega module (PAC-S10) for the LaserActive system allows for the use of not only Genesis games, but also the use of Sega CD games on the LaserActive. Initially retailing for $600 (module price alone, does not include $1000 LaserActive system), this was by far the most expensive way to play Sega CD games, but it also allowed for the use of Sega LD games specifically designed for the LaserActive. The module was installed into the front of the LaserActive system through a port specifically designed to take expansion systems and came coupled with a Genesis style controller with Pioneer stamped into the center.

Though not without its faults, the Sega CD was the platform that introduced quite a few popular games to the gaming community. The immensely popular RPG series Lunar was originally released on the Sega CD, as was the cult classic Snatcher. In addition to the two Lunar games, Working Designs also released Popful Mail and Vay on the Sega CD, both of which have very strong followings. The infamous Night Trap also made its first appearance on the Sega CD, causing Congress to look closely at the amount of violence in video games. This title was used repeatedly in the arguments that eventually culminated in a rating system for video games.

The Sega CD's bulky nature and often questionable games have made it more of a collectors' system than a gamers' system, and this is unfortunate. With quite a few stellar RPG's, action games and an abundance of sports titles, the Sega CD should be looked at closely by anyone that is interested in retro-gaming. And while they aren't the best games ever made, a few FMV titles might be fun for those interested in early installments of the genre.

The Sega CD system itself should not be the first option however, but instead those interested in playing these games should look for either the JVC X'Eye or the CDX as they are much easier to hook up and maintain.

"Gaming Gloves" were sold by several companies during the 80's to reduce thumb blisters from playing video games.

A/X-101

The Adventures of Willy Beamish

B.C. Racers

Battlecorps

3 Ninjas/ Hook (combo)   Sony Imagesoft   3 $5
Peter Pan and 3 Ninjas on the same compilation disc? This seems a bit odd to me. These actions games, mediocre at best, make an appearance on the Sega CD in this two for one game set. Neither really stands out as being any good, but instead are average games on the whole.

A/X-101   Absolute   4 $8
This space shooter is created by using FMV sequences that you view from the first-person perspective. Not standing out as being spectacular in any area, this limited game is hindered by its lack of interactivity and control.

Adventures of Batman and Robin
                        Sega   3 $4
A little misleading considering the fact that you really don't control Batman or Robin in this game, but instead drive the Batmobile for most of the game, and the Batwing for the rest. The game itself is entertaining and shouldn't be too difficult to come by, but the absence of any non-driving action sequences is really noticeable.

Adventures of Willy Beamish, The
                        Dynamix   3 $5
This action game places you in control of Willy Beamish, a kid with an attitude problem that needs to be fixed. This game was designed with the intention of showing children how to "mend their ways". As the story progresses, Willy becomes more and more adjusted to every day life. Not really intended for serious gamers, it can still be fun if you're not worried about the story and concentrate on game play.

Afterburner 3   Sega   4 $7
A continuation of the arcade favorite, Afterburner 3 offers more of the same action oriented fighter plane flying. The Sega CD seems to lack something in this installment however, leaving a grainy effect on most of the graphics. Control is adequate, but a lack of freedom in where you want to fly really reduces the re-play value of this game quite a bit.

AH-3 Thunderstrike   JVC   4 $7
This helicopter simulation places you in the cockpit of an AH-3 Apache with several weapon systems at your control. While the Sega CD lacks the power to create the same experience found on PC's, this is still a mildly fun game that requires a lot of practice to master.

Amazing Spiderman vs. Kingpin
                        Sega   5 $10

This Spiderman game is a side scrolling adventure that comes across pretty well. You can climb walls and use your web shooter to attack enemies and swing around different environments. The newer Playstation version is obviously better, but for 1993, this was a pretty good game.

Android Assault: The Revenge of Bari-Arm
                        Big Fun Games   4 $8
Taking the role of an robot named Bari-Arm, your job is to...wait for it...save the world. As the world's last defense against aliens, you must destroy everything in your path in this side scrolling action game. With the ability to turn into a space plane, the levels aren't just confined to jumping and shooting. A decent game, but certainly not anything exemplary.

Animals, The San Diego Zoo
                The Software Toolworks 6 $12
An interactive tour through the San Diego Zoo, information on the different animals present is accessed via interactive menus. It is difficult to understand why this title made it to a platform specifically designed for games. The 3DO version is understandable considering their marketing drive that was trying to push the system as a multimedia device, but the reasons for a Sega CD version are still a mystery.

B.C. Racers   Core Design   3 $5
This kart racer gives you the chance to assume the role of various cavemen on their prehistoric vehicles. While the levels can be difficult to navigate and often impossible to see, the game can still be mildly entertaining if you're a fan of games like Mario Kart.

Batman Returns   Sega   3 $5
Fighting the Penguin and Cat Woman, this port from the Genesis version adds new driving levels and improved graphics and sound. While not the best Batman game around, this is still an enjoyable side scrolling adventure.

Battlecorps   Core Design   4 $7
This is a first-person shooter that could have been improved in several areas, but by 1993 standards it was still pretty good. As with most first-person shooters of the day, however, this game suffers from limited graphical prowess and also has a poor frame rate.

Bill Walsh College Football
                        Electronic Arts   2 $3
This is a port of the Genesis game by the same name. And while sports games in general rarely stand out, this title could

Cell phone gaming is currently one of the fastest growing areas of video games.

have had many improvements that weren't in place. With little noticeable improvement over the previous version, there is no reason to own this title if you already own it for the Genesis.

Black Hole Assault   Bignet U.S.A., Inc   3 $4
This is a 2-D fighting game of pretty average quality. Control is pretty good however, and makes up for the lack of large characters. The soundtrack, while nothing is notable, is of relatively high quality, and is used mainly to add sound effects instead of a moving score.

Bouncers   Sega   5 $13
Definitely an example of "thinking out loud", in this basketball game you actually take the role of the ball itself. Utilizing power-ups and the opposing balls, you position yourself into the 10 foot high goal. While control can be a little frustrating at times, this title is a lot of fun, if for no other reason than the fact that it is completely different than anything else.

Bram Stoker's Dracula   Sony Imagesoft   2 $3
The back of the box begins with the words, "Bram Stoker's Dracula sucks..." It goes on to say other things, but these first four words really sum up the game as a whole. Digitized characters are the norm in this game and are controlled in a side scrolling fashion. Control seems to be jumpy from time to time, and the sound could have added a lot more to this game, but falls short as well. The game is very short, and although it is taken from the movie by the same name, this game simply does not do the movie justice. Short movie clips are interjected into the game play, but if leaving them out would have allowed for a longer game, they shouldn't have put them in at all.

Brutal - Paws of Fury   Gametek   4 $7
This 2-D fighting game places you in a tournament of champions...except this time around, you're an animal. With characters such as a bunny, rat and llama, this title is sure to entertain those who have become bored with the standard fighting game. Graphics and sound are very good, and control seems to be very accurate.

Bug Blasters: The Exterminators   Good Deal Games   9 $30
While this game is still available from Good Deal Games, it is definitely one of the rarest games available for the platform. While we will not give out actual release numbers, if you own a copy of this entertaining game, consider yourself one of the lucky few. And while it is true that most FMV games aren't much fun, the fact that this title was just recently released coupled with the very refined feel of this game make it one of the

more enjoyable titles for the system. Kill as many bugs as you possibly can using the light gun and see how far along you can move in this challenging game. It's a real pleasure to be able to play a new game for a system that was discontinued in 1996. This game is best played on the CDX and with the Menacer.

Cadillacs and Dinosaurs   Rocket Science Games   5 $10
This interactive movie should be entertaining for the amazing "cheese factor". Difficult to control at times, and with questionable graphics, this game still offers a decent challenge. Any game that puts an American car up against prehistoric lizards gets at least one try from me!

Championship Soccer '94   Sony Imagesoft   3 $5
Nothing spectacular or innovative places this soccer game squarely into the "average bin". Control could have been improved, though it doesn't stand out as being especially bad. Both sound and graphics could have been much better though, even in 1994.

Chuck Rock   Sony Imagesoft   4 $8
Chuck, of somewhat typical fame, makes an appearance on the Sega CD in this fun title. A side scrolling platform game with colorful characters and interesting levels, this title should be enjoyable for those who have worn their Super Mario Brothers carts out.

Chuck Rock II: Son of Chuck   Virgin   5 $12
Another appearance by the franchise on this system, though it was published by Virgin instead of Sony Imagesoft, the same great people at Core Design developed the game. More of the same entertaining platform action, this title offers great colors and good control. And while it is about the same in quality, most gamers seem to prefer the first installment for some unquantifiable reason

Cliffhanger   Sony Imagesoft   4 $7
If you thought the movie was good, you might enjoy this side scrolling action game. But if you're like the rest of the world and thought that the movie was just more of Hollywood's ever raging quest to squeeze more money out of you, then this game will be average at best. FMV sequences break up action sequences to add to the storyline and to give your thumbs a break. Yo Adrian!

Cobra Command   Data East   3 $5
This flying game is really more of an interactive movie than

Blackhole Assault

Cadillac's and Dinosaurs

Chuck Rock II, Son of Chuck

Cliffhanger

Several early NES releases are actually Famicom games that are attached to an adaptor and placed within a NES cartridge shell.

SCD

Compton's Interactive
Encyclopedia

Dark Wizard

Dragon's Lair

Dune

anything else. With limited control and simple firing functions, it's not very enjoyable for those that have had a taste of newer games in the genre.

Colors of Modern Rock Music CD / CD+G
Sega   6 $12
This title is a music CD featuring graphics that are presented along with the soundtrack as it plays in the Sega CD. This title should also be compatible with any CD+G player, though I haven't tested it.

Compton's Interactive Encyclopedia (Sleeve)
Tribune   4 $8
This encyclopedia was packaged with the JVC X'Eye and was useful before the internet became as readily accessible as it is now. However, its main purpose was to make the X'Eye appeal to an older audience in an attempt to make the X'Eye an addition to the entertainment center instead of an addition to the game room. This version came packaged in a cardboard sleeve instead of the typical Sega CD plastic case.

Compton's Interactive Encyclopedia (Case)
Tribune   6 $15
This title is exactly the same as above with the notable exception that is was packaged in the plastic case typical of Sega CD games. This version was not a pack-in title with the X'Eye, but instead was marketed after the X'Eye's release due to the belief that adults would buy this educational title for their children. It wasn't very popular and wasn't made in a very large quantity.

Corpse Killer   Digital Pictures   3 $5
This horrible FMV game, released on several consoles, should be avoided at all costs. Extremely grainy digitized graphics and bad sound make the gun accuracy problems seem almost enjoyable. The light gun is required.

Crime Patrol   American Laser Games 3 $5
This FMV title is based on the arcade game of the same name and requires the light gun. While not exceptionally bad, this shooter lacks a lot in originality and doesn't have the light gun accuracy necessary to make it enjoyable.

Dark Wizard   Sega   5 $12
This turn based strategy game is one of the better games for the Sega CD. Combining a story typically found in an RPG with strategic decisions normally found in war simulations, this title is a very entertaining game for the system and shouldn't be overlooked by anyone who has a chance to buy it.

Demolition Man   Akklaim   4 $7
Part side scrolling and part overhead view, this title follows the storyline found in the movie of the same name. Beginning the game in 1996, and then frozen to awaken in the future, you play the role of John Spartan in his quest to bring down your arch enemy. Graphics and sound are pretty decent, and control is easy enough to get used to.

Double Switch   Digital Pictures   2 $4
This interactive movie sets you squarely inside of a home filled with traps that you must spring at the right time in order to catch the bad guys. Yes, it's an FMV game, but one of the better installments in this genre. It can become repetitious if you don't catch on quickly though, as you will find yourself watching the same video clips over and over each time you begin a new game.

Dracula Unleashed   Sega   5 $10
Out to find the truth about your brother's death, you eventually stumble into a web of information suggesting that perhaps Dracula has returned. This is an interactive movie, but if you're a vampire fan, it should hold your attention. The actors are decent and the frame rate seems to be adequate to watch the game without getting frustrated.

Dragon's Lair   Readysoft   2 $5
Based on the arcade laserdisc game of enormous popularity, the Sega CD version offers adequate graphics and sound, but most importantly, control. While it is extremely difficult to master what button must be pushed at what time, enough practice will get you safely through the castle to save Daphne. The CD-I version offers superior video, but control is more difficult.

Dune   Virgin   3 $8
This first person shooter is based on the very popular books and movie. And while it doesn't necessarily do either justice, it is still an entertaining game when the story is factored into it. The graphics are nice as is the sound, though the controls can often be a little difficult to master.

Dungeon Explorer   Sega   5 $12
This action game has several RPG elements making it more enjoyable for many Sega CD fans. Fighting through dungeons, you will eventually gain experience points to raise your character a level and gold that can buy new weapons and armor.

Dungeon Master 2: Skullkeep
JVC   4 $8
This is a first-person RPG that is extremely long and complex.

282

The control style necessary to make this type of game work properly is very difficult to master and will often cause you to make costly mistakes. The Sega CD isn't the best system in the world for displaying 3-D graphics, and the result is a very flat world viewed through a first-person perspective. The level of difficulty can often times seem to be unfair, and it is not uncommon to move your party into harm's way simply because you were unable to accurately judge distances. While this game may be for the extremely dedicated, it is simply too hard to play for most casual gamers.

Earthworm Jim: Special Edition
                          Shiny   3 $5
This is an awesome installment in the EWJ series and should be played by any fans of Jim. Great colors, sounds and more levels than the cart version make this easily controllable game enjoyable for just about anyone who likes platform games.

Ecco the Dolphin   Sega   2 $4
Ecco does a pretty good job of impressing in his first Sega CD title. The graphics, as always, are very enjoyable to look at and the sound is awesome as well. Control is easy to learn and should be intuitive enough for even younger children to learn.

Echo: The Tides of Time   Sega   2 $4
This installment in the series, while still very enjoyable, didn't have the necessary upgrades to make it stand out as a stellar sequel. Don't misunderstand though, this title is still an awesome game that should be enjoyable for any fans of the series, just not quite as good as the first installment on this system.

ESPN Baseball Tonight   Sony Imagesoft   2 $3
A port of the Sega Genesis version, this title offers no significant improvement. It is hard to understand why this game would be brought in such similar style to a system that requires the Genesis to be owned. A below average baseball game, it is extremely common and inexpensive, and may be easier to find now than the Genesis version. And while there are improvements to this version over the Genesis version, none seemed worthy of the Sega CD getting its own installment

ESPN National Hockey Night
                          Sony Imagesoft   2 $3
You'll get to choose from actual teams from the 1994 season in this hockey game. Video clips taken from actual games often play during the game when a goal is made.

ESPN NBA Hangtime '95   Sony Imagesoft   2 $4
This average basketball game can get old quickly if you don't

have a friend to play with. But once the second controller is plugged in, and your loud mouthed friend quickly learns that you're better at a 7 year old basketball video game, the true loser will be known...but if he's really a friend, he won't keep pointing out that fact.

ESPN Sunday Night NFL   Sony Imagesoft   2 $3
While teams and logos are licensed, actual players are not. And while this may turn some serious sports fans away from this title, the number of play options should keep most people entertained. A large assortment of special plays will keep the game fun for quite a while, though on-screen selection of plays can make it easy for unscrupulous friends to cheat.

Eternal Champions: Challenge from the Dark Side
                          Deep Water   1 $5
This 2-D fighting games, though one of the most common, is a very fun title for fighting game fans. Elaborately illustrated characters (24 of them) and gruesome finishing moves are sure to please those who are looking for a little gore from their Sega CD.

Eye of the Beholder   FCI / Sega   4 $10
Based on the AD&D rules, this game should be a "must-have" for any RPG fan. Numerous adversaries to fight, and numerous character options will make this one of the better games for the system.

Fahrenheit   Sega   5 $7
This is actually the exact game listed in the Sega 32x/CD section. And by that I don't mean that it's the same content, it is the SAME GAME. The Sega CD and 32x versions were completed at the same time and packaged together in the same box. The Sega CD disc is actually used as a boot-disc for the 32x version. This version can be played separately however, but is simply a less refined version of the 32x game. So oddly enough, though they share the same package and basically the same content, they were sold as two games in one package. It just seems so odd because you would never see a double disc CD from a musical group proclaiming "Both Volume 1 and Volume 1 included!"

Fatal Fury Special   JVC   5 $13
This arcade game is best played on a Neo-Geo. There really can be no substitute, especially by the Sega CD. Though it's not particularly a bad fighting game, it simply can't begin to compare with the Neo-Geo version. This title should have been left un-ported.

Ecco: The Tides of Time

Eternal Champions

Eye of the Beholder

Fahrenheit

Space Invaders was the first arcade game to be made available on a home console.

SCD

Flashback: The Quest for Identity

Flink

Ground Zero TEXAS

Heimdall

FIFA International Soccer   Electronic Arts   1 $2
A great soccer game featuring some nice audio and great control, this should be the soccer game of choice for the Sega CD. While the graphics could have used a bit of work, it can't take away the fact that this extremely common game is very enjoyable to play.

Final Fight CD   Capcom   2 $3
This side scrolling game finds you fighting everyone on screen. Very popular in arcades, it makes a very good appearance on the Sega CD. Control seems a little stiff, but it was the same in the arcade. Sound and graphics are pretty good for this system, and fans of the side scrolling fighter should definitely check this version out.

Flashback: The Quest for Identity
**   U.S. Gold   3 $5**
Best known for its graphics, this game features some very interesting scenery. While on a quest to recover your memory and find out who you really are, you will encounter some very interesting environments. The first, and perhaps most beautiful level, takes place in the jungle. While the graphics don't take on a cel-shaded look, they have a very flat and even appearance. It really is unlike any other game that's ever been on the market, and due to graphical improvements in the decade since this game was created, it is doubtful that anything will ever be made to look like it again. The sound is also done very well. With sparse audio of any kind, when something does make a noise, you notice it immediately. The control will take a little while to master, but it is pretty basic and shouldn't give you too much trouble up front. The only drawback to this game is the fact that once you've seen the end, there really isn't any incentive to play it again.

Flink   Vic Tokai   4 $8
This is a side scrolling platform game that offers some unique level designs, along with some very interesting graphics and an easy control scheme. The audio is well done, and everything combined makes for an above average platform game.

Formula One World Championship: Beyond the Limit
**   Sega   2 $3**
This formula one racing game has very tight control and decent graphics, making it better than most F1 racers of the day. The sound is enjoyable also, though not exceptional.

Ground Zero Texas   Sony Imagesoft   4 $7
Pull out the light gun again! This game will require you to enter Texas armed and ready for combat. Accuracy in this title seems

to be pretty accurate and the graphics, while very grainy, do their job. While this is by no means a stellar title, it can be entertaining for a while, though it is doubtful that it will offer anyone very much replay value.

Heart of the Alien   Virgin   3 $5
This adventure game is actually the sequel to Out of this World, but offers very few redeeming qualities. Graphics, sound and control all suffer in this game making it very difficult to enjoy, and obviously diminishing any replay value to zero.

Heimdall   JVC   5 $7
This is a 3/4 isometric action adventure RPG in which you must...yes, save the world. Although the story obviously lacks some originality, the game itself is very enjoyable. Graphics are done very well with crisp edges and vibrant colors. Sound is handled well and control seems solid. There are several parts to this game, puzzle solving is just one of them. They become increasingly more difficult and occasionally monotonous. This is a long game, so you shouldn't expect to beat it in one sitting.

Hook   Sony Imagesoft   2 $4
This is the same side scrolling platform game that is featured on the 3 Ninjas/Hook compilation disc.

Hard Hits/Rock Paintings   Sega   3 $5
Actually a two disc set, this was a pack-in with the Sega CD. It isn't a game, but instead is a CD+G title that shows that the system can handle this type of CD.

INXS: Make My Video
**   Digital Pictures   4 $8**
Construct videos for several songs from INXS in this title. Unlike the others in this series of Digital Pictures games, this title's music is still enjoyable to most fans of the 80's and 90's.

Iron Helix   Drew Pictures   4 $8
This futuristic game is played through a first-person perspective and demands that you gain entry to a renegade ship and prevent it from launching its weapons against a peaceful planet. While the graphics could be improved, the control seems solid and the game is enjoyable.

Jaguar XJ220 JVC   JVC   3 $6
This is a mediocre driving game in which you are given the opportunity to drive the Jaguar XJ220 super car. While this isn't the best racing game ever made, there is nothing in particular that stands out as being bad. It doesn't portray a real feel of speed however, and this may annoy some more serious gamers

Super Mario Bros. 3 is one of the most common games ever made, with an estimated 20-30 million copies sold.

who have become accustomed to games like Gran Turismo 3.

Jeopardy!　　　　　Sony Imagesoft　3　$5
If you just can't get enough of Jeopardy on TV, then this is your chance to get just a little bit more. As with all versions of this game show on a video game console, once you have played it through enough times, the questions begin to repeat themselves, completely destroying any replay value.

Joe Montana NFL Football
　　　　　　Sega　　　　1　$1
This is a graphically enhanced version of the game's earlier release on the Genesis. Joe Montana also makes video appearances from time to time just to offer advice. And while this is an early title for the Sega CD, it just isn't very good.

Jurassic Park　　　　Sega　　2　$3
This game just isn't very enjoyable. While it is true that some people really like this title, the very short amount of game play necessary to completely finish this game, and the relatively unrelated tasks that need to be performed while playing really take away from what should have been a very fun game. Also, this game is incompatible with the CDX.

Keio's Flying Squadron　JVC　　8　$75
This extremely rare side scrolling shooter places you squarely on the back of a small dragon as you advance against the enemy in some of the most beautifully detailed environments to be found on the Sega CD. Much more common in Japan, this title seems to have only been released in very small quantities.

Kids on Site　　　Digital Pictures　5　$12
This interactive movie teaches children about heavy lifting machinery and other items found in construction sites.

Kris Kross　　　　Digital Pictures　3　$3
If you bought this title when it was new, you probably did so while wearing your pants backwards. Who can forget the two little rappers that made it popular to be dyslexic? Combine video clips from these two musicians to make your own videos in this strange use of FMV technology. A nostalgic title at best, it has almost no interactivity that will interest gamers.

Lawnmower Man, The　Sales Curve Interactive　4　$8
Based on the movie of the same name, this game features 8 levels of varied action. You will not only play through side scrolling levels, but will also play levels placed within the virtual reality world. While this game is average at best, the movie itself inspired the general public to seek out virtual reality as a

form of entertainment. And while VR hasn't make it to a mass consumer market yet, when it does I'm sure this game will be one of the first titles featured.

Lethal Enforcers　　　Konami　　2　$5
Extremely popular in arcades, this title comes to the Sega CD intact, and even included the light gun. Completely digitized graphics allow you to shoot at moving images of real actors in various scenarios including a bank robbery and the getaway chase.

Lethal Enforcers 2: Gunfighters
　　　　　　　　Konami　　3　$5
Trying to cash in on the popularity of the first title, this shooter takes place in the old west. Taking the role of a gunfighter, you must dispatch enemies in the streets as they pop up from every possible location before they have a chance to return fire. While not as popular as the first title, it is still a very fun light gun game for the system.

Links: The Challenge of Golf
　　　　　　　　Virgin　　1　$2
A very common game to find, Links is an average entry into the genre of golf games. The use of digitized scenery adds a touch of realism to a game that would otherwise be average in every way.

Loadstar: The Legend of Tully Bodine
　　　　Rocket Science Games　3　$5
Loadstar is a standard space shooter in which you control a spaceship armed with various weapons through multiple levels of varying difficulty.

Lords of Thunder　　Hudson Soft　5　$13
This side scrolling adventure was also available for NEC's Turbo Duo, and is much better on that system, but makes a decent attempt on the Sega CD. Relatively boring level designs can make the game seem to stretch out for quite a while, but continuous action should keep most gamers entertained for the amount of time it takes to complete this game.

Lunar: The Silver Star
　　　　　　Working Designs　5　$40
One of the best RPG's ever made for any platform, Lunar: TSS makes its debut on this system. It was later released on the Saturn (Japan only) and again on the Sony Playstation. This epic game brought some of the most unforgettable characters to video gaming and has one of the most compelling storylines of any RPG to date. While it is becoming more difficult to find, this

Jurassic Park

Keio Flying Squadron

The Lawnmower Man

Lunar: The Silver Star

Zelda's Adventure for the CD-i is the only Zelda title to feature real actors.

| Lunar: Eternal Blue | Mansion of Hidden Souls | Mad Dog McCree | Mickey Mania: The Timeless Adventures of Mickey Mouse |

game is an absolute "must have" for any fan of the genre. Turn based action and free roaming capabilities are the cornerstone of this title, but a wide variety of weapons and magic to choose from make it stand out.

Lunar: Eternal Blue
               Working Designs 6 $45
The sequel to Lunar: TSS, Eternal Blue takes place 1000 years after the first game ends. An equally compelling storyline and colorful characters make this game equal to its predecessor in every way. A large variety of enemies and the occasional returning character make this especially enjoyable for those that have played through the first game. An interesting note about this game is the fact that it is best played several months after the first is completed. The game was designed in a way as to utilize the fact that it wasn't released directly after the first title. After you have forgotten portions of the first game's storyline, it becomes more enjoyable to play this title since it relies on that fact. Images and characters from the first game are remembered by current characters in a way that wouldn't be as enjoyable if the two games were played back to back.

Mad Dog McCree   American Laser Games 3 $5
First seen in arcades, this title features fully digitized opponents that engage you in one on one gun fights. While it was entertaining at the time, enough practice with this game will prove that it is very short and offers very limited interactivity. The light gun is required.

Mad Dog McCree 2: The Lost Gold
               American Laser Games 4 $8
More of the same, you once again face off against digitized opponents in a quick draw contest. It appears that slight improvements to the graphics have been made, but it is obvious that this is an early attempt at using FMV in a home game.

Mansion of Hidden Souls   Vic Tokai   3 $5
This first-person point and click type adventure takes you through a mysterious mansion. You must find clues and solve puzzles in order to find your sister, who is lost within. The graphics in this game are astounding. The reason that they can afford to be so detailed is due to the fact that they are all still images, but they remain amazing nonetheless. Quite simply, if you're a fan of point and click adventures, this game should be in your collection.

Marky Mark and the Funky Bunch: Make My Video
               Digital Pictures 2 $3
Before he became an actor, Mark Wahlberg was known to the

world as Marky Mark. Standing shoulder to shoulder with other rapping greats such as Snow and Vanilla Ice, Marky Mark was one of the 1990's most forgettable rappers. This title allows you to make videos for three of his songs using various clips found on the disc. Not really any fun, this should still be entertaining for fans of 90's music and fashion.

Mary Shelley's Frankenstein/Bram Stoker's Dracula (combo)   Sony Imagesoft 3 $6
Just as Dracula was bad before, its appearance on this combo CD doesn't improve it. Mary Shelley's Frankenstein isn't any better and does little to improve the overall package. At least you're getting two games, though once beaten it is doubtful that you'll play either one again.

Masked Rider: Kamen Rider ZO, The
               Sega   4 $8
In your quest to save a missing child you must endure an interactive movie! This game, unlike most interactive movies, actually gives you the proper button to press onscreen. This makes the button mashing happen twice as fast, but at least you know what it is you're supposed to do. This type of game is often more enjoyable to casual gamers than regular interactive movies that offer no help. Though, once beaten, it is doubtful that it will be played again.

Mega Race   The Software Toolworks 3 $5
This is a futuristic racing game in which you drive cars loaded with weapons of all sorts. Fifteen tracks are included in this game and are surrounded by some very impressive environments. The control, graphics and sound are all done well, though the 3DO version is much smoother.

Mickey Mania: The Timeless Adventures of Mickey Mouse
               Sony Imagesoft 4 $9
This is a side scrolling adventure starring your favorite Disney characters. Very colorful graphics and clear sound are among the high points in this game, and control is near flawless. Great level designs and enjoyable animations make this one of the better games for the system, especially if you're a fan of Mickey.

Microcosm   Psygnosis 1 $1
FMV at its worst. This "rail" game offers extremely limited control and even less interaction. Traveling through the veins of a body, ala Fantastic Voyage, this title offers several different craft, but only on their respective levels. Monotonous and of extremely low replay value, this title is still a pioneer in a doomed genre.

Way of the Warrior for the 3DO was Naughty Dog's first video game.

Midnight Raiders Sega 3 $5
This FMV game quickly becomes tiresome due to the nearly complete inaccuracy of the shot registration. After a few minutes of missing targets that you know you hit, this game will most likely be turned off.

Mighty Morphin Power Rangers
  Sega 2 $3
When the Power Rangers were actually popular, this title seemed like an obvious necessity for any system. If you can get over the fact that you're controlling a Power Ranger, however, it can be mildly entertaining.

Mortal Kombat Arena 2 $4
When this title hit arcades, people were shocked and amazed. Digitized characters that could kill each other after successfully winning a best 2 of 3 contest were all it took to make this one of the best selling games in history. This is the best port of the arcade title on any home system, though the graphics do look dated and the control could have been improved. Still, short of buying the arcade machine itself, this is as close as you're going to get to the real thing.

My Paint: The Animated Paint Program
  Saddleback Graphics 5 $25
This is simply a paint program designed for use with the Sega CD. Though it isn't a complete paint program, it should still be entertaining for children. Of important note, this game will not work on the CDX.

NBA Jam Akklaim 1 $2
This is an updated version of the Genesis game of the same name. Small graphical improvements have been made over the original, and it is still fun to play, but noticeable load times.

NFL Trivia CapDisc 1 $2
As the title implies, this title is a trivia game that tests the player's knowledge of the NFL and its teams. This might be enjoyable for diehard football fans, but doesn't hold much interest for the casual gamer

NFL Greatest Teams: San Francisco vs. Dallas 1978-1993
  Sega 4 $10
Perhaps the only sports game for the Sega CD to have any rarity at all, this title puts you in the role of coach instead of quarterback. You pick the plays and then watch their execution via live footage taken from these two teams.

NHL '94 Electronic Arts 1 $2

This NHL game is fully licensed, but aside from that fact doesn't stand out in any way. Typical graphics and control make this yet another average sports game with no discerning features of its own.

Night Trap Digital Pictures 4 $25
One of the most influential games in video game history, Night Trap was singled out by Congress and the press alike for its gratuitous violence, and was eventually part of a campaign that instituted a mandatory rating system for all video games. This FMV title is entertaining to a point, but mainly because its grainy video, along with Diff'rent Strokes' Dana Plato, make it a nostalgic game for those who grew up in the 1990's.

Nova Storm Psygnosis 2 $2
This very common title features standard spaceship fighter action seen in nearly every other game of its kind. Released in 1994, this title was also available for the 3DO, on which it plays much more smoothly.

Panic! Data East 5 $10
This game has no point. This game is no fun. This game really should have never been made at all. Hell, it is not even a real game. Your character presses buttons onscreen in order to advance to the next "puzzle". Unfortunately, the puzzles apparently have no standard solution, so it becomes a series of random guesses. When the wrong guess is made, a badly animated sequence will take place. There is no apparent goal to this game, no obvious manor in which to solve the "puzzles" with which you're presented, and absolutely no fun whatsoever to be had. This is the worst game made for this system, hands down. Now, if you buy this title knowing that it isn't interactive and that the majority of people have absolutely no interest at all in this game, you might have stumbled onto a little secret. This title, though known by most of the world as the most horrible Sega CD game ever made, is often found very entertaining by fans of Monty Python and similar types of humor. Basically, the British and people that dress in period clothing and speak in poorly choreographed middle English (while working on a shirt made of chain male) will enjoy this title, but they're probably the only ones.

Pitfall: The Mayan Adventures
  Activision 3 $6
A more modern version of Pitfall, this title is a challenging platform game that allows you to swing from vines and fight several types of adversaries. This title is available on several other platforms, but the Sega CD version does an adequate job of handling the graphics and control. Still, limited diversity in the

Mighty Morphin Power Rangers   Mortal Kombat

Night Trap   Panic!

Can you describe the fatality of Sub-Zero in the first Mortal Kombat game?

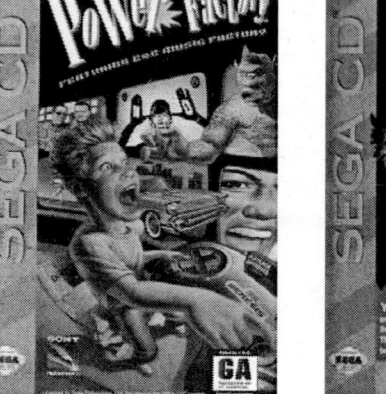

Popful Mail | Power Factory Featuring C&C Music Factory | Prize Fighter | Revenge of the Ninja

environments can quickly make this game seem tedious.

Popful Mail   **Working Designs 5**   **$28**
One of the "must have" RPG's from Working designs for the system, this title will be a big hit with fans of the genre. An interesting fact about this game is the fact that in order to save, all other information on your Sega CD's built in memory must first be deleted. The process used to save the data requires that the RAM be completely empty for some reason, making the use of a RAM backup cart for your other game saves essential. Or, as many gamers have done, simply use this game on a Sega CD system specifically set aside for its use.

Power Factory Featuring C & C Music Factory
                           Digital Pictures 2   **$3**
The once popular musical group makes a forgettable appearance on the Sega CD with this title. Construct videos to accompany songs from this group in this humorous title. Very rarely is something so quickly dated as games based on musical groups.

Power Monger   **Electronic Arts 3**   **$5**
This strategy game requires that you spend some time understanding what your goals are and how to meet your objectives. Immersive play and numerous options will keep you enthralled as you steadily build your empire go greatness. If you like strategy games, then you will enjoy this title. If you find strategy games lacking however, this game will not hold your attention long as the learning curve is a little steep for those new to the genre.

Prince of Persia   **Sega**   **4**   **$7**
The classic PC platform game makes its way to the Sega CD. Control and graphics are done very well, and the sound is about average. No real innovations were made though, and unless you're collecting for the Sega CD, this game is really no different than any other version found on countless systems.

Prize Fighter   **Sega**   **2**   **$3**
An interesting use of FMV, this title was a pack-in game with the JVC X'Eye. Black and white footage of your opponents is used in the first-person perspective, allowing you to react with the proper command at the right time. Control can be a bit tricky at times, and the graphics certainly haven't held up well, but it is an enjoyable title for diehard fans of boxing.

Puggsy   **Psygnosis**   **4**   **$7**
This side scrolling platform game was originally released on the Genesis and has pretty standard environments, though the sound and control are both done well. The graphics could have

easily been improved more than they were, but instead this seems to be a better sounding version of the same game found on the Genesis. This title seems to be designed for younger children though, considering the "cutesie" feel of the game.

Racing Aces   **Sega**   **3**   **$5**
Another good idea gone stupid. While the though of racing airplanes through mountainous terrain and shooting at your opponents sounds like a good idea, the Sega CD simply is not capable of supporting as much onscreen action as was necessary to make this game. Instead, it becomes an uncontrollable and unplayable flying game with no enjoyment.

Radical Rex   **Activision**   **4**   **$8**
Take the role of a dinosaur named Rex in this scrolling platform game. It offers two player support, but oddly enough does not work with the CDX unit. A fun game with colorful graphics, Radical Rex is easy to master however, and offers very little replay value once it is completed.

RDF Global Conflict   **Absolute**   **5**   **$12**
Take control of a "super tank" in this shooter and destroy everything onscreen. With several weapon systems at your disposal this game can be a lot of fun for shooter fans, but won't interest anyone looking for a good solid story. Graphics are done nicely, though they can be grainy at times. Sound is done pretty well, but control can be difficult to get used to in the varying roles you will undertake such as pilot and gunner.

Revenge of the Ninja   **Renovation**   **4**   **$7**
Onscreen commands will prompt you through this interactive cartoon in your search for your kidnapped girlfriend. The graphics are really nice and control, though limited to the onscreen commands, is responsive. Sound is done nicely, but like most other interactive movies, replay is very low once the game has been completed.

Revengers of Vengeance
                     Extreme Entertainment Group 3   **$5**
A little on the odd side, this game is part fighting game and part RPG/adventure. The fighting game portion is slow however, and doesn't really compare to a full fighting game. Other portions of this title will find you in an adventure mode where you must buy items and train your character. While this title may be a bit odd at times, it may be enjoyable for those looking for something different.

Rise of the Dragon   **Dynamix**   **4**   **$10**
An amazing game for the Sega CD, if you can't find a copy of

Sub-Zero would yank the head and spinal column from his opponent's body, then hoist it up as a trophy.

Snatcher, this may be your next stop. This interactive comic, or "graphic adventure" is illustrated very nicely and offers a high level of difficulty the first time through. On a mission to find who killed the mayor's daughter, you are quickly drawn into the middle of a far more sinister plot. This title is one of the "must-haves" for the Sega CD.

Road Avenger   Renovation   3 $5
This is an interactive driving movie. Combining these two genres was just a matter of time, and while it could be improved in many ways, this title isn't all bad. Quick reflexes are necessary in order to avoid onscreen obstacles, but often times it seems as if the controls just don't respond as well as they should. Onscreen prompts let you know which button should be pushed at the right time.

Road Rash   Electronic Arts   3 $5
Racing a motorcycle and beating the hell out of your opponents by whatever means necessary is a fun prospect for anyone, and the Sega CD version handles the digitized graphics pretty well. Updates on more modern systems have greatly improved on this title, but it is still entertaining to play this admittedly dated game from time to time.

Robo Aleste   Tengen   4 $8
This is a vertical shooter in which you pilot your ship through various obstacles and bosses ala Raiden. This game really has some nice graphics and the controls are very responsive. This should be a favorite of vertical shooter fans.

Samurai Shodown   JVC   4 $9
This is a port of the SNK classic of the same name. If you have never played the original, than you might actually enjoy this version. But once you've played this title on the Neo-Geo, you will never again want to play the Sega CD port.

Secret of Monkey Island   JVC   4 $8
Long load times and a very slow pace make this moderately interactive title less of a game than it should have been. Graphics look nice and the sound is good, and if it weren't for the long load times this game would be much more enjoyable.

Sega Classics Arcade Collection (4-in-1)
     Sega   3 $5
This compilation CD features Columns, Streets of Rage, Shinobi and Golden Axe.

Sega Classics Arcade Collection (5-in-1)
     Sega   5 $10

This compilation CD features the same four games from the 4-in-1 collection, but also includes the additional title Super Monaco GP.

Sewer Shark   Digital Pictures   1 $1
A "rail" game using FMV, Sewer Shark is one of the worst titles for this system. Originally a pack-in game designed to show the FMV capabilities of the Sega CD, it instead showed how horrible an FMV title can actually be.

Shadow of the Beast II   Psygnosis   3 $5
This side scrolling action game features RPG elements, but falls short of being very involving. The game quickly becomes tedious and repetitive.

Sherlock Holmes: Consulting Detective
     ICOM Simulations   3 $6
This is a standard point and click Sherlock Holmes mystery game with FMV sequences allow you to see the actor speaking about certain clues in this point and click mystery adventure. This title is still fun for both Sherlock Holmes fans and mystery fans alike.

Sherlock Holmes: Consulting Detective Vol. 2
     ICOM Simulations   5 $15
Different cases are used in this title which plays and looks just like the first installment. This title is preferable to the first one due to the fact that it wasn't available on as many platforms, making the cases and their outcomes less known to the average gamer.

Shining Force CD   Sega   2 $22
The amazing Genesis RPG series makes an appearance on the Sega CD in this amazing title. While it is still a relatively expensive title, it is still extremely fun for RPG fans and may prove easier to find than its Genesis counterpart.

Silpheed   Sega   2 $3
Considered by many to be the best space shooter on the Sega CD, this is an early release title (1993) that features some nice polygon effects as well as challenging levels. Inexpensive and common, there is no reason why this title should be overlooked by anyone with a Sega CD.

Slam City with Scottie Pippen
     Digital Pictures   2 $3
A FMV basketball title, Slam City pits you against various opponents in one on one street basketball. The control and digitized graphics are both horrible in this title and it should be avoided

Samurai Shodown

Sherlock Holmes: Consulting Detective Vol. II

Shining Force CD

Snatcher

What was the name of the Street Fighter II arcade trick that would lock each character as they were defeated, necessitating a machine restart?

Sonic CD   The Space Adventure   Star Wars Chess   Star Wars: Rebel Assault

unless you are collecting for this system.

too hard for seasoned gamers.

Snatcher   Konami   7 $45
An extremely difficult title to find, and a very fun one at that, Snatcher will not be cheap to obtain. This interactive story is presented in vivid still shots, much in the fashion of an interactive comic. This mystery game is very entertaining and has reached a cult status. Released on the Saturn in Japan only, this title is only available for the Sega CD in the U.S.

Sol-Feace   Wolf Team   4 $8
This is a side scrolling space shooter that is very similar to games such as Gradius and the classic game Vanguard. Very addictive game play and solid control will have you playing this game over and over, well past the point of completion.

Sonic CD   Sega   2 $3
More of the same that made Sonic so popular, this installment allows for time travel and features improved sound and graphics. While this isn't a major jump ahead of past sonic games it is still very enjoyable.

Soulstar   Core Design   3 $5
This 3-D space shooter places you behind the space ship as you fly through various terrain shooting everything onscreen. And while the graphics are nice for the Sega CD, this is hardly a new idea, and certainly doesn't involve any innovation.

Space Ace   Readysoft   3 $5
This is a port of the arcade laserdisc version by the same name. Control and graphics are both done nicely and should make any fan of the game happy. Like Dragon's Lair, it is difficult to know when to push what button, but that's the challenge of the game.

Space Adventure, The   Hudsonsoft   6 $20
Perhaps the most interesting title on the Sega CD, this is some what of a genre bender (no, not a gender bender!). Trapped somewhere between an interactive movie and a graphic adventure, this sci-fi tale uses short animated segments in which the proper button sequence must be used in addition to still frame artwork that helps to tell the story. A very compelling storyline and beautiful graphics grace this game. But not only is it difficult to find, but it also carries a mature rating.

Starblade   Namco   2 $3
This is an interactive movie in which you're along for the ride on this spaceship, but you control the guns. This title can prove challenging as the level of difficulty increases, but shouldn't be

Star Strike   Good Deal Games   9 $30
Another game produced by Good Deal Games, Star Strike is a shooter that places you in outer space. Some amazing visuals accompany the video within this entertaining game. And just like Bug Blasters, if you have a copy, you're one of a very select group.

Star Wars Chess   The Software Toolworks   5 $17
Basically an installment of Battle Chess, but with the use of Star Wars characters. This title will be very enjoyable for chess players who are also fans of the movies, but is just as entertaining for anyone wanting to play a quick game of chess. Animations make the death of an opposing piece that much more fun to watch.

Star Wars: Rebel Assault   JVC   3 $6
How many spacecraft from the Star Wars movies can you fly? Throughout this game you will fly several different ships as well as getting the chance to hop out of your speeder to shoot some storm troopers in third-person mode. And to top it all off, this game features the one thing that almost every Star Wars game has in it...the Death Star trench run.

Stellar Fire   Dymanix   2 $3
Blocky graphics are the first thing that you notice about this game, and from there its all downhill. While it does have some nice sound, the control seems very awkward and makes the game nearly unplayable. For a genre as common as the space shooter, it seems that a better job would have been done creating this game.

Supreme Warrior   Digital Pictures   3 $5
A perfect example of a bad use of FMV, this title puts you in the first person perspective while fighting various kung-fu fighters. And while the colors are vivid and your opponents are actual actors from Hong Kong, this title lacks what Prize Fighter had: true innovation. To compound things, the control is absolutely impossible to master, making this less of a game, and instead a movie that should have been titled, "Watching Someone Kick Your Ass."

Surgical Strike   Sega   3 $6
Move around in your hovering tank and take control of the guns in this interactive movie. This is an FMV game that offers limited interaction and is pretty standard for a title of this nature.

SCD

Terminator, The Virgin 4 $8
A lack of variety makes this side scrolling action game very repetitive. This game should have had more weapons choices, but unfortunately it remains pretty basic. While the control is solid and the sound is nice, the environments just don't seem to do the Sega CD justice. This title should have been refined before it was released, but instead it takes on a "rushed" quality.

Third World War Extreme 5 $13
This is a 2-D strategy game in which you take control of a country in your quest to fortify yourself and become powerful enough to survive an attack, or lead attacks of your own. A great game for strategy fans, this title has a small learning curve and should be easy enough for anyone to quickly become accustomed to.

Time Gal Renovation 4 $10
An interactive cartoon in which you must push the correct button when the onscreen prompt tells you to, this title has somewhat of a following. Also available for the Laseractive, both versions feature the same game play. Nice animation and sound accompany this title, and quick reflexes are essential. The interesting thing about these games is the fact that while playing, you can't enjoy the actual game itself since you're focusing on the prompt cue instead of the animations. Hook your Sega CD through a VCR so that you can record the action, and when the game is completed simply rewind the tape to watch the story all the way through.

Tomcat Alley Sega 2 $3
This is another FMV shooter that places you in the cockpit while aiming and shooting. The action can quickly become too fast the first time through, but after several attempts there should be no real challenge left.

Trivial Pursuit Parker Brothers 4 $7
The very popular board game from the 80's makes its appearance on the Sega CD in this title. Designed for adults, not by content, but instead by the fact that no children ever enjoyed playing Trivial persuit, this game wasn't a very good seller. After the questions have been played through a few times however, there is no challenge left in the game and its replay value is reduced to zero.

Ultraverse Prime/Microcosm (combo)
Sony Imagesoft 2 $4
Another odd combination, this CD compilation features the FMV game Microcosm with a side scrolling fighter called Ultraverse Prime. This is very similar in style to Final Fight in that it simply

places you against every person you meet on the street in a very rigid fight.

Vay Working Designs 4 $20
This is one of the "must-have" RPG's by Working Designs, though it is certainly not the best. On a quest to find five magical orbs in an effort to restore a special suit of armor that can save the world. You must buy new equipment, face varied enemies, travel through towns, etc. You control a four member party in this amazing game for the Sega CD.

Wheel of Fortune Sony Imagesoft 3 $5
This game does support two players, but it was obviously aimed at an older audience. This title can also quickly "wear out" after it has been played numerous times, though not as quickly as Jeopardy or Trivial Pursuit.

Who Shot Johnny Rock
American Laser Games 2 $3
A FMV shooter that supports the light gun, this game is very difficult at first, but quickly becomes much easier as you learn the enemies' pattern. Once the pattern is memorized, it can actually be watched like a movie with just the quick shot to the screen to continue along.

Wild Woody Sega 3 $4
Take the role of a pencil in this side scrolling platform game. Use your eraser to delete your enemies along the way. This game should be fun for just about anyone, though the difficulty level seems a little low for any serious gamers.

Wing Commander Electronic Arts 3 $6
When this game first came out for PC's, the world was stunned that graphics this good could be utilized during actual game play. And while they are degraded a bit on the Sega CD, the graphics still look amazing on this system. Pilot your craft against your enemies in this space simulation, and even practice flying in a virtual ship onboard the carrier.

Wirehead Sega 3 $6
While technically an interactive movie, this FMV game isn't played quite the same way. Instead of being told which button to press and then having to immediately respond, you are faced with several choices and much choose the right one before time runs out. Making the right choice advances you through the game while the incorrect choice will result in your capture.

Wolfchild JVC 3 $5
This side scrolling action game requires that you not only fight

Third World War   Time Gal   Vay   Wirehead

291

It is estimated that over 5 million E.T. carts for the 2600 were never sold.

World Cup USA 94

CD Back Up

Game Gun   American Laser Games   4 $8
Released separately for those who did not buy Lethal Enforcers.

Justifier Light Gun (Blue)   Konami   3 $8
This was the pack-in gun for the game Lethal Enforcers.

Justifier Light Gun (Pink)   Konami   5 $15
Available via mail-in offer after buying Lethal Enforcers.

off enemies, but also gain weapons and power-ups so that you can successfully fight the boss on each of the nine levels. Nice graphics and solid control make this game enjoyable, even for the seasoned gamer.

WonderDog   JVC   3   **$5**
WonderDog seems like an odd character to try and revive to the youth of the '90's, but he makes a starring appearance in this side scrolling adventure. Geared toward younger children (and probably their parents who would actually remember Wonder-Dog) this title offers only a moderate challenge. This doesn't stop the title from being graphically impressive however. Beautiful colors and animations make this game look great, and a great soundtrack adds the necessary sound.

World Cup USA 94   U.S. Gold   1   **$2**
An average soccer game with below average graphics, the audio must be complimented due to the fact that two of the songs included on the game were performed by the Scorpions.

WWF Rage in the Cage   Arena   3   **$5**
This standard wrestling game doesn't offer much over its Genesis counterpart. A few new animations have been added in, and the sound seems to be improved, but not much else has been changed. This title should be enjoyable for fans of wrestling, or those looking to find wrestlers from the early 1990's.

·HARDWARE

Sega CD system   Sega   4 $25
This is the original front loading system.

Sega CD2 system   Sega   2 $20
This unit mounts to the side of the Genesis and has a flip-top lid.

Sega CDX   Sega   6 $75
Compact and sturdy, this Genesis/Sega CD is the preferred Sega CD unit.

JVC X'Eye   JVC   5 $45
Built by JVC, this unit has the best audio quality and combines both the Genesis and the Sega CD into one unit.

JVC Controller   JVC   5 $10

CD Back Up   Sega   5 $20
This plugs into the cartridge slot in the Genesis and expands the available RAM for additional game save information.

Sega CDX

Contrary to popular belief, home video game consoles were around before arcade machines were.

Sega 32x

By: Lucus Barnes and Andy Slaven

If you're in the mood for insults and hoots of derisive laughter, just mention the words "Sega 32x" to a group of serious gamers. The Sega 32x is the redheaded stepchild of the videogame world, the unfortunate "console" that Sega (and the rest of the world) would rather forget. Surprisingly enough, the Sega 32x is quite memorable for two reasons.

1)   It is one of the least-successful gaming consoles ever produced.

2)   It is one of the main reasons behind the Dreamcast's demise and Sega's exit from the hardware business.

How could the little mushroom-shaped Sega 32x been the downfall of Sega, you ask? The 16-bit Sega Genesis had been a major success in the U.S. marketplace, leading Sega of Japan (reeling from the Japanese market failure of the Genesis' twin, the Mega Drive) to produce two add-ons for the Genesis. This was done in an attempt to prolong its life in the U.S. and remain competitive with Nintendo's Super Nintendo console. The first of these add-ons, the Sega CD, met with a cold reception from the game-buying public, but eventually gained some measure of respect along with some great RPG's, and a library of over 100 titles. Sega would have most likely survived the unpopularity of the Sega CD had it stopped while it was behind. The second of the add-ons, the 32x, was the proverbial "straw that broke the camel's back."

Sega of Japan thought that gamers would rather "upgrade" their existing 16-bit systems to 32-bit for a reasonable price rather than wait for the next wave of expensive 32-bit CD-based gaming consoles that were just around the corner: the Saturn and PSX. The 32x hardware team went through several weaker designs before finally settling on the dual-processor layout that was eventually released. The final design shares some basic hardware similarities with the Saturn, though the latter is far more powerful. The 32x utilizes twin Hitachi SH2 32-bit processors (from the same family as the chips found in the Saturn and Dreamcast), which can overlay 2-D and 3-D graphics on top of the visuals produced by the Genesis. The 32x also adds an additional two sound channels to the admittedly meager sound capabilities of the Genesis. The color palate and processing speed of the 32x is far greater than that of the stock Genesis, and the add-on is capable of displaying 3-D texture-mapped polygonal graphics similar to those found in early PSX and Saturn games. Regular Genesis games can be played directly through the 32x with no problems (with the exception of Virtua Racer), though the 32x does not enhance the 16-bit games in any way. Sega also re-released five "full motion video" CD games that feature sharper video than the Sega CD originals.

What was the most common handheld game system being played while waiting in line for a Sony Playstation 2?

32x

The Sega 32x was released to the American marketplace in November of 1994 at the price of $159.99 (with no pack-in game) and instantly sold out in many locations. *Doom, Virtual Racing Deluxe, and Star Wars Arcade* were the launch titles. Unfortunately, problems began to surface immediately. The add-on was difficult to install, especially on the older Genesis 1 model. Additionally, it was discovered that the 32x was incompatible with some older television sets, prompting Sega to release an adapter. The second series of games (*Cosmic Carnage, Metal Head*) were mediocre at best, and later releases like *Mortal Kombat 2* and *Primal Rage* offered little, if any noticeable improvements over the 16-bit originals. The add-on was an even bigger failure in the U.K. (the Mega Drive 32x) and Japan (the Super 32x), where sales of both the console and its games were truly dismal. The planned release of the Sega Neptune (a combined Genesis/32x hybrid) was unceremoniously cancelled.

Stores began to experience a huge wave of returned 32x merchandise, and game developers abandoned the system in droves, either moving existing 32x games to other platforms, or canceling them entirely. By Christmas 1995, it was all over. Toy behemoth Toys R' Us failed to include the 32x in its catalog, signaling the end of the 32x after only one year in the marketplace.

The amazing failure of the 32x was a devastating blow to Sega's reputation, and consumers steered clear of the Saturn, which had its own set of unique problems. By the time the Dreamcast was released, Sega's hardware division was doomed. They have since jettisoned their hardware aspirations altogether and are doing very well as a game developer.

Does the 32x deserve the amount of harsh criticism that it receives? In a word, probably. The technology is flawed when compared to "true" 32-bit systems like the Saturn, PSX, and to a lesser extent, the 3DO. Many of its games are mediocre "updates" of existing 16-bit titles, and the game library is very small. Regardless of its history and lineage, the 32x represents innovation, the kind of "thinking out loud" that we have come to expect from Sega.

The 32x is a great system to collect for, as most of its games are inexpensive and easy to find. It's also one of the few systems where acquiring a complete collection is a reasonably obtainable goal. Only 31 cartridge games were released in the states, along with 5 CD-based titles. The last 32x game released in the states, *Spiderman: Web of Fire*, is the rarest of all 32x titles, with a rumored production run of only 2000 copies. Only three games were available overseas that did not see a stateside release. These are *Gekijoban Sangokushi IV* (*Romance of the Three Kingdoms 4*), which was only available in Japan, while *FIFA Soccer '96* and *DarXide* were only released in the United Kingdom. The gorgeous 3-D shooter *DarXide* was the final 32x game ever released for the system, and is the most difficult 32x game to obtain for U.S. collectors. Only two confirmed prototypes, *X-Men* and *Virtual Hamster* have surfaced, but several more are rumored to exist.

***The 32x has limited compatibility with the various Genesis systems and the "Genesis clones." While only officially compatible with the Genesis 1 & 2 models, it will often work to some degree with other units. For instance, it will work with the Sega CDX, but is clearly stated in the CDX manual that this may cause electrocution, and even worst than that may ruin your CDX! We have personally been able to see a single frame of the opening sequence for several 32x games while it was plugged into a JVC X'Eye, but again, this can damage the system.

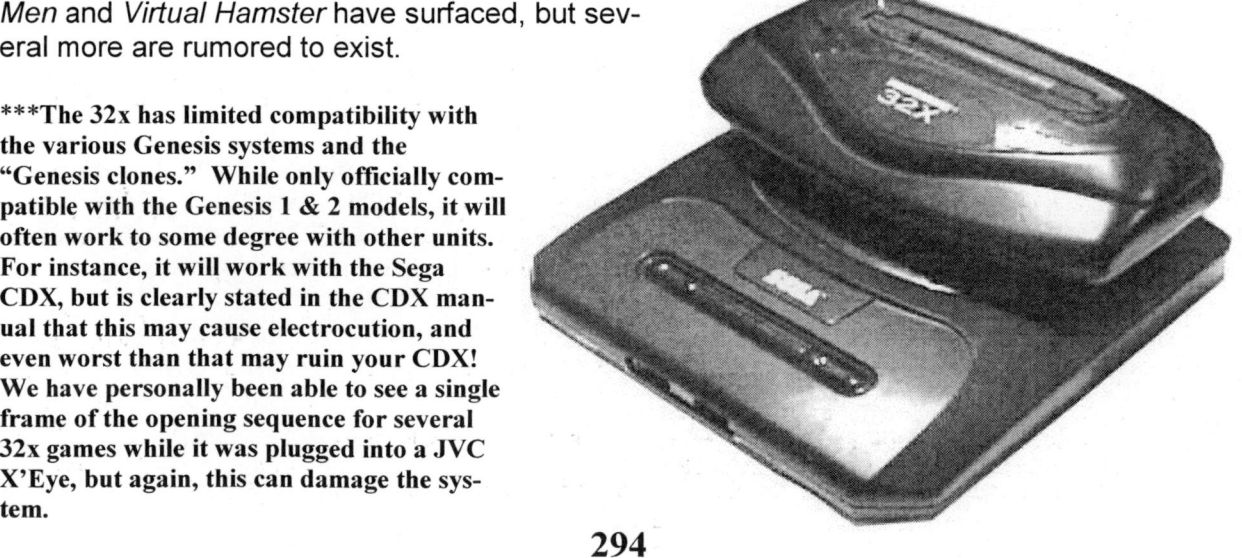

still a

After Burner

BC Racers

Kolibri

Metal Head

36 Great Holes Starring Fred Couples

Sega Sports 4 $7

This is not only exclusive to the 32x system, but also the only golf simulation in the entire 32x library. This game allows for you to play against the pros as either Fred Couples or as a character which you personalize. You are able to store and save up to 24 unique characters of your making. Unfortunately, this game pales in comparison to the golf games on the 3DO which were on store shelves at the same time.

After Burner Sega 3 $4

This version of After Burner is nearly arcade perfect, although it was already dated at its launch. Released in the arcades in 1987, the game itself was 7 years old by the time it was released on this platform.

BC Racers U.S. Gold 5 $15

A lot of potential can't save any game from being bad, and this is no exception. A racing game set in prehistoric times with colorful characters should be a lot of fun, but unfortunately bad controls and poor course design plague this game.

Blackthorne Interplay 5 $15

Originally appearing on the PC, the 32x version of this game is very impressive. A very dark platform game with RPG elements, you will find that careful timing and caution are a must when playing, as is the 6-button controller. Amazing graphics, an outstanding soundtrack, and more levels than the SNES version make this game very enjoyable.

Brutal: Above the Claw GameTek 4 $10

With a combination of cute, fuzzy animals and fighting to the death, you can't really go wrong with this game. With quick and responsive controls, the only real downfall of this game is fact that characters sometimes appear to be "lost" in the background. Twelve characters are selectable, all with their own set of moves.

Cosmic Carnage Sega 2 $3

This 32x exclusive was the first fighting game available for the 32x. Unfortunately for those who bought it at full price, it is also one of the worst games for the system. Poor graphical design, bland characters, horrible music and questionable control all add up to one gigantic disappointment.

Doom Sega 2 $3

One of the most famous games of all time, Doom makes a well received appearance on the 32x. While many believe that the game could have been made without a border (placed around a smaller viewable screen in order to allow for faster frame rates), meeting the launch date of the 32x seemed more important to Sega. Ten of 27 levels are missing from this version, but it is

great console version of this PC classic.

Knuckles Chaotix Sega 5 $15

You play as a team of two characters attached by a bungee cord in this unique twist to the Sonic game series. With one character whipping the other forward, you are then dragged along behind your partner. This new style of gameplay is enjoyed by some, but many feel it deviates too much from its Sonic roots

Kolibri Sega 6 $18

An absolutely beautiful release, this is by far the most beautiful game on the 32x. This game is actually a scrolling shooter where you take on the role of a hummingbird. With a relatively small number of levels, the high difficulty level keeps most people from finishing this game on the first day. And while it isn't the best shooter ever made, it is definitely worth finding just for the stunning backgrounds.

Metal Head Sega 3 $6

This is a bad addition to the genre of Mech games. Without the feeling of actually being inside of a Mech, and disappointing graphics, this game falls pitifully short of the benchmark set by so many others in this genre. An "unfinished" quality pervades the game and makes it nearly unplayable at times.

Mortal Kombat II Acclaim 4 $10

This is only a slight improvement over the Genesis version. With more colorful characters and good control, it makes one wonder why the backgrounds are still the same quality as the 16-bit version.

Motocross Championship

Sega 3 $5

With a small action field, horrible graphics, twitchy control and absolutely no fun to be had whatsoever, this 32x exclusive is best not played.

NBA Jam T.E. Acclaim 5 $10

With good scaling effects and graphics, this popular arcade port makes an impressive appearance on the 32x. While it was available on most consoles of the time, this system does a really good job of handling this translation of the game.

NFL Quarterback Club Acclaim 4 $7

With all 28 NFL teams, this Madden clone is a surprisingly good game for the 32x. Different play modes and solid control make this one of the better football games of its era.

Pitfall: The Mayan Adventure

Activision 5 $12

It seems that this title was available for every console ever

There have been no "homebrew" games released on cart for the NES.

made, but this version not only features the original Pitfall game hidden within, it also contains 3 levels exclusive to the 32x system.

Primal Rage   Time-Warner   4 $10
An average fighting game, Primal Rage on the 32x isn't much different than it was on the Genesis. With a little improvement to the color scheme, not much else stands out as being too different. But at least you get to urinate on your dead opponent if you're able to pull off the move.

R.B.I. Baseball '95   Time-Warner   5 $15
All 28 major league stadiums are present with detailed proportions and walls. Home Run Derby as well as other practice modes are also available on this baseball simulation. Unfortunately an irritating commentator chatters throughout, but not to the point of ruining the game.

Shadow Squadron   Sega   5 $15
A 3-D space shooter with complete freedom to fly anywhere, the only negative aspects of this game are the music and difficulty. The music is very simple and doesn't seem to match the mood of the game, while the difficulty may be too high for average gamers. The graphics and control are top notch however. This title should be in any 32x owner's library.

Space Harrier   Sega   3 $5
One of the most famous arcade games of all time makes a nearly perfect appearance on the Sega 32x. And while the game first appeared in 1985, it seems somewhat "ageless" as it still remain fun after nearly two decades. Appearing as recently as Sega's release of Shunmue, playable in an arcade early in the game.

Spider-Man: Web of Fire   Sega   8 $85
A 32x exclusive, and decidedly the most rare game for the system, this game suffers from very poor graphics. A side-scrolling brawler, your job is to defeat the villain Hydra and free the city from an electrical field he has enshrouded it in.

Star Trek: Starfleet Academy
                 Interplay   6 $20
A sad fact is that Star Trek, while undoubtedly popular in Movie and TV show format, is rarely the basis for a good game. This game is no exception to the rule, as it is often boring, has horribly sound and questionable graphics. The game places you as a cadet in the Starfleet Academy, attending classes and running simulations. This game is only for hardcore collectors and Star Trek fans.

Star Wars Arcade   Sega   2 $3
Relatively standard fare for a Star Wars game, this version does suffer from a "rail" effect. While it appears that you have complete control over where you can go, it quickly becomes clear that you are often restricted to a flight path that is unchangeable, though some levels do offer complete control of movement. And while everyone seems to enjoy playing Star Wars games, there have been many since that have greatly improved on this game. Necessary to complete a collection, but only a mediocre game at heart.

Tempo   Sega   4 $5
One of Sega's attempts to create a new mascot for their systems, Tempo is a very active platformer with very vibrant colors and good sound. The control, while average, still helps complete what is a very fun game. And while certainly not comparable to Sonic, it would have been nice to see more games based on this very colorful character.

T-Mek   Time Warner Interactive   7 $30
A conversion of an arcade game, it is often difficult to squeeze everything that was inherent in the arcade version into a cartridge-based system. This mech game uses sprites and scaling effects instead of polygon graphics. In order to make this technique work adequately, the screen was scaled down by placing a black boarder around the play field. The soundtrack consists of simple keyboard tunes, and the controls are made difficult by the lack of a dual-stick controller.

Toughman Contest   Electronic Arts   4 $10
What should have been an entertaining game, turned into just another bad boxing title. Based on the tournament of the same name, Toughman Contest uses a style similar to Punch Out for the NES, but doesn't offer the same control or amount of fun. 24 boxers are available, but this is simply an updated version of the equally bad Genesis version. It can be mildly amusing to play for a short time, but eventually the sluggish control will bring on frustration.

Virtua Fighter   Sega   5 $15
First appearing in arcades, this game was completely created using polygons and was unlike anything anyone had ever seen before. And while the 32x has difficulty recreating these polygons, the control scheme is still intact. Simple and responsive controls, combined with relatively simple looking graphics make this game a very solid fighter. And while not comparable to modern fighting games, it is important to remember that this game started the 3-D fighting game revolution from which Tekken and Soul Caliber were spawned.

Virtua Racing Deluxe   Sega Sports   2 $3
This polygon racer looks very simplistic by today's standards, but innovative digital control and addictive gameplay make this game more enjoyable than you would first think. While heavily dated, the 32x version features two tracks that were not available in the arcade version. Two additional cars were also

Space Harrier

Spider-Man: Web of Fire

Tempo

Virtua Fighter

When polled, what did 63% of gamers say was the most common reason for a game being bad?

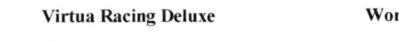

Virtua Racing Deluxe	World Series Baseball	Zaxxon's Motherbase 2000	Fahrenheit

added to this port, including the often favored stock car.

World Series Baseball   Sega Sports   4 $12
Minimal changes were made to the Genesis version of this game in order to bring it to the 32x. Sega always seemed to have an edge when making sports games and this one is demonstrates that fact adequately. But you have to ask why it was ported to this system with so few enhancements.

WWF Raw   Acclaim   4 $12
Either you love wrestling games, or you hate them. WWF Raw is pretty much a standard wrestling game by every account, with nothing standing out as exceptionally good or bad. If you're a wrestling fan though, this title does the genre justice and should be checked out if found at a reasonable price.

WWF WrestleMania: The Arcade Game
       Acclaim   5 $15
One dash of Mortal Kombat and two dashes of wrestling…and this is the result. With some very odd special moves and excessive violence, this game may actually break the seemingly set-in-stone rule of "love it or hate it" in regard to wrestling games. Graphical improvements over the Genesis version are very apparent, but the sound really suffers. Somewhat difficult to find, this game may appeal to mainstream gamers more than any other wrestling game.

Zaxxon's Motherbase 2000
       Sega   3 $5
Of important note, this game was not originally programmed to be of any relation to the great Zaxxon game seen in so many arcades and on so many consoles. The name "Zaxxon" was added after the game's completion in order to garner support from unsuspecting gamers. While it is a fun ¾ view game that is often challenging, it certainly doesn't live up to the standard set by its quasi-relative, the true Zaxxon.

CD GAMES

Corpse Killer   Acclaim   4 $5
Appearing on four consoles, many are forced to ask the question, "Why?" This game is a horribly digitized shooter based around the simple object of shooting things that are already dead. Bad control and mediocre sound are actually the high points of this game.

Fahrenheit   Sega   5 $7
A full motion video game based on firefighters, Fahrenheit isn't so much "bad", as it's just not any good. The most unique of all the SegaCD/32x games released, it is the only one of the five to come in the plastic case used for the Sega CD and Saturn releases. And oddly enough, both the full Sega CD ver-

sion and the 32x version are included in the package. Two completely separate games, of different quality, packaged together. But it is also important to know that the Sega CD disc is used as a "boot" disc for the 32x version, so both CD's must be present to play the more refined 32x version of the game.

Night Trap   Digital Pictures   3 $10
One of the most controversial games ever made, Night Trap first appeared on the Sega CD. Starring Dana Plato of *Different Strokes* "fame", the idea of helpless coeds being killed by monsters was evidently too much for Senator Lieberman to handle. Congress addressed the issue of video game violence, citing Night Trap as a prime example. A new rating system was quickly put into place shortly after. Many attribute this rating system solely to Night Trap. Too bad the rating system doesn't tell you how horribly cheesy this game is. Of historical significance to be true, but rarely considered to be any fun.

Slam City with Scottie Pippen
       Digital Pictures   3 $5
Ever wanted to play a game of basketball with Scottie Pippen? Well, evidently nobody else did either. Full motion video and basketball are shown to be completely incompatible in this poor excuse for a game. Grainy video and impossible control plague this game from the second it begins.

Supreme Warrior
       Digital Pictures   3 $5
And just when you thought it couldn't get any worse, along comes Supreme Warrior. Appearing on several consoles of the time, it is commendable that Digital Pictures was trying something innovative within the fighting genre. A first person fighter was certainly something new, but unfortunately the controls seem to have a mind of their own, and rarely respond at all. It is difficult to understand how a game this bad was actually released. It does use real Kung-Fu actors from Hong Kong though, so if you want to get a good laugh, it might be worth picking up.

HARDWARE

32x System   Sega   3 $15

Poor control.

Sega Saturn

By: Lucus Barnes and Andy Slaven

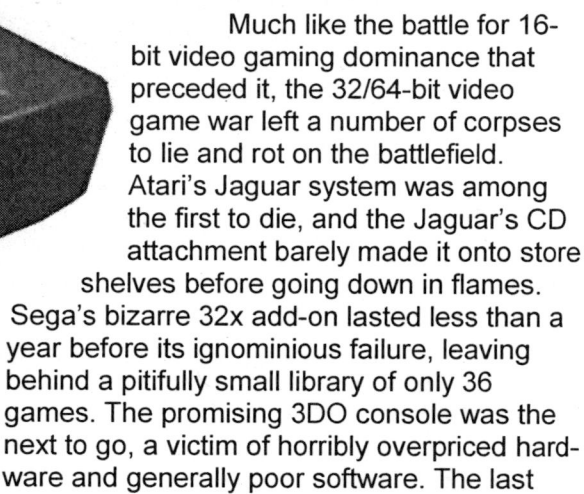

Much like the battle for 16-bit video gaming dominance that preceded it, the 32/64-bit video game war left a number of corpses to lie and rot on the battlefield. Atari's Jaguar system was among the first to die, and the Jaguar's CD attachment barely made it onto store shelves before going down in flames. Sega's bizarre 32x add-on lasted less than a year before its ignominious failure, leaving behind a pitifully small library of only 36 games. The promising 3DO console was the next to go, a victim of horribly overpriced hardware and generally poor software. The last console to fall was Sega's glorious Saturn, one of the most misunderstood and under-appreciated video game platforms ever ignored by the American public.

The Sega Saturn made its American debut in May of 1995, a full six months ahead of schedule. Sega's half-hearted attempt to outmaneuver their new rival Sony and get the Saturn to the marketplace earlier than the upstart Playstation failed miserably, alienating several major toy chains in the process. The first wave of software for the Saturn had been rushed through production, and the lack of development time was readily apparent. High-profile Saturn exclusives like *Daytona USA* and *Virtua Fighter* appeared glitchy and inferior when compared to much more polished Playstation offerings like *Ridge Racer* and *Battle Arena Toshinden*, immediately earning the Saturn the undeserved reputation of being the "weaker" of the two consoles. Additionally, many third-party game developers experienced major difficulties coming to grips with the overly complicated Saturn architecture, often resulting in Saturn games that looked worse than their Playstation counterparts. The fact that the Saturn was introduced at the whopping price of $400 didn't help matters either.

Things began to look up for Sega during the Christmas season of 1995 with the release of several very impressive new Saturn titles. The stunning ports of the popular arcade games *Virtual Fighter 2* and *Sega Rally*, in particular, silenced most of the critics and demonstrated that the Saturn really was as powerful as Sega claimed. Sega continued its upward trend much of the following year with a well-received promotion that bundled three popular games (*Daytona, Virtua Cop, VF2*) with each Saturn unit sold. Unfortunately, archrival Nintendo was about to cannibalize the sales of Sega's fledgling console and leave it sucking dust.

The Nintendo 64 was released just in time for Christmas 1996 and instantly became THE hot toy of the season, selling out in all stores. Sony's Playstation continued to rise in popularity at a rapid pace, but the Saturn had been dealt a fatal blow. An internet modem and a series of high-quality Saturn games like *Dragon Force, Sonic Jam*, and *Fighters Megamix* were finally released, but it was a definite case of "too little, too late." Sales of the console and its software dropped dra-

Some of the newer Neo-Geo AES games actually hold more data than CD-based games can!

matically, and many high-profile game developers began to cancel their upcoming Saturn titles. 1997 was a terrible year for Sega all around, and the Saturn was essentially dead by 1998. The "Final Five" Saturn games (*Burning Rangers, The House of the Dead, Shining Force III, Panzer Dragoon Saga*, and *Magic Knight Rayearth*) were released in mid 1998 in very limited quantities.

To be honest, the Saturn was doomed in America from the start, a victim of mismanagement on the part of Sega of Japan. The success of the Genesis could have easily lead to success for the Saturn as well, but Sega's reputation was severely tarnished with the releases of the Sega CD and the Sega 32x, two well-intentioned but under-whelming hardware add-ons meant to prolong the popularity of the aging Genesis. The exceedingly complex design of the Saturn hardware turned off many game developers, leaving Sega to support its console alone.

What makes the Saturn hardware so complex? Unlike the Playstation (which features a very straightforward and integrated design), the Saturn hardware houses EIGHT separate processors including two 32-bit Hitachi CPU's, two custom graphics processors, a very high-end Yamaha sound chip, and several additional chips that make sure all the components work together (legend has it that the second graphics processor was added late in the Saturn's development cycle in an attempt to boost the 3-D power of the Saturn to match that of the Playstation's.) This convoluted multi-processor arrangement, while powerful and versatile, proved to be the Saturn's achilles' heel.

In truth, the Saturn's complex architecture provides the Saturn with about 50% more raw processing power than the Playstation, and it is far superior at displaying 2-D graphics (in fact, the Saturn solidly outperforms the PSX, the N64, and even the vaulted Neo-Geo when it comes to displaying 2-D visuals.) Game developers that stuck with the Saturn realized that a properly programmed Saturn title could outperform its PSX counterpart, particularly in the area of overall speed. The Saturn console itself is quite resilient, and many first-generation Saturns are still functioning perfectly, long after their fragile PSX counterparts have broken down. The Saturn was the first console to feature true internet play capabilities, and the ability to add more RAM directly to the hardware lead to a string of stunning games for the Japanese market.

Truth be known, the Saturn is really an importer's machine. The Saturn was far more successful in the Far East, mainly due to Japan's insatiable desire for all things *Virtua Fighter* (coupled with the Saturn's ability to deliver perfect ports of arcade hits like *X Men Vs. Street Fighter* and *Vampire Savior* with the aid of a RAM cart). Fighting games and 2-D shooting games, in particular tend to be especially impressive on the Saturn, and many games don't require any knowledge of the Japanese language to play. The Japanese Saturn game library boasts over 700 titles, more than twice the amount of games released in the States (a fair number of them are adult-oriented "hentai" titles, where themes of lesbianism, bondage, and even homoeroticism abound.) Even today, the Saturn is still popular in Japan, though no new games have been produced for it in several years.

Collecting for the Saturn can be as cheap or expensive as you care to make it. The console itself is easy to find and can withstand a lot of abuse. Many of the more common releases can be obtained very inexpensively, and the oversized CD cases (a throwback to the Sega CD era) look awfully good when nicely displayed. Unfortunately, some of the best Saturn games (like *Panzer Dragoon Saga* or *Shining Force III*) had limited production runs and can cost considerably more than the average title. Many of the better imports, in particular, tend to get extremely pricey. Desirable games like *Battle Garrega* and *Dracula X* regularly break the $70 mark, and some of the rarer and/or more sought-after games like *Radiant Silvergun* and *Psychic Killer Assassin Taromaru* can easily break (and go far beyond) the $100 barrier.

Regardless of its poor (and completely undeserved) reputation in the United States, the Sega Saturn is a historically important console worthy of any serious collector's attention. With Sega now out of the hardware business, interest in their previous inventions is bound to increase. Get in while you still can!

What item is present in over 80% of all bootleg cartridge games?

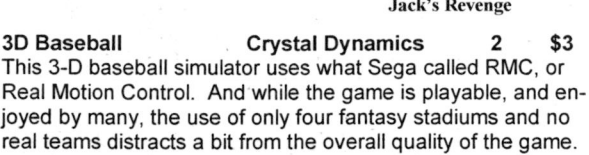

Albert Odyssey: Legend of Eldean

Alone in the Dark: One-Eyed Jack's Revenge

Batman Forever: The Arcade Game

Baku Baku

3D Baseball   **Crystal Dynamics**   2 $3
This 3-D baseball simulator uses what Sega called RMC, or Real Motion Control. And while the game is playable, and enjoyed by many, the use of only four fantasy stadiums and no real teams distracts a bit from the overall quality of the game.

Albert Odyssey: Legend of Eldean
                        Working Designs   6 $28
An overhead RPG from famed miracle workers Working Designs, many feel that this was a disappointing title. But with turn based combat and menu driven battle sequences, this is still among the great RPG's (just not up to Working Designs' standards.) You control five characters led by Pike, your main character. Your quest is to save your sister Laia after she was turned to stone in an attack on your village.

Alien Trilogy   **Acclaim**   3 $8
This is a first-person shooter based on the movies of the same name. This mediocre Saturn port is rumored to only utilize one of the Saturn's two available CPU's.   Common and relatively inexpensive, it should be easy enough to add to your collection, but game players seem to be divided as to how good it is. While it does convey an eerie atmosphere, gameplay suffers.

All-Star Baseball '97   **Acclaim**   2 $2
With six modes of play, real teams and real players, this game stands above 3D Baseball. Control and graphics are adequate, and announcer Jon Miller is used to commentate the game.

Alone in the Dark: One-Eyed Jack's Revenge
                        THQ   4 $12
The original survivor/horror series (that's right, Resident Evil wasn't the first one) makes an appearance on this system, if not a great one. Blocky graphics and often tricky control make for an average gaming experience. Taking place on a ship instead of a mansion takes away from the feel of the first installment, but it is a fun title to play if you're looking for something different.

A.M.O.K.   **Sega**   5 $15
This long-delayed 3-D submarine/mech shooter was one of the final Saturn releases and features a highly unique and appealing graphical style. With nine missions and bonus areas, you will be faced with a large variety of enemies regularly. A two player mode is also offered in which you can compete against each other or in a cooperative mode.

Andretti Racing   **EA Sports**   2 $5
One of many racing games available, this one is about average in every aspect. Control can be a bit off at times, but graphics

and sound are adequate throughout the game.

Arcade's Greatest Hits: Atari
                        Midway   5 $22
A collection of old Atari arcade classics, you will find that the translation is done well, but the use of a Saturn controller just won't feel right for anyone used to using a 2600 controller. This is much more difficult to find than the Williams compilation.

Arcade's Greatest Hits: Williams
                        Midway   3 $10
This compilation contains Asteroids, Battlezone, Centipede, Missle Command, Super Breakout and Tempest, all in good form, but is a little difficult to control with the Saturn controller.

Area 51   **Williams**   4 $15
A port of the very popular arcade game, the translation was done pretty well, and a very playable version of the game was created. While the digitized graphics appear less refined on the Saturn, the overall feel of the game is left intact.

Astal   **Sega**   3 $7
This is a respectable early-release platform game with gorgeous 2-D graphics. An interesting note about the packaging of this game is the fact that the name fails to appear on the spine, making it appear to have no title when stored next to other Saturn games.

Baku Baku   **Sega**   5 $20
A tough puzzle game to find, the object is to match the correct animal with the type of food falling on the screen. Addictive gameplay and good control will keep most players occupied for hours.

Bases Loaded '96   **Jaleco**   2 $3
While a license was obtained, and 700 real players and their teams were included in the game, it lacks a quality necessary in any baseball game: good control. Graphics are mediocre and sound is average, but the inability to control the players makes this game frustrating at times.

Batman Forever: The Arcade Game
                        Acclaim   5 $20
This is a bad game based on a movie franchise that went downhill after Tim Burton left. Not many would contest the statement that this game is barely worth the time it takes to load.

Battle Arena Toshinden Remix
                        Takara   2 $5
So, what was "remixed", you ask? One new character was

An "official" seal of quality.

added...sounds more like a stir than a mix. Or perhaps the title refers to the decreased quality in graphics over the Sony Playstation version. Either way, this fighting game is playable, just not all that enjoyable. Weapons are used in this game however, which offered Saturn owners a change of pace from the recently released Virtual Fighter 2.

Battle Arena Toshinden Ultimate Revenge Attack
Takara 3 $7

A step backwards in the series actually, one must wonder what is so "ultimate" about it. While the sound remains of relatively high quality, the environments and characters actually appear to be of reduced graphic stock. The playability of the game remains second rate.

Battle Monsters   Acclaim   4 $10
A digitized 2-D fighting game that pits odd monsters against each other, this lackluster title is not worth playing. Ugly environments, bad control and poor character design plague this title.

Battle Stations   EA   4 $12
This gunboat action/strategy game is interesting to play, but quickly becomes tiresome. A much more entertaining two player mode is supported though, and while the graphics aren't of the highest quality, control and sound are a little above average.

Battlesport   Acclaim   7 $12
Based on the highly-rated 3DO title, Battlesport was Acclaim's last Saturn release and had a very low production run but has yet to increase in value. And while the Saturn has the capability of improving upon the 3DO version, it almost seems as if this title lost quality, despite the fact that this is a carbon copy of the 3DO version.

Black Dawn   VIE   3 $7
Good helicopter simulations are hard to come by, but this game makes a relatively good appearance on the Saturn. With impressive graphics while in battle, great sound and decent control make this game very enjoyable.

Black Fire   Sega   3 $5
Don't confuse this helicopter action game with Black Dawn. Graphics are decent, but problems with sound and repetition of game play really take away from the overall enjoyment of this game.

Blast Chamber   Activision   4 $6
The objective is simply to escape the arena within which you are held captive, from chamber to chamber, before you're blown to bits. Simple concept, and fun in multi-player mode, but not much fun when playing solo.

Blazing Dragons   Crystal Dynamics   4 $5
Can't get enough of Cheech Marin? You're probably alone if you said "yes". But, nonetheless, Cheech is used for voice-overs within the game. You take the part of a dragon on his quest across the land collecting items and solving puzzles. It's animated style makes this title different than most other dragon games however, and is surprisingly enjoyable.

Blazing Heroes   Sega   5 $15
This is the same game as "Mysteria". The name was changed due to legal reasons, but aside from this, the games are identical.

Braindead 13   Readysoft   4 $10
In the same style as Dragon's Lair, you make control movements at the appropriate time in order to progress. Surprisingly fun, the animation is rendered very well by the Saturn, but many feel that the 3DO version is just as good, if not better.

Breakpoint Tennis   Ocean   1 $1
An average tennis game that is perhaps one of the most common titles for the system. Nothing stands out as too terribly bad, nor exceptionally good...it walks right down the middle of a road named "Mediocre".

Bubble Bobble: Also Featuring Rainbow Islands
Acclaim 5 $20

Two games in one, Bubble Bobble and Rainbow Islands, if you're bored with one, you can always play the other. Both based off games by the same names, these are both excellent ports of arcade classics from 1986 and 1987 respectfully.

Bug!   Sega   4 $8
This game's storyline has you acting in a movie. Your success will determine the success of the movie and visa versa. 16 levels of increasing difficulty should keep you busy for a while in this very entertaining game.

Bug Too!   Sega   4 $15
The obvious sequel to "Bug!", this title lacks the same innovation of the first. And while still a good game, the original formula and characters seemed more enjoyable. You can choose to play as Superfly or Maggot Dog in this title.

Burning Rangers   Sega   8 $60
One of the "final five" Saturn games, this amazing 3-D platform

Battle Stations   **Battlesport**   **Black Fire**   **Blazing Dragons**

Since the beginning of video games, there have only been two distinctive variations of game format: cartridge and optical discs.

| Bust-A-Move 2 | Casper | Congo: The Movie | Contra: Legacy of War |

shooter features futuristic environments, cool sound effects, and very impressive graphics. Only 5000 copies released in the U.S.

Bust-A-Move-2: Arcade Edition
Acclaim   4 $10
Can a game challenge the addicting nature of Tetris? Well, if there is one, it is any of the Bust-A-Move installments for any system. Your character, placed in the center-bottom of the screen has colored balloons that he must shoot into a field of other colored balloons. The object is to form combinations of 3 identical colors in order to remove them from the screen. Incredibly addictive, don't be surprised if you forget to eat, sleep, or even breath. It is that addictive!

Bust-A-Move-3   Natsume   5 $20
While all the installations of this game are entertaining, you would think that eventually a point of monotony would be reached. You would think. But with thousands of new puzzles to work through and the same addicting game play, there is no denying that this game will occupy a LOT of your time.

Casper   Interplay   4 $12
Based on the "friendly ghost" that our parents grew up with, this game has nice graphics and sound, but content seems to be directed at a younger audience.

Center Ring Boxing   JVC   5 $15
In this boxing game, the object isn't only to win, but to do so with a boxer that you created. Change the attributes of not only your fighter's appearance, but your performance as well through proper training. An interesting game for this system, it could be improved all around, but still fun.

Clockwork Knight   Sega   3 $7
Taking the role of a wind-up toy in the form of a knight, you are on a mission to save Princess Chelsea before dawn. Your opponents are made of other toys that have come to life, but with only five levels, the game can seem a bit short when played by any experienced gamer.

Clockwork Knight 2   Sega   5 $20
This is basically an expansion of the first installment more than it is a sequel. And while the story might have changed a bit, you're back in control of a toy knight, going on a mission through platform-levels and facing other animate toys. Graphical improvements make this slightly better than the first however.

College Slam   Acclaim   1 $2
With the license to use real college teams and logos, College Slam is a must-have for any fan of college basketball. A port from the arcade name of the same name, it plays and feels much like NBA Jam, which isn't really a bad thing. And while extremely common, it is still fun to play.

Command and Conquer
Virgin   4 $15
A port from the PC world, Command and Conquer is loved by millions, and it doesn't disappoint on the Saturn. It seems that almost everything was left intact during the conversion. Good solid game play, great sound, real time action/strategy, this will be a game that any fan of the genre will enjoy.

Congo: The Movie   Sega   3 $7
This is a dreadful, pixilated first-person shooter based on the equally bad movie. It uses the same engine as Ghen War however, and really fails to deliver any enjoyment on any level.

Contra: Legacy of War   Konami   4 $15
Not the 2-D Contra we know and love, but not all bad. This version comes with a pair of the old-style blue/red "3-D" paper glasses that are to be used with a special game mode (that doesn't work real well.)

Corpse Killer: Graveyard Edition
Digital Pictures   3 $4
It seems that this title is equally bad on all platforms. An action/shooter game where you must repeatedly kill Zombies, don't get the story line confused with the much more popular, and entertaining, House of the Dead series.

Courier Crisis   GTI   5 $12
Sometimes described as a shoddy mixture of Paperboy and Road Rash, this game is low on entertainment and replay value. It did have a low production, but also had a small fan base as well.

Creature Shock: Special Edition
Data East   4 $8
An improvement over both the PC and 3DO versions, this is still a futuristic "rail" game. This basically means that you have very limited control over the pace of the game and even the direction you head most of the time. Your main function is to shoot and avoid enemies.

Crime Wave   Eidos   5 $15
This is an intriguing adventure/racing hybrid with detailed graphics and a fatal flaw; the screen freezes every few second to load level data! This is inexcusable on a system with the Saturn's

capabilities and really detracts from the overall quality of the game.

Criticom — Vic Tokai — 2 — $2
A futuristic fighting game, Criticom is adequate in most areas and offers control better than that of Battle Arena Toshinden. And while it does have some flaws with the control scheme, it is a very playable game.

Croc: Legend of the Gobbos — FOX — 4 — $15
This 3-D platform game features a cartoon like style, but still features some of the best graphics seen on the Saturn system. Unfortunately this title is becoming increasingly difficult to find.

Crow: City of Angels — Acclaim — 4 — $15
This game can be put into the same category as Shaq-Fu: The worst games of all time. This is by far the worst movies translation by Acclaim, and is simply painful to play.

Crusader: No Remorse — EA — 3 — $5
This is your basic futuristic action/adventure game ported directly from its moderate success on the PC. You play the role of a "silencer", which is simply an elite soldier. Decent graphics and quality sound make this a fun title, but the control takes a little while to get used to.

Crypt Killer — Konami — 5 — $12
An average shooter with a choice of weapons, this should not be confused with the lesser game "Corpse Killer". Graphics and game play are on average, and the sound effects are above average for this genre.

Cyber Speedway — Mindscape — 3 — $5
A mediocre racing game set in the future, average graphics and sometimes frustrating control make this game less enjoyable after a few hours of play.

Cyberia — Interplay — 3 — $5
Cyberia actually refers to a doomsday device that was created to ensure world peace, however its power has been compromised by terrorists. As Zak, a computer hacker trying to redeem himself, your job is to infiltrate and stop Cyberia. An interesting plot and impressive environments for the time of this game's release make this game very enjoyable. It should offer at least 30 hours of game play.

D — Acclaim — 5 — $15
Definitely a cult classic, this game is short due to the internal game clock which counts down to the end...whether you're actu-

ally finished or not. Creepy cinemas and an excellent storyline make this title enjoyable on any platform, but especially for the Saturn.

Darius Gaiden — Acclaim — 4 — $5
This is a highly underrated 2-D shooter with well designed boss characters. This title is definitely recommended for fans of the shooter genre.

Dark Legend — Data East — 3 — $5
Your standard 2-D fighting game, the characters used are those from ancient China. With average control, average sound and average control, this game is often completely lost in the plethora of Street Fighter 2 clones.

Dark Savior — Sega — 5 — $20
The unofficial successor to the action/RPG Landstalker (Genesis) featuring isometric graphics and an intriguing battle system, this game suffers from a horrible musical score.

Darklight Conflict — EA — 4 — $5
Fused with an alien fighting ship at a genetic level, you will fly on numerous missions in this flight/space simulator. While it doesn't stand out in any particular area, its storyline is interesting and should hold your attention longer than most 3-D shooters of this nature.

Daytona USA — Sega — 1 — $1
This is the most common of all Saturn releases. Addicting game play will keep most interested, but glitches in the frame rate and graphics will turn some away from an otherwise enjoyable title.

Daytona USA: Championship Circuit Edition — Sega — 4 — $10
The addition of new cars, new tracks, and the ability of your car to suffer damage from collisions makes this game an improvement over the first, but the same frame rate and graphical problems are still evident.

Daytona USA: Championship Circuit Netlink Edition 6 — Sega — 5 — $15
Available only to those who ordered directly from Sega, this rarer version of the original game is identical in every way with the exception of its online capability via the Saturn Netlink device.

Decathlete — Sega — 5 — $15
A port of the arcade game by the same name, it is not very enjoyable for a single player, but can be a great game when

Crow: City of Angels

D

Dark Legend

Daytona USA

The secret "negative one" level on Super Mario Bros. has no end.

DefCon 5   Dragon Force   Dragon Heart: Fire and Steel   Earthworm Jim 2

played with multiple players.

DefCon 5   **Data East**   **4**   **$7**
Mainly a first-person shooter, different genres are mixed in for good measure, but in the end, the game fails on all levels. A bad and unresponsive control scheme mixed with substandard visuals and sound make this alien killing experience a forgettable one.

Die Hard Arcade   **Sega**   **3**   **$15**
A nearly arcade-perfect port, the only flaw of this game is its very short length. However, for as long as it lasts its enjoyable, and has a relatively high replay value.

Die Hard Trilogy   **Fox Interactive**   **3**   **$7**
Aptly named, you will play through parts of all three movies, each represented by a different genre. You will play not only a 3-D fighting portion, but also a light-gun compatible shooter, and an often violent driving game. A very enjoyable and impressive game for the Saturn.

Doom   **GTI**   **5**   **$10**
The Saturn was capable of much more than this, but unfortunately graphics and sound both suffer on one of the most famous first-person games ever made.

Double Switch   **Sega**   **3**   **$5**
Originally appearing on the Sega CD, this title is an interactive movie in which you must be in the right place at the right time in order to capture the bad guys before they harm anyone. Simple in concept, and certainly not anything new, this title can be fun the first time through. After you've completed the game however, the movie sequences become repetitious and very boring.

Dragon Force   **Working Designs**   **7**   **$65**
This addictive strategy game is widely considered to be the best in its genre, as well as one of the best (and most sought-after) games in the entire Saturn library. A definite must-have.

Dragon Heart: Fire and Steel
      Acclaim   **5**   **$10**
The best part about this game is the fact that it is short. Minimal effort was put into creating this translation of the movie Dragon Heart. Horrible graphics and sound only make the horrible control seem that much worse.

Duke Nuke'm 3D   **Sega**   **5**   **$15**
A great port of the PC favorite, this is proof that the Saturn is capable of creating good 3-D graphics.

Earthworm Jim 2   **Playmates**   **4**   **$15**
A great platform game with a very charismatic main character, this is among the top games for the Saturn. Great control, sound and graphics make this challenging game suitable for a large amount of replay.

Enemy Zero   **Sega**   **5**   **$15**
A creepy pseudo-sequel to "D", it stars the same character but is set in the distant future. New, scary, and occasionally irritating first-person hunts break up the monotony of the "graphic adventure" segments.

F1 Challenge   **Virgin**   **3**   **$5**
An average entry into the tangle of F1 racing games, this title hasn't aged well. With so many improvements to control schemes and graphics since this game's release, this title will probably only grace the shelves of collectors.

FIFA Soccer '96   **EA Sports**   **2**   **$2**
The soccer franchise that revolutionized the genre and revitalized a questionable sports game era, FIFA Soccer '96 is enjoyable and benefits from nice control and graphics.

FIFA Soccer '97   **EA Sports**   **2**   **$2**
With improvements over the first installment, this common soccer game is still amazing to play. It offers a level of control and perspective that are often mimicked by newer systems.

FIFA World Cup Soccer '98
      EA Sports   **3**   **$5**
Many options are available within this game as well, including the editing of rosters and different play modes. And if you don't like the perspective, a camera-change option is also available.

Fighters Megamix   **Sega**   **4**   **$15**
Quite possibly the best fighter on the Saturn (for 2 players), FM features cast members from Virtua Fighter 2, Fighting Vipers, Sonic, Virtua Cop 2, and even Daytona USA!

Fighting Vipers   **Sega**   **1**   **$1**
A massively underrated, and overproduced follow-up to Virtua Fighter 2. This is a great fighter, and even includes a girl on roller skates. How can you go wrong with that?

Frank Thomas' Big Hurt Baseball
      Acclaim   **2**   **$1**
One of so many baseball games, this entry is extremely common and extremely inexpensive. Average at best however, fans of Frank Thomas might find it entertaining, but game players might do well to look elsewhere for their baseball fix.

Galactic Attack   Acclaim   4 $10
Don't see many classic 2-D space shooters nowadays! Here's a good one. Simple control, graphics and sound are all straight-forward and solid, as is the case with most classic games.

Galaxy Fight   Acclaim   6 $12
A rare port of the Neo-Geo game by the same name, limitless levels (no boundaries) make "cornering" a thing of the past. Not nearly as good as the Neo-Geo version, but much more afford-able.

Gex   Crystal Dynamics   3 $7
The famed gecko makes his appearance on the Saturn. And while there are small improvements over the 3DO version, this title is mainly played for quick entertainment. A very popular character and franchise for about a year, not much was heard from Gex after his fame deteriorated.

Ghen War   Sega   3 $5
A tedious first-person shooter released early in the Saturn's short life, this title uses the same engine as "Congo: The Movie", making it flawed in too many ways to list.

Golden Axe: The Duel   Sega   4 $10
A continuation of sorts of the Golden Axe saga created in ar-cades by Sega, this title takes characters from fighting through levels and pits them against each other. An average fighter, it will be fun for any true fan of the Golden Axe series.

Grand Slam   VIE   2 $2
Average overall, a new control scheme for hitting and pitching make this game stand out as an innovator in the genre. And while game play is solid, sound could have been improved.

Grid Runner   Virgin   4 $5
Massively underrated party game. Get it now! Addicting 3 player action will keep you and your friends entertained for more time than most other multiplayer games (excepting Super Bust-A-Move 2.)

Guardian Heroes   Sega   7 $40
Famed developer Treasure graced the Saturn with a real rarity, a hack & slash adventure that's innovative and fun to play! Great control and an enjoyable sound track make this game better than most in its class.

Gun Griffon   Sega   4 $12
A decent mech game that many will enjoy, this title has a small following of loyal players, most of which have imported the im-proved second volume from Japan.

Hang-On GP   Sega   3 $7
Three tracks and six possible routes don't take much time to play through in this motorcycle racing game. If it had supported multiplayer gaming, it would have much higher replay value.

Heir of Zendor: The Legend of the Land
                 Koei   5 $10
What could have been a very fun game turns into a disappoint-ment from Koei. Airships and floating continents with turned based strategy/action sounds like it would be a lot of fun. And even a great storyline can't save it from very slow action, decid-edly less than average graphics and bad sound.

Herc's Adventures   Lucas Arts   6 $35
The makers of Zombies Ate My Neighbors! released this simi-larly-playing (and hilarious) game late in the Saturn's life, and nobody noticed it. A definite sleeper that should entertain any fan of the Saturn.

Hexen   GTI   2 $3
A first-person hack and slash game that offers spell casting for certain characters, this title appeared on several platforms. Unfortunately the full capability of the Saturn wasn't used, and grainy graphics are the norm in this title.

Hi-Octane   Bullfrog   3 $5
A futuristic racing game, average on the whole, will entertain those who are fond of cars outfitted with weapons. Unfortu-nately the game seems to move very slowly for a racing game.

Hi Velocity   Atlus   4 $10
Another 3-D racer on the Saturn, this title is a lot of fun with nice graphical and acoustic features. Speed is an attribute that this game carries relatively well and is among the better racing games for the system.

Highway 2000   Natsume   4 $7
A below average racing game with only 6 courses and 5 cars, a mediocre multiplayer feature is the only redeeming feature within this otherwise unplayable game.

Horde, The   Crystal Dynamics   4 $7
It has Kirk Cameron, and who could ask for more than that? This strategy game, with the occasional cinema, is entertaining and lighthearted. Many codes can be found on the internet that will basically allow for quick passage through a game that can otherwise take a while to complete.

Galactic Attack

Ghen War

Grid Runner

Herc's Adventures

Laid end to end, all the world's PSX units would reach a distance of around 11,000 miles.

The House of the Dead	In the Hunt	The Incredible Hulk: The Pantheon Saga	Loaded

House of the Dead, The
Sega   8 $50
One of the "final five" Saturn releases with only 5000 copies produced. This is a blocky and ugly yet infinitely an playable port of the arcade gun shooter smash. Finding this game will take longer than most others since a small cult following quickly buys every copy that becomes available.

Hyper 3D Pinball   Virgin   4 $10
A very fun and entertaining pinball game that offers good visuals and realistic control.

Impact Racing   Acclaim   3 $5
This combat oriented game can be very addicting. And while control isn't the best, driving takes a back seat (no pun intended) to the combat action.

In the Hunt   THQ   5 $25
This is a simply gorgeous 2-D submarine shooter that is ruined by horrendous slowdown. With five levels of side scrolling action, and one of vertically scrolling action, this game can become tedious at times. Weapons upgrades and changing enemies keep it exciting if you can just get past the glitch in the frame rate.

Incredible Hulk, The: The Pantheon Saga
Eidos   6 $12
Boring levels and a questionable storyline plague this title and make it less enjoyable than most other action games for the Saturn. Graphics, sound and control all suffer in this hard-to-find game.

Independence Day   FOX   4 $5
Based on the movie by the same name, this title is actually a flight simulator that has you knocking out alien generators in order to save the world.

Iron Man/X-O Man-O-War: Heavy Metal
Acclaim   5 $10
An odd pairing of super heroes to be sure, this title isn't very interesting for those that aren't fans of the comics from which these characters are derived. Side scrolling action is the theme in this game, through which you have the ability to fly. Your objective is to simply destroy everything possible, as is the case with most games in this genre.

Iron Storm   Working Designs   6 $30
A complex war strategy game translated by Working Designs, this title should be in every WWII buff's collection, along with anyone who is a fan of very long and engulfing strategy games.

You can choose to play as Germany, Japan or the U.S. in this war simulation. This is definitely one of the better titles for the Saturn.

Johnny Bazookatone   U.S. Gold   4 $5
Available on several systems, solid action and control make this a fun game to play for a short while, though it wears a bit thin only after a short while.

Last Bronx   Sega   5 $7
The last Saturn 3-D fighter, and this time they're armed! This massively underrated fighter was ignored in the arcade, and the well-translated sequel was ignored too.

Last Gladiators: Extreme Digital Pinball
TWI   5 $10
While seemingly a strange title for a Pinball game, the movie Titus staring Anthony Hopkins clearly shows that pinball was indeed played by gladiators. It also showed that the emperor of Rome drove around in a car, but that's not the point. Four unique tables in this exceptional pinball game should keep you busy for a while. Control, graphics and sound are all above average and make this game fun for any pinball fan.

Legend of Oasis   Sega   4 $15
A very enjoyable action game with mild RPG elements, this title is actually the prequel to "Beyond Oasis" for the Genesis. You take the role of Leon in a quest to beat Agito.

Loaded   Interplay   4 $8
This shooter, with an overhead perspective, tasks you with the simple objective to kill everything. Enjoyable sound and solid control will make this game enjoyable for anyone, though it carries a "mature" rating. Many believe that this version of the game actually has better graphics and sound than the Play-station version.

Lost World, The: Jurassic Park 2
Sega   5 $10
The ability to play as dinosaurs, in addition to human characters saves this game from becoming just another action game. Available on five other systems, the Saturn version is among the best.

Lunacy   Atlus   7 $30
A bizarre "graphic adventure" with gorgeous pre-rendered graphics and hilarious dialog ("the name that they call me is Sam.") Very Japanese, and very strange that this one made it over the ocean at all.

The sound of elephants is the loudest noise in the Genesis game Centurion: Defender of Rome.

Machinehead Eidos 3 $5
A first-person shooter at heart, you actually drive a hovercraft with an arsenal of weapons to destroy everything in your site. More fun than many first-person shooters due to the speed of your craft and weaponry available.

Madden NFL '97 EA Sports 1 $1
A very good installment of the largest football video game franchise in history, this version utilizes the Saturn's graphics very well and, more importantly, control seems to be very good.

Madden NFL '98 EA Sports 3 $5
The next installment in a long series, this title is a little disappointing after the '97 version. It seems that more improvements should have been made, but instead very minor updates were made, but no real game play is improved upon.

Magic Carpet EA/Bullfrog 5 $15
Riding a flying carpet in first-person perspective through 70 levels (yes, 70!), this title is among the favorites of many people. Involving game play and interesting environments make this a must-have for any Saturn owner.

Magic Knight Rayearth Working Designs 8 $50
This cute but dull "girly" RPG was one of the "final five" Saturn games (only 5000 copies produced) and was the final Saturn game ever released in the U.S. Delayed for nearly 3 years, it was the last game translated by Working Designs before they had a fight with Sega and jumped ship to Sony.

Mansion of the Hidden Souls
Sega 3 $5
An average interactive move that places you within an eerie mansion. As is the norm for this genre, being in the right place at the right time is the key to solving it.

Manx TT Super Bike Sega 5 $15
A very good entry into the motorcycle racing genre, this title has amazing graphics and control, along with enjoyable audio. And while it can be difficult to find, it is definitely worth picking up if you come across it.

Marvel Super Heroes Capcom 6 $25
Great 2-D Capcom fighter, this version is much better than the Playstation port. MSH is the only game released in the U.S. that had the ability to take advantage of the never-released USA 1 meg RAM cart (for extra frames of animation.) It will work with Japanese converter/Ram carts however. Joy!

Mass Destruction ASC 5 $12
This is a very entertaining, yet unappreciated tank shooter with very fast graphics. Addicting play will entertain even the most cynical gamers.

Maximum Force Midway 6 $10
Lower production than its predecessor Area 51, yet more readily available due to its often appearance in resale shops and online auctions.

Mech Warrior 2 Activision 4 $8
Nice graphics and sound are a plus in this mech game, but changeable controller configurations make the control scheme more intuitive. And while it does take some getting used to, a little practice will make this game very enjoyable.

Megaman 8: Anniversary Collector's Edition
Capcom 6 $30
A very good installment in the long running series that started on the NES, this title offers clean graphics and solid control. What more can be said? It's Megaman!

Megaman X4 Capcom 7 $35
Taking control of Megaman X or Zero (your choice throughout the game), you are back in the action in this classic platform game. Performing nicely on the Saturn, this installment should please any fans of the Megaman series, though it is very difficult to come across.

MLBPA: Bottom of the Ninth
Konami 2 $2
An above average baseball game for this system, graphics seem to be crisp and control is intuitive and easy to perform.

Minnesota Fats Pool Legend
Data East 5 $15
Bearing the name of one of the all time great pool players, this game certainly doesn't live up to his legend. The geometry seems to be a bit off and really has a negative effect on control. Nice graphics just can't make up for unrealistic game play in a pool simulation, not that the graphics are really that great to begin with.

Mortal Kombat 2 Acclaim 5 $20
While this title is considered the best in the series by many, and the graphics in the Saturn port are nearly arcade perfect, the reduced frame rate and load times DURING actual matches ruins this game completely.

Mortal Kombat Trilogy Midway 3 $10
This addition to the Mortal Kombat series is a brilliant idea gone

Machine Head

Magic Knight Rayearth

Manx TT Super Bike

Mech Warrior 2

What is the largest confirmed sum of money ever paid for a non-prototype video game cartridge?

Myst

Mystaria: The Realms of Lore

NASCAR 98

NBA Jam Extreme

stupid. With 32 characters to choose from, the variety is good, but the characters themselves are from three different MK games, resulting in horrible mismatches. The frame rate problems are still evident and loading, once again, ruins a game that should have been a lot of fun.

Mr. Bones Sega 5 $15
Bizarre compilations of mini-games starring a blues-loving skeleton, this is an interesting experiment with great music.

Myst Sunsoft 2 $3
The pioneering game that made a huge impact on the PC gaming world, Myst makes an average appearance on the Saturn. While it was amazing the first time it appeared on the PC, the Saturn is hardly pushed to its limits with still frame animation and a point and click interface. Still fun for those who haven't played the game however.

Mystaria: The Realms of Lore
Sega 7 $30
Re-released as Blazing Heroes to avoid a copyright conflict, this is the rarer of the two versions. This 3-D strategy/RPG offers free-roaming capabilities and turn based battles. And while it is often difficult to find and expensive to buy, it is still an enjoyable title.

NASCAR '98 EA Sports 5 $12
In this racing game you are able to choose from 24 actual NASCAR drivers and even use actual tracks. This game also supports two player action.

NBA Action Sega 2 $3
With a license from the NBA, you will be able to play with real players from real teams. You can also choose from actual plays from a playbook, or design your own, not that they're implemented very well in a basketball video game.

NBA Action 98 Sega 4 $7
A continuation of the first title, updated rosters are about the extent of the changes made to this game. Still enjoyable, but disappointing that improvements weren't made.

NBA Jam Extreme Acclaim 3 $5
A continuation of the NBA Jam series, the same type of game play can be expected from this title, featuring two on two match ups in which four players can go...head to head to head to head?

X **NBA Jam Tournament Edition**
Acclaim 2 $4

Power-ups, super dunks, injuries, etc. are just part of what makes this arcade style game enjoyable. And while it does fall behind in some areas such as graphics, it is still enjoyable to play with friends over.

NBA Live '97 EA Sports 2 $2
This licensed NBA game seems to fall a little short in both the graphical and control department. Very common and inexpensive, it might be worth a try if you're a huge basketball fan.

NBA Live '98 EA Sports 2 $2
An improvement over the previous year's installment, this title offers new modes of play, graphical and control enhancements. Of the two, this is a bit better considering the increased number of options and the more recent roster of players.

X **Need For Speed, The** EA 4 $10
This popular game franchise made this entertaining entry into the Saturn's collection with an average reception. Available on the 3DO as well, this version is much though, though, as the title might imply, it needs more speed.

NFL '97 Sega 2 $2
Though it is a licensed game including real teams and players, every aspect of this game is wanting of improvement. Graphics, control, frame rate, sound and enjoyment are all very low on this disappointing entry.

NFL Quarterback Club '96
Acclaim 1 $1
The title, while catchy, makes it seem that every other football game has you playing the part of a lineman or a defensive back. But, with a license, this game offers some of the top quarterbacks of the time and is enjoyable for fans of football.

NFL Quarterback Club '97
Acclaim 1 $1
Updated rosters are about the only change to this update to the series. Everything else seems to be left untouched from the first installment on the Saturn.

NHL '97 EA Sports 2 $2
Supporting up to 8 players at once (with the adaptor), this 3-D hockey game is a lot of fun for those who enjoy a fast paced sports game. This should be in every hockey fan's collection.

NHL '98 EA Sports 3 $4
An update to the previous year's version, all the violence of the real game is included. Solid game play and nice graphics make

this title enjoyable, but a lack of any major improvements to the game mechanics make the '97 version just as enjoyable.

NHL All-Star Hockey   Sega   1 $1
A licensed hockey game for the Saturn, and actually the first hockey game for the system, this is a decent effort that has options such as the trading of players in order to keep the game enjoyable. A 12 player mode is also available!

NHL All-Star Hockey '98
                        Sega   2 $3
This is not actually a true update of NHL All-Star Hockey, but instead is a continuation of the series name under a new design team. Unfortunately the same feel wasn't maintained and the series actually took a step backward, it's last step in fact. This version only supports 8 players as opposed to the original 12.

NHL Break-Away '96   Virgin   2 $2
A standard hockey game for the Saturn, and an early release at that. If you are looking for a decent hockey game on the system however, stick with NHL '97.

Night Warriors: Darkstalker's Revenge
                        Capcom   4 $15
Simply an outstanding game! In a world filled with 2-D fighters, this one sports some of the nicest graphics, sound and control of them all. A sequel to the lesser game Darkstalkers, this title is definitely the better of the two.

NiGHTS into Dreams...
                        Sega   3 $12
This simply gorgeous adventure game must be played to be appreciated, but it's still not for everyone. Iame bundled with Sega's superlative analog control pad, which the Sega Dreamcast's controller was later designed from.

Norse by Norsewest: The Lost Vikings 2
                        Interplay   5 $20
This puzzle based adventure game is the sequel to The Lost Vikings, not just an update. Entertaining game play and simple controls make this an enjoyable title.

Off-World Interceptor Extreme
                        Crystal Dynamics 2 $3
This is like taking a monster truck to another world with reduced gravity. Armed and ready to...drive? While there isn't much to the storyline, and the controls can sometimes be frustrating, the game is still fun to play, and easy enough to find.

Olympic Soccer   U.S. Gold   1 $1

Given a choice, you should definitely pick FIFA over this title, though it isn't a bad entry. Graphics aren't what they should be, and the control often times seems a bit cumbersome for players that should be moving much more agilely.

P.T.O. 2: Pacific Theatre of Operations
                        Koei   5 $20
This is another complex strategy game from the masters of complexity, Koei. Instead of focusing on shooting and bombing, this World War 2 strategy simulation focuses on the maneuvering of forces in order to secure the advantage over your enemy. A bit slow for some, this simulation should be enjoyable by history buffs and strategy gamers alike.

Pandemonium   Crystal Dynamics   5 $12
One of the best "3-D" (the action occurs on a 2-D plane) platform games every made. And while it is a little difficult to find, this title shouldn't set you back too much.

Panzer Dragoon   Sega   4 $15
This was a very early release for the system and was absolutely amazing at the time of its release. Gorgeous graphics and solid control promised a lot for the system, though the game does suffer from "rail effect" which severely limits your lateral and vertical limits. Basically, with the exception of collision avoidance, you really have no control over the direction of your dragon.

Panzer Dragoon II Zwei
                        Sega   5 $25
A beautifully updated sequel to the classic shooter featuring fine graphics and more complex game play. And though it still has the same "rail effect", control is nearly perfect as is the audio.

Panzer Dragoon Saga   Sega   7 $100
PDS is the most sought-after game in the entire domestic Saturn library, and with good reason. It is an incredible RPG with stunning visuals and a fascinating storyline, truly one of the greats. It is also one of the "final five" Saturn games, though it had a larger production run of between 10 and 15 thousand copies.

Pebble Beach Golf Links
                        Sega   4 $5
Better golf games have been made to be sure, including PGA Tour '97 listed below, but for a quick front 9 this game should entertain you. While graphics suffer, and sound is minimal, control is what a gold game is all about, and they are adequate for this game.

Night Warriors: Darkstalker's Revenge

NiGHTS into Dreams...

P.T.O. II Pacific Theater of Operations

Panzer Dragoon Saga

309

In addition to the arcade and console versions, Tetris is also available on cell phones, PDA's, and calculators.

Power Slave

Primal Rage

Pro Pinball

Resident Evil

PGA Tour '97   EA Sports   2 $2
A continuation of the series from the Genesis, improved sound and additional courses make this graphically enhanced golf game very enjoyable for golf aficionados.

Power Slave   .   Virgin   6 $15
This Egyptian-themed corridor shooter was the first game to really demonstrate the 3-D power of the Saturn. A low production number coupled with a low profile make this rarity and affordable game that most others won't have.

Primal Rage   Time Warner   4 $10
Made famous in the arcade, this port is less than it should have been. A promising franchise such as this should have been given more attention to improve frame rates and animations. And while it is still a decent fighting game featuring some very unusual prehistoric animals, it is disappointing on the whole.

Pro Pinball   Interplay   5 $12
This is what every pinball game should aspire to be, or rather what every pinball game maker should aspire for his creation to be. A great variety of mini-games and challenges are available via this title's main table. Instead of trying a new gimmick, this game simply does one thing well: imitates a pinball machine very well.

Quake   Sega   6 $12
This late-release shooter based on the PC classic boasts impressive visuals but no network option. This flaw doesn't make it a bad game, just one that didn't reach its potential, and this is a real shame. Still, a very fun game to play, If you can find a copy.

Quarterback Attack   Digital Pictures   1 $1
This interactive movie sets the camera man squarely inside the helmet of the quarterback. And while the concept was original enough, the game itself is less of a football experience and more of a timing experience. Pressing the right button at the right time in order to trigger the next video sequence is basically the extent of the game play.

Rampage: World Tour   Midway   5 $12
A continuation of the series made popular by the arcade and NES versions, this title features the same basic game concept: destroy buildings and eat people. Playing the part of a monster that climbs and destroys the buildings of cities across the world, this version shows improved graphics and control, though it hardly showcases the extent of the Saturn's capabilities.

Rayman   Ubi Soft   4 $25

A platform game with a character of considerable popularity, this version of the game has sharp graphics and very good sound. Control is very easy to learn and an increasing difficulty level keeps this game entertaining for a long time.

Resident Evil   Capcom   4 $20
The most popular survival/horror series around makes an entry into the Saturn market. While most believe the Playstation version to be superior, more solid control and impressive sound make this a true contender. A very eerie game that launched a swarm of sequels, the original is still viewed by many as the king of all horror games (though this title is obviously inspired by the original horror game "Alone in the Dark".)

Revolution-X   Acclaim   3 $7
A cult classic for Aerosmith fans, this shooter will have you fighting "The New Order", which is trying to control the world's youth by taking away entertainment. And while this game certainly has a small, but loyal following, the graphics are horrible and make it very difficult to enjoy the game. A game which relies on the sole control of a gun should look much better than this does.

Rise 2: Resurrection   Acclaim   3 $4
This 2-D fighting game suffers from jumpy movement and poor control. Even the sound track seems to be a bit scratchy at times, which is unforgivable for a game on the Saturn.

Road Rash   EA   4 $10
Available on many systems, this motorcycle racing/combat game is definitely entertaining. And while the graphics haven't aged very gracefully, they were above average for the time considering their digitized appearance.

Robo Pit   Kokopelli   3 $5
The interesting idea of a gladiatorial type combat game using robots instead of people sounds like an interesting idea. Unfortunately for anyone who bought this game, the graphics, control and sound all suffer to the point of making this title look like it belongs on the Genesis. And while it is considered to be a 3-D fighting game, the characters hardly look like they're anything but poorly designed 16-bit robots.

Robotica   Acclaim   2 $2
Good graphics and sound don't always make a game great, and this first-person shooter is a perfect example. All the elements are in place for it to be a great game with the notable exception of enjoyment. Since each level is randomly generated, there is no real depth to this game, and the action just becomes a senseless round of shooting.

What Genesis game has you slash at an opponent's legs until he kneels down, so that you may decapitate him?

Romance of the Three Kingdoms IV: Wall of Fire
Koei 6 $20

A continuation of the very popular strategy series, this title shouldn't disappoint fans of the previous games. Enhanced graphics and sound don't take away from the overall feel of this game, and it stays true to the original. Control in most strategy games is simple, as is the case here, so "adequate" is the only word that can be used to describe it.

Saturn Bomberman Sega 6 $40
Widely viewed as the best game in the addictive Bomberman party game series, the Saturn version can be multi-tapped to support up to ten players. This game is perhaps the only game available that will entertain 10 people who claim to be uninterested in video games. The immediately addictive game play will have everyone jockeying for a better seat around the TV so that they can blow the snot out of everyone else. Increasingly difficult to find, and a very fun game, this title is quickly increasing in value and scarcity.

Scorcher Sega 5 $15
This visually impressive late-release racer is virtually unplayable due to extremely lazy pre-release testing. It could have been so much more.

Scud: The Disposable Assassin
Segasoft 5 $10

While this title sports some impressively executed animations, and isn't the easiest title to find, it simply isn't any fun. Extremely repetitive level design and enemy character design make this a truly tedious experience.

Sega Ages Spaz 6 $35
Near-perfect versions of the arcade classics Afterburner, Outrun, Space Harrier grace this title. And if you're into the classic Sega games, the difficult task of tracking this title down should be worth the trouble.

Sega Rally Championship plus International Rally
Sega 2 $8

One of the best racing games ever made, period. And with the readily availability of it in most resale shops, this game can normally be found quite easily. It is nice to see a racing game with such good control come out for this system.

Sega Rally Championship plus International Rally: Netlink Edition Sega 5 $10
This is actually a port of the Japanese version of the game and could only be purchased directly from Sega. But the addition of the Netlink capabilities don't have any effect on the game itself

as it is otherwise identical.

Sega Touring Car Championship
Sega 5 $15

Actually based on an arcade game by the same name, this graphically challenged game might be enjoyable to some, but those looking for a more realistic game might be inclined to think that the controls are a bit touchy and the sound could have been greatly improved.

Sega Worldwide Soccer '97
Sega 2 $3

A very good soccer game for the Saturn, this title features 48 teams from around the world in addition to three different fields. Unfortunately only one player, Cobi Jones, is real, while the others sport generic numbers and names.

Sega Worldwide Soccer '98
Sega 4 $7

An update to the previous year's installment, not much was done to improve game play or graphics, though minor touchups can be seen. A very enjoyable soccer game on the whole.

Shanghai Triple Threat
Activision 5 $10

A classic game of strategy based on the Chinese game of Mahjong, the game really doesn't necessitate a system as powerful as the Saturn to make it enjoyable. Graphics and sound are adequate, and control is simple, though the rules of the game are the simplest of all. Simply remove the outside titles that are not "blocked" in by other tiles, along with a matching tile in the same situation, until there are no remaining tiles. Time limits and varied tile patterns will keep the game entertaining for hours.

Shell Shock U.S. Gold 4 $7
This 3-D shooter features 25 levels of action where you will destroy anything you can with a varied arsenal of weapons. Average in every sense, this game really doesn't stand out as being very good or bad, but can be fun for a quick game.

Shining Force III Sega 8 $70
One of the "final five" Saturn games, with only 5000 copies produced, SF3 continues the series tradition of exquisite strategy/RPG gameplay and is possibly the second most sought-after Saturn game behind PDS. And while this game actually had two additional installments released for it in Japan, the U.S. only received the single installment of Shining Force III.

Romance of the Three Kingdoms
IV: Wall of Fire

Saturn Bomberman

Sega Ages

Shining Force III

Shining Wisdom

Shinobi Legions

Sim City 2000

Sonic Jam

Shining the Holy Ark   Sega   7 $40
A tedious yet inexplicably popular 3-D RPG, this is a continuation of sorts of the Genesis title "Shining in the Darkness". Moderate difficulty and a decent length should keep most people busy for a while, but it can become boring at times if RPG's aren't your strong point.

Shining Wisdom   Working Designs   7 $40
A Zelda-type overhead RPG, but without as much fun. Translated by Working Designs, it is far from a horrible game and can be very entertaining if you like the genre.

Shinobi Legions   Sega/Vic Tokai   4 $15
An early-release sequel to the side-scrolling ninja classic, this game seems to be a bit out of character for the Saturn. It is very fun to play and fans of the series should be entertained, but this title didn't hit the mainstream with as much impact as the Sega Master System version did.

Shockwave Assault   EA   3 $5
One of so many space combat games, this average entry into the Saturn library should be fun for a quick gaming fix, but doesn't offer any real depth. Game play involves pressing the fire button as quickly as possible, and then pressing the fire button a little more. Control is average, and graphics, while nothing astonishing, are still crisp.

Sim City 2000   Maxis   5 $20
An update to one of the best selling games of all time, this game has you design, build and manage a city full of people and problems. Proper design will ensure that problems are kept to a minimum, but there will always be some problem that needs your attention. Updated graphics and situations make this version very enjoyable for any fans of the original.

Skeleton Warriors   Playmates   3 $7
Based on a mildly popular cartoon by the same name, this action/adventure was a good attempt that fell a little short of its mark. While control is very good, graphics and sound could have been improved, though it is obvious a lot of work went into the game's creation. And while this isn't the best game available for the system, it is definitely worth a look if you're tired of the same old action game.

Sky Target   Sega   5 $15
This is an underrated update to the classic shooter Afterburner featuring gorgeous but jumpy 3-D graphics. But with the exception of that graphical problem, the game is fun to play and should be enjoyed by anyone trying to find a good fighter plane shoot-em-up.

Slam & Jam '96   Crystal Dynamics   3 $5
When this game first appeared on the 3DO, people were jaw-dropped. And while it is still an entertaining game on the Saturn, many believe that it could have been improved in several areas before it's debut on this system. Control and graphics are still very good however, and the audio gives a realistic feel to the game.

Solar Eclipse   Crystal Dynamics   2 $5
This game is actually the sequel to Total Eclipse, which made its debut on the 3DO system. This is another typical space shooter that allows for multiple perspectives, and relies on quick thumbs to maneuver and shoot as quickly as possible.

Sonic 3D Blast   Sega   4 $15
Shouldn't a game with "3D" in the title actually be 3-D? This quasi-3-D title is entertaining and fun to play for fans of sonic, but is hardly the best on the Saturn. Once again, you must collect rings and run at incredibly high speeds in order to clear each level and continue on. This game, although fun, is a bit on the short side.

Sonic Jam   Sega   7 $40
A stunning compilation CD of Sonic 1, 2, 3, Sonic & Knuckles, plus a very enjoyable (but short) 3-D world game and a bunch of extras. This game has become very difficult to find and is sought after not only by Saturn collectors, but anyone even remotely interested in Sonic.

Sonic R   Sega   5 $15
This unusual racer starring Sonic and friends boasts some of the most impressive graphics ever to grace the Saturn. With as many racing games as there are, Sonic deserves one to his name more than any other character. Brilliantly designed levels, amazing graphics, and perfect sound come together to make this multi-player title one of the best of its kind. Unfortunately the extent of the multi-player mode is two people.

Soviet Strike   EA   3 $10
This overhead helicopter game should be entertaining for fans of the NES game Tiger-Heli. The enemies within the game are unique because they will not mindlessly face in your direction and fire, but instead will fire when advantageous and wait when it is not.

Space Hulk Vengeance of the Blood Angels
    EA   3 $7
This is a futuristic first-person/strategy game that places you in command of a small group of Marines encumbered by bulky

Since video games and the internet were introduced to the world, handwriting has become increasingly worse. Is there any connection?

mechanical suits. Proper planning and the careful execution of those plans will be necessary to be any good at this game.

Space Jam   Acclaim   5 $7
Based on the movie of the same name, this basketball game will allow you to choose from Looney Toons characters, as well as Michael Jordan, in order to help the cartoon characters regain their special powers. Game play is average, but the inclusion of such popular characters should keep casual basketball fans and cartoon fans alike entertained. Also, mini-games are available between periods.

Spot Goes To Hollywood
Virgin   5 $10
That's right, this is an advertisement for 7-Up, but nobody seemed to care since the main character, Spot, is fun to control in this side scrolling platform game. Solid control and entertaining animations make this game enjoyable for just about everyone.

Star Fighter   Acclaim   3 $5
This is a surprisingly uninspired port of the 3DO 3-D space shooter that is much better on the 3DO. It is enjoyable, but it is obvious that this game only uses a fraction of the Saturn's power, and could have been much better had more time been spent in its development.

Steep Slope Sliders   Sega   6 $20
A little-known, late-release snowboarding game that rates as one of the best of the genre. Great control and amazing graphics for the Saturn make this very enjoyable, especially with the amazing perception of speed this game portrays.

Street Fighter Alpha: Warrior's Dreams
Capcom   3 $10
An average installment to this ridiculously long series is entertaining for fans of the series, but is more of the same for those who have played the rest of the SF games. Control is good and graphics and sound are on par with the average Street Fighter game.

Street Fighter Alpha 2   Capcom   5 $20
One of the better installments in the series, this version has a good selection of characters, as well as improved environments and solid control. This installment will not disappoint fans of the series and should be entertaining for anyone who is a fan of the genre.

Street Fighter Collection
Capcom   6 $30

Two classic Street Fighter games, plus Street Fighter Alpha 2 Gold (an upgrade to SFA2 never released in American arcades) are included on this solid Street Fighter installment. And while the series seems to have an endless supply of titles, this should be worth the considerable effort it will take to track down a copy.

Street Fighter: The Movie
Acclaim   1 $1
A game based on a movie based on a game...? And just to make things worse, this game is absolutely horrible. Badly digitized graphics and very jumpy/unresponsive controls make this game a giant step back for the slow-to-evolve Street Fighter series.

Striker '96   Acclaim   1 $1
Often considered to be inferior to the other soccer games on the Saturn, this extremely common and inexpensive title should be fun for those interested in playing a quick game of soccer, but not for those looking for realism in a soccer game.

Super Puzzle Fighter II Turbo
Capcom   6 $35
This extremely addictive puzzle game, featuring characters from both Street Fighter and Dark Stalkers. If anything could challenge the addictiveness of Bust-A-Move 2 for the Saturn, this would be it.

Tempest 2000   Interplay   5 $12
An absolutely amazing update to the classic arcade game "Tempest", this version has improved clarity of graphics, improved audio, wonderful control, and an amazing amount of speed. You will either love or hate this game, but either way it will most likely hook you into finishing it.

Ten Pin Alley   ASC   4 $10
Decent graphics and sound take a back seat to good control and an infinitely re-playable game. Bowling has made an appearance on nearly every console ever released, but this version stands out as being one of the best.

Tetris Plus!   Jaleco   4 $10
What could have been a great installment in the series and for the Saturn turns out to be a disappointment. And while the original version is available for play, the new version included completely changes game play from what made Tetris so fun into something entirely different. And while innovation is admirable, perhaps a game that wasn't already loved by so many should have been the target of this type of change.

Space Jam   Steep Slope Sliders

Super Puzzle Fighter II Turbo   Tempest 2000

The U.S. education system thinks so.

Three Dirty Dwarves

Tunnel B1

Virtua Cop

Virtua Fighter Kids

Theme Park   **EA**   5 $20
Design, build and manage a theme park of your own, including roller coasters, concession stands, bathrooms, etc. What seems like a simple task can quickly become a very challenging simulation.

Three Dirty Dwarves   **Sega**   4 $10
This three-player game is a very entertaining and humorous side scrolling adventure in which you control dwarves armed for combat with various sporting items. Creative levels and solid control make this obscure game very enjoyable.

Thunderstrike 2   **U.S. Gold**   3 $7
This helicopter shooter offers seven available weapons and 27 different missions. About average in every aspect, it is a fun title to pick up for those interested in 3-D shooters.

TNN Motorsports: Hardcore 4x4
                    ASC   4 $7
This is a monster truck simulator in which various terrain and play modes allow for a good variation of levels. Control can be a bit tricky and the graphics and sound seem to suffer a bit on the Saturn, but monster truck racing is a very difficult sport to make completely boring. This title can be a lot of fun for anyone just looking for a quick game.

Tomb Raider   **Eidos**   2 $10
One of the most famous modern game franchises, Laura Croft stars in the only installment of this game on the Saturn. Pleasant graphics and sound make this fun game more enjoyable, and when the control scheme is learned, this title quickly becomes less of a game and more of an experience.

True Pinball   **Ocean**   4 $12
Four different tables and a changeable aspect (2-D or 3-D) offer a good amount of variety in this lackluster pinball simulation. And while the graphics can be impressive in hi-resolution mode, control seems a bit off, which is inexcusable for a pinball game.

Tunnel B1   **Acclaim**   4 $7
Taking the driver's seat in this hovercraft game will allow you to access a varied arsenal while trying to destroy various enemies in your way. Graphics and sound do their job, and the control seems responsive enough for this type of game. It is an enjoyable game, though it does get old quickly.

Ultimate Mortal Kombat 3
                    Williams   3 $7
This installment of the Mortal Kombat series contains 19 playable characters and decent control. And while the graphics and sound are on par with other games of the genre, this title lacks the type of innovation that made the first two titles so popular. Still, this should be enjoyable for diehard fans of the series, or anyone interested in being able to perform fatalities.

Valora Valley Golf   **Vic Tokai**   2 $2
While an otherwise average golf game, this version supports up to four players via the multi-player adapter for the Saturn. Be prepared to spend a good amount of time in front of the TV when playing with four people however, 18 holes can take quite a while to finish...especially when someone is a horrible golfer/player.

Virtua Cop   **Sega**   1 $1
An amazing leap in technology when it first appeared in arcades, this title makes a very good appearance on the Saturn. With support for the light gun, this game should see a lot of play time by fans of shooting games.

Virtua Cop 2   **Sega**   3 $7
With graphical and audio improvements over the first installment, and the same light gun support intact, this title is among the best shooters for the system.

Virtua Fighter   **Sega**   2 $1
The game that revolutionized the 3-D polygon fighting genre is intact on the Saturn, however the graphics have not aged well. No shading or textures, while not really noticed at the time this game hit arcades, are almost an eyesore by today's standards. But this game, while the graphics were revolutionary, is not about looking good, it's about controlling well. And the control is completely intact. Unfortunately, Saturn gamers of the time didn't see control as the most important element in this fighting game and were very upset with this title.

Virtua Fighter 2   **Sega**   1 $2
Amazing graphical updates to the first installment make this title even more popular than the first. And with the control scheme still intact, it would be difficult to find a better fighting game anywhere in the Saturn library.

Virtua Fighter Kids   **Sega**   4 $12
An interesting twist on the Virtua Fighter series, this installment offers children as the combatants of this title. Difficulty remains intact and this title is very enjoyable. Should you feel bad about thinking it entertaining to see children beating the snot out of each other? As long as you're not a regular attendant of local schoolyard fights, we think it's ok.

If you say the words "crap" or "shit" while playing Seaman on the Dreamcast, the seamen will fling poo at the glass.

Virtua Fighter Remix   Sega   7 $20
The little-seen "freebie" given to new Saturn owners as a play-able testament that the Saturn was more powerful than the first Virtua Fighter suggested. The game is nearly as good as VF2, featuring a much higher polygon count and texture mapping. Mailed out in a tiny cardboard sleeve, rather than normal plastic case.

Virtua Racing   Time Warner   5 $12
This game actually invokes quite a varied response from those who have played it. Many love the 3-D polygon attempt at rec-reating race tracks and cars. Others think that this game is horrible. Either way, it's first appearance on the Genesis re-quired an additional chip installed within the game and the 32x version is of questionable entertainment. But regardless of your stance on how good this game actually is, there can be no de-nying that it is an improvement over both previous installments.

Virtual Casino   Natsume   7 $25
This is simply a casino simulator that has slight graphical im-provements over those that came before. And while it offers a variety of games to choose from, the computer generated val-ues for cards and dice seem to form unrealistic patterns. Very difficult to find, and often expensive, this title is probably for collectors and compulsive gamblers only.

Virtual Hydlide   Sega   5 $15
This was the first RPG on the Saturn and is also the worst. Digitized graphics and horrible control don't go together very well in this laughable attempt by Sega.

Virtual-On: Cyber Troopers
Sega   4 $12
With large arenas and eight unique robots combine to form one of the best fighting/combat games for the Saturn. Controlling 3-D robots in an arena atmosphere, you must best your opponent twice before moving on to the next. This is a very enjoyable game with a lot of replay potential.

Virtual On: Cyber Troopers: Netlink Edition
Sega   5 $15
Available only from Sega, this version is identical in every way to the non-Netlink version with the exception that it allowed for online play with other Saturn owners. One of the more enjoy-able games to play via Netlink however, this version offered a unique experience for console owners of the time: online mech combat.

Virtual Open Tennis   Acclaim   2 $3

A very limited variety of players from which to choose, none of the real, and average graphics and sound make this easily con-trolled tennis game average in every way. Though, it is worth noting that only two tennis titles were released for the Saturn.

VR Golf   VR Sports   2 $2
This extremely common golf game is very generic and tries to recreate a 3-D feel to the game of golf. Unfortunately golf games of the time were much more easily, and succinctly, por-trayed by digitized graphics.

VR Soccer   VR Sports   1 $1
One of many soccer games for the Saturn, this title doesn't stand above any other, but is enjoyable for a quick soccer fix.

Warcraft 2: The Dark Saga
EA/Blizzard   5 $15
This real-time strategy game reached cult status on the PC, and makes a decent appearance on the Saturn. Relatively easy control scheme and adequate graphics and sound make this title enjoyable, though not nearly as much as the PC version.

Wing Arms   Sega   4 $12
A post WWII flight simulator that pits Japan, U.K., Germany and the U.S. in a combined force against a shared enemy, this title is an impressive effort early on in the Saturn's life. Most of the stages are over water though, so there isn't much of a chance to judge the ground effects in this game. This title should be en-joyable if you're looking for a break from the myriad of space shooters and modern jet combat games.

Winning Post   Koei   7 $40
A little-known horse racing simulation from Koei, this title's graphics don't do the system justice, but the nice variety from normal games that this title offers is a welcome addition to the Saturn's library. Good luck finding a copy though.

Winter Heat   Sega   6 $16
A very enjoyable multiplayer Olympic game ported from the arcade, this title is fun to play with friends, but can become tire-some when played alone.

Wipeout   Sega   3 $5
This futuristic racing game has solid control and decent graph-ics, though the different courses can quickly begin to look the same after a few hours of play time.

World Cup Golf Pro   U.S. Gold   4 $5
Yet another golf game for the Saturn, and yet another average entry. This title does offer some nice course designs though, it

Virtua Fighter Remix   Virtual On: Cyber Troopers

Virtual Open Tennis   Winter Heat

Left handed players of Galaga (and other one button games) commonly cross their arms, creating what is known as "The Galaga Cross."

| World Series Baseball II | Worms | WWF Wrestlemania: The Arcade Game | X-Men: Children of the Atom |

can be a real challenge to avoid strategically placed sand traps. Control is actually pretty good, though the overall experience doesn't stand out more than any other golf simulation for the Saturn.

World Series Baseball

Sega   2 $2

This fully licensed baseball game features not only all teams and players, but also four actual stadiums, including the now unused Astrodome. Control seems solid, but graphics could have been improved quite a bit on this early Saturn release.

World Series Baseball II

Sega   2 $3

A typical baseball title, this version offers the ability to send players to the minor leagues for no less than 15 days so that they can hone basic skills. Released in 1996, this game has players from the 1995 season filling the spots of the team rosters.

World Series Baseball '98

Sega   4 $10

Many graphical and audio improvements have been made to this installment as well as more realistic player personalization. Each character acts and reacts much more like their real life counterpart. This title should be a favorite among fans of the genre, though modern games look much better.

Worldwide Soccer: Sega International Victory Goal Edition

Sega   2 $4

This title just doesn't live up to even the most meager expectations. This type of early release is partly responsible for the bad reputation the Saturn got from early adaptors.

Worms   Ocean   5 $20

Taking your army of worms (yes, like earthworms) into combat in this 2-D strategy game is made even more entertaining by a large assortment of weapons. And while there is a time limit on each turn taken, it is sufficient to decide what you would like to do, with time to spare (60 seconds per turn).

WWF In Your House   Acclaim   3 $5

Pretty average for a wrestling game, this is substandard for a Saturn title. And while there are a variety of different environments available to fight in, it can't save this game from being like nearly every other wrestling game ever made.

WWF Wrestlemania: The Arcade Game

Acclaim   3 $7

This update of the 32x version is actually different than every

other wrestling game. Instead of trying to reproduce wrestling in a realistic fashion, special moves and features make this title stand out among the wrestling game genre.

X-Men: Children of the Atom

Capcom   6 $20

This 2-D fighting game pits X-Man against X-Man in one on one fighting. Great graphics and sound compliment the great control and execution of this hard to find game. This is one of the best 2-D fighters for the system, and it offers some classic comic book heroes to boot.

Demo CD's

Bootleg CD Sampler   Sega   1 $1

Bootleg CD Sampler II   Sega   1 $1

Christmas NiGHTS into Dreams... Sampler

Sega   7 $30

This Christmas theme bonus CD (bundled along with a magazine) featured the full version's first level that changed according to the Saturn's internal clock. Manually set the Saturn's time to Christmas Eve, Christmas Day, and New Years for a surprise!

NiGHTS into Dreams... Sampler

Sega   1 $1

Panzer Dragoon Playable Demo

Sega   2 $1

Rayman Playable Demo

Ubi Soft   3 $5

1997 Software bundle

Sega   2 $18

Sega had a special promotion from 11/27/96 until all units were sold in 1997. For every Saturn sold, Sega included a special boxed set featuring full versions of Daytona USA, Virtua Cop, and Virtua Fighter 2. The games were enclosed in small cardboard envelopes rather than the normal full-sized plastic cases

NES games in the U.S. have 72 pins, in Japan (Famicom) they have 60.

Unreleased Games

There seems to be a bit of confusion regarding some domestic Playstation games that were also scheduled to appear on the Saturn. Buster Brothers Collection, Iron & Blood, Street Racer, and Return Fire all appeared on American release lists and in American advertising, but none were ever released in the United States. Street Racer was released in Japan only for the Saturn.

HARDWARE

Sega Saturn   Sega   4 $35
There are actually two versions of the U.S. Saturn model with small cosmetic differences. The easiest way to determine the difference is the shape of the "power" and "reset" buttons on the console top. The first version had round buttons while the second version had oval buttons. Both consoles are available in similar quantities, and neither is sought after more than the other.

3D Control Pad   Sega   2 $5
This masterpiece of preciseness came bundled with Nights Into Dreams (and was also available separately) and is one of the best controllers ever made. It is often referred to as the "Nights controller".

6Player Multitap   Sega   4 $10
Their aren't that many games that actually utilize this peripheral, but it's an absolute necessity if you want to play Saturn Bomberman as it was meant to be played.

Arcade Racer   Sega   3 $7
Introduced not long after the original Daytona, this awkward driving controller is compatible with a lot of games but falls short of the 3D analog pad.

Backup RAM   Sega   2 $15
Unlike most of the newer consoles, the Saturn came equipped with its own internal memory (fueled by a tiny battery.) Unfortunately, it doesn't hold much data, making the memory cart a godsend for gamers who save a lot.

Control Pad 1   Sega   1 $1
The first version of the standard controller was supposedly designed for larger European/American hands, but its too big for most people and feels cheaply constructed.

Control Pad 2   Sega   4 $3
Essentially the original Japanese control pad, this second generation controller is much improved over the first one and is constructed with better-quality plastic.

Extension Cords   Sega   4 $2
Essential for gamers who like to sit far away from their TV sets, especially you lucky dogs with big screen TV's.

Hori Fighting Stick SS   Hori   6 $20
The only non-Sega item on this list, the Hori fighting stick is nearly arcade-like in quality and better than Sega's own Virtua stick. The stick "clicks" just right, and the button response is great.

Mission Stick   Sega   4 $8
Not only is the mission stick perfect for games like Panzer Dragoon and Black Fire, but it's interchangeable for lefties OR righties!

Netlink Modem   Sega   4 $15
This modem actually plugs into the RAM cart slot and came bundled with a browser CD. This is necessary for those wanting to utilize the online capabilities of such games as Saturn Bomberman and other online games.

Netlink Keyboard   Sega   5 $12
A necessity for those wishing to use the Netlink for more than just playing games. Sending emails and surfing the internet can seem nearly impossible without it.

Netlink Keyboard Adapter   Sega   5 $8
An adaptor that allows the use of a PC keyboard on the Saturn, this was a less expensive route for those who already owned a keyboard and simply wanted to use it on their Saturn.

Netlink Mouse   Sega   6 $15
The mouse is a must-have for cruising the net with your Netlink, and it is also supported by several games including Command & Conquer and Theme Park.

Stunner Arcade Gun   Sega   2 $5
Unlike Japanese gamers who got a proper (if huge) black gun, we Americans got stuck with a garish orange monstrosity. It's pretty accurate, though, but falls short of some of the third-party guns.

Virtua Stick   Sega   4 $10
While not quite as nice as the Hori stick, Sega's own fighting controller is a must-have for Virtua Fighter and Capcom fans.

You can shoot the seagulls in Metal Gear Solid 2 for the PS2.

Sega Dreamcast

By: Michael Collins

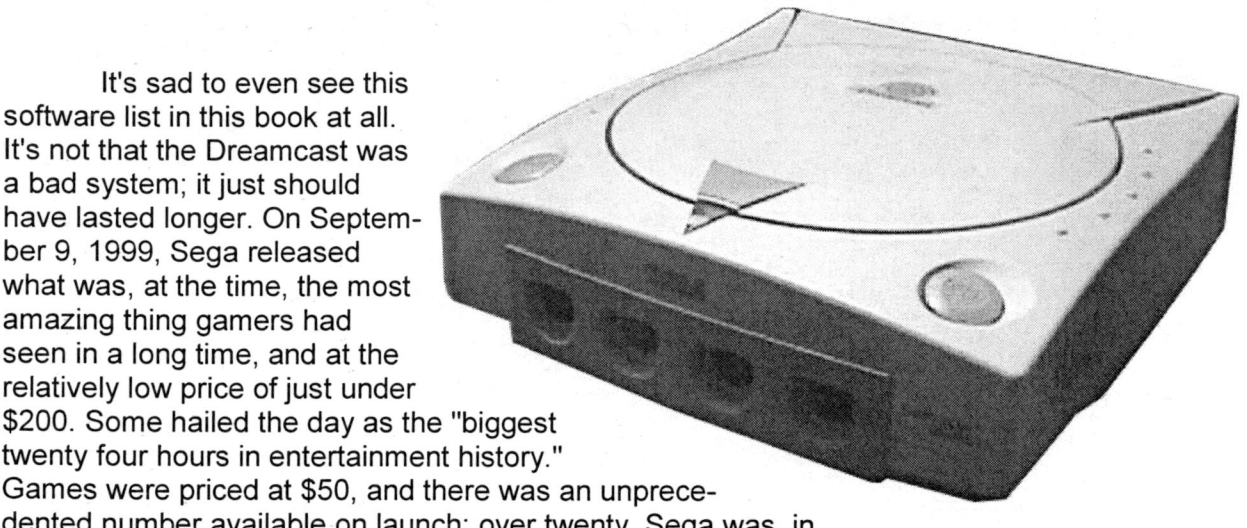

It's sad to even see this software list in this book at all. It's not that the Dreamcast was a bad system; it just should have lasted longer. On September 9, 1999, Sega released what was, at the time, the most amazing thing gamers had seen in a long time, and at the relatively low price of just under $200. Some hailed the day as the "biggest twenty four hours in entertainment history." Games were priced at $50, and there was an unprecedented number available on launch: over twenty. Sega was, in a word, excited, and for very good reason. Their sales projections put Dreamcast sales for the first 24 hours higher than any previous video game console, movie, CD, etc. They were right: 87 million dollars in sales rolled in on the first day alone.

Sega knew that the Dreamcast was their absolute last chance at staying in the hardware market, and they acted accordingly. Sega launched a $100 million marketing campaign, which included eye-catching full page magazine ads, coupled with magazine inserts and TV ads. Sega also set up Dreamcast tents at some large concerts, and even took Dreamcast vans across the country, giving out playtime and other freebies wherever they went. Still, some gamers were wary of Sega, having been "abandoned" in the past with the Sega CD, 32X, and Saturn. However, launch day won back a lot of those doubters.

The Dreamcast packs one hell of a punch under its hood with a Hitachi SH4 200MHz main processor and a graphics processor that puts a flamethrower to that of the PSX. Add 16 MB main RAM, 8 additional MB of video RAM, and another 2 MB allotted for sound, and it's easy to see why the Dreamcast can pump out the quality graphics, sound, and speed that it does.

The people at Sega have always been innovators, and innovate they did. Besides releasing a "next-generation" console a year before any of its competition, Sega also included a modem in the package that allowed users to get on the Internet right away with full web and e-mail capabilities. AT&T teamed up with Sega to provide access to the Net via their PlanetWeb service for as low as $9.99 a month. Although online gaming didn't become a reality until much later than originally planned, Sega had made a huge leap in putting the modem in the package from the start. When SegaNet became a reality, gamers from around the world were able to connect to online versions of the popular Phantasy Star Online, Quake III Arena, Unreal Tournament, and many others. While it wasn't the first time this was possible, Dreamcast gamers could even play in the same games as PC gamers for some titles. A broadband adapter was also released, but had a relatively short production run, and is now difficult to find.

Since Sega decided to make their own format for games, it was relatively hard to pirate Dreamcast games for a while. The format Sega used was the GD-ROM. Instead of only fitting

What was the game tournament called in the movie The Wizard?

650 MB, like the standard CD's of the time, a Dreamcast GD-ROM disc could hold a full giga-byte of information.

Modeled after the popular NiGHTS Into Dreams 3D controller for Sega's own Saturn, the Dreamcast controller is a very nice one, and was quite innovative in several areas. It featured the standard D-pad, a very nice analog stick, four buttons like that of the SNES or PSX, and the first analog buttons to appear on a console controller - the trigger R and L buttons. Another thing to note is that there were two ports in each controller to accept things like memory cards, VMU's (Visual Memory Units), and rumble paks. What is interesting about the VMU's is that they had a screen, and to accommodate this, the Dreamcast controller has an area cut out so that the VMU screen can be viewed at all times.

As stated earlier, and usually accepted as common knowledge, Sega has always been an innovator. It's not unusual then that even their memory card was very innovative. The VMU was a great idea -- it is essentially a memory card with a screen and buttons. In games like NFL2K, gamers were capable of picking their plays via the VMU's screen so that their opponents couldn't see their selection. Some mini games could be uploaded to the VMU and then taken anywhere for playtime. Sonic Adventure is a great example of this. Other games like Soul Calibur simply displayed animations on the VMU during gameplay while others, like Resident Evil CODE: Veronica, displayed important information about the player's status, like life percentage.

Several other peripherals were released for the Dreamcast. Despite the controversy over it because of gun violence in schools at the time, several light guns were released in America with limited support. House of the Dead 2 and Death Crimson OX are two of the few games that supported them. Online games made use of the keyboard and mouse in their usual ways, and Typing of the Dead made use of the keyboard in one of the most innovative games to come to the U.S. The infamous Samba de Amigo maraca controllers were also an interesting innovation that came from the folks at Sega. A few others that should be mentioned include a fishing controller, several arcade sticks, force feedback packs, and Aooii's Rally Wheel.

Of oourse, with all of these great add-ons, a very respectable library of games, and an ever-growing user base, it's easy to be confused as to why Sega pulled the plug on it all. With last year's announcement of ceased production of Dreamcast consoles, both developer and general public support for the Dreamcast waned, and the last commercial Dreamcast game, NHL2K2, has been released. After several price drops, a new Dreamcast could be purchased for the incredible price of only $49.99, which is lower than the price of the average GameCube, X-Box, or PS2 game. Buyers ran to stores in droves, and it is now very difficult to find a new Dreamcast at all.

Even with the ceased production of Dreamcast consoles, the system still lives on. Games can oftentimes be found for ridiculously low prices, considering the quality of the products, but these deals are becoming scarce quickly. Homebrew games, however, including 3D remakes of some of the classics (such as Snake and Asteroids), have been released for the system already, with many more expected on the way. Some homebrew developers have also programmed emulators for the Dreamcast, including ones that emulate the SMS, NES, SNES, Genesis, MSX, Game Boy, Game Gear, and many others. Two DivX players have been released, an MP3 player is out, and several JPEG viewers are also available. The best part: it's free!

The Dreamcast is far from being "dead." With a very respectable library of games to collect, tons of good ones in the lot, and an exploding homebrew and emulation scene, the Dreamcast is sure to have a long life ahead of it. It's STILL "thinking."

***Note: The Dreamcast section does not have dollar values attached to any of the games or hardware due to the fact that it is too early to determine them. Since old Dreamcast stock is still being sold, and games can be found in retail shops at clearance prices, it would be irresponsible to do so at this point. Also, the rarities listed are estimates as well, and will most likely fluctuate as more solid data is collected in the years to come. Due to the large quantity of demo CD's and non-game CD's, these titles have been incorporated into the main listing for convenience.

DC

18 Wheeler: American Pro Trucker

Alien Front Online

Alone in the Dark: The New Night-mare

Bangai-O

102 Dalmatians: Puppies to the Rescue
Eidos 2

102 Dalmatians is actually a surprisingly addictive, all around enjoyable platformer. It is extremely similar to Spyro the Dragon in that the object of the game is to save all of your puppy friends from Cruella deVille, collecting bones and other items along the way. While it is very easy (because it is obviously geared at a young audience), and the graphics are nothing spectacular, it's still a good time.

18 Wheeler: American Pro Trucker
Sega 5

This game is way, way too short. While it lasts, it's a lot of fun, though. There are several different truckers, different types of trailers, and some other extras to keep things interesting for a while, but like I said -- it is way too short of a game. Graphics are nice, and this is definitely recommended if you like arcade games.

4 Wheel Thunder   Midway   2
Midway's attempt at this high-speed, turbo-boosted racer was a good one. Great graphics, addicting gameplay, and extreme speed make this one of the better racers on the Dreamcast. However, the unforgiving AI can sometimes be an annoyance, because it is almost too good.

4x4 Evolution   Gathering of Developers   4
There's both good and bad with this one. While there is lots to do as far as customization and multiplayer gaming, the graphics are nothing spectacular and the control system just feels wrong.

AeroWings   Crave   1
This game can really be a lot of fun, but as a warning: there is a learning curve. Don't expect to pick this one up and pull off all of the coolest stunts right away. Controls are tight, and flight sim fans will go nuts over this game.

AeroWings 2: Airstrike   Crave   7
AeroWings 2: Airstrike is a nice update to its predecessor. Graphics are great, and all of the usual extreme details are in place, for all of the flight sim fans out there. One important thing to note is that AeroWings 2 is more action-based than the original, and includes several nice modes of play.

Air Force Delta   Konami   4
The only flight sim at launch, Air Force Delta was and is a decent game. The graphics are nothing spectacular, but the arcade-style dog fighting can really be a lot of fun.

Alien Front Online   Sega   4
Alien Front Online was a relatively late release. It's a tank-based combat game, and, as made obvious by the game's title, has online multiplayer capabilities. The graphics are nice, and there are good single player modes as well.

Alone in the Dark: The New Nightmare
Infogrames 4

The Alone in the Dark series has always been fun, and this installment does not disappoint. The environment graphics, while not fully interactive, are simply AMAZING, and the lighting effects are extremely nice. It's certainly a spooky game, and with two related quest modes to play through, this game is a lot of fun. The game certainly gives that eerie feeling of being alone in the dark in a strange, unusually scary place.

Armada   Metro 3D   2
Reminiscent of Asteroids, this game takes a few steps further from just being another shooter to being a shooter-RPG. The story and leveling elements are there to make this game stay interesting for a while. Although the graphics are far from what the Dreamcast is capable of, this game is worth a try.

Army Men: Sarge's Heroes
Midway 1

The object of this game is simple: save your men from death in different everyday settings. It's been done before, and because the game is essentially the same, the game has a major downfall. There's nothing new here.

Atari: Anniversary Edition
Infogrames 3

This is pretty standard, folks. It's a compilation of some of Atari's greatest hits, emulated in cabinet and full-screen modes. While most of the games play wonderfully, the Dreamcast controller is not the typical mid-80's joystick. Here are the games you'll get on the disc: Warlords, Super Breakout, Tempest, Asteroids, Asteroids Deluxe, Crystal Castles, Gravitar, Millipede, and Centipede.

Bang! Gunship Elite   RedStorm   4
The graphics in this game are simply gorgeous, but sadly, that is one of this game's best qualities. The beginning missions seem to be almost impossible, and even after clearing those, this 3D space shooter is nothing above average.

Bangai-O   Crave   5
This is somewhat of a unique 2D shooter on the Dreamcast. There is lots and lots of buildings get blown up, and gameplay can be very addictive. Over forty levels can be played through, as well. However, this game is not for everybody. Some will be very interested, but some will probably become bored quickly.

Bleem! for Gran Turismo 2
Bleem! 6

Gran Turismo 2 on Sony's PlayStation was (and still is) obviously a very popular game. While it may not be for everybody, the ability to play it with hardware acceleration on the Dream-

A standard Atari 7800 game weighs 68 grams.

cast is a great thing. The graphics look even better now, and the gameplay remains intact.

Bleemcast! for Metal Gear Solid
Bleem!   6

Buy this disc, and NOW! If you're a fan of Metal Gear Solid (and it's hard to imagine that you're not), then you will not be anything short of amazed at seeing it on your Dreamcast, running at full speed with hardware acceleration to top it off. Simply amazing. However, the controls gamers got used to on the PSX are a little different, obviously, because of the Dreamcast's lack of second L and R buttons. But, it all works out in a way that makes sense. Metal Gear Solid on the Dreamcast is bliss.

Bleemcast! for Tekken 3   Bleem!   6

Another great PSX game can be played on your Dreamcast. While the Metal Gear Solid disc is simply amazing, this one isn't quite as great. There is hardware acceleration, and the game plays very smoothly for the most part. However, there are a few spots where extremely slight slowdown can be noticed, but it's nothing major.

Blue Stinger   Activision   1

This is another launch title. However, it is sadly not as spectacular as some of the others. While the presentation of the game was wonderful, Blue Stinger is plagued by camera problems which really bring the game down as a whole.

Bomberman Online   Sega   5

Bomberman is back, and this time he's cell-shaded! While everybody may not be a fan of cell-shading, it is definitely a unique style of artistic presentation. Either way, the graphics are crisp, animations are cool, and the gameplay is, as always, extremely addictive. There are several different variations of the classic, and of course, the game is another of Sega's games to allow Dreamcast gamers to play online.

Bust-A-Move 4   Acclaim   4

Not a whole lot new here. This installment in the Bust-A-Move series is just as cute and colorful as the rest, and gameplay is as usual, pretty much the same. It is still lots of fun though, and definitely recommended if you've never played a Bust-A-Move game.

Buzz Lightyear of Star Command
Activision   5

Buzz Lightyear of Star Command should probably only be purchased if it's for a child or for the sake of collecting. The graphics are extremely simple, and sub-par for the Dreamcast. Controls are not very accurate, and although it could have been a lot of fun, the game feels like it was slopped together.

Caesars Palace 2000   Interplay   4

There is good reason that this game is not as famous as the casino that it is based on. As with many casino-themed games,

it's just not very much fun. There are plenty of the usual casino games to play, but there's nothing here to make gamers want to come back for more.

Cannon Spike   Capcom   3

Cannon Spike is a great game, plain and simple. While it doesn't have the extreme replayability that some games do, or tons of extras to unlock like Mars Matrix, it is definitely worth a look. The arcade-style shooting is fast-paced, and the graphics are great.

Capcom Vs. SNK   Capcom   2

Two of the greatest video game developers' greatest fighting game characters all packed in on the same disc is never a bad thing. For 2D fighting fans, this game is a must. It's tons of fun, has a nice engine, and there are tons of extras to unlock.

Carrier   Jaleco   1

While this game has been compared to Resident Evil, it thankfully doesn't have as many impossible puzzles or as much backtracking as some of the RE games do. There is more action in Carrier, and thankfully, less running back and forth.

Centipede   Hasbro   2

Thankfully, the classic version of Centipede is included on the disc with this 3D update. However, if you've already got the original, don't bother with this update. Some games really do not belong in the third dimension, and this attempt at bringing Centipede to it was certainly not a good one.

Championship Surfer   Mattel   3

Unless you're REALLY dieing for a surfing game, stay away from this one. Championship Surfer's graphics are boring, gameplay is boring, and the sound is boring, too. The learning curve is immensely steep, and considering how boring the game is, what's the point?

Charge N Blast   Infogrames   1

Charge N Blast is another arcade to Dreamcast port with essentially no extras thrown into the bag. While visuals are nice and gameplay is true to the original, there's nothing to keep gamers coming back for more.

Cheats and Codes Vol. 1   Interact   5

Chicken Run   Eidos   3

The gameplay and graphics of this game are very true to the movie that it is based upon. Some people have even compared the game to Konami's Metal Gear Solid, because of the espionage-action elements of the game. However, while Chicken Run is a solid title, don't expect that type of quality in it.

Chu Chu Rocket!   Sega   1

Chu Chu Rocket is one of the cooler Dreamcast games out

Blue Stinger

Caesars Palace 2000

Capcom Vs. SNK

Centipede

When polled, what were the top two concerns of video game collectors?

| Chu Chu Rocket! | D2 | Daytona USA | Dino Crisis |

there. Puzzle gamers will go nuts over this one, as it is addictive and fast-paced. This game was also the first game to have online multiplayer capabilities on the Dreamcast.

Coaster Works   Xicat   5
Coaster Works is a solid simulation game, and although there is obviously nothing in the way of a two-player mode, it is recommended for roller coaster fans. The game concentrates solely on building the biggest and baddest coaster, rather than actually managing a theme park, like in Roller Coaster Tycoon.

Confidential Mission   Sega   2
Confidential Mission is one of the very few light gun games on the Dreamcast, and while it is often overlooked, it deserves a chance. Some even consider this game to be better than the smash hit House of the Dead 2.

Conflict Zone   UbiSoft   5
Conflict Zone is a real-time strategy game that unfortunately is not as good as it could have been. Possibly due to the fact that it was a late release and support for the Dreamcast was dwindling, the game has no mouse or keyboard support, and for RTS veterans, it is obvious that these are musts.

Crazy Taxi   Sega   1
Not much to say here, really. It's an excellent arcade port of a very addicting game. It's easy to get into, there are a few extra modes, and it's just tons of fun. However, it does get boring after a while. Still, it is recommended.

Crazy Taxi 2   Sega   3
This is essentially the same thing as the original, with the same fast-paced, adrenaline-pumping style of gameplay, and a few new twists. More than one passenger can now be picked up at a time, and at the simple push of a button, gamers can send their taxis sailing through the air.

D2   Sega   4
The sequel to the game that originally appeared on the 3DO (and later PSX and Saturn), this game is a good experience but lacks in some areas. The graphics and feel of the game are great, but the voice acting is terrible and completely out of sync with the characters' mouths. Gameplay is interesting, but nothing revolutionary.

Dave Mirra Freestyle BMX   Acclaim   4
Although the graphics are not incredible by any means, the gameplay of this title makes up for anything lacking in the way of visuals. The engine is tight, and the stunts in this game are fun to pull off. If you liked Tony Hawk's Pro Skater, check this out. If not, stay away from it -- they're pretty similar in style.

Daytona USA   Sega   4

Daytona USA is one of the best racing arcade to Dreamcast ports out there. The lush graphics and blazing speed are intact, and the ability to play online only adds to the experience.

DC-X   Fire International   5
DC-X is essentially a boot disc allowing gamers to play all of their import Dreamcast games on their domestic console with no problems.

Dead or Alive 2   Tecmo   5
While somewhat similar to the acclaimed Soul Calibur, this game doesn't have the lasting appeal that Soul Calibur did. There aren't as many fighters, and there's basically nothing to unlock. While the graphics are great, the fighting areas incredibly detailed, and the fighting engine decent, it's just not enough to last for an extended period of time.

Death Crimson OX   Sammy Entertainment   6
Another of the few light-gun Dreamcast games, Death Crimson OX is mediocre at best. Basically, it follows the standard formula for light gun games, with not much else to offer: shoot, repeat.

Deep Fighter   UbiSoft   6
Deep Fighter is one of the very few video games set underwater. Thankfully, the graphics in this game are the usual Dreamcast standard - wonderfully detailed. The game centers around story-inspired missions, with a touch of strategy on the side.

Demolition Racer: No Exit   Infogrames   5
Similar in concept to Metropolis Street Racer, however not quite the same in execution, Demolition Racer's gameplay is centered around racing in style. Of course, this "style" means bashing opponents as many times and with as much force as is possible. As far as graphics go, they're nothing spectacular, but they're not the worst the Dreamcast has to offer, either.

Dino Crisis   Capcom   4
If you didn't play Dino Crisis on PSX yet, this game may be for you. However, if you have, don't expect much more than a rehashed version of the same game with updated graphics and not much else.

Dinosaur   UbiSoft   2
Another movie-based video game that many feel is subject to the same sub-par treatment as others in this category. The game is mainly puzzle-based, and graphics are average for the Dreamcast.

Disney World Magical Racing Tour   Eidos   5
It seems that for every popular video game franchise, there has been a related cart racing game released within the last few

years. Now, Disney has joined the bandwagon, and although the game itself is a decent one, Magical Racing Tour does nothing innovative for the sub-genre of racing games that it belongs to.

Donald Duck: Goin' Quackers
UbiSoft   7

Since this game is aimed at a young audience, it is rather easy and short. However, the lush graphics and decent game engine really make this title worth playing. While it isn't on par with Rayman 2, which is also by UbiSoft, it does deserve a look.

Draconus: Cult of the Wyrm
Crave   4

While this game is sure to please the medieval hack and slash fan, it really could have been a lot better. Graphics look great in still shots, but when playing, they don't feel so smooth. Still, this game is an average one that has some good points.

Dragon Riders: Chronicles of Pern
UbiSoft   4

Unfortunately, this title doesn't belong on the pedestal that some of UbiSoft's other games do. It is a plot-driven action game, but is plagued by camera problems.

Dream VCD Player   SRC   5

This is pretty self-explanatory. The Dream VCD Player allows users to watch VCD's on their Dreamcasts. A remote control is even included with it so that users don't have to use their Dreamcast controllers.

Dreamcast Generator Demo Disc Vol. 1
Sega   5

Dreamcast Generator Demo Disc Vol. 2
Sega   5

Dreamcast Magazine Demo Disc Vol. 3
Sega   5

Dreamcast Magazine Demo Disc Vol. 4
Sega   5

Dreamcast Magazine Demo Disc Vol. 5
Sega   5

Dreamcast Magazine Demo Disc Vol. 6
Sega   5

Dreamcast Magazine Demo Disc Vol. 7
Sega   5

Dreamcast Magazine Demo Disc Vol. 8
Sega   5

Dreamcast Magazine Demo Disc Vol. 9
Sega   5

Dreamcast Magazine Demo Disc Vol. 10
Sega   5

Dreamcast Magazine Demo Disc Vol. 11
Sega   5

Ducati World Racing Challenge
Acclaim   4

Acclaim has put out some very high-quality games and some very low-quality games. Unfortunately, this is the latter. The graphics are poor, the driving engine feels like it was thrown together, and this game is just completely unpolished.

Dynamite Cop
Sega   2

Dynamite Cop is a very short experience. Don't expect to even really get $10 worth out of this one - it ends in less than an hour, and then there's not much of a reason to play it over again.

Ecco the Dolphin: Defender of the Future
Sega   3

Finally, an update to the Genesis classic, Ecco the Dolphin! It's too bad it wasn't a very good one. The graphics and environments in this game are simply gorgeous, but they aren't so good that they make the game fun. Unfortunately, that's the major problem with this 3D update to the original - it's too hard and frustrating.

ECW Anarchy Rulez!   Acclaim   4

ECW Hardcore Revolution
Acclaim   2

You probably either hate wrestling games like the smell of burning rubber or you love them like your own children. ECW Hardcore Revolution is obviously a wrestling game, and is basically the same re-hashed game that most wrestlers are. There is plenty to do and customize, but there's nothing new or exciting that hasn't been done many times before.

Elemental Gimmick Gear
Vatical   3

An old-school style action-adventure RPG, E.G.G. is a decent title that is worth playing through. While it isn't for everyone, the puzzles are fun, the cut-scenes are great, and the boss battles are a blast. The game is 2D though, and the graphics, while crisp, are nothing overly amazing throughout most of the game. The story is also kind of confusing, since the game suffers from apparently bad translations.

ESPN International Track and Field
Konami   4

This game belongs on the NES. While the graphics and sound

Donald Duck: Goin' Quackers

Dragon Riders: Chronicles of Pern

Ducati World Racing Challenge

Ecco the Dolphin: Defender of the Future

What video game system is most commonly collected for?

| ESPN NBA 2 Night | Evolution 2 | Floigan Brothers | Frogger 2: Swanpy's Revenge |

may seem like they're from a Dreamcast game, the gameplay certainly does not. It's essentially a very slightly updated version of Track and Field on the NES, and while it can be a somewhat enjoyable party game, even that doesn't warrant a purchase -- after all, there's no Dreamcast Power Pad!

ESPN NBA 2 Night   Konami   3
Stick to Sega's NBA 2K series, and stay far, far away from this piece of trash. While sports games aren't for everybody, this game isn't "for" anybody at all.

Evil Dead: Hail to the King
**   THQ   5**
Based on the Evil Dead storyline, this game is both good and bad. For fans of the series, it's decent, because it does stay true to its roots and is presented well. However, the game is short and the graphics are below what is expected on the Dreamcast.

Evolution   UbiSoft   1
While it is no Final Fantasy or Chrono Trigger, Evolution is a pretty solid RPG. The story is decent, the controls are tight, and the game is pretty much fun all around. As far as graphics go: the game runs at a constant 60 frames per second, and the textures are nice. However, the game does suffer from one thing in particular -- overly long and uneventful dungeons. They just seem to drag on entirely for too long.

Evolution 2   UbiSoft   4
Evolution 2 seems vaguely familiar. It's really not all that different from its predecessor -- although the graphics have had an update, not much else has. It seems very repetitive, and the dungeons in it are even more boring than the first. Worse still, there are less save points, so if one dies, much of the same repetitiveness must be repeated once again.

Expendable   Infogrames   2
Expendable is a decent adventure game that has some problems, but is an all-around good time. The graphics are simply stunning, and while the controls are sometimes frustrating, they could have been worse.

F1 World Grand Prix   Sega   5
This game feels like a real F1 race. It has the official license, and therefore has everything that goes along with it -- the drivers, the cars, and the tracks. The graphics in this game are pretty good, and while there is sometimes a drop in framerate, it doesn't drastically affect gameplay. However, the multiplayer mode is weak -- only two players can race against one another, and there are no computer opponents.

F355 Challenge   Acclaim   5
F355 Challenge is incredibly detailed. Your car (of which you unfortunately only have one choice) can be customized and

tweaked down to the very last detail. It's lots of fun to play, and the detail is great, but if you're not into extremely deep and detailed racers, don't bother with this one.

Fatal Fury: Mark of the Wolves
**   Agetec   6**
This is a SNK game. Buy it. Now. Fatal Fury: Mark of the Wolves has the absolute best 2D animation I've ever seen on the Dreamcast. In fact, I might go so far as to call it the best 2D animation I've ever seen, period. The resolution may not be quite as high as some other games, but this thing just flows. The fighting engine is what you would expect for a Fatal Fury game -- great. The game does suffer from a few things, though -- poor menus and a lack of extras to unlock.

Fighting Force 2   Eidos   2
It's basically a 3D beat-em-up, and it's even more unoriginal than the original. As is typical of beat-em-ups, the enemies in Fighting Force seem to be recycled all too often, and while there is a decent arsenal of weaponry at your disposal, it's just not all that exciting.

Flag to Flag CART Racing   Sega   4

Floigan Brothers   Sega   5
Floigan Brothers is short. Really short. The graphics and gameplay, however, do make it worth your while. It has a very cartoony feel, which many other games have not been able to capture. Puzzles in this game are easy, and so is the game in general. There is an online trading area as well, but no real online play.

Frogger 2: Swampy's Revenge
**   Hasbro   2**
Among the updates to classic games, Frogger 2 stands out as a good one. The game has plenty of levels (30) to keep classic junkies busy, and there are several nice four-player multiplayer games.

Fur Fighters   Acclaim   1
You'll take control of a cute, furry animal in this action/puzzle-based adventure game. Not your sort of thing? What if you have guns? Fur Fighters is an interesting game, and while it is fun for a while, it doesn't last forever. The gameplay is rather repetitive, and there's just not very much depth here.

GameShark CD-X   Interact   2

GameShark Lite   Interact   4

Gauntlet Legends   Midway   4
Gauntlet Legends thankfully stays true to its roots and is tons of fun. This game feels and plays just like its arcade counterpart, and is just as addicting. There are lots of extras, it's as mind-

less as ever, and it is definitely recommended.

Giga Wing   Capcom   5
The Dreamcast should have had more shooters like this one! Shooter fans will have a blast with this one, and although it is kind of short, it's a blast while it lasts. As is with most Capcom shooters, there is a ridiculous amount of stuff on the screen at any given time.

Giga Wing 2   Capcom   6
Giga Wing 2 is even more fun than the original, with more ships and more levels. However, it too is too short. Multiplayer mode is a blast, and the variety in ships keeps things fresh.

Grand Theft Auto 2   Rockstar   5
With all of the recent buzz about Grand Theft Auto 3, some people are wondering what GTA2 was like, because they may have missed it. Well, it's a good time, but it's no GTA3. The port to the Dreamcast isn't the best -- the controls don't work quite as well as they should. The game itself is a good time, but I found it more enjoyable to just drive around with invincibility on, blowing things up at will than actually completing the missions.

Grandia 2   UbiSoft   2
One of the two biggest and baddest RPG's on the Dreamcast, Grandia II should be at least played by everyone who has a Dreamcast. The story is nice for the most part, the game itself is fun (although there are points where it is boring), and the music is simply amazing. Also note: this game came with the soundtrack CD packed in.

Grinch, The   Konami   3

Gunbird 2   Capcom   5
Capcom's 2D shooters are always a blast, and this one is no exception to the rule. Of course, it is somewhat limited as far as replay value goes, though, because it is pretty short. For shooter fans, it will be a great and long-lasting experience, but for casual gamers, it won't last too long.

Gundam: Side Story 0079   Bandai   6
It's really surprising that this game was ever released in America, especially considering that it's Bandai's only Dreamcast release. Still, it is a mech game, and generally considered a solid (but short) one.

Heavy Metal: Geomatrix   Capcom   3

Hidden & Dangerous   Take2 Interactive   5
Hidden & Dangerous is a World War II simulation game. The missions are somewhat interesting, but frankly, are nothing spectacular. Aside from the gameplay itself, this game feels very unpolished and buggy.

House of the Dead 2   Sega   3
If you're a fan of shooting games and don't know what this game is all about, you've been living in a hole for too long. While House of the Dead 2 is extremely short, it's always fun to come back to once in a while, and with light gun support added in, it is a very enjoyable game.

Hoyle Casino   Sierra   5

Hydro Thunder   Midway   3
Hydro Thunder was great fun in the arcades, and while this port doesn't quite stack up to the original, it is certainly a great game. There are plenty of tracks, boats, and difficulties to keep racing fans busy, and the visuals in this game are simply amazing.

Illbleed   Jaleco   3
Illbleed is a typical survival-horror game, with poor controls and animation. As far as this genre goes on the Dreamcast, stick with Alone in the Dark or one of the Resident Evil games.

Incoming   Interplay   2
As with many shooters, this game is great for shooting fans, but not necessarily the most immersive experience for the casual player. And, while the controls in Incoming don't feel natural at first, they're not too bad once you've gotten used to them.

Industrial Spy: Operation Espionage
     UFO   7

Internet Browser 3.0   PlanetWeb   7

Iron Aces   Infogrames   6
An above average action-based flight sim, Iron Aces is worth picking up. It doesn't have the extreme detail that some flight sims have, but it is a good time, especially for those who are intrigued by World War II, which is where the game is set.

Jeremy McGrath Supercross 2000
     Acclaim   3

Jet Grind Radio   Sega   1
If you haven't yet played Jet Grind Radio, you should. JGR uses a cool new (and increasingly popular) style of graphics - cell-shading. The game centers around spray-painting walls, cars, and pretty much anything in site to mark your gang's territory. There are several cool rollerblading skaters to play as, other gangs and police to deal with, and even a custom graffiti design mode.

JoJo's Bizarre Adventure   Capcom   2
JoJo's Bizarre Adventure is bizarre, all right, and is based on the anime series of the same name. The game is a 2D fighter, which is one of the things Capcom is known to do best. Besides the outrageous characters and moves, the story mode adds

Giga Wing 2

Grandia II

Gunbird 2

Incoming

What is the difference between production Dreamcasts and early demonstration units sent to stores?

DC

| JoJo's Bizarre Adventure | The King of Fighters Dream Match '99 | KISS Psycho Circus | Marvel Vs. Capcom |

some replayablity to the game, since it's always a little different with each fighter.

Kao the Kangaroo   **Titus**   6
Kao the Kangaroo had a short production run for good reason -- it's not all that much fun. While the graphics are decent and the game not too bad in and of itself, Kao suffers from major control problems. And, the game really doesn't do anything new, and because of this, is pretty darned boring.

King of Fighters Dream Match '99, The
     SNK   5
For hardcore fighting game fans, this is a must-buy. There's not much to be said about most King of Fighters games that hasn't been said already. This is a slower-paced, but completely enjoyable fighter. However, there is no story mode, which is important to note.

King of Fighters Evolution   **Agetec**   5
Once again, SNK fans are treated to a cool new version of classic KoF. In KoF Evolution, there is a cool "striker," which can be brought out briefly during fights to help briefly. The coolest thing about this is that there are tons of extra strikers to be unlocked, and "evolved" to higher, stronger levels. Besides the strikers, there is a huge cast of fighters to pick from, and plenty of gameplay modes to try out.

KISS Psycho Circus   **Gathering of Developers**   5
KISS Psycho Circus probably won't even please the most devoted of KISS fans. There is very little of anything related to KISS in the game, and with other, better, first-person shooters out there, Psycho Circus has little to offer.

Last Blade 2: Heart of the Samurai
     Agetec   6
Last Blade 2 is one of the more overlooked fighting games on the Dreamcast. Although it doesn't have the speed or flare of Marvel vs. Capcom 2, or the animation quality of Fatal Fury: Mark of the Wolves, it does have a relatively deep fighting engine, cool fighters, and a pretty solid feel.

Legacy of Kain: Soul Reaver
     Eidos   5
Haven't we seen this before? Yes, we have. Still, Legacy of Kain: Soul Reaver makes a great appearance on the Dreamcast. With the graphical power the DC has, this game really comes alive, since some very cool lighting effects were used.

Looney Toons Space Race
     Infogrames   6
Kart racing seems so dull anymore! Thankfully, Space Race is one of the better ones out there, and probably close to the best available on the Dreamcast. This game uses cell-shaded graphics, like that of Jet Grind Radio, and they look great. (After

all, Looney Tunes is a cartoon.)

Mag Force Racing   **Crave**   6
Mag Force Racing is essentially a typical high-speed racer. Rather than hovercrafts, superspeed motorcycles, or spaceships, though, Mag Force Racing is all about racing with tripods. The graphics in the game are pretty decent, and although the control isn't the tightest that there has ever been in these types of games, there are plenty of wicked tracks, vehicles, and difficulties to keep the fun of playing alive.

Maken X   **Sega**   4
While the graphics are amazing and the gameplay concept creative, Maken X isn't the brightest crayon in the box. The control scheme is simply awful, and sadly, this takes away too much from this game to make it a classic.

Mars Matrix   **Capcom**   5
Ah, another 2D Capcom shooter on the Dreamcast. Mars Matrix is definitely the best of them all. With nice, clean graphics, ridiculously addicting gameplay, several modes to do it in, and tons of extras to keep things fresh, Mars Matrix excels upon all levels. Get this game, now.

Marvel Vs. Capcom   **Capcom**   2
Aside from 2D shooters, 2D fighting games are what the folks at Capcom know best. This game is no exception to the rule, and in fact is a game that no fighting fan should be without. While the combo system isn't as deep as some games, Marvel vs. Capcom is a blast. There are tons of fighters to choose from, blazingly fast gameplay, and an awesome two-player experience.

Marvel vs. Capcom 2   **Capcom**   5
If you thought Marvel vs. Capcom was even remotely good, you'll be amazed by the sequel. With even faster gameplay than its predecessor, a cool three-fighter tag team to play with, 56 (yes, fifty-six) fighters on the disc, and other extras included, this game is an absolute must-buy!

Matt Hoffman's Pro BMX   **Activision**   5
Designed along the same lines of Tony Hawk's Pro Skater, Matt Hoffman's Pro BMX is a very solid game. There are a few collision glitches, however, and it isn't quite as addicting as THPS, but is definitely worth a try if you're a fan of this genre of games.

Max Steel: Covert Missions
     Mattel   5
Has Mattel ever done anything worthwhile for video games? If they have, this certainly isn't it. Aside from some pretty decent graphics, this game is a real piece, and I don't mean the good kind. Gameplay is just dull, and the replay value is therefore obviously lacking. Stay away from this one.

326

Production DC's were equipped with a modem, demo units had a hollow piece of plastic in its place.

Maximum Pool   Sierra   6
While most pool video games in the past haven't been worth looking at more than the outside cover, Maximum pool is actually a decent game. It certainly doesn't stretch the power of the Dreamcast's hardware, and it's not quite like a real pool table, but with solid gameplay and an online mode, Maximum Pool is somewhat of a surprise.

MDK2   Interplay   4
With some of the better graphics in a game on the Dreamcast, great gameplay, and some craziness only outdone by the likes of JoJo's Bizarre Adventure, MDK2 is a game that no Dreamcast owner should be without. It is played in a third person perspective and uses a control scheme similar to that of Turok. One important thing to note, however, is that the game is pretty much a one-timer. After it's over, there's not the same joy in playing through it again.

Metropolis Street Racer   Sega   4
This is the best racer on the Sega Dreamcast. Period. With an arcade feel and the detail of a racing sim, MSR is a must buy. All of the games 200+ circuits are set in San Francisco, Tokyo, and London. The interesting thing about MSR is that, as the game states, "It's not about how fast you drive. It's about how you drive fast." Style and speed make a perfect match in this must-own Dreamcast racer.

Midway Greatest Arcade Hits Vol. 1
     Midway   5
This game certainly doesn't push the Dreamcast to its limits in any way, shape, or form, but for classic gamers, it is a great buy. The games included on the disc are: Robotron 2084, Sinistar, Joust, Defender, Defender 2, and Bubbles.

Monaco Grand Prix 2   UbiSoft   4
With six modes of gameplay, including a retro mode, Monaco Grand Prix has a lot to offer. There are also eleven racing teams and sixteen tracks in the game.

Mortal Kombat Gold   Midway   5
It's been a long time since there was a Mortal Kombat game worth a purchase, and this one certainly isn't it. This is essentially the same Mortal Kombat game that we all played years ago, with updated graphics and improved sound. The fighting engine still has little depth, and fatalities offer the only reason to play the game through after the first time.

MP3DC   Blaze   6
Blaze's MP3DC offers CD-based MP3 and VBR file playback on the Dreamcast, and supports play list creation, file browsing, and song/artist display.

MP3DC   Pelican   6
Pelican's MP3DC is essentially does the same thing that Blaze's MP3 player does. It supports individual MP3 playback, as well as the use of play lists.

Mr. Driller   Namco   5
Few puzzle games can be so simple yet so complex, and pull it off in a way that is as addicting as this. Mr. Driller is a modern-day sequel to the classic Dig-Dug, with graphics and sound that are above average for a puzzle game. As with most great puzzle games, the addictive gameplay make Mr. Driller a great game.

Ms. Pac-Man Maze Madness
     Namco   5
Ms. Pac-Man Maze Madness is one of the best re-makes of a classic game that I've seen in a long, long time. The game is addictive, the graphics are great, and there are some really cool extras, like a great multi-player mode and an arcade-perfect translation of the original.

MTV Skateboarding   THQ   5
Why do companies like THQ release games like this? MTV Skateboarding is an obvious clone of Tony Hawk's Pro Skater, and a very poor one at that. It just isn't fun. Stay away from it.

Namco Museum   Namco   5
With classic compilation games galore being released in recent years, and Namco being one of the torch carriers in bringing them out, one would think that their first compilation on Dreamcast would at least be a little... bigger. Only six games were included on this disc, which is even less than the original PSX release. Sure, Dig-Dug, Galaga, Pole Position, Pac-Man, Ms. Pac-Man, and Galaxian are all great games, and they're emulated wonderfully here. It's just disappointing that Namco didn't do anything beyond that.

NBA 2K   Sega   1
EA Sports finally lost its pedestal of always having the best basketball games on the block. Sega and Visual Concepts deliver what is one of the best basketball games ever. The play-calling is sometimes a chore, but otherwise, NBA 2K is a masterpiece. The graphic artists were meticulous, and the computer AI is actually competitive.

NBA 2K1   Sega   1
NBA 2K1 is pretty similar to its predecessor, but has a few new features and revisions that make it a little bit better. The most notable new feature is probably the ability to play online. The AI is also more offensive in 2K1, and this essentially boils down to more intense, and more enjoyable, gameplay.

NBA 2K2   Sega   3
More online play and a few more improvements make NBA 2K2 the best of the NBA 2K series on the Dreamcast. Visual Concepts completely changed the game by allowing gamers to interrupt animations to do other moves, passes, or shots. In

Max Steel: Covert Missions   MDK 2   Mr. Driller   Ms. Pac-Man Maze Madness

The degradation of information stored on ROM's over time is known as "bit-rot"

NBA 2K2

NCAA 2K2

NFL Blitz 2001

NFL Quarterback Club 2000

doing this, they made the game a lot more enjoyable, because players had more control over the action of the game.

NBA Hoopz   Midway   5
NBA Hoopz is very reminiscent of NBA Jam -- it's all about fast, furious, adrenaline-pumping gampeplay. It's too bad it's not very immersive. NBA Hoopz has a good feel, and can be a lot of fun, but with the terrible AI (that plays poorly or wonderfully depending on the score), it just doesn't stack up to any of the NBA 2K games.

NBA Showtime: NBA on NBC
         Midway   4
See the review for NBA Hoopz -- this game isn't very different. Showtime's arcade-style gameplay can be a blast for a while, but it doesn't have the depth it needs to be a long-lasting single-player experience. Two-player mode can last for quite a while, but unless that's you're main motive in buying a basketball game, stay away from this one.

NCAA College Football 2K2
         Sega   5
Based on the NFL 2K engine, and from the same fine folks at Visual Concepts, NCAA College Football 2K2 is both amazing and disappointing. As a football game, it excels. However, as a *college* football game, it does not. Even the detailed stadiums, 118 Division I-A teams, the Rose Bowl, and online play don't give the uplifting feeling of a Saturday afternoon of college football.

Next Tetris: On-line Edition, The
         Crave   2
Tetris is arguably the best puzzle game of all time. Tetris is cool. Online gaming is cool, too. Add in updated graphics, nice music, and a few new quirks to gameplay, and you've got one of the best damn Dreamcast puzzle games in the land. If you're even remotely a fan of this type of game, get this one, and now.

NFL 2K   Sega   1
NFL 2K was, on September 9th, 1999, the best football game ever made. The great play-calling menus (and optional play calling via the VMU), the meticulously detailed graphics, and the great gameplay modes and options made NFL 2K one of the premier reasons to own a Dreamcast.

NFL 2K1   Sega   1
While the number of updates to NFL 2K was somewhat minimal, there was one *major* update that made NFL 2K1 a game that any sports fan had to own. That major update was online multi-player support. While there were some gamers on SegaNet who made headaches for others, NFL 2K1 worked quite well online, and this made the game many times better than it would have been without it.

NFL 2K2   Sega   2
Visual Concepts released another simply amazing football title in what is NFL 2K2. The major improvement to note is that the running game of 2K2 was much improved over 2K and 2K1. Other small improvements were made all around, and online gameplay is still an option that adds seemingly infinite replay-ability to the game.

NFL Blitz 2000   Midway   3
Besides SNK's Neo Geo, the Dreamcast was really the first home console that offered arcade-perfect translations. NFL Blitz 2000 is a perfect example of this. Fast, action-packed gameplay make this game a nice break from the NFL 2K series, but since it lacks the depth of other football games, it isn't as immersive.

NFL Blitz 2001   Midway   4
With updated graphics, a few extra modes to try out, and not much else, NFL Blitz 2001 is pretty much the same old game. It's still fun, but it's still the same.

NFL Quarterback Club 2000
         Acclaim   2
With games like NFL 2K2 and even NFL Blitz 2001, there is absolutely no reason to play this game. Horrible AI, sloppy graphics, and even sloppier controls make NFL Quarterback Club 2000 a game that has almost no merit and one that should be avoided completely.

NFL Quarterback Club 2001
         Acclaim   4
Why does Acclaim keep releasing these games? They just are not fun... at all. QB Club 2001 has essentially no improvements over QB Club 2000. The AI still cheats, the graphics are still sloppy, and the controls are still exactly what they should not be -- uncontrollable.

NHL 2K   Sega   3
Although NHL 2K isn't the best of Sega's new sports titles, it is still a very solid game. As far as hockey games go, it is a fast-paced, exciting one. The graphics are really nice, and ice effects are of particular excellence. One area that this game lacks though is in the area of extra modes -- there basically aren't any.

NHL 2K2   Sega   5
Thankfully, the Dreamcast's last commercial release in the United States is a good one. Visual Concepts takes over the designing reigns of the NHL 2K series, and it shows. Pretty much everything is improved -- in particular, there are more commentary sound clips for less repetitiveness, better graphics, tighter control, and thankfully, there are many more gameplay modes than were in NHL 2K.

A standard SNES cartridge weighs 80 grams.

Nightmare Creatures 2 Konami 4

Nightmare Creatures 2 could have been a lot better than it was. With tighter controls, less repetitiveness, and MUCH-improved graphics, it could have been a pretty cool game. However, the fact that all of these and more are problems for the game make it a less than average game in a sea of above average Dreamcast titles.

Omikron: The Nomad Soul
Eidos 4

Ooga Booga Sega 5

Tons of levels, awesome replayablitiy, and an online mode that rivals the addictiveness of Everquest make Ooga Booga's action/adventure gameplay something that no Dreamcast owner should miss. As for the graphics: they are somewhat simple and cartoony, but still decent. Check it out.

Outtrigger Sega 4

If you're a FPS fan and have a bunch of friends or access to the SegaNet, check out Outtrigger. While the single-player experience is a good one, this game is mainly driven by the multi-player options.

Pen Pen Tricelon Infogrames 4

Pen Pen Tricelon could have been so much better. Based on the triathlon, players must race with penguin-like creatures in three different events per race: walking, sliding, and swimming. This is very creative as far as racing games go, and works quite well. The racers are cool, and the tracks are lots of fun, too. The main problem with Pen Pen then is not the gameplay. It is the lack of extras. With only four tracks and several variations of each, Pen Pen gets old way too fast.

Phantasy Star Online Sega 1

Phantasy Star Online is a mixed bag of beans. Offline, the game is fun, but isn't really worth playing through more than once, as the story is somewhat lacking. Online, however, Phantasy Star Online is a different story. Many gamers have spent hundreds, if not thousands of hours playing this game online.

Phantasy Star Online Version 2
Sega 2

Although it is a good update to the original, and fans of PSO will be happy, PSO Version 2 isn't quite what it was cracked up to be. Online gameplay was no longer free with Ver. 2, and the single player experience was still pretty much a one-timer.

Plasma Sword Capcom 3

Capcom 2D fighters are always a lot of fun, but unfortunately, many of them are so similar to one another that it's hard to decide which to buy. While Plasma Sword isn't by any means a bad game, it's not an overly amazing one, either. It does nothing to further the fighting genre, and the game's graphics are sub-par for the Dreamcast.

POD: Speedzone UbiSoft 4

Among other racers on the Dreamcast, POD stands right in the middle. There are games like Metropolis Street Racer that are infinitely better than it, and there are games like Test Drive 6 that are many times worse. Where the single player mode is shallow, the two player mode is slightly better. However, this isn't much of a reason to buy the game, because it is unpolished all-around and has a limited track selection.

Power Stone Capcom 5

A 3D Capcom fighting game? These don't come along very often. Thankfully, Power Stone is one of the best. It's fully 3D and fully interactive environments make it a very unique experience. However, it is important to note that while the two-player mode is a blast, the single-player game is sub-par for a Capcom fighter.

Power Stone 2 Capcom 6

Power Stone 2 builds on what was one of the most revolutionary fighting games in a long time, and makes it better. More gameplay modes and more customization make the single-player game last longer than it did on the original. With four player multiplayer mayhem and even crazier arenas, Power Stone 2 is a game that any fighting game fan should own.

Prince of Persia Mattel 5

Project Justice Capcom 5

As a continuation of the Rival Schools storyline, Project Justice succeeds, but as an amazing fighting game among the competition it has on the Dreamcast, it fails. The game is a decent amount of fun, and the story modes keep things interesting for a while. However, the fighting engine is not very deep, and this is what keeps Project Justice from being one of the best fighting games on the Dreamcast.

Psychic Force 2012 Acclaim 4

Q*bert Majesco 2

Q*Bert may have the potential to become a good 3D game, but this version of the classic was not it. The game is as simple as ever, but it gets boring quickly. Classic gamers will probably find themselves playing the original Q*Bert mode more, which is thankfully emulated perfectly on the disc.

Quake III Arena Sega 1

Online fragging has never been this good. Quake III was and is one of the best reasons to go online with your Dreamcast, and with a great single-player game for those times when you have to be offline, this game is well worth a purchase. While it may not run at quite the speed or resolution some PC buffs have become used to, Quake III still looks amazing on the Dreamcast. However, it is important to remember that a keyboard and mouse are absolute necessities for this game.

Nightmare Creatures II   **Ooga Booga**

Phantasy Star Online   **Power Stone**

How many buttons are on top of the first version of the SNES console?

Rainbow Six: Rogue Spear   Railroad Tycoon II   Ready 2 Rumble Boxing   Record of Lodoss War

Railroad Tycoon 2   Gathering of Developers   6

It's a wonder that so few simulation games were released for the Dreamcast, and even more remarkable that one of the few would be Railroad Tycoon II. With nearly a hundred missions and scenarios, special attention to details, and a surprisingly easily-navigated interface, Railroad Tycoon is a great game for hardcore and casual sim fans alike.

Rainbow Six   Majesco   5

Rainbow Six is one of the deepest, most immersive Dreamcast games ever released. However, this game is not for the casual gamer -- the control scheme takes some getting used to, and so much training is needed before jumping into the heart of the game that only the serious gamer will really be into this.

Rainbow Six: Rogue Spear

Majesco   5

All of the detail, customization, and realism of the original Rainbow Six are still in tact in this PC port or Rogue Spear. It's too bad that Red Storm didn't add any bonuses in for the Dreamcast audience. As with its predecessor, this game isn't for everybody. Hardcore fans of games like Unreal Tournament should probably stay away, but otherwise, Rogue Spear probably deserves a look.

Rayman 2: The Great Escape

UbiSoft   5

UbiSoft released an amazing game they called Rayman 2. While the story isn't overly original, the gameplay is addictive, and the graphics are some of the best available on the Dreamcast. But, be warned: Rayman 2: The Great Escape can be addicting and platformer fans will be hooked. The game is somewhat short, but for the time that it lasts, it isn't likely that you'll want to put it down.

Razor Freestyle Scooter   Crave   5

Obviously, this game is intended for younger audiences, but it's not half bad. Or, depending how you look at it, it's not half good either. Razor Freestyle Scooter centers around the same idea that Tony Hawk's Pro Skater and Matt Hoffman's Pro BMX do. Players must ride around a specific area, doing tricks and collecting points and items wherever they go. Sadly, this game doesn't live up to what is now expected in this genre, and although it isn't the worst THPS rip-off to come out, it's not the best, either.

Ready 2 Rumble Boxing   Midway   2

Boxing games have been a scarce thing in recent years, but Midway released what many consider to be the best-ever, and certainly the most notable since Super Punch Out. At 60 frames per second with tight controls and cool characters, Ready 2 Rumble is a game that will definitely get some playtime on your Dreamcast, should you pick it up.

Ready 2 Rumble Boxing: Round 2

Midway   4

Maybe there wasn't much that Midway could have done to update Ready 2 Rumble, but this game is still a little disappointing. The game itself is still just as fun as the original, the graphics are more detailed, and the humor has been upped a notch. Still, there's not much new here. It's probably a little better than the original, but it's so close to being the same thing that it's hard to say.

Record of Lodoss War   Crave   5

It's somewhat amazing that a game like Record of Lodoss War, which is based on a Japanese anime series, would be released in America. However, it's a good thing it did come out here, because this is one Hell of a good game. Record of Lodoss War is a hack 'n' slash RPG with a great story, cool side quests, and some other interesting extras I'll leave for you to find out about.

Red Dog: Superior Firepower

Crave   6

Red Dog is one of those games that come along, get passed up on store shelves, and deserve more recognition than they get. This is an action game in which players take control of a tank, kill the bad guys, and save the Earth from them. Of special interest in this game is the multiplayer mode, which adds a decent amount of replayability to it.

Reel Fishing Wild   Natsume   5

With Sega's fishing games on the Dreamcast, there isn't much of a reason to own this game. Sub-par graphics, shallow gameplay, and boring everything else make Natsume's Reel Fishing Wild a title to steer clear of.

Resident Evil 2   Capcom   4

This is pretty much a straight PSX to Dreamcast port of the classic Resident Evil 2. The graphics are only slightly updated, and there's not much added in for Dreamcast owners. For fans of the game, it's a decent buy, and for those who enjoyed CODE: Veronica but haven't played this yet, it's a great buy.

Resident Evil 3: Nemesis   Capcom   4

Resident Evil 3 is Capcom's second PSX to Dreamcast port of a Resident Evil game. Again, there isn't much of a change in the game besides slightly upgraded graphics, but for those who haven't tried this one out yet, it is certainly worth a spin.

Resident Evil CODE: Veronica

Capcom   4

Resident Evil meets the Dreamcast in what is an amazing experience. CODE: Veronica certainly captures the look and feel of what the series has come to be known for. Creepy graphics, areas, and lots of zombies to shoot with minimal amounts of ammo are just a few of the things Capcom had up their sleeves when they made this game.

Re-Volt   Acclaim   3
RC racing games are few and far between, and this one is awesome. Re-Volt has tight control, intelligent AI, and a general feel of actually racing a tiny RC car around tracks set in areas like a neighborhood street. Re-Volt also has a very nice four-player mode and a decent track editor for added replayability.

Ring: Terror's Realm, The   Infogrames   4
Even the best of plots can't save some games. Bad controls, ugly graphics, terrible voice acting, and a host of other problems keep The Ring from being the survival horror game it could have been.

Rippin' Riders   Sega   3
While Rippin' Riders isn't on par with 1080° Snowboarding on the N64 or even with Acclaim's Trickstyle on the Dreamcast, it is a fairly solid title. Graphics, sound, and control are above average, and the game is a good time all around. For fans of snowboarding games, Rippin' Riders is definitely worth a look.

Roadsters   Titus   3
If you haven't figured it out already, a large percentage of Dreamcast games are above average. However, if there weren't any that were below average, we wouldn't have anything "above average" at all. Roadsters is one of those below average games. It suffers first and foremost from control, and later from pretty much everything else. Be it the graphics, the framerate, or the lack of decent multiplayer fun, Roadsters is one of those games that really shouldn't have ever been released.

Samba de Amigo   Sega   2
Samba de Amigo is *so cool*. The object of the game is simple: shake your maracas to the beat of the music. It is so simple, yet so addictive. And, with the option of real maraca controllers, this game stands out as one of the most unique games this side of the Pacific.

San Francisco Rush 2049   Midway   3
Although this game lacks decent AI opponents, the insane track designs make San Francisco Rush 2049 a nice break from the realism of Metropolis Street Racer and Sega GT. This game is a blast. Multiplayer battle mode adds hours and hours of playtime to Rush 2049. Remember, though: this game is what may be referred to as an adventure racing game. For fans of Beetle Adventure Racing, Extreme-G, and others, this is a perfect choice.

Seaman   Sega   3
If you haven't seen this game in action, you should. Remember the Tamagotchi fad a few years back? Seaman is a more advanced, intellectual, and badmouthed version of that. With the game comes a microphone which is plugged into a Dreamcast controller, as a VMU or rumble pak would be. This allows for communication between the player and his or her Seaman, a combination of a fish and a man. While the game was very revolutionary, it didn't quite live up to its hype, and as with any video game, there's only so much to do.

Sega Bass Fishing   Sega   2
Sega Bass Fishing brings fishing games to a whole new level of completeness. The gameplay is incredibly fun and the fish, lures, and environments are just as incredibly detailed. Even for non-fishers, this game is worth looking into.

Sega Bass Fishing 2   Sega   4
Since Sega pretty much hit the nail on the head with Sega Bass Fishing, the sequel is much of the same thing with a few extras. A tutorial mode is helpful for beginners, the graphics are even more detailed than the original, and there are even more customization options than before. Definitely worth dusting off the old fishing controller one more time.

Sega GT   Sega   4
As far as racing games go on the Dreamcast, Sega GT is one of the best. Extreme attention to detail was paid to this game, and it shows. For hardcore racing sim fans, this game is a must own, and for casual racing fans, it is still a great buy.

Sega Marine Fishing   Sega   4
As an arcade to Dreamcast port and as another Dreamcast fishing title, Sega Marine Fishing succeeds on all levels. The great play mechanics of Sega Bass Fishing are here, and there are several new modes not found in the arcade original. Check this one out.

Sega Rally 2   Sega   5
Sega Rally 2 could have been so much better. While the arcade-style gameplay is there, the sense of extreme competition is not. It can be somewhat immersive for a while, but the high difficulty in later levels of the game and the poor multiplayer mode really take Sega Rally 2 down.

Sega Smash Pack Vol. 1   Sega   1
Sega's own classic compilation is a good one. Twelve classic Sega games on one GD-ROM certainly warrant a purchase. Here's what you'll get: Sonic the Hedgehog, Golden Axe, Shining Force, Wrestle War, Streets of Rage 2, Columns, Vectorman, Phantasy Star II, Virtua Cop 2, Revenge of Shinobi, Altered Beast, and Sega Swirl.

Seventh Cross: Evolution   UFO   4
As the title of this game states, it's all about Evolution. Too bad NEC didn't decide to let Seventh Cross evolve as a piece of software before they released it. Some of the worst graphics on the Dreamcast and poor gameplay keep this game from being as good as it was intriguing at first glance.

Resident Evil 2   Resident Evil CODE: Veronica   Samba De Amigo   Seaman

What feature did the SNES controller introduce?

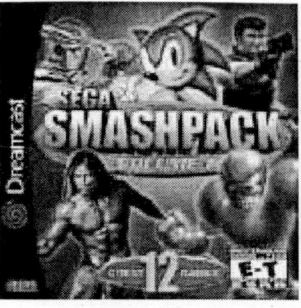

Sega Smash Pack Vol. 1

Skies of Arcadia

Shenmue

Sonic Adventure

Shadowman   Acclaim   4

Shadowman was one of the most unique games to hit the N64 and PSX. Shadowman's ability to travel between worlds make this game a huge and engrossing experience which, accompanied by nice graphics and sound, make it a worthy purchase for any Dreamcast collection.

Shenmue   Sega   2

Shenmue 2 really should have come out here in America, because the original was somewhat of a disappointment. While Shenmue was certainly one of the most realistic, epic games ever released, it just isn't as good as it could have been. The lack of action for this pseudo-RPG really brings it down.

Shenmue: Limited Edition   Sega   6

Shenmue: The Rehashed Version. Aside from the included music CD and very slight packaging variations, this limited edition of Shenmue is the same game. Only for hardcore Shenmue fans or Dreamcast collectors.

Silent Scope   Konami   6

For lots of anti-terrorist sniping fun, give Konami's Silent Scope a shot. Although it does suffer from a lack of extra modes, Silent Scope is still a solid game for any shooting fan. And, while the graphics aren't quite on par with some other Dreamcast games, the gameplay is what makes this title shine.

Silver   Infogrames   4

Skies of Arcadia   Sega   2

Arguably the best conventional RPG available for the Dreamcast, Skies of Arcadia shouldn't be missed. The graphics, sound, gameplay, and story of this game all come together to form one solid, unified piece of art. Random encounters can be annoying at times, but even this does not bring this game down from being one of the best RPG's the Dreamcast has to offer.

Slave Zero   Infogrames   1

Slave Zero sounded pretty cool before the Dreamcast launched. It's too bad that it wasn't. The horrendous framerate, poor controls, and uninspiring gameplay keep Slave Zero from being even remotely enjoyable.

Sno-Cross Championship Racing   Crave   5

Snow games are usually really cool. As cool as ice, in fact. Sadly, Sno-Cross Championship Racing isn't cool at all. It suffers from choppy framerates and extremely boring, frustrating gameplay. Poor graphics and a lack of extras only add to the holes that this game is laced with.

Soldier of Fortune   Crave   5

Another great Dreamcast first-person shooter? Soldier of For-

tune certainly is. While the graphics and framerate aren't quite on par with others like Unreal Tournament, the gameplay (both single and mutiplayer) makes up for any flaws there. Soldier of Fortune may not be the biggest-name title out there, but it is one that is worth looking into.

Sonic Adventure   Sega   1

Sonic Adventure is FAST. In fact, Sonic himself never knew he could move at such a speed. This game is, put simply, one of the best Sonic games ever made. Thankfully, Sonic has made the jump back into 3D quite well, and with several playable characters, unique adventures for each, a VMU mini game, and other extras, Sonic Adventure is a must-own game for platformer gamers everywhere.

Sonic Adventure: Limited Edition
Sega   7

Several months before the Dreamcast's launch in America, Sega teamed up with Hollywood Video to bring U.S. gamers a full (but not completely polished) version of Sonic Adventure, which was, at the time, one of the most anticipated games of the Dreamcast's impressive release lineup.

Sonic Adventure 2   Sega   3

The extra modes of Sonic Adventure 2 warrant purchasing this game alone. As in the original, extra modes abound, including an unlockable cart racing mode, the Chao mini-games, and more. Boss battles are also just as exciting as in Sonic Adventure, and Sonic's new nemesis, Shadow, adds a whole new level of deepness to the series.

Sonic Adventure 2 Demo Disc
Sega   2

Sonic Shuffle   Sega   2

Sonic Shuffle was Sega's answer to Nintendo's Mario Party. Unfortunately, it wasn't a very good answer. Sonic's video game board game has less mini games than Mario Party, and they're not as simple, either. This makes Sonic Shuffle somewhat of a chore, and as we all know chores to be, that equates to a boring gaming experience.

Soul Calibur   Namco   1

Soul Calibur was one of Namco's few games on the Dreamcast, and definitely by far the best. There's not much to say about this game that hasn't been said already. As a multiplayer game, Soul Calibur is a blast, for the most part. As a single player game, though, it is short-lived. Arcade mode is extremely easy and there are no difficulty settings to change that. For casual fighting game fans, this game is a must-own, but for hardcore fighters, Soul Calibur may not be worth a purchase.

Soul Fighter   Mindscape   2

Soul Fighter is everything that the average 3D beat-em up is --

repetitive, boring, and... repetitive again. While Soul Fighter does have more of an action-adventure feel than a game like State of Emergency, there just isn't enough depth to keep things interesting. Hacking and slashing can only last for so long, and unfortunately for Soul Fighter, that amount of time is very short.

South Park: Chef's Luv Shack   Acclaim   1
For fans of the TV show, Chef's Luv Shack will be a short, but enjoyable game, IF you have a bunch of friends around who enjoy the show just as much. However, single player mode in this game is, after a short time, boring and uneventful.

South Park Rally   Acclaim   5
Some cart racing games are bad. Some are really bad. South Park Rally is so bad that it's even worse than Paula Jones in a boxing match. It's ugly, out of control, and completely unenjoy-able. While there is a lot of humor from the show, this is pretty much the only perk of the game, so unless you're a hardcore South Park fan, steer clear of this one. In fact, even if you are a hardcore fan of the show, do not buy this game.

Space Channel 5   Sega   2
Sega released several decidedly unique games for the Dream-cast, including the likes of Jet Grind Radio, Samba de Amigo, and 18 Wheeler. Space Channel 5 is another game that fits into the bunch, and is starred by the sassy space reporter, Ulala. In it, Ulala must dance to the beat of different songs to out-dance her opponents. It's simple and lots of fun. And, the sound track is amazing, as would be expected for a dancing game. Recom-mended.

Spawn: In the Demon's Hand
                                Capcom   4
Capcom releases so many amazing games that it's confusing that a game like Spawn: In the Demon's Hand could come from them. While the multiplayer game is mildly enjoyable for a time, the single player mode is so dull that there's really no reason to play for more than five minutes. Repetitive, uninspiring every-thing keep Spawn and the gang from having a decent video game, once again

Spec Ops 2: Omega Squad
                                Ripcord   5

Speed Devils   UbiSoft   4
Good old arcade racing with a few new twists makes a great appearance on the Dreamcast. Nice graphics and cool track design make this game a great one alone, but there are two special features to note. When passing police cars, if a player maintains a certain speed, he or she earns money, and players also have the ability to bet on races, somewhat similar to that in Metropolis Street Racer.

Speed Devils Online Racing
                                UbiSoft   6
Speed Devils Online is, as was expected, basically the same old game with online support added in. Most of the single player game remains unchanged, but there is a new track included with the update. So, unless you really want to play this game online, there's not much else new here to mess around with.

Spider-Man   Activision   5
As with any game with a super-hero main character that can swing from building to building (yes, I realize how many there are), the Dreamcast's Spider-Man port suffers from all kinds of camera problems. Controls are also sometimes difficult, and the graphics haven't seen much upgrading from the PSX ver-sion of this game. Still, it is considered by many to be a great action game, and deserves a look by most.

Spirit of Speed 1937   Acclaim   4
The concept of driving old race cars is pretty interesting. It's too bad that LJN didn't put the idea to good use. Poor graphics, poor sound, poor control, long load times, and a host of other negatives of Spirit of Speed make it one of the worst Dreamcast racers around.

Sports Jam   Agetec   4
Sports Jam is a 128-bit version of an 8-bit game. Oddly enough, it's actually a good time. It centers around specific sports events, much like World Events did on the NES. Some of the events include: soccer corner kicks, basketball three-point shooting, and various football drills.

Star Wars Demolition   LucasArts   4
Star Wars games have been a mixed bunch. Some of the greatest and some of the worst games ever have come from this license. Star Wars Demolition is essentially Vigilante 8 with Star Wars vehicles and characters. It's not a very new concept, but it's still a good time.

Star Wars Episode I Racer
                                LucasArts   5
Episode I Racer was a great game on the N64. Sure, this ver-sion is decent, but with absolutely no improvements and no considerable extras packed in, this game falls short of what it should have been. Even the graphics saw no updating. It's sad, too, because with the power of the Dreamcast, this game could have been incredible.

Star Wars Episode I: Jedi Power Battles
                                LucasArts   5
Although Jedi Power Battles did receive a huge graphical over-haul from the PSX original, there isn't enough changed in the game's control mechanics to make this as good as it could have been. Still, this is a huge surprise, considering how poor the original was.

Soul Calibur

South Park: Chef's Luv Shack

Speed Devils

Spirit of Speed 1937

What word did Apple disallow Bandai to use when marketing the Pippin @world in the U.S.?

DC

| Star Wars Episode 1 Racer | Street Fighter III: Double Impact | Super Magnetic Neo | Sword of the Berserk: Gut's Rage |

StarLancer   Crave   5
Space shooters like this don't come along too often. Fortunately, for those who missed the PC original, StarLancer has made an appearance on the Dreamcast, and a fairly nice one. Good graphics, a nice control scheme, and solid gameplay are just a few of the things this game has to offer.

Street Fighter Alpha 3   Capcom   4
It's a wonder how many Street fighter games can be released and still retain all of the quality that they have become known for. Street Fighter Alpha 3 is no exception, and for those who played the PSX version, all of the extras are unlocked, so you won't have to reacquire everything.

Street Fighter III: Double Impact
     Capcom   4
Yet another Street Fighter game, Double Impact is still on par with the rest of the series. The graphics are some of the best for 2D Dreamcast fighters, and the gameplay is, as usual, incredibly amazing.

Street Fighter III: Third Strike
     Capcom   4
Capcom released this game with hardcore fighters in mind. Although it doesn't have the speed or flare of Marvel vs. Capcom or Street Fighter Alpha 3, this game's fighting engine is deep and solid. Casual fighting fans will enjoy this game, but it is especially recommended for the hardcore fighters out there.

Striker Pro 2000   Infogrames   4
Since there are so few soccer games available for the Dreamcast, Striker Pro 2000 is, while flawed, probably the best. An authentic European setting, crisp graphics, and a few extras to unlock will keep soccer fans busy for a while.

Stupid Invaders   UbiSoft   6
Stupid Invaders is a rather interesting Dreamcast title. It is a puzzle/adventure game, and is best described as a very humorous and atmospheric (yet beautiful) video game. Even though it was a somewhat later release, it is still a high-quality game.

Super Magnetic Neo   Crave   2
Super Magnetic Neo is a truly unique puzzler-platform game. As Neo, you must utilize your positive and negative magnetic powers to advance through different levels and areas of the game. Although it is simplistic and easy, it's fun, and the bonus rounds keep things fresh.

Super Runabout: San Francisco
     Interplay   5
It's not as bad as South Park Rally, but it is certainly no Metropolis Street Racer, either. Poor controls and a general feeling of a tarnished and unfinished game keep Super Runabout from being anything worth much of your time. There are a de-

cent number of options, but the aforementioned problems keep them from being what they could have been.

Surf Rocket Racers   Crave   3
Think Wave Race 64. Too bad this game is too shallow to hold its own against a game like this. Graphical effects are nice, as is pretty much everything else. However, it's not the best water racing game on the Dreamcast -- stick with Hydro Thunder.

Suzuki Alstare Racing   UbiSoft   4
I guess this is what UbiSoft gets for releasing a game that they didn't develop themselves. This game could have been decent, but is mediocre in all areas. Where the controls are solid, the gameplay is boring. Where the graphics are decent, the sound is horrible.

Sword of the Berzerk: Guts' Rage
     Eidos   1
Senator Lieberman preys on games like this. As suggested by the title, this game has oodles of blood and guts, and is certainly not for the young or those with weak stomachs. But, for those who can get past the gore, this hack 'n' slash action adventure game is quite enjoyable.

Sydney 2000   Eidos   4
When we were all younger, Track & Field was a blast. Then again, that was on the NES and this is on the Dreamcast. Repetitive gameplay in the form of mindless button mashing for most of the Olympic events makes this game nothing but a bore after a short while. There is some odd form of addictiveness to it, but not a very enthralling one.

Tech Romancer   Capcom   5
Among all of the 2D fighters on the Dreamcast sits Tech Romancer. It is certainly unique, because it is based on Japanese anime, the fighters are giant robots, and it actually saw release in America. As is expected from Capcom, this is a quality fighting game, but it isn't necessarily their best.

Tee Off Golf   Acclaim   5
Aside from the mini-golf mini game in 102 Dalmatians (which is excellent), Tee Off Golf is pretty much the only option golfing gamers have on the Dreamcast. Even though it is a blatant rip-off of Hot Shots Golf, it turns out to be a good one. Single player and multiplayer modes alike are a lot of fun, and the graphical and sound elements of the game are above average as well.

Tennis 2K2   Sega   3
Tennis 2K2 takes what was arguably the best Tennis game ever made and makes it better. There are even more professional tennis phenoms to play as, like the Williams sisters. Tennis 2K2's World Tour mode is completely engrossing, and the new

underspin shot adds even more control and depth to the game. Multiplayer is, as was in the original, a blast. If you haven't played Virtua Tennis or Tennis 2K2 yet, you must!

Test Drive 6   Infogrames   1
Do not buy this game. With as many amazing racers on the Dreamcast as there are, it's sad that a game like this was even released. Test Drive 6 is horrible -- choppy graphics, boring gameplay, and horrid controls make it a title to avoid at all costs.

Test Drive Le Mans   Infogrames   4
Nice tracks, tons of amazingly fast cars, realistic sound effects, and unrelenting speed make anybody who played Test Drive 6 wonder what Infogrames did with that one and why it wasn't as amazing as Test Drive Le Mans. This is one of the better games on the Dreamcast. Check it out.

Test Drive V-Rally   Infogrames   4
There is a huge difference in quality between the other two Dreamcast Test Drive titles. Fortunately, Test Drive V-Rally is on the end of the spectrum with Test Drive Le Mans, although it is a different style of racer. With twenty-six cars, eighty-six tracks, tight controls, and more, V-Rally is arguably as good, if not better than Sega's own Sega Rally 2.

Time Stalkers   Sega   2
Time Stalkers is a rather unique RPG, but was short and lacked what draws many gamers to the genre -- a compelling story. As stated, though, the game does have a rather unique feature. As the game's main character, players can capture enemies and use them in battle. Random, rather boring dungeons (and the loss of all experience upon leaving them) also bring this game down from the likes of Grandia II.

TNN Hardcore Heat   ASC   3
TNN Hardcore Heat has so much going for it. It's just too bad that poor controls keep it from being as enjoyable as it should have been. The single player mode especially could have been amazing, but without control of your vehicle, it's just too frustrating.

Tokyo Xtreme Racer   Crave   1
There are so many solid Dreamcast racing games! Tokyo Xtreme Racer may not be the best, but it is without a doubt a great game. Although there are some control issues and the single (yet massive) track can become somewhat of a bore, this game is still addictive, and the multiplayer mode is worth a try as well.

Tokyo Xtreme Racer 2   Crave   7
Tokyo Xtreme Racer 2 continues with an improved version of the immersive quest mode of the original. So, to put it simply, if you loved the concept behind Tokyo Xtreme Racer, you'll probably love the sequel, because there is even more to do.

Tomb Raider: Chronicles   Eidos   3
While this game is a little bit more fun than The Last Revelation, it's not *that* much better. The Tomb Raider series should have gone the way of the Dodo long ago, and Chronicles is a testament to that. It's all the same old thing.

Tomb Raider: The Last Revelation
                    Eidos   1
It is really amazing that Eidos still proudly touts the Tomb Raider flag. With games like this, I don't understand how they can manage to do it financially, either. As is the case with Tomb Raider: Chronicles, there is absolutely nothing new here. I suppose if you've never played a Tomb Raider game before that this may be remotely amusing, but for most of us, this has been old for years now.

Tony Hawk's Pro Skater   Crave   1
If you haven't played one of the incarnations of Tony Hawk's Pro Skater yet, you've probably been living in a cave somewhere, and it is truly amazing that you got your hands on this book. Great graphics, addictive gameplay, and lots to do and unlock make Tony Hawk's Pro Skater a great game for Dreamcast owners. Even real skateboarding was never this much fun.

Tony Hawk's Pro Skater 2   Activision   3
This game is ridiculous. Ridiculously amazing. It sports an incredible professional mode, an amazing sixty pre-made skate parks for free-skating and two player modes, a create-a-skater option, and a park editor. The graphics and sound are even improved upon the original. Yes, you read all of that correctly. Yes, you need this game.

Toy Commander   Sega   3
Toy Commander takes some of the ideas of controlling a small toy, like in a game like Re-Volt and improves upon it. The environments in this game are amazing, and they really allow gamers to feel very small -- as if they were a toy. Toy Commander's challenging and varied missions keep it interesting for quite a while. Recommended

Toy Story 2   Activision   5

Trickstyle   Acclaim   1
Continuing the trend of extreme sports in a whole new way, Trickstyle ends up being a surprisingly enjoyable experience. The graphics are simply amazing, and the combination of racing and stunts on futuristic hoverboards in equally futuristic settings make Trickstyle a rather unique game.

Typing of the Dead, The   Sega   4
This is one of the coolest, most unique games you'll find on the Dreamcast. While it is essentially House of the Dead 2 as a typing sim, it is the best damn typing sim around! With full typing tutorials included, this game is an absolute blast, and for most, a much better choice than Mario Teaches Typing.

Tee Off

Test Drive 6

Tine Stalkers   Tomb Raider: The Last Revelation

335

Toy Story 2

The Typing of the Dead

Ultimate Fighting Championship

Vanishing Point

Ultimate Fighting Championship
Crave   3

Fighting games like this do not come along very often. Ultimate Fighting Championship is what many consider to be the most realistic fighting game of all time. Obviously, this is something not seen very often, with super flashy, combo-driven fighters dominating store shelves everywhere. Amazing graphics and great gameplay make this one Hell of a game.

Unreal Tournament   Infogrames   3

Unreal Tournament was a smash hit when it came to PC's everywhere, and for good reason. While the Dreamcast port falls just a tad short of the PC original, it is certainly one of the best 3D deathmatch games available for Sega's little box. With modes including deathmatch, capture the flag, and team variations of each, the single-player mode last for quite a while. And if that doesn't quench your thirst for blood, there is always the great multiplayer mode, on or offline.

Urban Chaos   Eidos   6

Urban Chaos is another Dreamcast game that could have been so much better than it was and is. The concept is similar to that of Grand Theft Auto, but is centered around upholding the law by any and all means possible, rather than breaking it. However, poor controls and framerates, problems commonly found in bad Dreamcast games, abound in Urban Chaos.

Vanishing Point   Acclaim   5

At first, Vanishing Point seems to be another Dreamcast racer that looks pretty but has horrible controls. Fortunately, after access to a few new cars is gained, the game gets a lot better. Nice graphics and a variety of vehicles not commonly seen in racing games give Vanishing Point that new car smell for quite a while. Among other Dreamcast racers, it isn't the best, but it holds its own.

Vigilante 8: 2nd Offense   Activision   5

Although it doesn't do much of anything original, Vigilante 8: 2nd Offensive is still a ton of car-bashing fun. There aren't many things as cool as futuristic vehicles with futuristic weapons being controlled by interesting characters, all set in the 1970's. Is it Twisted Metal? No. Is it just as fun? Definitely.

Virtua Athlete 2000   Agetec   3

Games completely centered around button mashing should be a thing of the past. Sure, the graphics of Virtua Athlete 2000 are decent, but with mindless, boring gameplay like this, who cares?

Virtua Fighter 3tb   Sega   5

Virtua Fighter 3tb should have received *much* more credit than it did or probably ever will. Namco's little fighter completely over-

shadowed this game for most, and that is unfortunate, because Virtua Fighter 3tb has incredible depth for a fighting game. The graphics don't have the flare and the moves don't have the simplicity of Soul Calibur, but Virtua Fighter 3tb is still an amazing game. Check this one out if you haven't already.

Virtua Striker 2   Sega   4

Stick with Striker Pro 2000. Sega's own Virtua Striker 2 is an average soccer game at best. It's a good thing that this game's graphics are above average, because it's easy to get the feeling of watching the game play itself rather than actually feeling a part of the game.

Virtua Tennis   Sega   1

As with Tennis 2K2, if you haven't played this game yet, you should. Amazing gameplay, graphics, sound, and an almost ridiculously long single player mode make this game a real hit. Tennis fans and non-tennis fans alike will have a great time with Virtua Tennis.

Virtual-On: Oratorio Tangram
Activision   6

Mech games can be really amazing, and although it does have some considerable faults, Virtual-On: Oratorio Tangram is a surprisingly deep, long-lasting one. The main problem the game has is the control scheme: without the almost completely necessary twin sticks, everything seems kind of whacked. Otherwise, this game is another arcade-perfect translation of the Dreamcast. Wahoo!

Wacky Races   Infogrames   5

Wacky Races is probably the best kart racing game on the Dreamcast. Just a few of this game's perks include: tons of tracks, cool new characters to unlock, and solid gameplay. Definitely give this one a whirl if you're a fan of games like Mario Kart and Diddy Kong Racing. Don't expect the same level of quintessence, but do expect an all-around good game.

Web Browser   Sega   1

Web Browser 2.0   Sega   1

Wextrix+   Xicat   2

Wetrix was a surprisingly new concept a few years back when it was released on the N64. Although not quite as new as before, Wetrix+ still makes a big splash. As with any puzzle game, the gameplay is what makes this game a blast that will last. Pretty graphical effects and a nice two-player mode are just two of the added bonuses.

Who Wants to Beat Up a Millionaire
Berkeley   4

On what console did the Street Fighter series make it's home debut?

Wild Metal　　　　　　Rockstar　　　2
Is there a story in this game? Well, yes. I just wish I had it presented to me before I started playing. Wild Metal is an action game with lots of explosions, cool tanks, and creatively designed levels. While the story isn't incredibly important in the game, a little more development of it would have been nice.

World Series Baseball 2K1　Sega　　　1
Maybe Sega shouldn't develop their own sports games anymore. Visual Concepts does a lot better of a job. World Series Baseball 2K1 is a gorgeous game, but is, without a doubt, the red-headed stepchild of the Sega Sports 2K series. The AI is horrendous and the lack of manual fielding (yes, the lack of manual fielding) is completely unforgivable. Just try to

World Series Baseball 2K2　Sega　　　3
Thank goodness! Visual Concepts takes the reigns of another Sega Sports series and saves the day. World Series Baseball 2K2 is an incredible improvement over the original. Manual fielding is now an option, batting and pitching mechanics have been tweaked, and even the amazing graphics of WSB 2K1 are improved.

Worms Armageddon　　　Hasbro　　　3
Ah, bliss. Worms Armageddon is the perfect combination of easy gameplay and complete insanity in what is one of the best multiplayer puzzle games on the Dreamcast. Single player is enjoyable, but playing Worms Armageddon with a friend is a lot more entertaining.

Worms World Party　　　Titus　　　5
Worms World Party brings more classic Worms mayhem to the Dreamcast! The simple gameplay and craziness of previous Worms games are intact, and with even more multiplayer gaming (including the option of going online), World Party is a game that puzzle fans shouldn't miss.

WWF Attitude　　　　　Acclaim　　　2
Wrestling games certainly aren't for everybody. For the most part, it seems that gamers either love them or hate them. WWF Attitude is sure to please wrestling fans with a nice wrestler creation mode, tons of pre-created wrestlers, nice animations, and solid gameplay. However, as stated previously, this game isn't for everybody.

WWF Royal Rumble　　　THQ　　　3

Xploder DC　　　　　　Blaze　　　6
Xploder DC is similar to Interact's GameShark line of cheating devices. It includes over 2,000 codes for over 140 different Dreamcast titles, and has the option of entering unencrypted codes.

Xtreme Sports　　　　Infogrames　　4
Xtreme Sports was somewhat of a surprise. The graphics are truly breathtaking, and although some of the game's many events are kind of ugly (like hang-gliding), the game is actually pretty enjoyable. I expected this game to be another below average "Xtreme" sports game that tried to be a snowboarding, off-road racing, and all-in-one package that falls short in all areas. Thankfully, that isn't the case at all. It's not incredible, but the all-around balance of multiple sports events in the same game is nice. In some ways similar to Pen Pen Tricelon.

Zombie Revenge　　　　Sega　　　2

HARDWARE

Sega Dreamcast　　　　Sega　　　2

Sports Dreamcast　　　Sega　　　5
This console is black and was released in limited quantities in the U.S.

Standard Controller　　Sega　　　1
One of the best controller designs to date, the analog stick is one of the most accurate analog sticks ever made, second only to the N64's controller.

Standard Keyboard　　　Sega　　　4
A necessity for those wanting to write email and visit message boards with their Dreamcast, this keyboard is well built and is adequate for the job.

Standard Light Gun　　MadCatz　　3

Standard Mouse　　　　Sega　　　4
This tool is very useful for internet use and is pretty much standard when compared to PC mice.

Broadband Adapter　　　Sega　　　7
The best way to utilize the DC's internet functions, this allows for an Ethernet connection to be made and works surprisingly well, if you can find one.

Fishing Controller　　　Sega　　　2
This fun controller gives all the fishing games on the DC much more enjoyable and you will often find yourself getting very involved when using this controller.

VMU　　　　　　　　　Sega　　　1
Designed to not only hold information for game saves, but also to be used as a game on its own with the use of its own screen, this "visual memory unit" was a refreshing touch of innovation for the gaming community.

Wacky Races

World Series Baseball 2K2

Worms World Party

WWF Attitude

NEC's TurboCD, in the form of Fighting Street.

SNK Neo-Geo AES

By: Vincent Yang and Andy Slaven

In March of 1990, SNK introduced a high-end console: The Neo-Geo AES (Advanced Entertainment System). The system was far more powerful than any other system of the time (NES and TurboGrafx), and the specs are still impressive today with 430K VRAM, 64K SRAM, and 56 megabits of DRAM. Even the Playstation and other, more modern systems can't match the 2D power of the Neo-Geo.

When the system was introduced in Japan, it was intended for rental at local video stores. SNK thought the system and its games would be too expensive for average gamers. However, gamers proved SNK wrong by buying the system and games, at which point the rental idea was scrapped. SNK introduced Neo-Geo to the US shortly after its Japanese release, but these prices were unheard of in the U.S. The Gold system (which came with 2 large controllers and one game of your choice) sold for $700 and each game was priced at $200.

Sales in the U.S. were very slow, and this prompted SNK to change its strategy. The MVS (Multi Video System) was created in order to boost revenues. The MVS is basically a standard Neo-Geo AES system placed inside an arcade cabinet, but the port size for the cartridges were changed to negate compatibility. The engineered incompatibility prevented MVS owners from purchasing and using the cheaper AES carts for use in their arcade machine. An interesting feature about the MVS/AES compatibility is the fact that since the ONLY difference is the size of the slot in which the cartridge is inserted, memory cards made for the AES system could be taken to an arcade and used on the MVS machines that allowed it.

In 1993, SNK introduced Samurai Shodown (which was misspelled on the released game as well). This game brought a lot of attention to the Neo-Geo and boosted sales for the year. However, the excitement died down, and most games made after 1994 were done so in very small quantities, resulting in extreme rarities in some cases. The rarest games were made in 1996 when there were no guaranteed preorders.

Due to the high returns received from fighting games in the arcade, and the extremely easy conversion from MVS to AES format, the overwhelming majority of Neo-Geo games are fighting games. This does offer a lot of replay value, and obviously Neo-Geo fans couldn't get enough of fighting games, so SNK continued to focus on this genre. In the early days of the Neo-Geo (1990-1991) there was a larger variety of games. While some wish that this trend of diversity would have continued, it simply did not happen. While some very popular non-fighting games were released later in the lifecycle of the Neo-Geo (namely Metal Slug), it was the seemingly endless supply of fighting games, such as King of Fighters (KoF), that has prolonged the life of the Neo-Geo so greatly.

In October 2001 SNK declared bankruptcy, and the era of Neo-Geo seemed to be over. However, the former owner, Mr. Kawasaki, personally bought the rights to the 16-bit Neo-Geo

More than 90% of all video game buyers (consoles) are over the age of 18.

coinops and home system. The new company is called "SNK Neo-Geo." Games are to be developed by Brezzasoft and Eolith, while the MVS games will be distributed by Sun Amusement. With this new support, the Neo-Geo may yet last another 10 years.

The Neo-Geo is not just a video game system, it's a cult, a religion. It is also about passion and dedication toward traditional 2D animation and game play. The system has kept the interest of its fans longer than any system and has gamers paying the big bucks for its games.

Key factors to the Neo-Geo's cult status are:

1) Quality

Both the system and the games are of superior quality. The system comes with well-built arcade sticks and a very sleek design. All of the games are packaged in large cases with much attention given to the insert art. But the main draw of the system is its software. With most of the games being above average, only a few can actually be considered "bad." Most titles are fun to play, even if they are not the most graphically advanced. Even the older titles hold the interest of many Neo-Geo gamers.

2) Arcade Perfect

This is the first system that allowed the customer to actually play the exact same game that was in the arcade. It may be true that the system's specs may seem outdated, but it feels awesome when you get the carbon copy at home. It really is like bringing the arcade back home with you.

3) Longevity

Launched March 1990, the system still has a strong following, and games are still scheduled for release. It is true that they are few and far between these days, and some might argue that the Game Boy and PC-Engine (TurboGrafx 16) come close to having lasted longer, but both of the aforementioned systems have gone through a number of upgrades. The Neo Geo, however, has remained essentially unchanged since its release. And the game will work perfectly on the system bought in 1990. Incredible!

4) 2D Animation

No other company pays attention to the detail and quality of cartoon animation like SNK. Unlike most systems that see substandard titles being produced toward the end of product cycle, the Neo-Geo's games keep getting bigger and better. King of Fighters 2001 is weighed at 892 megs, the largest Neo-Geo game ever. This, compared with 30 meg titles introduced in early 90's, is staggering.

5) Universal Compatibility:

There are absolutely no territorial lockouts. All Japanese games will play on U.S. systems, and visa versa. Due to the fact that all games, regardless of their country of origin, are identical, the language used within the game is determined by the version of the system used. An American system can play a Japanese cart in English, or a Japanese system can play an American game in Japanese. Only a few systems, such as the LaserActive, offer this type of unrestricted compatibility.

| Baseball Stars Professional | Crossed Swords | Fatal Fury | Fatal Fury Special |

3 Count Bout SNK 4 $40
The only wrestling game for the Neo-Geo, this wrestling game is difficult to master and hardly shows off the system's muscle.

Aero Fighters 2 Video System 6 $75
One of the best shooters for Neo-Geo, there are 8 different types of planes to choose from and 20 stages. The level of difficulty is on par with Tiger Heli and Raiden.

Aggressors of Dark Kombat ADK 7 $60
This is one of the stranger fighting games for the Neo-Geo, but worth a look.

Andro Dunos Visco 8 $50
This is the first game made by Visco. The creatures and themes are very similar to those found in R-Type.

Alpha Mission 2 SNK 5 $40

Art of Fighting SNK 3 $20
Many consider the difficulty on this arcade favorite to be unrealistically high. With a very limited number of players and opponents, this game doesn't offer much replay value.

Art of Fighting 2 SNK 3 $35
This is a large improvement over the first Art of Fighting. The characters are huge and moves are easy to pull off, but difficulty is maintained.

Art of Fighting 3 SNK 8 $250
This installment is considered to be the best of the series, and often ranks among the top fighting games on the system.

Bang Dead NGF 10 $350

Baseball Stars Professional SNK 5 $25
This is a very simple take on the sport of baseball. With no real teams or statistics to worry about, this game is all about getting a quick baseball fix. Many players complain that the computer cheats however.

Baseball Stars 2 SNK 5 $60

Blues Journey ADK 4 $40
This is a simple platform game that many equate to Super Mario Brothers, but it rarely is thought of as highly.

Burning Fight SNK 5 $25
Played in similar fashion to Final Fight, this game simply doesn't do justice to the system or side scrolling fighters.

Crossed Swords ADK 4 $35

About as close as you're going to get to an RPG on the Neo-Geo. This is a quasi-first-person game with limited attacks and limited monsters.

Cyber-lip SNK 6 $50
Konami was almost upset at the creation of this Contra clone. Almost. It is such a bad game that Contra looks and plays amazingly in comparison.

Diggerman NGF 10 $125

Double Dragon Technos 8 $250
This is a head to head fighting game based on the Double Dragon characters.

Eightman Pallas 6 $75
You play the character of a robot with a malfunction. As a result, you travel through the streets fighting anything that gets in your way. Instead of a normal punch, your character pushes an energy wave a short distance in front of his hand. While this game has a near cult status, it's not very entertaining after the first level.

Fatal Fury SNK 4 $25
An early fighting game for the Neo-Geo, the control seems to be adequate, but not up to par with the obviously more advanced fighting games released years later.

Fatal Fury 2 SNK 2 $25
This sequel offers small improvements to the original. Characters seem to be a bit sharper and control seems to have been improved. And with this game being more common than the first, it is the obvious choice of the two.

Fatal Fury 3 SNK 3 $70
What many consider to be the best in the series, yet more improvements all around make this a fun game to play, and compared to other games on the system, it is considered a bargain at $70.

Fatal Fury Special SNK 2 $50
Fatal Fury Special is actually the combination of all the characters from Fatal Fury and Fatal Fury 2, not just a sequel. Fighting mechanics and graphics are on the same level as Fatal Fury 2.

Football Frenzy SNK 4 $25
A lack of any realism makes this football game suitable for only quick games. Not much depth is associated with sports games on the Neo-Geo, and this is no exception.

Garou: Mark of the Wolves SNK 6 $400

It is estimated that only 1% of all video games in Malaysia are original...99% are pirate copies.

Galaxy Fight Sunsoft 5 $65
This is Sunsoft's first game for the Neo-Geo, and it is very diffi-cult. This fighter is a favorite of many however due to the fact that the playing field is infinite in that there are no boundaries.

Ghost Pilots SNK 7 $40
SNK's answer to the popular Capcom game 1942, it may be prettier, but the control seems to be a bit off.

Karnovs Revenge Data East 5 $40
So close to the composition of Street Fighter II, this game prompted legal action from Capcom. While some characters closely resemble those found in SFII, this title can still stand on its own merits.

King of Fighters 94 SNK 3 $75
The first in a long line of fighting games, the first installment was a very popular arcade game in certain parts of the country.

King of Fighters 95 SNK 3 $100
With improvements over the previous title, this series seems to improve with each installment. And while fighting can seem to be a repetitious genre, each title in this series is worth owning.

King of Fighters 96 SNK 3 $150

King of Fighters 97 SNK 3 $125

King of Fighters 98 SNK 3 $130
While not much more can be said for the longest running series of fighting games on the Neo-Geo, the artwork on this title is among the favorites of many Neo-Geo collectors. Oddly enough, it features no one fighting on the cover as you can see in the photo below.

King of Fighters 99 SNK 4 $150

King of Fighters 2000 SNK 7 $300

King of Fighters 2001 Eolim/SNK 6 $300
The latest installment and perhaps the best yet, this title is sure to please any fan of the Neo-Geo. Characters and control are top notch, and it appears that after a decade of improvements, this title has reached 2D fighting game perfection.

King of the Monsters SNK 4 $25
Many consider this installment better than its sequel. You can choose from more characters and the movements, while still difficult, are often easier to pull off.

King of the Monsters 2 SNK 5 $30
A mediocre sequel to a mediocre game. Difficulty is still high, but environments, characters and sound are average at best.

And the controls, while useable, are very difficult to master. Special moves seem almost impossible to perform at times.

Last Blade, The SNK 5 $175
Definitely a fighting game worth playing, it is by far one of the best games for the series. And while its sequel is better, for the price you just can't find a better fighting game.

Last Blade 2, The SNK 7 $350
Considered by many to be the best fighting game on the Neo-Geo, this game is sure to amaze anyone not familiar with the amount of detail that SNK puts into its games.

Last Resort SNK 6 $90

League Bowling SNK 6 $45
This game is good for getting your "bowling fix", but doesn't offer much in the way of realism.

Magician Lord ADK 4 $30
One of the best platformers for any system, this early release is relatively easy to come by and is a nice break from all the fight-ing games on the system.

Metal Slug Nazca 9 $1100
This is perhaps the most sought after game for the Neo-Geo. With only a few hundred copies known to exist, solid game play, and beautiful graphics and sound, this game is a perfect exam-ple of a game that is both scarce AND fun. That combination causes for a hefty price tag though, with this cart often fetching insane prices on Ebay.

Metal Slug 2 SNK 7 $400
With two additional characters to choose from and increased number of vehicles (including a camel), this installment is con-sidered by many to be superior to the original. However, like the first game in the series, slow-down is often encountered when too many moving items are on screen at once.

Metal Slug 3 SNK 6 $175
More stages, more vehicles, more enemies, more routes and more action mean that this game is amazing. It is considered by most to be the best in the series.

Metal Slug X SNK 7 $325
With only a few differences, this game is pretty much identical to Metal Slug 2. A few of the enemies have been shifted around, and some of the glitches from part 2 have been corrected, but not much else is different. Of note however is the fact that now your character can "over eat" rations and become fat on all stages, not just the 4th stage as was the case in Metal Slug 2.

Mutation Nation SNK 6 $30

The King of Fighters '98   The Last Blade 2   Metal Slug X   Neo Turf Masters

Matthew Broderick was sent Galaga and Galaxian arcade machines for a period of two months to practice with for the movie "War Games".

Samurai Shodown

Samurai Shodown II

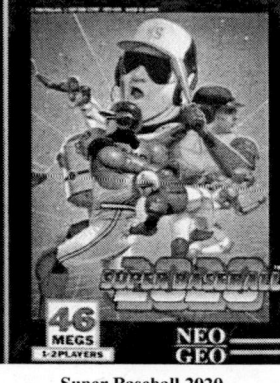

Super Baseball 2020

The Super Spy

Nam 75   SNK   6 $30
Similar in control and style to "Operation Wolf", this shooter utilizes a side scrolling technique while you maintain the first person perspective. Unfortunately, no light gun controller is available for the Neo-Geo, so a joystick must suffice.

Neo Turf Masters   Nazca   9 $750
Perhaps even rarer than Metal Slug, this game demands a high price not only for its scarcity, but also for its addictive play. A golf game of surprising depth (when compared to other sports games on this system), if you are able to find one, it is definitely worth picking up.

Ninja Combat   ADK   4 $25
A laughable sidescrolling game for a great system, this release shows off none of the system's real power.

Ninja Commando   ADK   7 $90

Ninja Masters   ADK   8 $525

Real Bout: Fatal Fury   SNK   4 $200

Real Bout: Fatal Fury Special
         SNK   5 $200
A continuation of the series, control and graphics are still impressive, while certainly not on the same level as "Last Blade 2" or "King of Fighters 2001".

Real Bout: Fatal Fury 2   SNK   5 $220
There is no doubt that this is an amazing game, and preferred by many players over any other in the series.

Riding Hero   SNK   4 $25
Even with arcade and career modes, this game isn't very much fun and the graphics aren't much to brag about.

Robo Army   SNK   5 $30

Samurai Shodown   SNK   2 $30
Perhaps the closest SNK came to dethroning Street Fighter 2 as the top fighting game in the arcades, this game (and subsequent sequels) allows players to use weapons and features the blood (Japanese consoles only) that was lacking from Street Fighter 2.

Samurai Shodown 2   SNK   2 $45
This sequel was just as popular on the home system as it was in the arcade. This game was the reason many people bought the Neo-Geo to begin with, and even after years of advancement, this is the title in the series that most remember.

Samurai Shodown 3   SNK   3 $120
While living up to the second installment of this series would be tough regardless, SS3 disappointed many fans. Many complained that the game seemed "rushed into production". And while it certainly lacks the unwavering support of SS2, it is still a fun game with precision control and beautiful graphics.

Samurai Shodown 4   SNK   6 $240
While the most expensive title in this series, it is definitely a top notch fighting game. Graphics, control and sound are used very well together and this game really shows off the capabilities of the system. Again, not necessarily the favorite of fans of the series, but still a very high quality game that most fighting game fans should enjoy.

Savage Reign   SNK   4 $90

Sengoku   SNK   5 $40
An interesting side scrolling fighting game with good environments and good character design. And certainly worth the money if you are able to find one.

Sengoku 2   SNK   6 $110

Sengoku 3   Noise Factory   6 $200
Somewhat of a surprise, this August 2001 release is the last game released under SNK. With improvements in several areas including graphics and sound, this game should keep fighting fans happy for a while, even if the number of selectable characters is a bit low.

Soccer Brawl   SNK   5 $25

Spin Master   Data East   6 $45
This is the only game I can think of off-hand that uses a yo-yo as a weapon.

Stakes Winner   Saurus   7 $250
A surprisingly unique game for the Neo-Geo, horse racing doesn't seem to be a typical release for any system, much less one that is known specifically for its fighting games. Fun, and often addictive when played with friends, it is far from capable of competing with so many other great games for the system.

Street Hoop   Data East   7 $75
Much like the rest of the sports games on this system, this game's lack of depth takes away from an otherwise fun basketball arcade game.

Super Baseball 2020   Pallas   4 $25
This is baseball, without real teams or players, controlled in an obviously arcade style. It is enjoyable to play from time to time

You need 9 pieces of candy to "phone home" in the Atari 2600 game "E.T."

and is one of the more affordable games for the system.

Super Sidekicks	SNK	4	$25
Super Sidekicks 2	SNK	3	$40
Super Sidekicks 3	SNK	6	$75
Super Spy	SNK	4	$30

Why is it that ninjas in both video games and American Ninja movies have machine guns? Isn't that against whatever rules there are in the "ninja handbook"? It kinda takes the "stealth" out of stealth assassin. This is a fun game with regrettably repetitive action. Unlimited continues make it a game of patience instead of a game of skill.

Thrash Ralley	ADK	4	$30
Top Hunter	SNK	6	$45
Top Player's Golf	SNK	4	$25

A surprisingly addictive golf game for the system. Unfortunately control doesn't handle very well, and distances and power don't seem to be handled very well. But fun nonetheless.

Viewpoint	American Sammy	7	$00

Released in 1993, this is a ¾-view isometric shooter and is one of the most sought after titles for the system. Six stages and good techno music make this game a lot of fun.

Voltage Fighter Gowcaizer	Technos	8	$280

A fighting game innovation allows you to utilize your defeated opponent's special move in place of your own.

Windjammers	Data East	6	$110

That's right, it's a Frisbee game! Played in the style of Pong, in an overhead and left to right fashion, this game is entertaining for a while, but it quickly becomes repetitive

World Heroes	ADK	3	$10

The first in the series, it may not be the best, but it is still a very good fighting game. And while not on the same level as many other fighting games for the Neo-Geo, it was far ahead of its time when it was released.

World Heroes 2	ADK	3	$30
World Heroes 2 Jet	ADK	4	$40

Battling your opponents in groups of three, you must defeat two of them to progress. This is a bit different than normal since you only face each opponent once, regardless of the outcome.

World Heroes Perfect	ADK	6	$190
ZuPaPa	NGF	9	$250

Of important note is the fact that many MVS (arcade only) carts have been converted into AES (home) compatible carts. These games, for the purpose of this book, will be classified as "home-brew" games since they were created by individuals without permission from SNK. This being the case, this book will not cover them until a later volume.

HARDWARE

Neo-Geo AES	SNK	5	$250
Old Style Joystick	SNK	4	$40
New Style Joystick	SNK	4	$40
Memory Card	SNK	6	$25
Hotel Unit	SNK?	10	$2500

This machine is certainly an oddity. Only two are confirmed to exist, and a third is rumored, but the quality would hint at the fact that more must have been made. Apparently made by SNK themselves, each known version actually has a different arrangement of audio and video outputs. The machine is set to take coins and uses MVS (arcade) carts, but it is designed to be connected to a standard TV. Also, it takes standard AES (home) system joysticks.

This system has been nicknamed the "hotel system" by those trying to make a guess at its purpose, but nobody is sure as to its origins or purpose. Since it plays unmodified MVS carts on a standard TV and uses AES joysticks, this system is somewhat of a "missing link" in the Neo Geo world.

Neo-Geo "Hotel Unit"

   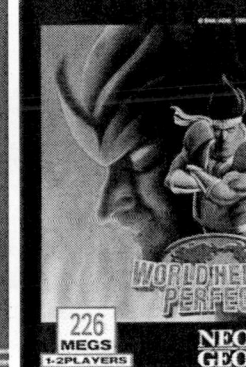

Voltage Fighter Gowcaizer   **View Point**   **Windjammers**   **World Heroes Perfect**

Mario has been featured in five separate cartoons throughout his career.

SNK Neo-Geo CD

By: Vincent Yang and Andy Slaven

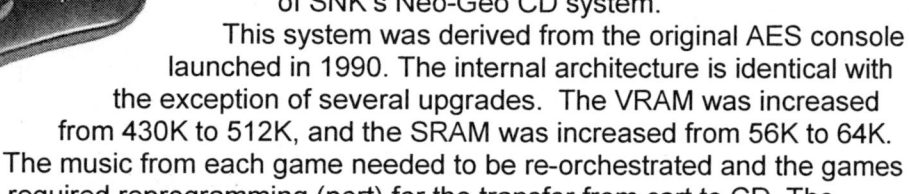

Since the early 1990's, the Neo-Geo Advanced Entertainment System (AES) has been a popular, yet very expensive platform, limited to the wealthiest and most dedicated gamers interested in arcade style games. In 1994, SNK of Japan came up with the concept of a CD based system that was intended to attract a more mainstream audience. This is what prompted the creation of SNK's Neo-Geo CD system.

This system was derived from the original AES console launched in 1990. The internal architecture is identical with the exception of several upgrades. The VRAM was increased from 430K to 512K, and the SRAM was increased from 56K to 64K. The music from each game needed to be re-orchestrated and the games also required reprogramming (port) for the transfer from cart to CD. The games, due to the less expensive CD format when compared to cartridge, ranged in price from $39 to $59. This, compared to the $200-$269 for cartridge based games on the AES, was a much preferable option for Neo-Geo fans on a budget.

The Neo-Geo CD, as different in appearance as it was to the cartridge AES system, uses the same AV cable as its cartridge counterpart. Also, the Neo-Geo CD (top loading version) came standard with two control pads instead of the single joystick that came bundled with the cartridge system. This wasn't a popular feature among hardcore fighting game fans however. The CD unit also has the added feature of allowing gamers to save data without the use of memory cards due to its internal RAM. The most appealing feature that the Neo-Geo CD has in common with its cartridge counterpart is the fact that all games are universally compatible. When using a U.S. system, games are displayed in English, and Japanese consoles display games in Japanese. Just like the cartridge system, certain games are censored for content (such as Samurai Shodown's blood and King of Fighter's "jiggling boobies"). While some titles are censored in such fashion, codes are available so that they can be played in their intended form, without censorship.

SNK of Japan launched the Neo-Geo CD system on Sept 9, 1994, at which time a limited edition front-loading model (only 30,000 were made) and 19 titles were made available. This first model came standard with one joystick that is identifiable by its rounded shape as opposed to the very blocky cartridge system standard joystick. They sold out completely on the launch date. With an original price of around $500, it is evident that gamers were interested in saving money on buying the games and not the system itself. Encouraged by the public's response, SNK later made a less expensive (and more common) top loading model of the Neo-Geo CD system. This top loading model is what is considered to be the standard Neo-Geo CD model, and is what was later released in the U.S. A third model was eventually released, only in Japan, in 1995 and was dubbed the Neo-Geo CDZ. It came equipped with a faster CD-ROM drive (about 1.5x) and offers quicker loading times for many games due to this fact.

It wasn't until the end of 1996 that U.S. gamers would get the opportunity to buy the Neo-

What is Super Mario Bros. for the NES most often credited for?

Geo top loading system (the only Neo-Geo CD version released in the U.S.) By this time, U.S. gamers were already won over by the Nintendo 64 and the Sony Playstation. What caused SNK to delay the U.S. launch until this time is still unknown, but considering its meager sales numbers, it is apparent that it was a costly mistake. Since U.S. and European titles are identical in every way (packaging included), surplus consoles were easily transferred to the U.K. and other European countries for resale.

During 1994 and 1995, SNK had high hopes that the Neo-Geo CD system would attract casual gamers to the Neo-Geo platform. Despite the reduced price of games, most fans of SNK titles remained loyal to the more expensive cartridge system. Due to reduced frame rates, and often unbearable load times associated with the CD system, games just weren't as enjoyable as they were in cartridge form. There are four major reasons as to why the Neo-Geo CD system was a relative failure worldwide:

1) SNK's Neo-Geo cart system is arcade-perfect in every way. It is a true carbon copy of exactly what gamers played in the arcade. The CD system, however, had re-orchestrated music and changed (often enhanced) graphics. Most gamers felt that this defeated the purpose of owning a Neo-Geo system and refused to support it.

2) The need to reprogram games into a CD format proved to take more time than the direct port from Arcade carts (MVS) to home carts (AES). This conversion took important resources away from SNK's arcade development, making the necessary sales numbers for CD based games higher than actual sales figures.

3) Emulation on PC's allowed gamers to get the same quality as CD-based titles, but without the cost. Hardcore Neo-Geo fans would either play the arcade or cartridge systems, but would not pay for a CD system that could so perfectly be emulated on a PC.

4) Competition from other CD-based consoles was enormous at the time. The Sega Saturn and Sony Playstation were powerhouses that SNK had not counted on. Also, the load times on these consoles aren't nearly as long as those on the Neo-Geo CD, and a larger variety of games drew in a larger installed consumer base than SNK could create with a library consisting mainly of fighting games.

It should be noted that games made in 1994-1995 have the highest rate of conversion from cartridge to CD format, while many excellent games made in 1996 were never ported to the CD system. However, despite its flaws, the Neo-Geo CD system did have several games developed for it that were never released in cartridge form. In addition to these games, some very hard-to-find, and prohibitively priced games can be found for much cheaper on the Neo-Geo CD (Neo Turfmasters immediately comes to mind). As a point of interest, all games published after July 21st, 1995 are encrypted to prevent piracy.

While the Neo-Geo CD never made much of an impact in the U.S. market, it is a formidable platform regardless of its makers' marketing mistakes. A very well-built and stylish design, coupled with a library of high quality games, makes this system a favorite among many gamers who aren't willing to pay the often outrageous prices that Neo-Geo AES carts demand. Certainly not without its flaws, this system is still a wonderful addition to any collector's or serious arcade fan's collection.

***Note: Since Neo-Geo CD games contain the same content as their cartridge counterparts, the description of most games will be very brief, but any important differences will be noted. For more information on the content or story of each game, please refer to the Neo-Geo AES section.

The creation of the side scrolling platformer.

Aggressors of Dark Kombat   Burning Fight   Double Dragon   Fatal Fury

3 Count Bout SNK 4 $18
This is a wrestling game with controls that are difficult to master

Aero Fighters 2 Video Systems/SNK 4 $35
This shooter sports eight different planes and 20 stages.

Aero Fighters 3 Video Systems/SNK 5 $45
This title was not released on the U.S. cartridge system and features improvements over Aero Fighters 2, though it is still not equal to the MVS release.

Aggressors of Dark Kombat
ADK/SNK 4 $15
An unusual fighting game for the Neo-Geo with virtually no storyline.

Alpha Mission 2 SNK 6 $50
Improvements over the first Alpha Mission are included in this sequel, including the ability to modify your ship. This is a 2-D space shooter viewed from the top.

Art of Fighting SNK 3 $15
An early fighter for the AES makes a decent appearance on the Neo-Geo CD, but is still very difficult.

Art of Fighting 2 SNK 3 $15
The improvements apparent in the AES cartridge version aren't as evident on the CD system due to frame rate degradation.

Art of Fighting 3 SNK 6 $25
An impressive port of the cartridge version, it is still very difficult to find even on the Neo-Geo CD.

Baseball Stars Professional SNK 4 $20
Basic arcade control is used to play this very simple baseball game. The CD version plays just as well as the cartridge version.

Baseball Stars 2 SNK 5 $30
Small improvements over the first version make the action even faster in this baseball game. A shift from actual rankings and statistics to that of a pure win/lose game made this very popular in Japanese arcades, and is very enjoyable on the Neo-Geo CD.

Blues Journey ADK/SNK 4 $20
A platform game with solid yet simple game play. This title is too easy for many serious gamers.

Burning Fight SNK 8 $60
For some reasons, Burning Fight on NGCD is the second rarest Neo-Geo CD title available. This title often demands twice the going rate of the cartridge version.

Bust-A-Move Taito/SNK 6 $30
This very addictive game was not released on cartridge for the AES, but instead came straight to the CD. Due to the fact that levels load completely at the beginning, there is no loading time during actual game play.

Crossed Swords ADK/SNK 4 $20
This is an over-the-shoulder view adventure game in which you wield a magical sword in order to defeat a limited variety of monsters.

Cyberlip SNK 7 $60
A side scrolling shoot-em-up that is very similar to Contra or Metal Slug, this title doesn't have the variety necessary to hold the attention of most gamers.

Double Dragon Technos/SNK 4 $35
This is a fighting game based on the characters from the Double Dragon series with unique level designs and quality graphics.

Fatal Fury SNK 4 $15
An early entry to the Neo-Geo library, this conversion does a good job of reproducing the relatively simple graphical style of the cartridge version.

Fatal Fury 2 SNK 2 $15
Small improvements over the first installment make this more common and less expensive title an obvious option to the first.

Fatal Fury 3 SNK 2 $20
Frame rate reduction is evident in this version, but not to the point of making it unplayable. On the contrary, unless you are familiar with the cartridge or arcade versions, it is almost unnoticeable.

Fatal Fury Special SNK 2 $20
This game features all the characters from both Fatal Fury and Fatal Fury 2.

Football Frenzy SNK 5 $20
A football game dedicated to quick action instead of statistics, this game is enjoyable for those who wish to get in a quick game.

Galaxy Fight Sunsoft/SNK 4 $25
This fighting game has no horizontal boundaries making "corning" a tactic of the past.

Ghost Pilots SNK 5 $20
Control is still a little difficult on the CD version of this overhead plain shooter.

When polled, what system did most RPG fans say was the greatest RPG system of all time?

Karnov's Revenge Data East/SNK 4 $20
A game very similar in appearance and style to Capcom's Street Fighter 2, this title doesn't play nearly as well.

King of Fighters 94 SNK 2 $20

King of Fighters 95 SNK 2 $25

King of Fighters 96 SNK 2 $30

King of Fighters 97 SNK 3 $40

King of Fighters 98 SNK 3 $35

King of Fighters 99 SNK 6 $40
Despite been the largest Neo-Geo game ported to CD, the loading time on this game is surprisingly short, with some clever loading arrangement and loss of animation during character selection. Many wonder why it took so long for SNK to figure out the tricks on programming for Neo-Geo CD.

King of Monsters 2 SNK 4 $25
With the first title obviously missing from the CD library, the less enjoyable second installment makes a decent appearance on the Neo-Geo CD.

Last Blade SNK 5 $35
Long load times and reduced frames of animation are evident in this otherwise incredible fighter.

Last Blade 2 SNK 6 $50
With incredibly long loading times after even the simplest of actions, it is not uncommon for load time to take nearly 4 minutes from selecting a fighter to actually being able to play the game. What should have been a great game is ruined by the amount of time it takes to actually play it.

Last Resort SNK 4 $40
This is a side scrolling shooter that is virtually identical to the cartridge version.

League Bowling SNK 6 $30
A fun title that supports multi-player, controls are among the simplest for any game on the system.

Metal Slug Nazca/SNK 7 $95
It would make sense that such a sought after cartridge game would have been made more readily available, but instead it is still extremely difficult to find on the Neo-Geo CD.

Metal Slug 2 SNK 6 $65
More common than the first installment, this very fun title still won't be easy to find for this system. Additional characters and vehicles make this installment a favorite of many.

Mutation Nation SNK 4 $15
This is a side scrolling action game that plays nearly as well as its cartridge counterpart.

Nam 75 SNK 5 $15
This shooter, similar to "Operation Wolf" in the arcade, uses side scrolling movement and first person perspective.

Neo Turfmasters Nazca/SNK 7 $30
One of the best games on Neo-Geo CD, yet very hard to find. To play this game, turn off the announcement option else it loads about 5 times during the course of each hole simply for quick announcements. This is another example of a game that should have been made in larger quantities for the Neo-Geo CD.

Ninja Combat ADK/SNK 4 $10
A side scrolling game for the Neo-Geo CD that doesn't fare any better than its cartridge counterpart.

Ninja Commando ADK/SNK 5 $15
A vertically scrolling action game, this game is enjoyed by many and hated by others. If you're a fan of the genre then it should be enjoyable.

Ninja Masters ADK/SNK 8 $55
A fighting game with a rather standard selection of characters featuring unique moves and control.

Puzzled SNK 6 $20
This puzzle game was not available on the AES cartridge system, but instead came directly to the Neo-Geo CD.

Rally Chase ADK/SNK 6 $20
This title is actually the same as Thrash Rally on Neo-Geo.

Real Bout: Fatal Fury SNK 5 $35
Another fighting game ported to the Neo-Geo CD, this title does have noticeable reduction in animation rates but is still enjoyable.

Real Bout: Fatal Fury Special SNK 3 $20
Solid control is maintained after the conversion of this popular cartridge game to the CD system. It still lacks the finished look that makes some of the newer games for the Neo-Geo look so impressive.

Real Bout 2: The Newcomer SNK 4 $25
Another installment in this popular series, control is still a strong point.

Last Resort   Mutation Nation   Puzzled   Real Bout: Fatal Fury Special

Samurai Shodown III	Samurai Shodown IV: Amakusa's Revenge	Sengoku II	The Super Spy

Riding Hero   SNK   4 $15
This motorcycle racing game wasn't impressive it its original version, and it still fails to impress. I suppose that makes the porting process a success, but the game is still a failure.

Robo Army   SNK   4 $15
This side scrolling adventure game has some impressive graphics and animations, but the control can take a while to get used to. Interestingly though, it seems easier to play when using the non-joystick control pad instead of the standard controller.

Samurai Shodown   SNK   2 $20
Of course a classic like this would make an appearance on the Neo-Geo CD. Certainly the best CD version available, 3DO and other systems that tried to mimic this game produced an experience that is laughable when compared to this one.

Samurai Shodown 2   SNK   2 $25
Still an amazing game, even on the Neo-Geo CD, the cartridge version can be found for about the same price.

Samurai Shodown 3   SNK   3 $20
While not the favorite of fans of the series, this installment was ported over to the Neo-Geo CD in the hope of attracting more fighting game fans to the system.

Samurai Shodown 4: Amakusa's Revenge
          SNK   4 $30
This installment does lose some of its luster when ported to the Neo-Geo CD, but is still a very playable game that can be found for much less than the expensive cartridge version.

Savage Reign   SNK   4 $25
This weapons based fighting game is less than impressive regardless of the system it is played on. With uninspired music, graphics and control that seems unresponsive, this common title isn't much fun on the Neo-Geo CD or the cartridge system.

Sengoku   SNK   5 $20
One of the very early titles that were ported to CD yet very rare, though not as tough to find as Burning Fight.

Sengoku 2   SNK   5 $25
With graphical improvements over the first installment, this title is an enjoyable side-scroller that uses interesting characters and abilities.

Soccer Brawl   SNK   4 $15
The ability to beat the hell out of an opposing soccer team makes the sport of soccer actually sound interesting. And being able to shoot your opponents almost makes it seem like a sport even Americans would enjoy. But the control of this game, coupled with awful graphics and sound, make it a disappointing

sports title that should be avoided.

Stakes Winner G   Saurus/SNK   6 $25
This game is the same as Stakes Winner on the cartridge system. The reason for renaming it is unknown.

Street Hoop   Data East/SNK   6 $30
A basic basketball game that is enjoyable for those wanting to play without worrying about real teams or players.

Super Baseball 2020   SNK   4 $30
This is a futuristic baseball game presented in a simple format focused on game play.

Super Sidekicks   SNK   4 $30
Strategy takes a back seat in this action oriented soccer game originally designed for the arcades.

Super Spy, The   SNK   5 $15
Side scrolling movement and first person perspective are brought together for this repetitive game.

Top Hunter   SNK   5 $35
This side scrolling combat game offers adequate graphics and control, but doesn't stand out as being exceptional.

Top Players Golf   SNK   4 $25
Basic golfing makes its way to the CD system intact. Still fun to play, load times weren't too bad on this version.

Viewpoint   American Sammy/SNK   5 $35
Much easier to find on the CD system than on the cartridge system, and certainly less expensive, the music is a favorite among many players in this shooter.

Voltage Fighter Gowcaizer
          Techno/SNK   5 $45
Take your opponents' skills as you defeat them in this fighting game.

Windjammers   Data East/SNK   5 $30
Frisbee at its worst. What could have been an entertaining game quickly gets old and becomes nothing more than a colorful Pong game without the nostalgia.

World Heroes   ADK/SNK   3 $15

World Heroes 2   ADK/SNK   2 $15
Fourteen characters are playable in this enjoyable fighting game. And while noticeably better in cartridge format, it is still enjoyable on the Neo-Geo CD.

The first prototype of the Atari 2600 was orange.

World Heroes 2 Jet   ADK/SNK   2 $20

World Heroes Perfect   ADK/SNK   6 $30
Sixteen characters are playable in this installment of the series and offers a "hero gauge" that, when charged, allows for more spectacular moves to be pulled off and for your character to take less damage.

HARDWARE

Neo-Geo CD System   SNK   6 $200

Arcade Stick (Rounded)   SNK   4 $40

Centipede was designed by a woman.

Quasi Systems

Quasi systems are interactive game systems that do not fit the typical criteria associated with a video game console. Typically it is the general lack of true interaction that causes a system to be classified in this section, but unusual media types (such as VHS tapes), or a library that consists mainly of edutainment (such as the Sega Pico).

Action Max
By: Andy Slaven

Worlds of Wonder is probably best remembered (if indeed it is remembered for anything) for the creation of the 1986 sensation known as Laser Tag. Wearing a vest with a sensor and armed with a low level laser pistol (including a very cool scope), you would chase your opponents around the neighborhood shooting your laser at them while they secretly placed their hand over the sensor to make hits impossible. Cutting edge technology at the time, Laser Tag was the number one Christmas present of the year.

Trying to build on this success, Worlds of Wonder released the Action Max in 1987. The Action Max is a console that hooks into a standard VCR and allows for limited interaction with special VHS tapes played on a standard television. The only controller for this system is a light gun that is plugged into the console, and then aimed at the screen to fire at various targets that would appear via the VHS tape's output. Various game tapes were released and offered different scenarios, from shooting fighter jets to blasting ghosts. In order to determine your progress, a "hit" is shown by a red light that uses a suction cup to affix itself to the TV screen. When a successful shot is fired, this light will flash.

Unfortunately for those who purchased this machine, it quickly became apparent that simply playing through the short game tapes a few times was enough practice to anticipate every onscreen enemy. The games were, quite simply, too easy once the patterns were learned. Unlike cartridge based games of the time, there was no variation from game to game, and this is, in large part, one of the reasons for this system's failure. Unlike the Captain Power "Power Jet XT-7," there were no programs airing on TV that would support this system, and unlike the InteractiveVision, the target audience was old enough to quickly grow bored with repetitive play.

With only a handful of game tapes ever released for the Action Max, it is often forgotten when reviewing the history of video games. Due to the lack of a truly interactive media library, this system has found itself as a quasi system. With a sleek gray and white exterior, and knobs on the system reminiscent of the dedicated Pong systems of the 1970's, this system is still a favorite among fans of the obscure and those in need of a dose of nostalgia.

.38 Ambush Alley	Worlds of Wonder	Sonic Fury	Worlds of Wonder
Blue Thunder	Worlds of Wonder		
Hydrosub: 2021	Worlds of Wonder	**HARDWARE**	
Rescue of Pops Ghostly, The	Worlds of Wonder	Action Max System	Worlds of Wonder

The first cartridge based handheld system was named the Microvision.

Atari XEGS

By: Andy Slaven

When most gamers think of Atari, they immediately think of the Atari VCS (2600). Atari wasn't completely dedicated to console gaming, they also had a wide variety of personal computers. Labeled numerically, these computers were given such creative names as the Atari 800XL or the Atari 65 XE. The "XE" line was actually the replacement for the "XL" line and was intended to boost the computer division's sales. Numerous versions of these computers were released, each with a slight improvement over the last. This constant "stepping" effect meant that nothing released by the division would really shock the world. Instead, many consumers were disheartened by the fact that after buying a computer, Atari was almost certain to quickly release a slightly better model.

Trying to bridge the gap between computers and gaming systems, Atari used the 65XE technology to design a game system. In 1987 Atari released the XEGS (XE Game System), the result of combining an Atari computer with the look and feel of a game machine. Most computers during this time were inseparable from their keyboard interface, but the XEGS was completely detached from its keyboard and could be used with only an Atari joystick. Designed to work as either a computer or a game system, when the keyboard was attached to the system, it would act as a computer by starting in Atari BASIC. If the keyboard was detached the system would start using the built in game Missile Command.

The Atari XEGS originally sold for $199 and included a joystick, light gun and several game cartridges. The joystick looks identical to those used on the VCS with the notable exception that it is gray, to match the color of the XEGS. The light gun is a nice addition, though there aren't many games that support it. Many gamers complain about the accuracy of the light gun due to its peculiar horizontal tracking system. The gun will often be accurate on the vertical plane, but will shoot off the mark horizontally. The keyboard attachment could be bought separately by those wanting to expand the system's capabilities. While the system itself was packaged as a game system, and indeed supports over 200 games available on cartridge, it is still a computer at heart.

Due to the fact that the titles available for this system weren't specifically designed to operate solely on the XEGS, but were in fact intended for several different computer systems, this machine is classified as quasi-system. This isn't to say that cross-compatibility is a bad thing, but without a unique library of games, the XEGS is just a repackaged computer that is designed to make playing computer games easier. For reference however, the XEGS will play almost any game made for the Atari XE or XL line of computers.

Innovation in gaming is usually a very good thing, and consumers are normally appreciative of such efforts, but the XEGS was a failure. Poor consumer support for the system (probably due to the fact that computer buyers didn't want a game machine, and video game buyers didn't want a computer) and meager media coverage quickly saw the Atari XEGS to its grave. Supporting some classic arcade favorites as well as games that were previously only available on disk, the XEGS (or the 65XE for that matter) would make a nice addition for any gamer looking for something different.

Atari is actually a Japanese word that means "prepare to be attacked."

LJN Video Art

By: Andy Slaven

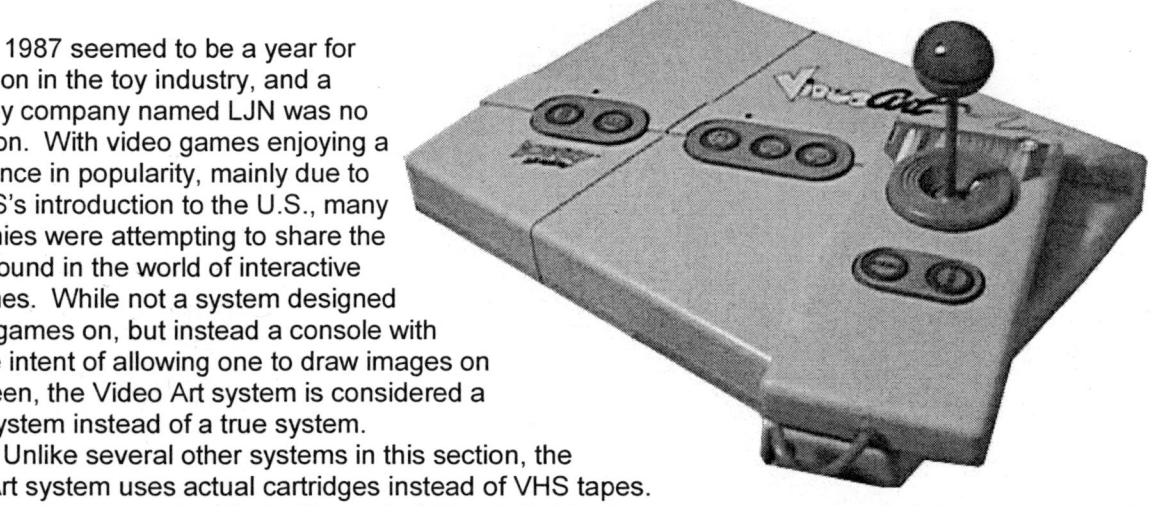

1987 seemed to be a year for innovation in the toy industry, and a small toy company named LJN was no exception. With video games enjoying a resurgence in popularity, mainly due to the NES's introduction to the U.S., many companies were attempting to share the profits found in the world of interactive TV games. While not a system designed to play games on, but instead a console with the sole intent of allowing one to draw images on the screen, the Video Art system is considered a quasi-system instead of a true system.

Unlike several other systems in this section, the Video Art system uses actual cartridges instead of VHS tapes. Each cartridge comes bundled with a colorful book that includes stories, uncolored pictures, poetry and the like. A small selection of cartridges was released shortly after the system itself, though the "Video Art Activity Cartridge" was included with each system sold. It is interesting that three very large franchises (Disney, Looney Tunes, and Marvel) would allow their characters to be used on such a small system, however the actual interaction with these characters is basically limited to drawing over the top of them, or coloring their costumes.

Included with each system was one joystick style pad that was used as the primary interface, though buttons on the system itself could affect the onscreen image as well. The controller has an analog stick, which is not self centering, and two buttons that can be used to "lock" the drawing path into a horizontal or vertical motion to assure straight lines. At the top of each controller is a clear slide that can be moved left or right to select the color desired. This very simple design makes the Video Art system easy for young children to use. As an obvious sign of inexperience in the market, LJN designed the controller with a ten inch cord. Granted, the cord is similar to that of a phone cord, and does allow for stretching, but only to a total length of one meter.

LJN's Video Art system didn't grab the attention of very many people, and only offers very limited entertainment, but is a piece of video game history regardless. If the titles had offered more interaction with the characters and offered some sort of game element, this would have been a true system. Instead, without the element of a "game," this system can't be considered a video game console. This system saw a shelf life of around one year before it was put on clearance and all remaining stock sold.

A Trip to the Zoo	LJN	My Favorite Doll	LJN
Disney Coloring Book	LJN	On the Move	LJN
Disney Story Book	LJN	Video Art Activity Cartridge	LJN
Looney Tunes	LJN		
Marvel Super-Heroes	LJN		
My Dream Day	LJN		

HARDWARE

Video Art System	LJN

In the game Donkey Kong, "Mario" is actually a character called "Jumpman."

Mattel Captain Power

By: Andy Slaven

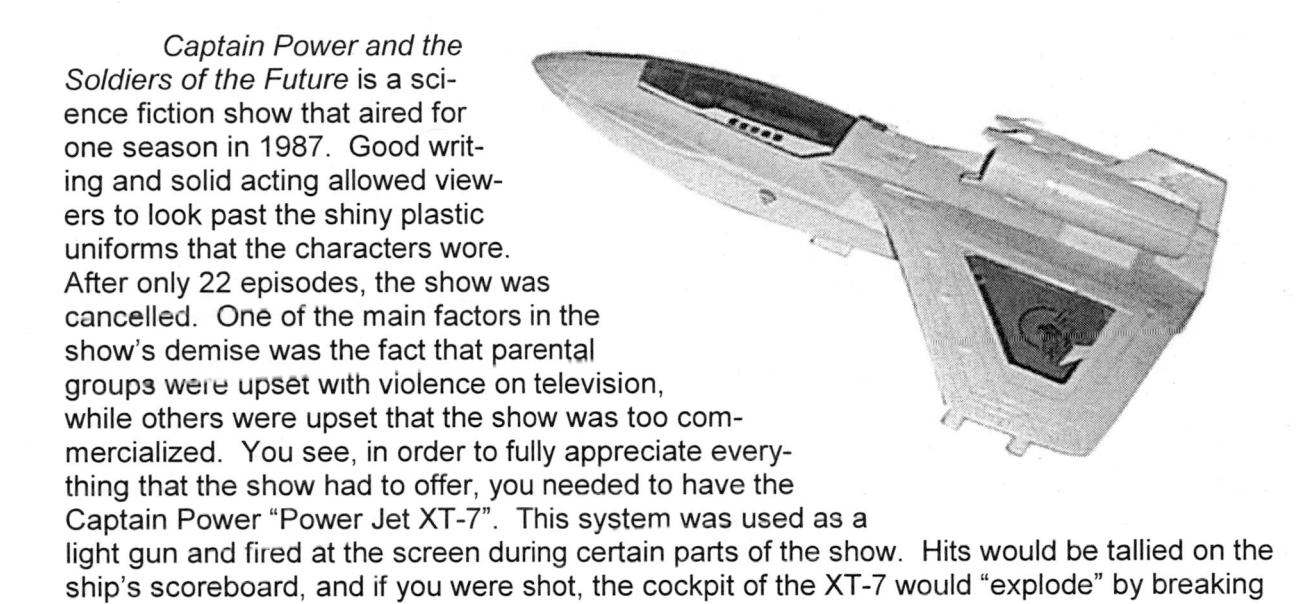

Captain Power and the Soldiers of the Future is a science fiction show that aired for one season in 1987. Good writing and solid acting allowed viewers to look past the shiny plastic uniforms that the characters wore. After only 22 episodes, the show was cancelled. One of the main factors in the show's demise was the fact that parental groups were upset with violence on television, while others were upset that the show was too commercialized. You see, in order to fully appreciate everything that the show had to offer, you needed to have the Captain Power "Power Jet XT-7". This system was used as a light gun and fired at the screen during certain parts of the show. Hits would be tallied on the ship's scoreboard, and if you were shot, the cockpit of the XT-7 would "explode" by breaking into several pieces as it was ejected from the ship.

While this type of interaction was very fun for children, and evidence actually shows that sales of the Power Jet XT-7 were brisk, Mattel decided that there was too much controversy surrounding the show and its toy tie-ins and cancelled support for the show. In a stroke of irony, several parents' groups then complained that they had purchased the Power Jet XT-7 for their children, and now it was useless since the show was cancelled.

The "game" itself was actually part of the television show, and without the show being broadcast, the Power Jet XT-7 could only be used properly if the "Training Missions" had been bought on VHS (sold separately of course.) These three tapes were made available from Mattel so that the viewers of the show could practice before actually trying it out on an episode. The training tapes were made for three different skill levels and offered several missions in which one could practice firing at onscreen objects. This type of interaction, very similar to that of the Action Max by Worlds of Wonder, was all that kids were left with after the show was cancelled. Fortunately for fans however, Hi-Tops began to bring the episodes to VHS so that the Power Jet XT-7 could still be used. Six tapes were produced by Hi-Tops, several with multiple episodes. This brings the total game library for the Captain Power XT-7 to 9 VHS tapes. Though they aren't listed, fan groups have recently produced CD compilations that contain all 22 episodes from the first season.

While the Mattel Captain Power XT-7 will never reach the fame of the NES, or even that of the relatively obscure Action Max, its interactive capabilities with programming later made available on tape places it within the quasi-system realm. With an extremely loyal fan base, expect to see episodes of Captain Power playing again in the U.S. within a few years. Currently, the only country still airing episodes of Captain Power is Canada, on the Space Channel (Sundays 9 A.M. Est).

What inventory item was renamed for the GameBoy version of Metal Gear Solid?

QSI

A Fire in the Dark	Hi-Tops
Bio Dread Strike Mission: Skill Level 2	Mattel
Ferryman, The	Hi-Tops
Final Stand	Hi-Tops
Flame Street	Hi-Tops
Future Force Training: Skill Level 1	Mattel
Intruder, The	Hi-Tops
Raid on Vocania: Skill Level 3	Mattel
Shattered Past	Hi-Tops

HARDWARE

Power Jet XT-7	Mattel

EPISODES
(IN BROADCAST ORDER)

Shattered

Wardogs

The Abyss

Final Stand

Pariah

The Mirror in Darkness

A Fire in the Dark

The Room

The Ferryman

And Study War No More

The Intruder

The Rose of Yesterday

Flame Street

Gemeni and Counting

And Madness Shall Reign

Judgement

A Summoning of Thunder: Part One

A Summoning of Thunder: Part Two

The Eden Road

Freedom One

New Order: Part One—The Sky Shall Swallow Them

New Order: Part Two—The Land Shall Burn

Retribution: Part One

Retribution: Part Two

The Ferryman

Final Stand

Raid on Volcania

Shattered Past

NUON

By: Andy Slaven

NUON is not so much a game machine as it is a technology. Much like the 3DO technology that was licensed out to various companies for use in their respective consoles, so it was done with NUON. This technology was purchased and used in several different models of DVD players and allowed for games specifically designed for it to be played on any DVD player enhanced with NUON capabilities.

Using a 128-bit processor, the function of the NUON technology wasn't simply to play games and multimedia titles, but it also enhanced the performance of any DVD player that was equipped with it. DVD players that did not support the NUON technology were still capable of playing movie discs with NUON enhancements, but would not benefit from those enhancements, nor would it be able to play games designed for NUON.

A would-be failed marketing strategy was employed to separate NUON enhanced DVD players from video game consoles. Instead of the titles being referred to as games, they would instead be deemed "DVD-Interactive" and sold with other digital video media such as DVD's and CD's. Unfortunately for VM Labs, the creator of the NUON technology, this strategy didn't pay off. Consumers saw the feature as an uninteresting addition to DVD players, and video game consumers saw the technology as less-than-adequate to support their gaming needs.

Both Toshiba and Samsung offered NUON enhanced DVD players with varying success, but it was the dismal sales of the software that eventually ended the life of NUON. Each system had a remote similar to that of a TV remote, and gamepad remote controllers were also available as both pack-ins (depending on the DVD player model) and from third parties.

Some of the games stand out as being innovative themselves, such as Freefall 3050 AD. In this title, game play occurred as your character was, oddly enough, free falling through various levels in which the action would occur. Other titles however, such as Merlin Racing were built on existing genres that had already been proven. This particular title is very similar in style to Mario Kart, though the use of a game pad was almost necessitated by the complexity of game play.

NUON is yet another example of innovation in video games that the average consumer just wasn't willing to embrace. Similar in overall function to that of the LaserActive, with the ability to play both games and movies (with the obvious intent primarily on reaching a movie-going audience), it is not surprising that this technology met with a similar fate.

With limited sales of software, and the average NUON consumer simply looking for a nice DVD player, both the software and hardware are almost certainly going to be collectable in the years to come.

***Note: Listed within this section are games that have not yet been released, but were at one point scheduled for distribution. It is still unclear if any of these titles will make it to market, though it seems unlikely. VM Labs was forced into bankruptcy in 2001, and the technology sold off. While the future of NUON is unclear, future releases are very unlikely.

What system was so popular that an entire generation was unofficially named after it?

QSI

Ballistic	Infrogames
Freefall 3050 AD	DVD International
Iron Soldier 3	VM Labs
Merlin Racing	DVD International
Next Tetris, The	Toshiba
Space Invaders XL	VM Labs
Tempest 3000	DVD International

Unreleased Games

aMaze

Bust-A-Move 4

Breakout

Bugdom

Game of Life, The

Monopoly

Myst

Pitfall: The Mayan Adventure

RC de Go!

Riven

Shangahi: Mahjongg Essentials

Speedball 2100

Star Trek: Invasion

zCards

Iron Soldier 3

Merlin Racing

Space Invaders XL

The Next Tetris

The NES, causing some to derive the term "Nintendo Generation."

Sega Pico

By: Andy Slaven and Michael Collins

Most serious gamers have never heard of the Sega Pico and even fewer have ever owned one. The simple reason for this is that it was designed for children between 3 and 7 years and offers no games in the sense that most gamers would think of. Instead of focusing on any type of action or RPG elements, this system's main focus was edutainment.

Dubbed "The computer that thinks it's a toy", the Pico's design is similar to that of a laptop computer. Instead of a keyboard interface and LCD screen, the Pico had a stylus and touch sensitive pad, and the visuals were displayed on the TV to which it was connected. There is also a directional pad to be found on the system that can be used to control onscreen actions. The games are known as "storyware" and take the form of a small book that is placed into the system much like a normal cartridge would be. Once the book is opened, the "game" would begin. As pages are turned, onscreen visuals were changed in order to match those of the book. Interaction is minimal, but the software was intended to teach basic academic skills.

Coming from Sega, this type of system is very unusual. With a firm base in fighting and arcade style games, many wondered why this system was made at all. Some speculate that it was an attempt to test the video game marketability toward young children, and to possibly begin an attempt at taking some of Nintendo's firm grasp on that market. While the system does retain popularity among parents with young children, sales did not justify pursuing the edutainment genre any further.

Unfortunately for collectors that must have everything, Pico prices remain high due to its continuing viability as an early learning tool. Due to the fact that children between 3 and 7 aren't as demanding when it comes to digital entertainment, Pico systems can be seen selling online regularly for over $40, and games also demand a reasonable price.

Originally released at $139 in 1994 with software beginning at $40, the Pico saw relatively low sales. Sega eventually began a series of price cuts until all remaining stock was sold. With many popular characters, including Mickey Mouse and the Muppets, the system and its software also holds an interest for collectors of items other than video games.

Due to the fact that the Pico is overlooked by many video game collectors it should be relatively easy to find one at a reasonable price.

The RCA Studio II originally retailed for $150.

QSI

Magic Crayons

Mickey's Blast Into the Past

Tails and the Music Maker

A Year at Pooh's Corner

101 Dalmatians: Math Antics
Sega
This title was later re-released by Majesco.

Adventures in Letter Land with Jack and Jill
Sega

Berenstain Bear's - A School Day
Sega

Crayola Crayons: Create a World
Sega

Ecco Jr. & The Great Ocean Treasure Hunt
Sega
A seemingly odd choice of character for an educational title, Ecco Jr. is the most difficult of all Pico titles to find.

Great Counting Caper with the Three Blind Mice
Sega

Lion King: Adventures at Pride Rock
Sega
This title was later re-released by Majesco.

Magic Crayons   Sega

Magical School Bus   Sega

Mickey's Blast Into the Past
Sega

Muppets on the Go   Sega

Musical Zoo   Sega

Pepe's Puzzles   Sega

Pocahontas Riverbend Adventures
Sega

Richard Scarry's Huckle and Lowly's Busiest Day Ever
Sega
This title was later re-released by Majesco.

Sesame Street Alphabet Avenue
Sega
This title was later re-released by Majesco.

Smart Alex and Smart Alice: Curious Kids
Sega

Sonic the Hedgehog's Gameworld
Sega
This title is an obvious attempt at luring some of the older children in the Pico's targeted age range.

Tails and the Music Maker   Sega
While Tails never gained the same fame as his mentor Sonic, this title demonstrates what might have been a unique franchise marketing strategy: Introduce a less popular character to younger children so that when they're old enough to appreciate regular video games, it will be a much more equitable character to produce games for.

Year at Pooh's Corner, A   Sega
This title was later re-released by Majesco.

HARDWARE

Sega Pico   Sega

One modern gaming system has more computing power than all of NASA when it took over the space program.

View-Master InteractiveVision

By: Michael Collins

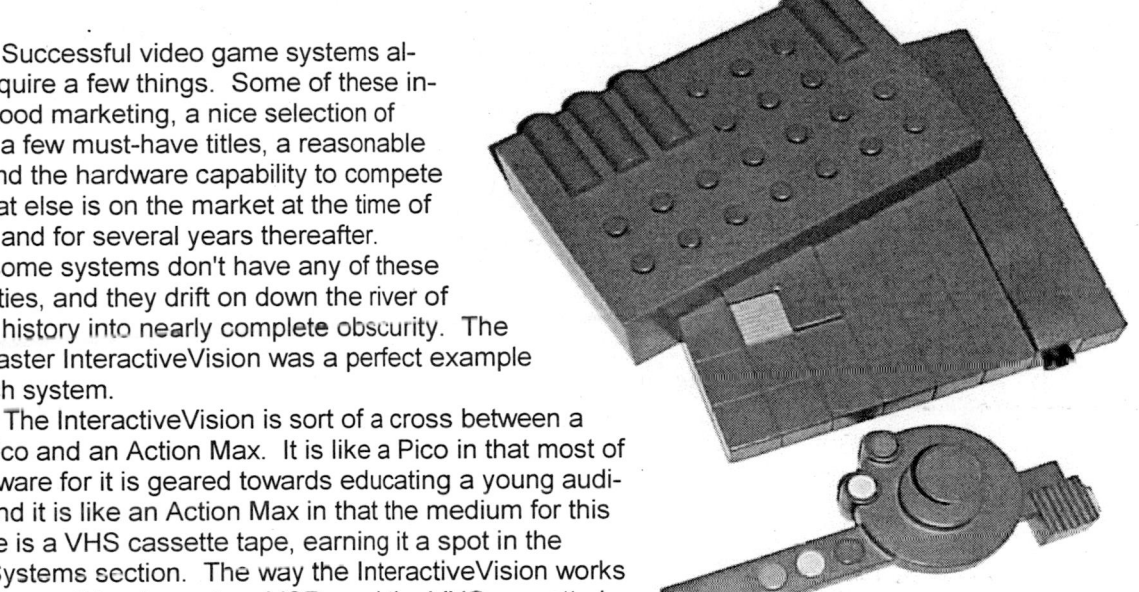

Successful video game systems always require a few things. Some of these include: good marketing, a nice selection of games, a few must-have titles, a reasonable price, and the hardware capability to compete with what else is on the market at the time of release and for several years thereafter. Sadly, some systems don't have any of these necessities, and they drift on down the river of gaming history into nearly complete obscurity. The View-Master InteractiveVision was a perfect example of a such system.

The InteractiveVision is sort of a cross between a Sega Pico and an Action Max. It is like a Pico in that most of the software for it is geared towards educating a young audience, and it is like an Action Max in that the medium for this software is a VHS cassette tape, earning it a spot in the Quasi Systems section. The way the InteractiveVision works is as follows: It hooks up to a VCR, and the VHS cassette is played in the player. The InteractiveVision loads a program off of the tape, which runs on a timer. Independent from this, the tape plays like any other. Computer graphics from the program the InteractiveVision is running are then overlaid on the video, and a game can be played. In a nutshell, that's how it works.

Two packages of the console itself were available (one with a pack-in of Disney's Cartoon Arcade and another with Sesame Street: Let's Learn to Play Together), and by the time View-Master's console was off store shelves, only seven "games" had been released. Both packages came with the system, cables for hookup, instructions, and one of the most uniquely shaped joysticks to have ever been made. The joystick itself looks a lot like a fishing controller, and surprisingly, isn't too uncomfortable. (However, it can be difficult to figure out which way it is supposed to be held.) Still, the joystick itself is too bulky, and some of the buttons are in awkward locations in relation to the control stick.

As stated earlier, only seven titles were actually released for the InteractiveVision. All of them were children's titles, and only one (Disney's Cartoon Arcade) can really be considered a game. There were two Muppets games, the single Disney game, and four Sesame Street titles. All of them are fairly difficult to find, but compared to the others, the pack-in games are more common.

When the InteractiveVision was released to the public, it was not well received. The original retail price of $130 wasn't an attractive price for a child's educational toy. The target audience was too narrow to allow the system to last very long, and even the would-be buyers didn't know that the InteractiveVision even existed due to poor marketing. Everything considered, the system is unique in concept and design, but will most likely only be desirable to diehard collectors.

Disney's Cartoon Arcade

Muppet Madness

Muppets' Studios Presents: You're the Director

Sesame Street: Let's Learn to Play Together

Sesame Street: Let's Play School

Sesame Street: Magic on Sesame Street

Sesame Street: Oscar's Letter Party

For multiplayer games on the 3DO, controllers must be linked together since the system only has one controller port.

WebTV Plus
By: Andy Slaven

WebTV is a common alternative to using a computer for internet access and became relatively popular in the mid 1990's. Due to its lower cost and readily available interface with a standard television, this device was seen as an innovation that allowed those less technically inclined consumers an affordable and easy option to utilize the internet. It is also commonly used by those who simply wish to keep their computers safe from internet based viruses. Regardless of the intent of the users, WebTV has become an easy access tool, and several companies have built various models over the past decade.

Phillips Magnavox, Mitsubishi, and Sony each have their own version of the newest installment in this hardware line, the WebTV Plus. In addition to simply being able to connect to the internet, this system allows for the use of specific online game programs. Due to the lack of any real interchangeable media, and the fact that the primary function of this unit is still internet access, the WebTV is listed as a quasi-system. The games listed below are readily available on the internet for free download, and new games are likely to appear as fans of this system continue to make them. The average WebTV Plus retails for around $200, though prices vary depending on brand and the possible inclusion of the keyboard. The standard unit comes with a controller similar to that of a TV remote, but composing email messages almost necessitates the use of a keyboard.

Alien: The Interactive Story	Javascript Aliens	Strickman Murder Mystery, The
Battleship	Mars or Bust	Tic-Tac-Toe
Castle Quest	Mastermind	Triumph
Chess	Mine Sweeper	Turbulence
Concentration	MISSED	Twilight Castle
Cyber Dungeon	Monarchy	Utopia
Coom	Murder Barney the Dinosaur	Victorian Crime Club, The
Dread	Plastic Surgeon to the Stars	Virtual Paintball
Earth: 2025	Pong	Web Kingom
Electric Lighthouse Hangman	Space Merchant	Whack-A-Nixon
Gold Runner	Stellar Crisis	Who is Jack the Ripper?
		You don't Know Jack

In Super Mario RPG, both Mario and Bowser are fighting on the same side!

Import Systems

This section is far from a complete listing of consoles released outside of the U.S., and in fact only contains those from Japan. From the numerous systems that were candidates for coverage within this section, those chosen were done so for their historical significance and overall appeal to the average gamer.

Bandai Playdia

By: Andy Slaven

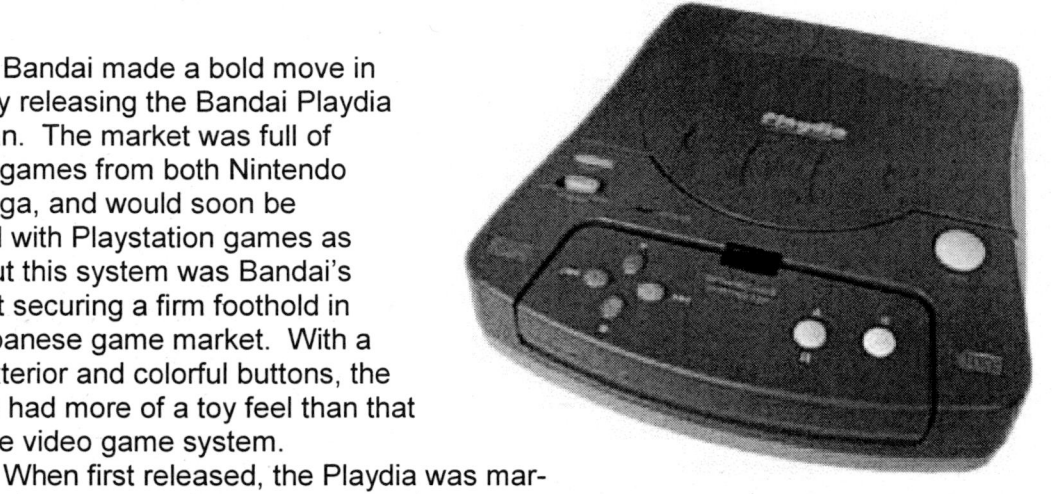

Bandai made a bold move in 1994 by releasing the Bandai Playdia in Japan. The market was full of quality games from both Nintendo and Sega, and would soon be flooded with Playstation games as well, but this system was Bandai's hope at securing a firm foothold in the Japanese game market. With a blue exterior and colorful buttons, the system had more of a toy feel than that of a true video game system.

When first released, the Playdia was marketed as a family oriented machine that could offer entertainment for everyone, from young children to adults. Early titles included games such as "Ultraman: Welcome to Alphabet" and were intended for educational purposes. This strategy never caught on however, and Bandai was forced to reevaluate its marketing techniques.

It is the later releases on this system that draw the attention of both gamers and collectors however. Gundam, Sailor Moon and two Dragon Ball Z games mad appearances on the Playdia and are all highly sought after. "Earth Side" and "Space Side" are the two variations of Dragon Ball Z on this system and are extremely collectable. They demand insane prices when they can be found, though they are average games at best.

Even the inclusion of these titles to the Playdia's library wasn't enough to satisfy consumers, so Bandai allowed the release various "Idol CD's" for the system. These "games" feature young Japanese girls in various states of undress. While this type of title is very common among those found on the FM Towns Marty, it seems odd that a console initially designed as a family oriented system would so quickly become host to second rate softcore pornography.

Since the Playdia was initially intended for the entire family (Japanese family that is), the controller is very small by American standards and can be difficult to use. The directional pad (on the left) is actually four separate buttons, each representing a direction. There are two action buttons in yellow and white, and the controller itself is wireless. Not a common feature, and certainly more expensive than a corded controller, this type of convenience was seen on the Phillips CD-I, but met with limited success due to poor design. The Playdia controller however, is comfortable for those with small hands. When not in use, the control pad can be returned to a small alcove built into the front of the system, and can function as typical component buttons like you would find on a DVD player, or in this case a VCD player.

The Playdia, while offering some nice features and a very unique design, will not hold much interest for serious gamers. Unless you are a diehard Dragon Ball Z or Sailor Moon fan, this system doesn't offer much in the way of "must have" titles.

What four types of games can the Genesis play when properly equipped with adaptors or add-on systems?

FM Towns Marty
By: Andy Slaven

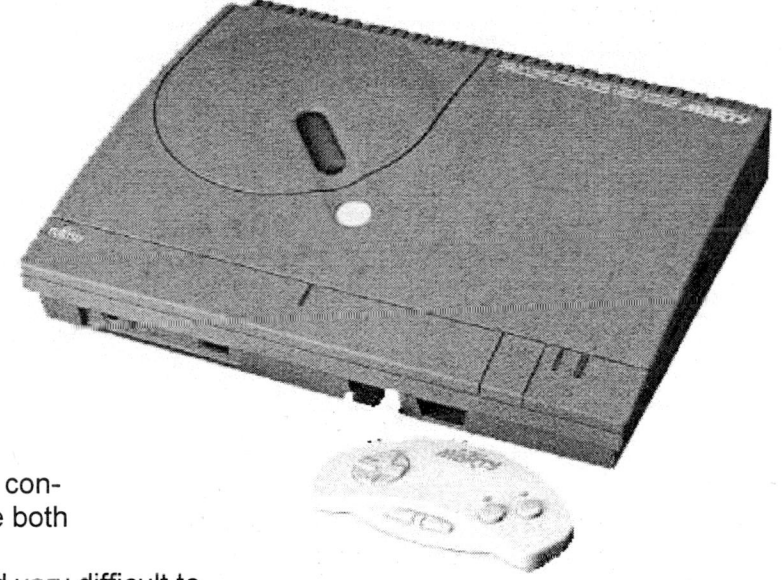

Originally released in 1991 with a 386 processor, the FM Towns Marty was later upgraded to a 486 (oh the speed!) This 32-bit system features both a CD drive, hidden under the flip top lid, and a 3.5" floppy drive accessible from the front. The controller, oddly enough, is white and does not match the gray exterior of the system itself. Though the system was only sold with one controller, there is a second controller port for multi-player games. In addition to the standard controller, a mouse and keyboard were both available for this system.

While relatively obscure and very difficult to find, you might be surprised at the number of games this system is capable of playing. In addition to the FM Towns Marty's unique library of games, it is also compatible with many of the games released on the moderately successful line of FM Towns computers. In 1991, most games were released for the PC on 3.5" floppy disks, and this is what the floppy drive is most commonly used for. The keyboard and mouse are essential while playing many of these games, and are a great asset when wanting to expand the capabilities of the system. As PC games were slowly moving over to the CD format, the FM Towns Marty could also accommodate many of these titles via the CD drive. While not compatible with all the games released on the Fujitsu line of computers, the library of available games is very impressive for such a little known system.

Known mainly for a library of adult anime (hentai) games, the FM Towns Marty also had several quality mainstream games released for it. The most notable is 3x3 Eyes, an action adventure game that was also released on the PSX, Saturn, Super Famicom, Turbo Duo and the FM Towns line of computers. One factor that really limited the number of games specifically designed for the system was the two button controller. While this didn't seem like much of a hindrance in 1991, it would later prove inadequate for more advanced games.

This systems obscurity and fleeting popularity makes it among the more difficult consoles to find, even with the aid of the internet. Systems without any games often cost in excess of $300, and games normally demand at least $50 apiece. The sleek design and large library of games makes this item popular among import gamers. While most won't admit it, the extremely large library of hentai games remains a large reason why this system is so desirable.

NEC PC-FX
By: Andy Slaven

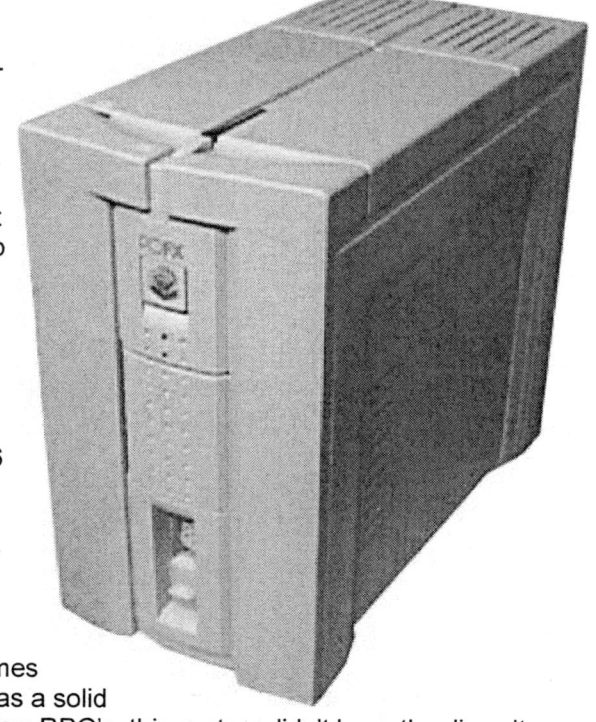

NEC's fifth major foray into the video game market manifested itself in the form of the PC-FX, released in Japan only on December 23rd, 1994. This 32-bit CD based system has the unique styling of a conventional PC, standing vertically instead of the traditional horizontal systems. But instead of opting for the traditional front loading CD tray, NEC designed the system with a flip top lid on top of the system, with control ports located near the bottom of the console and centered. This PC style casing allowed for easily installed hardware upgrades, though few were ever released. Among these expansions are the FX-BMP memory card and the PC-FXGA, a PC interface card allowing connection to the PC-9800. The controller for the PC-FX is relatively standard, with 6 primary buttons and both run and select buttons in the center. A mouse controller, the FX-MOU, was also made available and is supported by a few games on the system.

Quite simply, the PC-FX is a 2-D workhorse. It does have the ability to produce 3-D graphics, as has been demonstrated via prototype games, but no 3-D games were ever released for this system. Released instead was a solid library consisting of anime games, puzzle games and a few RPG's, this system didn't have the diversity necessary to compete with the Sony Playstation or the Sega Saturn. One game, Battle Heat, stands out in the library of games however. Very unique, even by today's standards, Battle Heat is an interactive anime fighting game. Pressing a button at a specific time will seamlessly switch to a different course of animation and perform the fighting move selected. While the game does take a little getting used to, and can become boring during an extremely long round, this title stands out as having exceptional graphics. While the control takes a while to get used to, and the sound is sparse during game play, the opening sequence of this game alone is proof of what the PC-FX is capable of. Also, a few of the PC-FX titles could be considered hentai, though not nearly as many as were available for the FM Towns Marty. While these games have extremely loyal followings in Japan, their fan base is much smaller in the U.K. and the U.S. Surprisingly, this system was slated for release in the U.S. either in late 1995 or 1996, depending on how NEC viewed the market. Unfortunately problems with Hudson Soft and apparent signs that the average consumer wasn't willing to purchase this machine led NEC to rethink its strategy, and instead leave it as a Japan-only system. The last game was released on August 24th, 1998, though it was rumored that several others would be released. While both NEC and Hudson Soft promised time and time again that they would continue to support the system, nothing ever materialized.

While certainly underrated by most consumers, the PC-FX lasted for nearly 4 years in Japan and harbors a strong fan base. More importantly, this system has become quite popular among import collectors. With a library of over 60 games, there is a wide variety of titles to be enjoyed. Unfortunately, the anime games, for the most part, require that you have a working knowledge of Japanese, so most American consumers are going to be limited to the puzzle games for the system.

The PC-FX may not have the most diverse library of games, and it may suffer from occasional control problems, but this machine is capable of some amazing things. Unfortunately NEC had experienced some dismal failures in the U.S. market, and it was unwilling to take that chance again. PC-FX consoles are becoming difficult to find in good condition, though they can normally be found online for around $200, with games ranging from $20-$80.

Who's face was reportedly visible in a certain rock formation in the Japanese version of Pilotwings 64?

NEC SuperGrafx

By: Andy Slaven

NEC, makers of the TurboGrafx-16, released this interesting system in Japan only in 1990. With a price of 39,800 Yen (around $400), it certainly wasn't an inexpensive entry into the video game console war. A 16-bit system at heart, the SuperGrafx was not only capable of playing games specifically designed for it, but also PC-Engine (Japanese TurboGrafx-16) as well. A switch on the side of the machine could be turned to "PC-Engine mode" or to "SuperGrafx mode" in order to allow the system to be configured properly for the game that was inserted. The controller is very similar in style to those used on both the PC-Engine and the Turbo Duo and still offers the standard two button configuration with a "run" button in the center.

Competing mainly against the Super Famicom (Japanese Super Nintendo) and the Megadrive (Japanese Genesis), the Supergrafx had two very tough competetors. It has even been theorized that NEC specifically created this system in an attempt to lure potential Sega and Nintendo consumers to the NEC console, regardless of the loss incurred by NEC. While the intent of this console was to continue the success of the wildly popular PC-Engine, it never reached a broad audience and quickly died off.

With a miniscule library of five games (costing as much as $110 when new), the only real redeeming quality of this machine is its reverse compatibility. When used in conjunction with the right system card and the CD attachment, this system is capable of playing every game intended for use on the PC-Engine, CD-ROM, Super CD-ROM and games designed for use with the Arcade Card.

Oddly enough, NEC shouldn't have been so worried about Nintendo and Sega, but instead with itself. The Turbo Duo, still popular in Japan, was drawing most of the SuperGrafx's potential customers. The ability to play the small library of games specifically designed for the SuperGrafx simply wasn't enough of an incentive to entice Duo owners to spend another $400, plus the price of games. Perhaps the biggest tragedy associated with this system is the fact that Strider was slated for release, but never was due to the system's failure.

Unpopular even in Japan, the SuperGrafx has gone almost completely unnoticed in the U.S. While an American release was rumored for a while, NEC's realization that there was no true market for this system quickly ended any hopes of that happening. Demanding a premium price on the internet, these systems are becoming increasingly difficult to find in good condition. The games, while not extremely rare, also demand high prices due to the very small community of collectors for this system.

1941: Counter Attack	Hudson Soft	Ghouls 'n Ghosts	NEC
Aldynes	Hudson Soft	Grand Zort	NEC
Battle Ace	Hudson Soft		

Jesus Christ's

Nintendo 64DD

By: Andy Slaven

The Nintendo 64DD is a brilliant concept that Nintendo didn't think the U.S. market was ready to embrace. This add-on to the Nintendo 64 is a storage device that uses custom magnetic 64MB disks. Loading faster than CD-ROMs and allowing for rewritable capabilities, this format really is a nice hybrid that overcomes several problems associated with both CD and cartridge formats. The primary purpose of this system was to allow for more storage of game data, but would also allow for updates and upgrades to existing games. In addition to allowing this new format to be played on the N64, the 4MB of RAM is used in tandem with that of the N64, bringing the total to 8MB RAM for the combined unit. This allows for more complex graphics and better sound quality, in addition to larger games.

With over 40 games promised for the system, only a handful were released in Japan, causing many Nintendo fans to be disappointed by their purchase. The Legend of Zelda: Ocarina of Time was originally slated as one of the 64DD releases, but was moved to cartridge format instead. But even after the game's release it was rumored that an expansion would be available on the 64DD. This situation raises the main interest that this system holds for consumers; upgrading an existing game to allow for more game play with improved graphics and sound. Sports titles would have benefited from updated rosters, adventure games would feature new levels, and RPG's would have expanded quests, all for the price of a 64DD disk, which would be far less expensive than a full cartridge. This prospect was the driving force behind many of the unit's sales, but instead those who adapted were disappointed with mediocre drawing programs (sold with an included mouse controller) and a few action games.

Nintendo had the ability to create a CD based add-on, but instead chose a proprietary format that only they would be able to produce. Much in the same way the N64 carts were produced, Nintendo held the exclusive rights to produce these disks, making a nice profit from each game sold. Nintendo refuted this theory by stating the 64DD's technology allowed for faster load times than CD's ever could and would not settle for anything less than instantaneous access. Regardless of the reasons why this format was chosen, Nintendo could not close the growing gap between their systems and Sony's Playstation.

While the Nintendo 64DD library is very limited, the system itself is very sleek and a trophy among import collectors. A steady stream of these units is available on the internet, but this unit will often cost in excess of $200 without any games. Games normally cost in excess of $50 apiece and most are difficult to play without an understanding of the Japanese language. What should have been a great leap for video games turned into a disappointment by Nintendo, though given the chance, it seems that this system would have sold relatively well in the U.S. Had more interesting titles been created for it (including the rumored Dragon Quest [Dragon Warrior in the U.S.]), this system might have had the support necessary to facilitate a U.S. launch.

Some Japanese schools will cancel a school day to coincide with the release of popular video games.

Vintage Advertisements

Some interesting advertisements were released for both the systems and games featured in this guide. A few were chosen because they were interesting, some because they are among the most memorable ever made, and still others because they have rarely been seen (such as the (a)world ad) We hope you enjoy them.

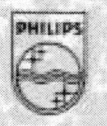

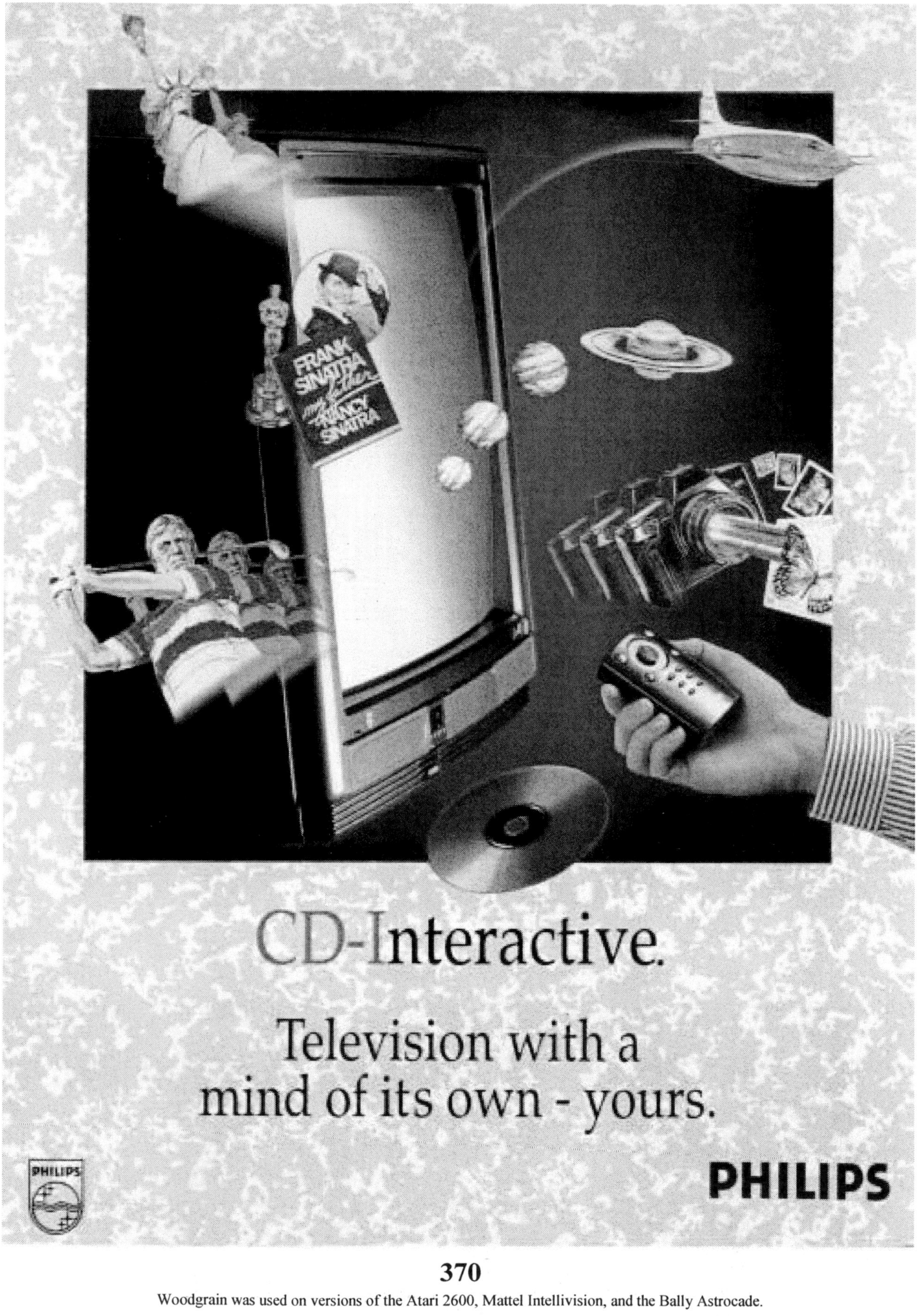
FRANK SINATRA
NANCY SINATRA
CD-Interactive.
Television with a
mind of its own - yours.
PHILIPS
PHILIPS

Woodgrain was used on versions of the Atari 2600, Mattel Intellivision, and the Bally Astrocade.

YOU WON'T RECOGNIZE THE FAMOUS COMPUTER IN THIS AD. OR THE VALUE.

You'll never know the amazing things this black box can do just by looking at it.
Not only does CDTV® play your audio CDs but it can bring words, music and pictures to life
on your television. CDTV simply connects to your TV and stereo and through its ingenious marriage
of computer, audio and video technologies lets you play with a new generation of interactive CDs.
CDTV is based on the Amiga® and if you buy the CDTV/P system before June 30th it
comes with AmigaDos®, a keyboard, floppy drive, mouse, Grolier's Electronic Encyclopedia™,
Lemmings™, Appetizer pack and a savings of up to $848.00.*

Just pick up a CDTV Multimedia Player and you'll have a full 1Mb Amiga 500 with the potential
to be a home video editing system, a home reference library, a children's learning tool,
a music studio and a language learning lab. All within reach of your sofa.

For the name of the closest authorized Amiga dealer or for your free
CDTV Welcome Tour video tape call 1-800-66-AMIGA, in Canada, call 1-800-661-AMIGA.

Look into CDTV Multimedia. You'll be amazed at what you see.

C® Commodore®

CDTV™
INTERACTIVE MULTIMEDIA

Circle 193 on Reader Service card.

The Commodore 64 has over 15,000 titles available for it, when floppy disk games are included in the total.

PREPARE TO FLY.

COMING AUGUST

•

ONLY ON

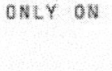

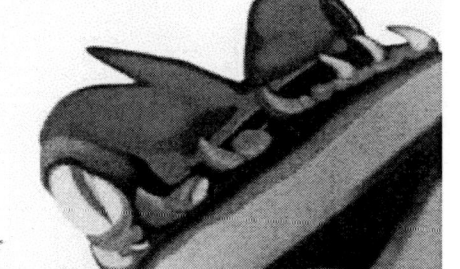

Nintendo is more than 100 years old, starting in the 19th century as a playing card company.

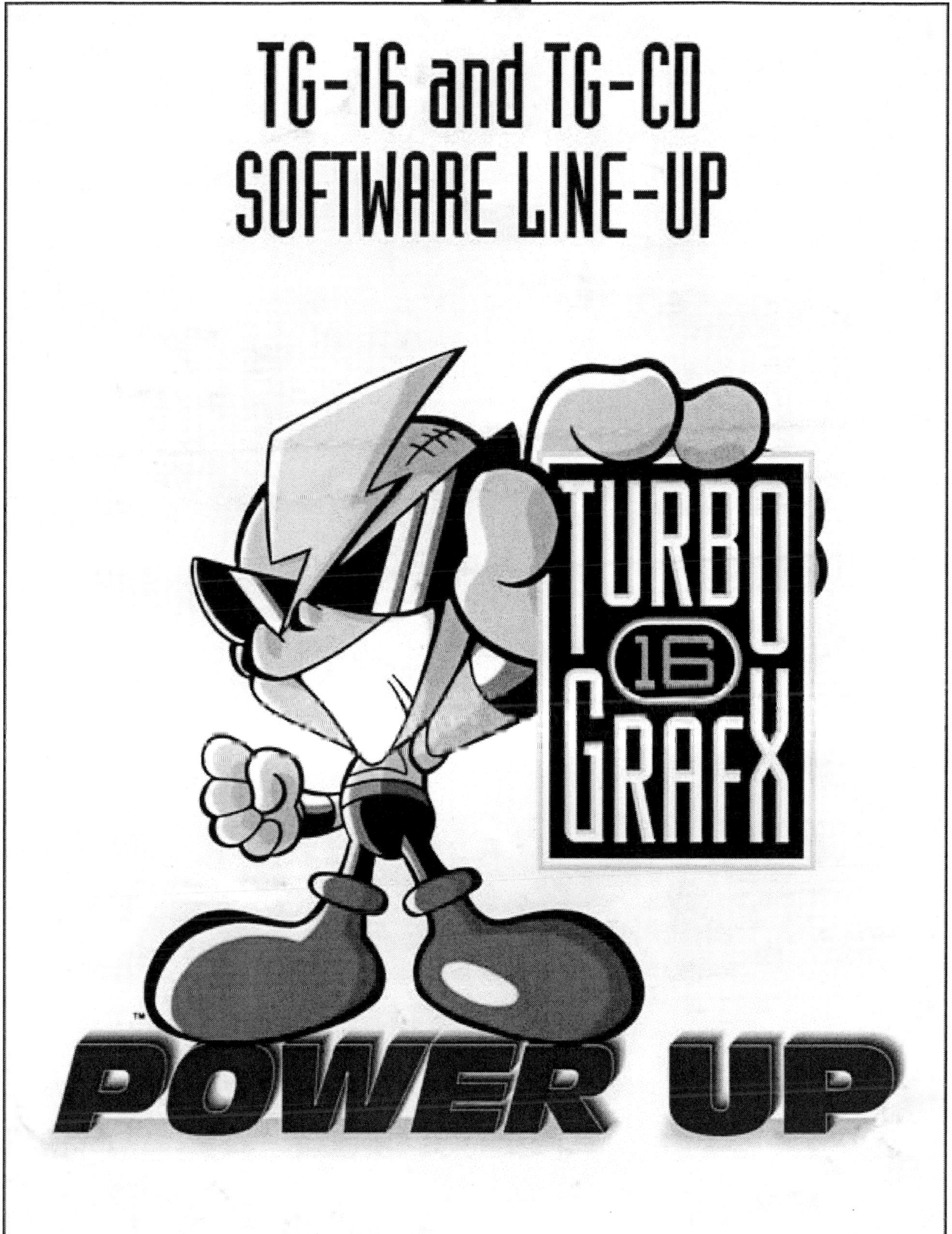

TG-16 and TG-CD
SOFTWARE LINE-UP

When polled, 12% of gamers thought that the NES power light was blue.

374

Phoenix: The Fall and Rise of Videogames, by Leonard Herman, is an exhaustive history of video games from the beginning to 2001.

375

The CDTV controller is nearly twice as wide as the NES controller.

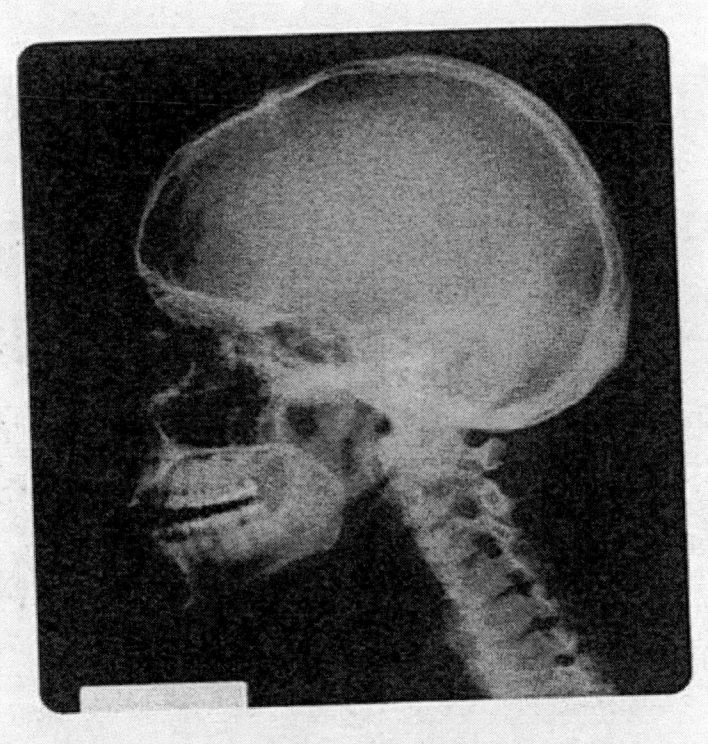

More homebrew games have been made for the Atari 2600 than for any other system.

Computer Space was the first arcade game ever released.

378

Xenophobe for the NES was inspired by the movie Alien.

When run over with a car, a copy of Super Mario Bros. for the NES was still playable. But don't try it yourself!

U.S. Console Timeline

1949
Ralph Baer receives an assignment as a budding engineer that leads to his original conception of interactive games played on a television.

1967
Ralph Baer's original vision comes true with the creation of "Chase", the first video game playable on an ordinary TV.

1972 (Classic Era Begins)
Magnavox Odyssey

1975
Atari Pong home console

1976
Fairchild Channel F

1977
Atari VCS (Atari 2600)
RCA Studio II

1978
Bally Professional Arcade
Magnavox Odyssey 2
APF MP-1000

1980
Mattel Intellivision

1981
TI-99/4A

1982
Vectrex
Atari 5200
Colecovision
Commodore 64
Emerson Arcadia 2001
GCE Vectrex

1984
Video game console market crashes.

1985   (Neo-Classic Era Begins)
Austrian rock singer Falco records…"Rock Me Amadeus!"
Nintendo Entertainment System
RDI Halcyon

1986
Sega Master System
Atari 7800
Action Max

1987
Atari XEGS
LJN Video Art
Mattel Captain Power

1989
NEC's TG-16
Sega Genesis
NEC's TG-CD
Viewmaster InteractiveVision

1990
SNK Neo-Geo AES

1991
Super Nintendo
Amiga CDTV

1992
Sega CD
Phillips CD-i
NEC's TurboDuo

1993
Atari Jaguar
3DO
Pioneer LaserActive

1994
Sega 32x
Atari Jaguar CD
Amiga CD32
Sega CDX
JVC X'Eye
Memorex VIS
Sega Pico

1995
Sega Saturn
Nintendo Virtual Boy

1996
Nintendo 64
Pippin @world
Neo Geo CD

1998
WebTV Plus

1999
Sega Dreamcast

2000
Playstation 2
NUON

2001 (Neo-Classic Era ends with the death of the Dreamcast)
Microsoft Xbox
Nintendo Game Cube

It is rumored that millions of unsold E.T. carts for the Atari 2600 are being stored in a secret location.

Glossary

3DO – Officially unknown, it is believed to stand for "3 Dimensional Objects".

64DD – A Japanese-only release, the term actually means 64 Disk Drive in reference to the Nintendo 64 and its add-on system.

AES – Advanced Entertainment System

ALG – American Laser Games

AVE – American Video Entertainment

C64 – Commodore 64

CDTV – Commodore Total Dynamic Vision

CG – This can mean computer graphics or computer generated, and refers to video created through the use of computer generated graphics when used in the later.

Clump – This is a term commonly used to describe the effect seen in digitized video when large sections of the picture bleed together, or are covered by colors obviously not intended by the programmer.

Cart – Simply an abbreviated term for the word "cartridge".

DC – Short for the Sega Dreamcast

Easter Egg – This term refers to any secret hidden within the game that cannot be reached by conventional methods. Typically an Easter Egg takes on the form of entering a sequence of button presses at a specific time.

Engine – The very core of the game itself, this term refers to the fundamental properties found within the game such as the type of physics used, collision detection, etc.

FMV – Full Motion Video

HES – Home Entertainment Suppliers

INTV – The abbreviation for the Mattel Intellivision

LD – Laserdisc

MVS – Multi Video System

Mac – Short for Macintosh, referring to the line of Apple computers released from 1984 to present.

Memory Card – This is an interchangeable memory storage device that was introduced with the Neo Geo AES system, and is commonplace among current consoles.

N64 – Nintendo 64

NTSC – This stands for National Television Standards Committee and refers to the type of television used in the U.S. and Japan.

NEC – Nippon Electric Company

NES – Nintendo Entertainment System

O2 – A common abbreviation for the Magnavox Odyssey 2 system.

PAL – This stands for Phase Altering Lines and refers to the type of televisions used in European countries.

PC – Personal Computer (though this term is usually referring to IBM compatibles and not Macintosh.)

PSX – This refers to the Sony Playstation.

Platformer – This is a type of game which typically involves side scrolling action in which occasional jumps must be made from one "platform" to another.

Plethora – OK, this term was used a few times in the book, and it basically means, "a whole lotta something". But after hearing El Guapo say it in "The Three Amigos", it was hard not to use it at least once in the book.

Polygon – A three dimensional object that is created by the game console. Polygon generation takes more processing power, and is typically seen only on newer consoles.

Port – This describes the process of moving an existing game from one system to another. It also applies when describing the conversion from an arcade format to any home console.

Random Generation – This is a technique used by programmers that randomly generates level designs. It is typically frowned upon in newer games as this typically means that there is a less involving story line, but when used in older games it often ads replay value.

RAM – Random Access Memory, for the purpose of this book it refers exclusively to the built in memory storage unit found within a video game console.

ROM – This stands for "Read Only Memory" and typically refers to the binary image stored within a cartridge.

RPG – Role Playing Game

SMS – Sega Master System

SNES – Super Nintendo Entertainment System

TG-16 – TurboGrafx-16

TTI – Turbo Technologies Incorporated. This division was formed when NEC and Hudson Soft joined forces.

VCD – Video Compact Disc

VCS – Commonly referred to as the Atari 2600, the system's official name was the Atari VCS, or Video Computer System.

VGB – Video Game Bible

VIS – In reference to the Memorex VIS, it stands for "Video Information System".

XEGS – XE Game System, referring to the game system based on the Atari XE line of computers.

There are no external screws on Neo-Geo AES cartridges.

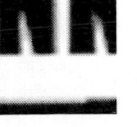

If you have questions or comments about this book, feel free to visit our open forum at:

www.videogamebible.com

Any questions concerning the ordering of this book in quantity should be directed to:

videogamebible@hotmail.com

As with any book this large, errors and omissions are always a concern, and with your help, any discrepancies can be corrected for the second
volume in this continuing series of video game guides. Polls were conducted with the use of the VGB website and personal polling within different game stores.

COMING SOON

Video Game Bible: Handheld
Covering all U.S. released handheld video game consoles

Video Game Bible: 1972-1984
Covering all U.S. released video games prior to the NES

Video Game Bible: Complete
Covering all systems from 1972-release date, with truncated reviews

Video Game Bible: Pocket
Covering all U.S. systems ever released, but in a very portable size

Video Game Bible: PAL
Covering all European released video game consoles

Video Game Bible: Japan
Covering all Japanese released video game consoles.

And finally, for those of you wondering what the boxes that occasionally appear at the top of seemingly random pages are for:

These were created for your amusement, but the fun is figuring out how to use them. The only hint that we can give is that the solution is mathematical. Have fun, and thank you for your patronage!

A standard Genesis cartridge weighs 51 grams.

ISBN 155369731-6

9 781553 697312